CROFTS PHYSICAL EDUCATION SERIES
Charles Harold McCloy, *General Editor*

Tests and Measurements

in

HEALTH

and

PHYSICAL
EDUCATION

Tests AND Measurements

IN

HEALTH

AND

PHYSICAL EDUCATION

By

CHARLES HAROLD McCLOY

AND

NORMA DOROTHY YOUNG

Third Edition

New York

APPLETON-CENTURY-CROFTS
EDUCATIONAL DIVISION
MEREDITH CORPORATION

Copyright, 1954, by

MEREDITH CORPORATION

All rights reserved

This book, or parts thereof, must not be used or reproduced in any manner without written permission. For information address the publisher, Appleton-Century-Crofts, Educational Division, Meredith Corporation, 440 Park Avenue South, New York, N. Y. 10016.

760–15

LIBRARY OF CONGRESS CARD NUMBER:
53–7241

51279

Copyright renewed, 1970, by Amanda McCloy Capen, Emma McCloy Layman, Edward McCloy, Robert W. McCloy and William A. McCloy

Copyright renewed, 1967, by Amanda R. Capen, Emma McCloy Layman, Edward McCloy, Robert Winston McCloy and William A. McCloy

Copyright, 1939, 1942, by F. S. Crofts & Co., Inc.

PRINTED IN THE UNITED STATES OF AMERICA

390–61351–7

Dedicated to a
great humanologist,
VIRGIL M. HANCHER

PREFACE

A BIBLIOGRAPHY of the tests and measurements developed in physical and health education since the publication of the second edition of this text in 1942 would in itself constitute a small book. Hence the selection of the tests and measurements to be included in this edition was a major task. If there were several good tests covering the same field, a selection of these tests was made for inclusion in the book. Some good tests had to be referred to by title and source because of copyright restrictions. Purely psychological tests have, in general, been omitted in view of the fact that tests of that type are better selected by clinical psychologists than by physical or health educators. In general, except for tests produced in the authors' laboratory, only published tests appear in the book.

Tests and measurements can be used fruitfully only if the underlying theory is understood. Hence explanations have been advanced both for the understanding of the tests and measurements and for the stimulating of further research in this area.

Fifteen chapters in the third edition are new, or are complete revisions of chapters in the second edition. Most of the other chapters in the second edition appear with extensive revisions in the third edition. A few of the chapters deserve special mention.

Chapter 2 on "Factors Basic to Measurement in Physical and Health Education" is a new chapter, and indicates further directions for research in tests and measurements in physical and health education.

Chapter 14 on "Strength," Chapter 15 on "Endurance," and Chapter 23 on "Cardiovascular Tests" contain tests that are useful in programs of adaptive therapy, corrective therapy, and physical reconditioning or physical rehabilitation.

In Chapter 19 on "Special Abilities," sections on flexibility, response time, eye dominance, handedness for athletics, and depth perception have been added.

Chapter 23 on "Cardiovascular Tests" contains a detailed analysis of the materials basic to such measurements.

Chapter 25 on "Potentiality for Different Sports" contains many tests that should be of service in a differential diagnosis of potentialities for performance in athletics.

Chapter 28 on "Anthropometry" is a new chapter, and makes available the work of the senior author and others in the field of applied anthropometry. This chapter should be of special value for classes in adaptive physical education and for various health-education groups, especially those interested in following the treatment of over- and underweight.

Appendix A, which is an addition to the second edition, is a condensed text on statistics. It contains in sufficient detail a description of the statistical methods needed for research in tests and measurements in physical and health education. Appendix A, together with the exercises for that Appendix in Appendix C, may well be used as the basis for a two-semester-hour laboratory course in statistical methods.

The laboratory manual that accompanied the second edition has been replaced by Appendix C, which contains laboratory exercises outlined in connection with the various chapters. Data are given for elementary-school, junior-high-school, and senior-high-school boys and girls, which data may, in non-laboratory courses, well be used as a basis for the computation of various scores.

SUGGESTED ASSIGNMENTS

I. For a two-semester-hour course the following assignments are suggested: Sections 1-7; 63-187; 194-215; 220-26; 231-35; 237-41; 253-65; 267-372; 378; 381-84; 387-89; 394; 403-11; 415-17; 420-23; from 424-45 instructor should select tests to be covered; 446-84; 495; 498-501; 505-09; 514-21; 522-42, instructor should select tests to be studied by class; 543-74; 575 (7) and 575 (8); 590-607 (instructor should give demonstrations of how to measure, and explain how to compute normal weights, etc.); 608-42.

II. For a three-semester-hour course it is suggested that the following assignments be added to those in I: Sections 8-62; 188-93; 243-52; 266; 373-77; 379-80; 390-93; 485-92; 502-04; 575-89; 689-92.

III. For a four-semester-hour course, the whole text may be covered.

Finally, it must be remembered that tests and measurements will make constructive contributions to programs of physical and health education only if they are administered according to directions. Just as "figures do not lie, but liars figure," so tests and measurements that are highly valid may prove almost useless when improperly used and inadequately interpreted.

ACKNOWLEDGMENTS

To former graduate students and to other researchers for the materials acknowledged by footnotes on the pages on which the materials are presented.

To the following persons, departments of physical education, organizations, and publishing companies for permission to reproduce tests, measuring devices, and tables: Nancy Bayley and Leona M. Bayer for the androgyny patterns of body form (Fig. LII); Vaughn S. Blanchard for the Detroit Decathlon and Pentathlon (Sec. 118, Tables 3-4) ; Karl W. Bookwalter for height-weight class divisions for high-school girls (Sec. 144) ; Lucien Brouha for the step tests for measuring physical fitness (Secs. 498-99, Table 107) ; C. L. Brownell for a scale for measuring anteroposterior posture (Sec. 457, Fig. XXXIII) ; H. C. Carlson for the fatigue-curve test (Sec. 337) ; H. H. Clarke for a method of measuring the height of the longitudinal arch of the foot (Sec. 468, Fig. XLI) ; Harriet L. Clarke for a functional physical-fitness test for college women (Sec. 500) ; F. W. Cozens and the Lea and Febiger Publishing Company for height-weight class divisions of college men (Sec. 138) ; C. W. Crampton for the blood-ptosis test (Sec. 485, Table 103) ; Billie L. Crook for a scale for measuring anteroposterior posture (Sec. 458, Fig. XXXIV) ; Thomas K. Cureton, Jr., for a test for endurance in speed swimming (Sec. 346, Table 84) ; Roland A. Fisher and Frank Yates and the Oliver and Boyd, Ltd., Publishing Company for the table of t (Table 135), which was abridged from Table III in *Statistical Tables for Biological, Agricultural, and Medical Research* by those authors; Darwin A. Hindman for a revised method of scoring the Schneider test (Sec. 287, Table 105) ; to the Iowa Child Welfare Research Station and to the Department of Publications of the State University of Iowa for breathing-capacity norms (Table 125) from *Individual Differences in Breathing Capacity* by Helen G. Kelly, and for anthropometric materials (Secs. 590-601) from *Appraising Physical Status: the Selection of Measurements*, and *Appraising Physical Status: Methods and Norms* by the senior author; Department of Physical Education for Women of the State University of Iowa for the Iowa Posture Test (Sec. 453, Fig. XXX) ; Granville B. Johnson for physical-skill tests (Sec. 210, Fig. XIII) ; P. V. Karpovich for cardiovascular tests (Sec. 490, Table 106) ; to Frank L. Kleeburger for the University of California Physical-efficiency Test (Sec. 370, Fig. XXVI) ; to Everett F. Lindquist and the Houghton Mifflin Publishing Company for the table of the z function for values of r (Table 145) from *Statistical Analysis in Educational Research* by that author; E. G. Martin for tests of muscular efficiency (Sec. 308) ; G. W. Mueller for the Philadelphia Age Aims (Sec. 351, Table 86) ; National Recreation Association for the badge tests (Sec. 350, Table 85) ; Charles C. Peters for the Doolittle method of computing multiple correlations and multiple regressions (Sec. 677, Table 143) ; J. Marion Read for formulas for the prediction of basal metabolism (Secs. 505-06) ; E. C. Schneider for a cardiovascular measure of physical fatigue and efficiency (Sec. 486, Table 104) ; Sigma Delta Psi fraternity for a test of athletic ability (Sec. 371) ; George W. Snedecor and the Iowa State College Press for the table of r and R values for probabilities of .05 and .01 (Table 144) and for the table of F (Table 146) from the sixth edition of *Statistical Methods* by that author; Department of Physical Education of the University of Southern California for the

University of Southern California Posture Standards (Sec. 456, Fig. XXXII) ; Craig Taylor for the maximal pack test (Sec. 503, Table 108) ; W. W. Tuttle for the pulse-ratio test (Sec. 495, Fig. XLVII) ; and Department of Physical Education of Wellesley College for the Wellesley Posture Standards (Sec. 461, Figs. XXXVI-VII).

To the following persons who gave valuable suggestions in the preparation of various materials, but who are, of course, wholly free of responsibility for the shortcomings of these materials: Nancy Bayley and Leona M. Bayer for criticism of the material on somatic androgyny (Table 113), which material was suggested by a table published by those authors in the *American Journal of Physical Anthropology* for December, 1946; Luis Bisquertt S., of the University of Chile, for making available the reference to the Martinet Test (Sec. 493) ; Wendell Johnson for suggestions used in the formulation of a test of handedness (Sec. 411) ; Scott N. Reger for assistance in the preparation of the tests of hearing [Sec. 575 (8)]; William H. Sheldon for assistance in the preparation of the material on the characteristics of endomorphs, mesomorphs, and ectomorphs (Table 111) ; L. L. Thurstone for assistance that resulted in the isolation of basic factors in the area of physical and health education (Chap. 2) ; and S. M. Woo, of China, and numerous physicians of mission colleges and universities of China for their assistance (from 1921 to 1924) in the preparation of the material on medical examinations (Chap. 27).

To the following persons who prepared the illustrations new to this edition: Dale Ballantyne, Kendall W. Hamlin, and William A. McCloy.

To the following persons who typed preliminary drafts of the manuscript: Bettye J. Allison, A. Douglas Macrae, Josephine M. Maddox, Mary E. Maxwell, and Edith M. Parman; and to Alice D. Hamlin who typed a large part of the final draft of the manuscript and who typed most of the tables in form for photographic reproduction.

C. H. M.

N. D. Y.

CONTENTS

TABLES

FIGURES

xix

Tests and Measurements

in

HEALTH

and

PHYSICAL
EDUCATION

PART I

Introduction

CHAPTER 1

PURPOSES

1. INCREASE OF KNOWLEDGE

THE USE OF measurement for the increase of knowledge is, in the long pull, the major purpose of measurement in physical and health education. Although only a few persons have the training and the interest to engage in this use of measurement, they are the ones who are responsible for the devising of means by which programs of physical and health education may be improved.

2. IMPROVEMENT OF INSTRUCTION

Measurement is a *sine qua non,* not only for a program in which adequate provision is made for individual differences, but also for a program in which attention is given primarily to likenesses of persons.

3. Classification. In order that a teacher may organize an advantageous program for all his pupils, he needs at the beginning of the school year to classify his pupils according to both their capacities and their achievements. Furthermore, in order that a teacher may most wisely guide all his pupils into the types of activities in which the pupils are likely to succeed, he needs especially to have information concerning the capacities of the pupils.

4. Achievement. In order that a teacher may know whether his pupils have accomplished the objectives set for various phases of the program and whether they are ready for subsequent phases of the program, he needs to measure, from time to time, the achievement of his pupils. Likewise, in order that a supervisor and an administrator may obtain information concerning the status of the programs for which they are responsible, they need, from time to time, to measure the achievement of the pupils in those programs.

5. Diagnosis of difficulties. In order that a teacher may help his pupils

1

whose achievements are inadequate, he needs not only to re-examine the general capacities of the pupils, but also to measure specific capacities and such items as nutritional status.

6. Motivation. Although all measurements of achievement are useful for purposes of motivation, achievement quotients, that is, achievement in relation to capacity, are the most productive of results in this respect.

7. PURPOSES OF THIS BOOK

Measurements are useful in education if they help the teacher to improve his service to his pupils. Hence the teacher needs to know what methods can be used profitably for the measurement of various qualities and what the limitations of these various measurements are. Measurements are also useful in increasing knowledge if they are highly refined. Hence the researcher needs to know what highly refined measurements have been devised in order that he may continue the process. In the pages that follow, an effort has been made to present the measurements that appear to be useful to both teachers and researchers.

CHAPTER **2**

BASIC FACTORS

8. INTRODUCTION

IN THE LATE nineteen-twenties and early thirties the publication of practicable methods for analyzing data statistically for underlying factors or components made possible a new approach to the study of problems involved in measurement.[1] The technical aspect of these methods as applied to problems in physical and health education has been discussed elsewhere.[2]

There are two types of factors: (1) orthogonal factors and (2) oblique factors.

An orthogonal factor might be called a "pure" factor, for it is statistically independent of, and uncorrelated with, other orthogonal factors. Just as hydrogen and oxygen are elements that are independent of, and uncorrelated with, each other, so strength and speed of muscular contraction are factors that are statistically independent of, and uncorrelated with, each other. If such factors as strength and speed of muscular contraction are plotted geometrically, the axes and the planes that pass through the factors are orthogonal; that is, the axes are, regardless of the number of planes involved, at right angles to each other.

An oblique factor might be called a compound factor, for it is comprised of two or more orthogonal factors, with each of which it is correlated. Just as water is compounded of hydrogen and oxygen, on each of which elements it is dependent and with each of which it is correlated, so power (see Chap. 9) is a factor that is statistically dependent upon, and correlated with, the factors of strength and velocity. If such a factor as power is plotted geometrically, it falls between the orthogonal planes that pass through the factors of strength and speed of muscular contraction, and hence is called an oblique factor.

[1] Charles E. Spearman, *The Abilities of Man, Their Nature and Measurement.* L. L. Thurstone, *A Simplified Multiple Factor Method and an Outline of the Computations.*

[2] Charles H. McCloy, "The Factor Analysis as a Research Technique" in *Research Methods Applied to Health, Physical Education, and Recreation.*

9. FACTORS IN PHYSICAL QUALITIES

10. Muscular strength[3] (orthogonal). Since strength is prerequisite to all physical activity, it appears in all factorial analyses of physical performances. Also, the trait or quality of strength may appear in the form of one or more factors; for example, an oblique factor of strength of the arms may appear in contrast with a general factor of strength of the whole body.

11. Speed of muscular contraction[4] (orthogonal). Persons of the same size and strength differ in the speed with which they can move their limbs. The factor herewith involved is called the factor of speed of muscular contraction.

12. Dynamic energy[5] (probably oblique). Persons able to lift the same weights or to pull springs of the same tension, or to run and jump with the same speed, differ in the speed with which they can use their strength explosively, that is, in the speed with which they can "throw their strength" into action. The factor herewith involved is called the factor of dynamic energy.

13. Ability to change direction[6] (probably oblique). Persons with the same training and of the same strength and speed differ in the efficiency of their footwork. The factor herewith involved is called the factor of ability to change direction.

14. Muscular endurance[7] (orthogonal). Persons of the same strength differ in the number of times they can repeat performances. The factor herewith involved is called the factor of muscular endurance. Muscular endurance as a factor should not be confused with muscular endurance as a quality, which quality is a combination of muscular strength and blood supply to the muscles.

15. Circulorespiratory endurance[8] (orthogonal). Persons with the same

---

[3] Aileen Carpenter, "An Analysis of the Relationships of the Factors of Velocity, Strength, and Dead Weight to Athletic Performance," *Research Quarterly,* March, 1941.

McCloy, "The Apparent Importance of Arm Strength in Athletics," *Research Quarterly,* March, 1934.

———, "The Measurement of Speed in Motor Performance," *Psychometrika,* September, 1940.

[4] McCloy, "The Apparent Importance of Arm Strength in Athletics," *loc. cit.*

———, "The Measurement of Speed in Motor Performance," *loc. cit.*

[5] Esther E. Cope, "A Study of the Component Factors of the Iowa Revision of the Brace Motor Ability Test" (M.A. Thesis, State University of Iowa, 1938).

[6] Donald D. Gates and R. P. Sheffield, "Tests of Change of Direction as Measurements of Different Kinds of Motor Ability in Boys of the Seventh, Eighth, and Ninth Grades," *Research Quarterly,* October, 1940.

Frances Sierakowski, "A Study of Change-of-Direction Tests for High School Girls" (M.A. Thesis, State University of Iowa, 1940).

Kathryn E. Young, "An Analytic Study of the Tests of Change of Direction" (M.A Thesis, State University of Iowa, 1937).

[7] McCloy, "Endurance," *Physical Educator,* March, 1948.

[8] *Ibid.*

amount of strength and muscular endurance differ in the efforts they can exert before becoming thoroughly "winded." The factor herewith involved is called the factor of circulorespiratory endurance. Circulorespiratory endurance as a factor should not be confused with circulorespiratory endurance as a quality, which quality is a combination of muscular strength, muscular endurance, and strength and endurance of the heart.

16. Agility[9] (probably oblique). Persons equally efficient in strength and in velocity vary in their ability to change position rapidly. The factor herewith involved is called the factor of agility.

17. "Dead" weight[10] (orthogonal). Persons apparently equal in measurable physical qualities vary in athletic ability. Part of this variation has, in a number of studies, been accounted for by differences in the weight of the skeleton, the skin, the viscera, the vessels, and the inactive muscles, and especially by differences in the weight of the fat. The factor herewith involved is called the factor of "dead" weight.

18. Flexibility[11] (probably orthogonal). Persons apparently equal in many measurable physical qualities differ in the range of movement possible at the various joints. The factor herewith involved is called the factor of flexibility.

19. FACTORS IN MOTOR EDUCABILITY

Persons apparently equal in the physical qualities discussed in Sections 10 to 18, and apparently equal in training and in experience, differ in their ability to learn motor skills.

20. Insight into nature of skill [12] (probably orthogonal). The person who is most aware of the nature of the skill that he is trying to learn, learns the skill most rapidly. The possession of this quality is probably highly

[9] Cope, *loc. cit.*

Gates and Sheffield, *loc. cit.*

Kenneth Hill, "The Formulation of Tests of Motor Educability for Junior High School Boys" (M.A. Thesis, State University of Iowa, 1935).

Sierakowski, *loc. cit.*

[10] George F. Brady, "The Effect of Excess Weight upon Motor Skills" (Ph.D. Dissertation, State University of Iowa, 1951).

Carpenter, *loc. cit.*

McCloy, "The Measurement of Speed in Motor Performance," *loc. cit.*

[11] Cope, *loc. cit.*

Thomas K. Cureton, Jr., "Flexibility as an Aspect of Physical Fitness," *Supplement to Research Quarterly*, May, 1941.

Florence L. Hupprich and Peter O. Sigerseth, "The Specificity of Flexibility in Girls," *Research Quarterly*, March, 1950.

Jack R. Leighton, "A Simple Objective and Reliable Measure of Flexibility,' *Research Quarterly*, May, 1942.

[12] Lex V. Combs, "A Comparison of the Efficacy of the Whole Method and of the Whole-Part-Whole Method of Teaching Track Activities" (M.A. Thesis, State University of Iowa, 1932).

Cope, *loc. cit.*

Hill, *loc. cit.*

dependent upon an understanding of the principles of mechanics underlying the skill.

21. Depth perception.[13] This factor is involved in the ability of a person to judge the distance of objects and of persons from himself. Whether or not depth perception is an orthogonal factor is not entirely clear. It is dependent upon several different processes or elements which, however, may possibly be combined into one mental process (see Secs. 412-14).

22. General-kinesthetic sensitivity and control [14] (orthogonal). This factor is involved in the ability of a performer to sense, by means of proprioceptors in muscles and in joints, positions of the body and of various parts of the body, and to control allied movements with accuracy.

23. Balance[15]

Eyes and balance in movement in general (orthogonal). Although the *general* contribution made by the eyes to balance may combine with other factors, the factor is basic to balance, and it is apparently statistically independent of the next two factors.

Eyes and balance in forward-and-backward movement (orthogonal). The contribution made by the eyes to balance in forward-and-backward movement, such as balancing crosswise on a narrow beam, may involve accommodation or convergence of the eyes, and hence implies an accuracy of discrimination in the proprioceptors of the muscles controlling the eyes.

Eyes and balance in sideward movement (orthogonal). The contribution made by the eyes to balance in sideward movement, such as balancing on a narrow beam running lengthwise of the foot, may be a function of the change of the angle of the head in relation to the vertical plane, or it may be related to a parallactic phenomenon. Since this factor functions only if the eyes are open, it is apparently different from the factor that follows.

Vertical semicircular canals and balance (orthogonal). The contribution to balance made by the two vertical sets of semicircular canals, which seem to function together, is primarily in forward, backward, and sideward movements around transverse and anteroposterior axes.

Horizontal semicircular canals and balance (orthogonal). The contribution to balance made by the horizontal semicircular canals is largely

---

[13] William S. Duke-Elder, *Text-book of Ophthalmology I*, pp. 1070 ff.

[14] Ruth I. Bass, "An Analysis of the Components of Tests of Semicircular Canal Function and of Static and Dynamic Balance," *Research Quarterly*, May, 1939.

Bernath E. Phillips, "The Relationship between Certain Phases of Kinesthesis and Performance during the Early Stages of Acquiring Two Perceptuo-Motor Skills," *Research Quarterly*, October, 1941.

Vernon R. Wiebe, "A Study of Tests of Kinesthesis" (M.A. Thesis, State University of Iowa, 1951).

Olive G. Young, "A Study of Kinesthesis in Relation to Selected Movements," *Research Quarterly*, December, 1945.

[15] Bass, *loc. cit.*

in movements in which the head rotates in a horizontal plane around a vertical axis, or in the plane of the horizontal set of canals. Examples of such movements are pirouettes in dancing, spinning in dancing and in skating, and balance stunts on a narrow beam running lengthwise of the foot, with the trunk bent forward ninety degrees.

Tension-giving reinforcement (probably oblique). One factor has been found to be present in activities involving balance when the performer stands on a narrow beam, and not present when the performer stands on the floor. This factor has been considered to be involved with an increased sensitivity of the mechanisms of balance brought on by an increased tension on the sole of the foot. It is highly probable that this function of balance is related to the factor of general-kinesthetic sensitivity and control.

Kinesthetic sensitivity and control (see Secs. 248-52).

24. Perceptual speed [16] (probably orthogonal). This factor is involved in the ability of a person to perceive quickly the nature of the situation and to initiate activities appropriate to the situation. The initiation of these activities is dependent also on such factors as the performer's insight into the nature of the skill, and on depth perception. It is possible also that physiological response-time—apparently a neurological factor—may also be involved with the factor of perceptual speed.

25. Ability to visualize spatial relationships[17] (orthogonal). This factor is involved in the ability of a performer not only to see where objects and performers are, but also to realize what their geometrical inter-relationships are at the time and what changes they may undergo. In most motor performances this factor is probably combined with the factor of insight into the nature of the skill and with the factor of depth perception.

26. Sensory-motor co-ordination I [18] (orthogonal). This factor is involved in the motor co-ordination of the eyes with the head, the hands, and the feet, as in the heading, the hitting, the catching, the striking, and the kicking of balls. It is highly probable that this factor never appears alone, but that it appears in combination with the factors of depth perception, gen-

---

[16] Thurstone, *A Factorial Study of Perception.*

———, *Mechanical Aptitude III, Analysis of Group Tests* (Psychometric Laboratory, University of Chicago, 1949).

———, "The Perceptual Factor," *Psychometrika*, March, 1938.

———, *Primary Mental Abilities.*

——— and Thelma G. Thurstone, *Factorial Studies of Intelligence.*

[17] Theresa Anderson and C. H. McCloy, "The Measurement of Sports Ability in High School Girls," *Research Quarterly*, March, 1947.

Jake H. Moser, "An Attempt to Devise a Simple Method of Measuring Potential Football Intelligence" (M.A. Thesis, State University of Iowa, 1938).

Thurstone, *Primary Mental Abilities.*

[18] Robert H. Seashore, "Stanford Motor Skills Unit," *Psychological Monographs*, 1928.

Arthur J. Wendler, "A Critical Analysis of Test Elements Used in Physical Education," *Research Quarterly*, March, 1938.

eral-kinesthetic sensitivity and control, and insight into the nature of the skill.

27. Sensory-motor co-ordination II (probably oblique). This factor is involved in a performer's ability to adapt his muscular system to an external weight and to another force. This type of motor co-ordination is illustrated by what happens when a person catches a tossed ball that he thinks is a twelve-pound shot, but which he finds to be a dirty indoor baseball. Much of the accurate response that is responsible for good form in many types of motor performance is probably dependent upon the presence of this second factor of sensory-motor co-ordination. This factor is, in many situations, related to insight into the nature of the skill and to kinesthetic sense. It may be correlated with general-kinesthetic sensitivity and control.

28. Judgment concerning time,[19] height,[19] distance,[19] and direction[20] (orthogonal). This factor is involved in the ability of a performer to judge various relationships of objects and of persons with himself. The function of this factor is illustrated in "leading" a performer in passing a ball, in judging a fly ball or a line drive in baseball, in judging a pitched ball in batting, and in catching a forward pass. This factor is almost always associated with depth perception, with the ability to visualize spatial relationships, and with an insight into the nature of the skill. It is frequently closely related to the first factor of sensory-motor co-ordination. The latter factor, however, is principally concerned with the approximation of the body or of parts of the body to various implements, while the former factor is concerned with the adaptation of the performer to changes in time, height, distance, and direction.

29. Co-ordination for complicated unitary movement[21] (orthogonal or oblique). This factor is involved in the ability of a person to execute such a performance as a back somersault or a somersault with a full twist. This factor, which probably never functions alone, is undoubtedly related to an insight into the nature of the skill, general-kinesthetic sensitivity and control, the ability to visualize spatial relationships, the first factor of sensory-motor co-ordination, and judgment concerning time, height, distance, and direction.

30. Co-ordination for combination of movements.[22] This factor is involved in the ability of a performer to execute a series of movements that follow

---

[19] Wendler, *loc. cit.*

[20] Hamlin Blix, unpublished study.

[21] David K. Brace, *Measuring Motor Ability.*

Cope, *loc. cit.*

Thomas J. Cross, "A Comparison of the Whole Method, the Minor Game Method, and the Whole Part Method of Teaching Basketball to Ninth-Grade Boys," *Research Quarterly,* December, 1937.

[22] Cross, *loc. cit.*

Granville B. Johnson, "Physical Skill Tests for Sectioning Classes into Homogeneous Units," *Research Quarterly,* March, 1932.

one another rapidly. Its function is illustrated by such activities as the pole vault; the pivot and dribble in basketball; and the round-off, the back handspring, and the back somersault in tumbling. This factor is probably associated with an insight into the nature of the skill, general-kinesthetic sensitivity and control, the ability to visualize spatial relationships, the first factor of sensory-motor co-ordination, and judgment concerning time, height, distance, and direction.

31. Arm control [23] (probably oblique). The function of this factor is illustrated by balancing, by many twister exercises in tumbling and in diving, and by the aid given by the reaction of the arms in broad and high jumping. This factor is undoubtedly related to an insight into the nature of the skill, general-kinesthetic sensitivity and control, and co-ordination for a combination of movements.

32. Accuracy of direction [24] (probably oblique). This factor is involved in the ability of a performer to project implements rapidly, as in throwing balls for accuracy. Such accuracy of direction implies decreasing the angle of the error of projection. This factor has as yet not been adequately analyzed. It undoubtedly involves the ability to visualize spatial relationships, the ability to make quick and adaptive decisions, depth perception, an insight into the nature of the skill, general-kinesthetic sensitivity and control, the second factor of sensory-motor co-ordination, and co-ordination for a complicated unitary movement.

33. Sensory rhythm. [25] In physical education the following items of sensory rhythm appear to need consideration: (1) a feeling for beat or regularity of intervals, (2) a feeling for interval or duration, (3) a feeling for stress or intensity, and (4) what might be called "a harmony of rhythmical feeling" (knowing "when it is right"), which item is probably related to an insight into the nature of the skill and to general-kinesthetic sensitivity and control, and (5) a feeling for proper timing, which item may be related to the two factors that follow.

34. Timing

Eye-motor timing (probably oblique). This factor is probably related

[23] Cope, *loc. cit.*

[24] D. C. Moffett, "A Study of Accuracy of Direction in Motor Skills at Different Distances as Determined by the Relative Size of the Angle of Error," *Research Quarterly*, December, 1942.

Harve A. Oliphant, "A Study of Improvement in Shooting Baskets as Related to the Amount of Practice" (M.A. Thesis, State University of Iowa, 1939).

Gunter Voigt, "Über die Richtungspräzision einer Fernhandlung," *Psychologische Forschung* XVI:1 and 2 (1932).

[25] Blix, unpublished study.

Eloise Lemon and Elizabeth Sherbon, "A Study of the Relationships of Certain Measures of Rhythmic Ability and Motor Ability in Girls and Women," *Supplement to Research Quarterly*, March, 1934.

Carl E. Seashore, *The Measurement of Musical Talent.*

Eugene Wettstone, "Tests for Predicting Potential Ability in Gymnastics and Tumbling," *Research Quarterly,* December, 1938.

to the first factor of sensory-motor co-ordination, to an insight into the nature of the skill, and to general-kinesthetic sensitivity and control.

Duration of time (probably oblique). This factor might be characterized by a feeling for the duration of time. Its function is illustrated in the upstart or "kip" on a horizontal bar, in which exercise the intervals between the parts of the performance must be accurately timed. This factor is probably related to a feeling for motor rhythm. This subfactor appears to be related to an insight into the nature of the skill, depth perception, general-kinesthetic sensitivity and control, the ability to visualize spatial relationships, and judgment concerning time, height, distance, and direction.

Insightful timing (probably oblique). This factor is involved in the ability of a performer to execute an activity properly with a minimum of practice because the performer understands how to time his movements. It is undoubtedly related to an insight into the nature of the skill, the ability to visualize spatial relationships, and a feeling for timing.

35. Motor rhythm[26] (probably oblique). Motor rhythm, as measured by the Stanford Motor-skills Unit, has been demonstrated to have a significant correlation with gymnastics ability and with timing. It has also been found that the rhythmical element that can be measured by the Koerth Pursuit Test in the Stanford Motor-skills Unit is related to success in gymnastics. This rhythmical element is believed to be related to the motor-rhythm factor.

36. Quick and adaptive decisions.[27] This factor is undoubtedly related to an insight into the nature of the skill, perceptual speed, the visualization of spatial relationships, and judgment concerning time, height, distance, and direction.

37. Aesthetic feelings (probably oblique). This factor is involved in the feeling of a performer for perfection of movement. It is very probably related to an insight into the nature of the skill, general-kinesthetic sensitivity and control, balance, the ability to visualize spatial relationships, co-ordination for a complicated unitary movement, co-ordination for a combination of movements, arm control, sensory rhythm, timing, and motor rhythm. Much less information is available on this factor than on most of the other factors.

38. The following factors are prerequisite to the successful learning of motor activities: (1) muscular strength, (2) dynamic energy, (3) ability to change di-

[26] Blix, unpublished study.

McCloy, "An Analytical Study of the Stunt Type Test as a Measure of Motor Educability," *Research Quarterly,* October, 1937.

Robert H. Seashore, *loc. cit.*

Wettstone, *loc. cit.*

[27] Anderson and McCloy, *loc. cit.*

McCloy, " 'Blocks Test' of Multiple Response," *Psychometrika,* September, 1942

Robert H. Seashore, *loc. cit.*

Stanley M. Smith, "The 'Blocks Test' as a Measurement of Adaptive Athletic Response" (M.A. Thesis, State University of Iowa, 1943).

rection, (4) flexibility, (5) agility, and (6) lack of an undue amount of "dead" weight (e.g., a lack of excess fat). The following qualities or abilities, which have not as yet been analyzed into their component factors, are also prerequisite to such learning: (1) peripheral vision or ability to perceive objects with reasonable clarity out in the edge of the visual field, (2) good acuity of vision, (3) ability to concentrate or to keep the mind on the activity—metaphorically speaking, "to keep the eye on the ball," (4) understanding of the principles of mechanics underlying the techniques of the activity, and (5) absence of disturbing or inhibiting emotional complications, such as fear of the water in learning to swim.

39. FACTORS IN PHYSICAL GROWTH [28]

40. Fatty growth. This factor is evident in the growth of subcutaneous tissues and in accumulations of fat on the body. It is a strong factor in endomorphic growth.[29]

41. General growth.[30] This factor is most evident in the growth of long bones, in growth in height, and in linear growth, generally. Certain aspects of this type of growth also appear to a certain degree in measurements other than those of pure-linear growth. The factor of general growth is a strong factor in ectomorphic growth.

42. Cross-sectional growth. This factor is evident in the growth of the girth, the breadth, and the depth of the chest, and in the growth of the circumference of the limbs. It is a strong factor in mesomorphic growth.

43. Omomorphic growth. This factor is evident primarily in the growth of the width of the shoulders, and in growth above the waist as contrasted with growth below the waist.

44. Neural growth.[31] This factor is evident in the growth of elements concerned with the nervous system and its appendages such as the cerebrum, the cerebellum, and the eye, and, indirectly, with the growth of the diameters of the skull.

45. Lymphoid growth.[32] This factor is excessive in early youth, reaching its peak during pubescence and falling to a low level in later life. It is evident in the growth of the lymph glands, the tonsils, and other lymphoid structures.

46. Genital growth.[33] This factor is evident in the growth of the genital organs and glands, and in the growth of organs concerned with secondary sex characteristics. It is, for the most part, latent until just a few years

---

[28] J. A. Harris and Others, *The Measurement of Man*, Chap. 4.

McCloy, "An Analysis for Multiple Factors of Physical Growth at Different Age Levels," *Child Development*, December, 1940.

[29] This term and other terms related to types of growth are defined in Chapter 28.

[30] This factor should not be confused with the factor of general growth described by Harris and Others, which factor includes not only the factor of general growth described in the text above but also the factors of fatty growth, cross-sectional growth, and omomorphic growth.

[31] Harris and Others, *op. cit.*

[32] *Ibid.*

[33] *Ibid.*

preceding pubescence when it begins to awaken, as it were, and then is very active throughout the period of puberty and adolescence.

Many of the factors of physical growth may be influenced by gene heredity, and also by hereditary functions, and sometimes by pathological changes in the various glands of internal secretion.

47. FACTORS IN CHARACTER [34] (Probably Orthogonal)

In the following factors each of the terms following the name of the factor has in it something that is common to all the traits listed under the factor. It is this "something that is common to all" that characterizes the orthogonal factor involved.

48. "Individual-social" or individual good citizenship.[35] Integrity, initiative, trustworthiness, thoroughness, conscientiousness, poise, ability to exert a wide influence on others, ability to work hard on one's studies, dependability, and honesty.

49. "Group-social" or group good citizenship. Ability to be a good follower, fairness, integrity, respect for the rights of others, loyalty, perseverance, co-operation, desire to be liked by others, and, usually, fondness for large social gatherings.

50. Self-mastery. Self-denial, moral courage, sociability, coolheadedness, ability to recover readily from anger, striving to excel in the field of one's chief interest, and, frequently, better-than-average athletic ability.

51. Individual self-sufficiency. Moral courage, modesty, good sportsmanship, resourcefulness, and perseverance.

52. Good adjustment. Cheerfulness, persistence, active engagement in social pleasures, lack of tendency to become angry easily or to crave admiration unduly, or to give way to fits of depression.

53. Individuality, "standing out from the crowd." Athletic ability, good appearance, popularity, sociability, good health, poise, and tendency to work hard.

54. Sociability. Tendency to work hard at pleasures, quickness of apprehension, exertion of wide influence on others, and originality of ideas.

55. Conscientiousness. Thoroughness, perseverance, accuracy, diligence, self-sufficiency, good judgment, attentiveness, and ability to concentrate on one's task.

56. Buoyant individuality. Impulsive kindness, cheerfulness, quickness of apprehension, kindness on principle, and, usually, a good sense of humor.

57. Positive-action tendencies. Energy, aggressiveness, adaptability, conviction, resourcefulness, initiative, ability to discipline others, and, usually, originality of ideas.

58. Positive attitudes. Self-confidence, energy, enthusiasm, vitality, and alertness.

[34] McCloy, unpublished studies.
[35] "Social" as the opposite of "antisocial."

59. Leadership. Fairness, aggressiveness, popularity, enthusiasm, resourcefulness, desire to excel in the activities of one's interest, co-operation, and conscientiousness.

60. FACTORS IN PERSONALITY [36] (Probably Orthogonal, see Sec. 479)

61. FACTORS IN CARDIOVASCULAR CONDITION [37]
(Probably Orthogonal, see Sec. 481)

62. The factors listed in this chapter present part of the challenge that is before the research worker in the field of measurement in physical and health education. At the present time there exists only a small number of methods of measuring factors one at a time. Many of the methods of measurement are of a "shot-gun" variety; that is, a mixture of a number of factors, rather than individual factors, is measured. Such a test as the Sargent Jump (see Chap. 9), for example, which is designed to measure power, is positively correlated with the factors of strength and speed, and negatively correlated with the factor of "dead" weight. Further, certain methods for typing body build result in analyses representing a mixture of factors of growth. Research workers should attempt to devise accurate methods of measuring orthogonal factors (e.g., velocity) and oblique factors (e.g., power).

[36] Emma McCloy Layman, "An Item Analysis of the Adjustment Questionnaire," *Journal of Psychology,* July, 1940.

[37] McCloy, "A Study of Cardiovascular Variables by the Method of Factor Analysis," *Proceedings,* Second Biennial Meeting, Society for Research in Child Development, October, 1936.

Mary Agnes Murphy, "A Study of the Primary Components of Cardiovascular Tests," *Research Quarterly,* March, 1940.

PART **II**

Methodology

CHAPTER **3**

CHARACTERISTICS OF MEASUREMENTS

63. The most important quality of any measurement is its **validity,** that is, the accuracy with which the measurement represents the item under consideration. However, everything that can be measured cannot be measured with the same degree of accuracy. Ability to perform a standing broad jump, for example, can be measured with a much higher degree of accuracy than can ability to play basketball, for the distance of the standing broad jump can be measured to within one sixteenth of an inch, while ability to play basketball can only be rated by categories. Ability to play basketball, however, can be rated with a higher degree of accuracy than can character traits, for performance in basketball is more specific than are manifestations of character traits. Hence, contrary to a statement appearing in many textbooks on methods of research, there is no general rule concerning the degree of validity necessary for a measurement to be useful. On the one hand, a fairly valid measurement of an item that can be measured with only a fair degree of accuracy may be a useful measurement. On the other hand, a fairly valid measurement of an item capable of being measured with a high degree of accuracy may be of questionable usefulness.

A measurement may have an unsuspected validity. Stunts designed to measure motor educability may, for example, be valid measurements of strength rather than of motor educability, just as problems designed to measure the ability of a fourth grader in arithmetic may be valid measurements of the ability of the fourth grader to understand the English language rather than of his ability in arithmetic.

64. If a measurement is valid, it is also **reliable;** that is, measurements successively obtained upon one group or upon comparable groups are consistent with each other. Although a valid measurement is a reliable measurement, a reliable measurement is not necessarily a valid measurement

15

of the quality it was designed to measure. Consistent results may be obtained, for example, from successive administrations of a test designed to measure motor educability. If strength rather than motor educability is measured by the test, the measurement although reliable is not valid as a measure of motor educability.

65. The reliability of a measurement is largely dependent upon its objectivity, that is, the degree to which consistent results are obtained from the use of the same method of measurement by different persons. The objectivity of a measurement is, in turn, largely dependent upon the standardization of the procedure for using the method of measurement and for scoring the results. Such standardization, in turn, is largely dependent upon the clarity of the directions for the method of measurement.

66. Valid methods of measurement that can be used with at least forty pupils at one time or in one hour and that require no or little equipment are, perhaps, the only ones that are highly useful for a program of physical and health education. If two methods of measurement are equally valid, but one requires more time and equipment for its use than does the other, the latter is, even for purposes of research, more useful than the former. However, if the only valid method of measurement that exists is time consuming and expensive, it may be useful in that it may be the means by which a significant increase in knowledge may be made.

Successive administrations of a test designed to measure quickness of learning usually yield invalid results because of the amount of learning due to the first administration. Duplicate forms in which the elements of the two forms are different should be provided for such a test.

Only those methods of measurement, whether they are designed for a program of physical and health education or for purposes of research, are useful of which the results are capable of interpretation.

CHAPTER **4**

DEFINITIONS OF TERMS OF STATISTICS

67. IN THIS CHAPTER are presented definitions of the statistics referred to in this textbook. Methods for computing these and other statistics commonly used in the analyses of data in the field of physical and health education may be found in *Appendix A*.

68. The **range** of data is the difference between the value of the highest datum and that of the lowest datum. If the lowest body weight of fifty subjects is 95 and the highest is 180, the range of the weights of the fifty subjects is 85.

69. Class intervals (CI) are groups in which data are classified in order that the data may be interpreted conveniently and effectively. The data for the squat jumps in Table 8 (p. 48) are classified in eighteen class intervals, and the size of the class interval is 4.

70. The **frequency** (f) is the number of data in each class interval. The *number* (N) is the sum of the numbers of the data in all the class intervals. In the data for the squat jumps in Table 8 the frequency for the highest class interval is 1, and that for the lowest class interval is 3. The sum of the numbers of the data in all the class intervals is 498.

71. The **arithmetic mean** (Mn) is the sum of the values of all the data divided by the number of the data. If the weights of five subjects are 95, 150, 100, 120, and 145 pounds, the arithmetic mean of the weights is 122. The **median** (Mdn) is that datum above and below which 50 per cent of the data lie. The median of the weights of the five subjects is 120.

72. Normal probability curve. If chance is operative, as in a large number of data, the data are massed at the center, and there is a gradually diminishing number of data toward the lowest and the highest datum. This phenomenon is in accordance with the binomial expansion of $(1 + 1)$. For example, if $(1 + 1)$ is expanded algebraically, the first three expansions are as follows: $(1 + 1)^2 = 1 + 2 + 1$; $(1 + 1)^3 = 1 + 3 + 3 + 1$; $(1 + 1)^4 = 1 + 4 + 6 + 4 + 1$. If $(1 + 1)$ is expanded an infinite number of times (readily done by the calculus), the so-called normal probability curve is obtained. A **normal distribution** is one that exhibits the characteristics of the normal probability curve.

In data falling in a normal distribution the **standard deviation** (SD) may be interpreted as follows: 68.26 per cent of the data lie between one standard deviation above and one standard deviation below the mean; 13.59 per cent of the data lie in the second standard deviation above the mean, and

13.59 per cent of the data lie in the second standard deviation below the mean; 2.145 per cent of the data lie in the third standard deviation above the mean, and 2.145 per cent of the data lie in the third standard deviation below the mean; .135 per cent of the data lie above three standard deviations above the mean, and .135 per cent of the data lie below three standard deviations below the mean. The standard deviation is especially useful in equating two groups and in determining the adequacy of a sample. If, for example, it were wished to conduct a study on two groups of fifty subjects each that were comparable with respect to weight, equal or nearly equal standard deviations of the weights of the two groups would usually be considered to indicate that the two groups had been equated with respect to that factor.

73. The **critical ratio** (CR) is a device commonly used to determine whether the difference between statistics (e.g., means) of two sets of data is a difference due to chance (i.e., sampling errors) or whether the difference is a "true" difference (i.e., the populations from which the sets of data were drawn are different in the items measured). In data falling in a normal distribution the critical ratio may be interpreted as follows: a critical ratio of 1 indicates that, if an experiment were repeated on one hundred groups of the same number of subjects drawn from the same population, a difference as large as the one obtained in the original experiment would, by chance alone, be expected in 32 (i.e., $100 - 68$) per cent of the groups, and hence, in all probability, the difference is not statistically significant; a critical ratio of 1.96 indicates that such a difference would, by chance alone, be expected in 5 (i.e., $100 - 95$) per cent of the groups, and hence, very probably, the difference is statistically significant; and a critical ratio of 2.58 indicates that such a difference would, by chance alone, be expected in 1 (i.e., $100 - 99$) per cent of the groups, and hence, most probably, the difference is statistically significant.

74. The degree of relationship between two or more series of data may be obtained by the process of correlation. The values of a **coefficient of correlation** (r) vary from $+ 1.0$, a perfect positive relationship, to -1.0, a perfect negative relationship. These are pure numbers and do not indicate the value of a coefficient of correlation in terms of a percentage. The significance of this pure number might be explained as follows. Assume that one hundred persons each pitched ten pennies and recorded the numbers of heads, and then repeated the process. If the number of heads pitched by each person in the first pitching were compared with ("correlated against") that of the second pitching, the r between the two sets of pitchings would be 0; that is, the result would be due entirely to chance. Then assume that one hundred persons each pitched ten pennies and recorded the number of heads, and then, leaving three pennies lie, repeated the process with the other seven pennies and recorded the number of heads of the seven pennies pitched plus those of the three pennies that were not pitched. Then the r between the two sets of pitchings would be .3, which value would indicate the proportion of heads common to both sets of pitchings.

If there is a relationship between two series of data, one series of data may be predicted from the other. The accuracy of the prediction depends upon the size of the degree of relationship. There is, for example, a rather high relationship between scores made in the running high jump and those made in the standing broad jump. Hence if an individual's record in the running high jump is known, his record in the standing broad jump may be predicted fairly accurately. The equation for predicting the score is called a **regression equation**.

Although the interpretation of the values of r depends upon the variables under consideration, the following is a fair guide: r of .00 to .20 = negligible relationship; r of .20 to .40 = slight relationship; r of .40 to .70 = substantial relationship, and r of .70 to 1.00 = high to very high relationship.

75. A **coefficient of product-moment correlation** (r) expresses the relationship between two variables.

76. A **coefficient of biserial correlation** (r_{bis}) expresses the relationship between a continuous variable (one that can be measured in regular increments) and a variable that can be conveniently measured only by a classification into two categories (dichotomous variable). The number of baskets made in thirty seconds is a continuous variable. If the numbers of baskets made by players who failed to make the squad and the numbers of baskets made by players who succeeded in making the squad are tabulated, the two groups of players constitute the dichotomous variable.

77. A **coefficient of triserial correlation** (r_{tris}) expresses the relationship between a continuous variable and a variable that can be conveniently measured only by a classification into three categories (trichotomous variable). The standing broad jump can be measured in inches and hence is a continuous variable. If the number of inches jumped by groups of prepubescent, pubescent, and postpubescent boys are tabulated, the three groups of boys constitute the trichotomous variable.

78. A **coefficient of partial correlation** expresses the relationship between two variables when the influence of one or more other variables has been "held constant" or "partialed out." For example, there is a positive correlation between performance in the shot-put and chronological age. The correlation of age with the shot-put, however, is probably not due to age alone, but to the fact that older boys are taller and heavier than younger boys. Hence the correlation between age and the shot-put may be due partly to differences in height and in weight as well as to differences in maturity. The correlation between the shot-put and age, with the influence of height and of weight eliminated, is much lower than the correlation between the shot-put and age. The effect of holding height and weight constant may be illustrated as follows. If the data on the ages, the heights, the weights, and the shot-put records of several thousands of subjects were written on separate cards and these cards were dealt into piles according to height so that in each pile were records of boys of one height only, and then each height pile were dealt into subpiles according to weight, there would be a large number of small piles in each of which the heights and the weights were the same. In each of these piles height and weight would be "constant." If now the ages were correlated against the shot-put records for each of these piles, the correlation would be between age and the shot-put, with height and weight held constant. The average[1] of these numerous r's between the shot-put and age would correspond, roughly, to a coefficient of partial correlation between the shot-put and age, with height and weight held constant. The symbol for a coefficient of partial correlation is an r with two subscripts followed by a period followed by one or more subscripts ($r_{01.23}$). The variables correlated precede the period. The variables held constant follow the period. The *order* of a coefficient of partial correlation is indicated by the number of variables held constant.

79. By means of a **multiple regression equation** scores in one variable may be predicted from scores in several other variables; for example, the weight of an adult male (age, 18 to 24 years) may be accurately predicted from the following multiple regression equation (in metric units): weight = .236 (height) + .964 (chest girth) + 1.140 (hip width) + 2.480 (knee width) − 112.8. The *weightings* of .236, .964, 1.140, 2.480, and −112.8 are determined algebraically from the r's, the SD's, and the Mns. The r between weight and the items on the right of the equality sign is equal to the **coefficient of multiple correlation** ($R_{0.1234}$: 0 = weight; 1, 2, 3, and 4 = height, chest girth, hip width, and knee width, respectively).

80. In a **factorial analysis,** which is a method of correlational research, several factors are isolated, and coefficients of correlation, which are called "factor loadings," are obtained between each of these factors and the individual variables or test items. The usefulness of this method is that the factors which emerge from the computations frequently cannot be obtained readily in any other manner. For example, in such a variable as the standing high jump, the relative contributions of strength and contraction speed of muscle (positive contributions), and of "dead" weight (weight not contributing to success in the performance, a negative contribution) may be determined.

---

[1] Only r's that do not vary greatly in size may be averaged with justification. See: Henry E. Garrett, *Statistics in Psychology and Education*[4], p. 146.

CHAPTER 5

RATING

81. THIS CHAPTER is concerned with methods of constructing and using rating scales. Rating scales for specific purposes may be found in Chapters 21, 22, and 29.

82. Ratings are subjective estimates. They are useful, primarily, for the measurement of items for which no objective method of measurement exists or for the measurement of items for which the existing objective method of measurement is impracticable.

The use of ratings may, in some instances, be preferable to that of equally valid and equally practicable objective methods of measurement. If objective measurements were always interpreted in relation to the person concerned, the two indicated methods of evaluation would, theoretically, be equally adequate. Frequently, however, objective measurements are interpreted only in relation to the group concerned. Since ratings, however, are based on the observation of the person being rated, they are, of necessity, interpreted in relation to the person concerned, and hence tend to cause the rater to become acquainted, on an individual basis, with the person being rated.

83. CHOOSING ELEMENTS OF ITEM TO BE RATED

(1) The opinions of experts concerning what the important elements of the item to be rated are may be secured. If ability to play basketball is to be rated, opinions of expert basketball coaches may be secured concerning what the elements of that ability are. (2) The item to be rated may be analyzed into parts. All the activities of a basketball player during a game, for example, may be noted and classified, and then tabulated for their frequency of occurrence. The importance, as well as the frequency of occurrence of each element, should be considered. A basketball guard, for example, in the present-day five-man defense dribbles slowly down the back court much more frequently than he tries to make a basket. Making a basket, however, may be considered to be of more importance than dribbling. A player's dribbling in such a way that it results in a teammate's scoring may be considered to be of still more importance than the dribbler's occasional attempt to make a basket.

84. DEFINITION OF ELEMENTS TO BE RATED

The elements to be rated need to be defined in such a way that they not only may be understood but also that they cannot be misunderstood. The reliability of ratings is dependent in no small degree upon the rater's understanding what the elements are that are being rated. If, for example, ability to block in football is being rated, the rater needs to know whether successful blocking means "performance of the standardized movements skillfully whether or not the opponent is taken out" or "performance of the standardized movements successfully with the opponent's being taken out." The elements should, in so far as it is possible, be defined in terms observable by the rater. If, for example, character is being rated, the elements of character should be presented in terms of behavior observable in the gymnasium and on the athletics field.

In addition to a general definition of the element to be rated, the characteristics of the highest, the lowest, and the middle rating should be given. If, for example, an element is rated in seven categories, the requirements for ratings *1*, *4*, and *7* should be specified.

85. RATING DEVICES

If a standardized method of rating is used, the ratings of a number of raters made at the same time may be compared with each other, and the ratings made at one time may be compared with those made at other times. If the standardized method of rating is of such a nature that the rating is done by categories, the ratings can be treated statistically. The following rating devices vary in their efficacy. Some are presented primarily in order that attention may be called to their shortcomings.

86. Absolute ratings. An item may be arbitrarily rated in terms of a percentage on a scale that runs from *0* to *100*. This method of rating is usually more inaccurate than most of the other methods of rating proposed in this chapter. Raters tend not to rate below 50 per cent, and to average at least as high as 75 per cent. Such a high average is due to the fact that raters are accustomed to consider marks lower than 70 to 75 per cent to be failures. Because of the inconsistency of raters' interpretations of percentages, then, this method of rating is not recommended.

87. Man-to-man rating scale. In the man-to-man rating scale each rater selects five persons who are representatives of five different degrees of the ability being rated. A rating of 100 is assigned to the best representative, 0 to the poorest, 50 to a representative midway between the best and the poorest, 75 to a representative midway between the average and the best, and 25 to a representative midway between the average and the poorest. Each rater, then, rates, according to his own scale, all the persons under consideration. The man-to-man rating scale is a cumbersome method, and may cause attention to be given to the specific characteristics for which each of the five representatives is best known rather than to the level of the ability that each person has been chosen to represent. Since different raters using this method tend to be inconsistent with each other in their ratings, the method is not highly recommended.

88. Ratings according to categories. Usually five categories are sufficient. However, if raters tend not to use the first and the fifth category, a rating scale comprised of seven categories is recommended. After the ratings have been made, the ratings in the first and the second category may be combined, and those in the sixth and the seventh category may be combined; hence the result is a five-category scale.

Defined categories. The following is an example of a rating scale made up of seven defined categories for the evaluation of athletic ability: 7 = all-conference material; 6 = varsity material; 5 = subvarsity or substitute material; 4 = good intramural material; 3 = poor intramural material; 2 = not good enough for regular intramural teams—a "dub"; and 1 = very poor skills—terrible!

Nondefined categories. The persons who are average in the ability being rated may be indicated by 0; the persons slightly better or poorer than average by +1 and by −1, respectively; the persons decidedly better and poorer than average by +2 and by −2, respectively; and the excellent and the very poor persons by +3 and by −3, respectively. The successful use of this kind of rating scale requires a sort of mathematical sense, and is probably not so good as the preceding or the following scale.

89. Ratings according to curve of probability. The following scale is one of the best types of rating scales made up of categories: 5 = excellent—6%; 4 = good—25%; 3 = fair—38%; 2 = poor—25%; and 1 = very poor—6%. In this type of scale usually only five categories are needed. If seven categories are desired, the following ratings and percentages may be used: 7 = superior—2%; 6 = excellent—9%; 5 = good—23%; 4 = average—32%; 3 = poor—23%; 2 = very poor—9%; and 1 = just terrible—2%. In both the preceding scales the percentages may, and usually will, because of the usual variations of samples, vary somewhat from the ones suggested.

A rating scale based on the curve of probability can be used with justification only if the group being rated represents a random sample. All the pupils in a gymnasium class or all the pupils in one grade would, in a sizable school, very probably constitute a random sample. A university football squad would not constitute a random sample; it would, rather, represent, in truncated form, the top segment of the curve of probability. If this top segment, a varsity squad, for example, is to be rated, it is advisable to use a scale with seven categories representing more than the varsity group, and to assign numerical values to the lines separating the adjacent intervals as well as to the middle of each interval. Such a rating scale is illustrated in Figure I (p. 24). If a varsity squad is rated by such a scale, no varsity player is likely to receive a rating lower than 8, and hence 8 to 14 constitutes a scale with seven categories representing the top 34 per cent. The categories 8 to 10, 10 to 12, and 12 to 14, then, represent 68 per cent (23 ÷ 34), 26 per cent (9 ÷ 34), and 6 per cent (2 ÷ 34), respectively, of the varsity players. The percentages for each of the ratings from 8 to 14 are approximately as follows: 8 = 42%-52%; 9 = 26%-36%; 10 = 12%-18%; 11 = 4%-7%; 12 = 1%-3%; 13 = 1%-2%; and 14 = 0-1%. Since the distribution represented by ratings 8 to 14 is not a normal one, there will be numerous players in the lowest category and perhaps no player in the highest one or two categories.

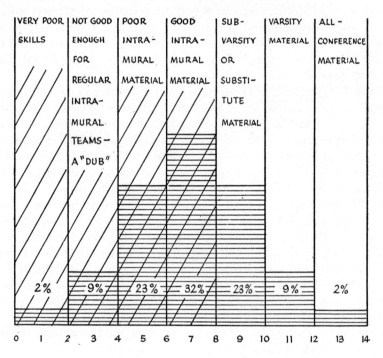

FIGURE I. Rating Scale for a Group of Varsity Players

90. Graphic scales. Graphic scales are considered to be excellent rating devices.

Linear scale. A line is divided into five equal intervals, with the interval at the extreme left labeled "poorest" and the interval at the extreme right labeled "best." The rater places an X in the interval that represents the degree of the quality possessed by the person being rated. Rating by means of this type of linear scale is probably not so effective as either of the two following methods.

A linear scale based on the curve of probability and a linear scale with the categories described may be combined for a rating scale. This type of combined scale is an excellent one for use if the evaluations are made by inexperienced raters.

In all the graphic scales described, the rater places an X in the interval that represents the degree of the quality possessed by the person being rated. If in doubt whether to place an X in one interval or in an adjacent interval, the rater may place an X on the line separating the two intervals. Placing the X on a line adds four categories to the scale with five categories, and six categories to the scale with seven categories. The scoring of the ratings is simplified if the base line of the scale with five categories is ten centimeters long, and if the base line of the scale with seven categories is fourteen centimeters long. If a centimeter ruler is so placed beneath the base line that the left end of the ruler coincides with the left end of the base line, 1 on the ruler coincides with the middle of the first interval, 2 with the line between the first and the second interval, 3 with the middle of the second interval . . . 9 with the middle of the fifth interval . . . 13 with the middle of the seventh interval.

Extreme-ly poor	Very poor	Poor	Average	Good	Excel-lent	Superior
2%	9%	23%	32%	23%	9%	2%

Very poor	Poor	Average	Good	Excel-lent
6%	25%	38%	25%	6%

Linear Scales according to Probability

General Aggres-siveness

Never "starts things"; always waits until the situation forces action

Always takes part in whatever is going on; makes things happen

Dribbling Ability

Very poor. Usually has the ball taken away from him by the opponents

Fair. Retains the ball most of the time

Very good. Almost impossible to stop and always retains control of the ball

Linear Scales with Categories Described

91. Lapp Rating Method.[1] Each pupil is given a list of the names of the members of the class, and is requested to put a + before the names of 25 per cent of his classmates whom he considers to be the best fourth in the quality being rated, and a − before the names of 25 per cent of his classmates whom he considers to be the poorest fourth in the quality being rated. The +'s and the −'s are then tabulated. The score for each pupil is the difference between the number of +'s and the number of −'s. In a class of forty the highest score is 40 +'s, and the lowest score is 40 −'s. A score of 0 indicates that a pupil is average in the ability being rated. The scores based on the number of +'s and −'s may be converted into scores comparable with scores derived from the use of a scale with five or seven categories. The range (in a class of forty the maximum range is 81, that is, from 40 +'s to 40 −'s, with 0 counted as a score) is divided by the number of categories (5 or 7), and values are assigned accordingly. In a scale with five categories, for example, −40 to −25 is recorded in the first interval, −24 to −9 in the second interval, −8 to +8 in the third interval (0 scores are recorded in the middle category), +9 to +24 in the fourth interval, and +25 to +40 in the fifth interval.

A pupil's rank in a group determined by the number of +'s and −'s that he receives from classmates may, by the conversion of the ranks into percentages, be compared with his rank in another group and/or with his rank determined by a different number of raters. A ranking of 27 in a group of 40, for example, is equivalent to 68 per cent, while a ranking of 27 in a group of 37 is equivalent to 73 per cent. The percentages may also be converted into T-scores (see Secs. 123-24).

The Lapp Rating Method has the advantage that the raters are not requested to rank, or to assign numerical values to, the persons being rated.

92. VALIDITY OF RATINGS

The average rating of a number of raters is usually more valid than the rating of one rater. The validity of a rating is increased, approximately in accordance with the Spearman-Brown Prophecy Formula (see Sec. 686), by the addition of competent raters. However, a rating made by one competent rater is more valid than the average of ratings made by ten incompetent raters.

The combination of the ratings of a number of subitems is usually more valid than a rating of the item as a whole. The validity of a rating is increased, approximately in accordance with the Spearman-Brown Prophecy Formula, by the careful fractionating of large items. The subitems may also be weighted according to their importance; for example, in the rating of basketball players for their value to the team, timing ability

[1] Personal communication from Vernon W. Lapp.

would probably be weighted more heavily than ability to dribble accurately at full speed.

The rating of a definitely stated item is more valid than that of an indefinitely stated item. Moral courage and egotism, for example, would probably be rated less validly than perseverance, while "continues to fight when the team is behind" would be more validly rated than "perseverance."

The validity of a rating is affected by the rater's degree of assurance of his rating. A rater's degree of assurance may be recorded as follows: $0 = $ a mere guess; $1 = $ slight inclination; $2 = $ fair assurance; and $3 = $ positive assurance. In a study on the ratings of character (see Sec. 475) the ratings were valid when the rater's degree of assurance was 2 or 3, and invalid when the rater's degree of assurance was 0 or 1.

In the same age groups a rating made by a person of the same sex is usually more valid than a rating made by a person of the opposite sex, at least so far as physical activities and traits of character are concerned. The sex of the rater is of little importance, however, in the case of the rating of young children by adult teachers.

The validity of a rating is frequently lowered by what is called the "halo effect." Thus raters tend to rate a person whom they like, or toward whom they are favorably disposed, too high in everything; and they tend to rate too low a person to whom they do not respond favorably. To avoid this effect as much as possible, the rater should be requested to rate the first item for each person, then the second item for each person, and so on.

The validity of a rating is increased if the raters are given instruction and practice in how to use the selected rating device, and if they discuss their ratings with one another. If a rater has a strong prejudice that would affect his rating, his rating should not be counted; for example, if a rater were strongly prejudiced against a child who occasionally used profanity, or if he were strongly prejudiced in favor of a child with an excellent posture, he would be likely to introduce a certain kind of "halo," which effect would impair the validity of the rating.

93. RELIABILITY OF RATINGS

(1) The ratings of all the raters may be intercorrelated, and the ratings made on one occasion may be correlated with ratings of the same persons made a week or two later. (2) The ratings of a group of raters may be correlated with previously validated ratings. (3) The rating assigned to each person by each rater may be compared with the average rating assigned to that person by all the raters. The comparison may be expressed in terms of the number of intervals of deviation from the average. If, for example, a scale with seven categories is used, and the average rating assigned to a person by a group of raters is represented by the fourth in-

terval, then ratings that fall in the third and the fifth interval represent a deviation of one interval from the average rating. Any rater whose ratings deviate by more than one interval from the average rating of the group of raters should be requested to re-examine his ratings.

The reliability of ratings may be increased both by the increase of the number of competent raters and by an increase in the number of relevant subitems being rated. The increase by both methods is, approximately, in accordance with the Spearman-Brown Prophecy Formula. The reliability of ratings made by two competent raters (r obtained for the two ratings = .6667), for example, is increased from .80 (the reliability of the *sum* of the two ratings computed by the Spearman-Brown Prophecy Formula) to approximately .86 by the addition of one skilled rater, and to .89 by the addition of two more skilled raters. An average coefficient of inter-correlation of .90 [2] has been obtained between three coaches' ratings of a football squad. The r of reliability of the combined ratings, as computed by the Spearman-Brown Prophecy Formula, is .967.

[2] Personal communication from George Wells.

CHAPTER 6

TEST CONSTRUCTION

94. ELEMENTS TO BE MEASURED

IF THE ITEM to be measured is not a specific element, but rather a general quality (e.g., motor ability), the specific elements that make up the general quality need to be determined.

General-athletic ability has been analyzed by Cozens,[1] on the basis of opinions of experts, into the following specific elements: (1) arm-and-shoulder-girdle strength with some abdominal strength; (2) arm-and-shoulder-girdle co-ordination; (3) hand-eye, foot-eye, arm-eye co-ordination; (4) jumping or leg strength; (5) endurance (sustained effort); (6) body co-ordination, agility, and control; and (7) speed of legs with co-ordination of body.

Sixty-one specific elements were, on the basis of opinions of experts, selected by Kistler for classifying high-school boys for physical activities. These elements were classified in the following categories: "age-height-weight-build, strength, skill, health, personality, educability, and motor ability." [2]

Motor ability has been considered by Brace[3] to be made up of elements concerned with the readiness with which new activities are learned.

95. CRITERION

A criterion that adequately represents all the components of the item to be measured needs to be established. If a valid criterion already exists, it may be used for the validation of new tests. This method, to date, has not been widely used in physical and health education. Intelligence tests, on the other hand, have not infrequently been validated by being correlated with a number of composite scores obtained from other intelligence tests that had been proved to be highly valid. The criterion, in order to be acceptable, must be valid regardless of how complicated it turns out to be.

96. Composite score for large number of activities. If one or more activities

[1] Frederick W. Cozens, *The Measurement of General Athletic Ability in College Men*, p. 127.

[2] Joy W. Kistler, "The Establishment of Bases for Classification of Junior and Senior High School Boys into Homogeneous Groups for Physical Education," *Research Quarterly*, December, 1937, p. 13.

[3] David K. Brace, *Measuring Motor Ability*.

are used for the measurement of each of the specific elements of a general quality, the criterion for the general ability may be represented by the composite score of the activities. Cozens, for example, used as a criterion for general-athletic ability the sum of the T-scores for forty-one motor tests, each of which was considered to represent some aspect of the seven specific elements into which general-athletic ability had been analyzed. In the measurement of a general ability this type of criterion is the most useful.

97. Comparative success of two contrasted groups. A criterion may be established on the basis of differences between the performances of two contrasted groups. A criterion for innate ability to play basketball, for example, may be based on differences between certain performances of an intramural and a varsity basketball group. Each group executes the selected motor performances. Those motor performances between which the two groups show the greatest differences in terms of the standard deviations of the differences are selected as criteria. In order that the differences in performance may not be due primarily to differences in training and in experience, skills indirectly related to basketball should be selected for measurement rather than ones directly related to basketball. The Johnson Test for Basketball Potentiality (see Sec. 553) is an example of such a type of selection.

The following method for the establishment of a criterion is a variation of the method described in the preceding paragraph. Initially, instead of two contrasted groups, one large group (e.g., 400 college men) representing a large range of ability executes the performances, which are scored compositely as described in the preceding section. On the basis of these scores, two contrasted groups are selected, one composed of the performers that received the highest 25 per cent of the scores, and the other composed of the performers that received the lowest 25 per cent of the scores. The scores *for each performance* are then tabulated for each group, preferably with the scores of the highest 25 per cent of the group being tabulated on one side of a vertical line, and the scores of the lowest 25 per cent of the group being tabulated on the other side of the vertical line. Those performances in which the distributions of scores for the two groups do not overlap constitute valid tests (Table 1, p. 31), while those performances in which the distributions of scores for the two groups overlap markedly do not constitute valid tests (Table 2, p. 31), for the latter performances do not distinguish between competent and incompetent performers.

98. Rating by experts. A rating scale with approximately seven intervals should be used. If the performers are difficult to rate in, say, five to seven categories, they may be rated simply as *cans* and *cannots*. Seventy-five candidates for a freshman basketball squad, for example, might be divided into two groups: (1) those accepted for the squad and (2) those not accepted for the squad. The relationship between the performances with

Table 1

OVERLAPPING (SMALL) OF TWO DISTRIBUTIONS OF SCORES

Pull-ups (no.)	Performers (no.)	
	Highest 25 per cent	Lowest 25 per cent
15	1	
14		
13	1	
12	3	
11	Mn = 9.25 8	
10	SD = 1.42 25	
9	11	
8	8	
7	2	
6	1	1
5		4
4		8 Mn = 2.72
3		11 SD = 1.51
2		13 CR = 3.1
1		16
0		7
	N = 60	60

Here there is almost no overlapping between the distributions of the number of pull-ups of the best and the poorest 25 per cent of the performers, and there is a large
difference between the means. According to this set of
scores (fictitious data), pull-ups should differentiate
well between the motor ability of good and of poor performers.

Table 2

OVERLAPPING (LARGE) OF TWO DISTRIBUTIONS OF SCORES

Free Throws Made out of 25 Trials (no.)	Basketball Players (no.)	
	Highest 25 per cent	Lowest 25 per cent
20	1	
19	0	1
18	3	2
17	6	4
16	13	12
15	Mn = 15.33 14	9 Mn = 14.43
14	SD = 2.01 10	10 SD = 2.49
13	6	6 CR = .281
12	4	4
11	0	6
10	2	2
9	1	2
8		2
	N = 60	60

Here there is a great amount of overlapping between
the distributions of the number of free throws made
by the best and the poorest 25 per cent of the players, and there is a very small difference between
the means. According to this set of scores (fictitious data), the number of free throws made out of
twenty-five trials would not differentiate well between the basketball ability of good and of poor
players.

respect to the two groups may be determined by a coefficient of biserial correlation.[4] Similarly the performers may be rated in three categories: (1) those accepted for the squad, (2) those retained for training but not accepted for the squad, and (3) those not retained for training. In this case the relationship between the performances with respect to the three groups may be determined by a coefficient of triserial correlation.[4]

99. Artificially devised standards. The following seven performances[5] were devised for the formulation of a criterion of motor educability that is independent of strength.

Finger ladder-up. Move index fingers and thumbs upward alternately to create illusion of continuous climbing. Score = number of times that performance is executed in ten seconds.

Finger ladder-down. Move index fingers and thumbs downward alternately to create illusion of continuous descending. Score = number of times that performance is executed in ten seconds.

Meeting of fingers. Starting position: standing, arms raised sideways to level of shoulders, forearms extended, eyes closed. Keeping forearms extended at level of shoulders, bring ends of index fingers together in front of face. Score = number of trials necessary for three successful performances.

Grasping nose and opposite ear. Grasp left ear with right hand, and nose with left hand. Release left ear and nose, and clap hands. Grasp right ear with left hand, and nose with right hand. Release right ear and nose, and clap hands. Score = number of times that performance is executed correctly in fifteen seconds.

Grasping nose and opposite ear without clapping hands. Score = number of times performance is executed correctly in fifteen seconds.

Raising indicated finger. Cross wrists, with palms facing each other, in front of face. Clasp fingers, rotate hands downward toward body, and then upward and forward. When administrator of test indicates a given finger without touching it, raise finger indicated. Score = number of times that indicated fingers are raised correctly in ten trials.

Chopsticks. Move, with two pencils held in fingers of one hand, as many peanuts as possible from one plate to another. Score = number of peanuts moved successfully in fifteen seconds.

The performances were T-scored, and the sum of the T-scores was the criterion. This criterion did not prove to be a useful one in the studies cited; it is cited here solely as an example of an artificially devised criterion.

100. Analyses of courses of study. A criterion especially usable for measurements of knowledge may be established on the basis of materials included in a number of courses of study. A criterion so established,

---

[4] The biserial or the triserial method of correlation may be validly used *only* if the dichotomous or the trichotomous variable is normally distributed. Such an assumption is not always valid in relation to candidates for an athletics team (see Sec. 89).

[5] Gertrude Barton, "A Comparative Study of the Brace Type of Test and the Johnson Type of Test as Measurers of Motor Educability in the Senior High School Girl (M.A. Thesis, State University of Iowa, 1935).

Hazel M. Roads, "A Comparative Study of the Brace Type of Test and the Johnson Type of Test as Measurers of Motor Educability in the Senior High School Girl as Shown by Two Selected Criteria" (M.A. Thesis, State University of Iowa, 1936).

however, is an indication of what is being taught and not necessarily of what should be taught.

101. Increase of scores with age. The average motor ability of boys of senior-high-school age and of girls eight to at least fourteen and one-half years of age increases with each year of life. Hence, in these groups, the average score in motor performance each year should be greater, or certainly not less, than that of the preceding year. If, for example, an average score in motor performance for persons fourteen years old were less than that for persons thirteen years old, the validity of the method of measurement would be questionable.

102. PRELIMINARY SELECTION OF METHODS OF MEASUREMENTS

All the valid tests for the elements of the ability to be measured should be assembled, and, in the absence of such valid tests, new tests for the same purpose should be devised. A selection of these tests should be made on the basis of the following considerations. (1) Tests that require the use of expensive apparatus should be eliminated unless the test is being formulated for a specific situation in which such apparatus is available. (2) Tests in which performance is unduly limited at either end of the range should be eliminated unless other tests are included that compensate for this deficiency. If, for example, a test results in the successful performance of 75 per cent of a group, either it should be eliminated, or it should be compensated for with a test resulting in the unsuccessful performance of 75 per cent of the group. (3) Tests with inadequate means of being scored should be eliminated. (4) Tests that can contribute to the development of the skill of the performer without losing their value as methods of measurement should be retained in preference to tests without such values. In the measurement of the ability to make baskets in basketball, for example, a test that affords the performer an opportunity for practice in this activity is preferable to an artificial method of measurement that involves skills not used in the playing of basketball.

103. PRELIMINARY TRIAL OF SELECTED TESTS

After procedures for administering the selected tests have been standardized, the tests should be administered to a group of sixty to one hundred persons typical of the group for which the test is being devised. At least two trials should be given for every performance, and both scores recorded for further use (see Sec. 104). If these records are to be included in the final study, usually the better score of the two trials is used. The results of the preliminary trial should be analyzed, and eliminations of tests made on the bases that follow.

104. Reliability. Unreliable tests should be eliminated. With one exception the reliability may be determined by a correlation of the results of one trial with those of another trial. (This is one reason for having at least two trials in the preliminary study.) The exception concerns tests of the speed with which a person learns new skills. In this case the reliability may, if the tests are arranged in order of difficulty, be determined by a correlation of one half of the results that have been selected at random with the results of the other half, or by a correlation of even-numbered tests with odd-numbered tests.

The degree of reliability required for the retention of a test is dependent partly upon the number of tests in the final battery. If there are only two or three tests in the final battery, the reliability of each test should be, in terms of an r, at least .75. If, for example, the r of reliability of each of two tests is .80, the r of reliability of the combination of the two tests is about .89. If there are more than three tests in the final battery, a lower reliability is acceptable for each test than if there are fewer than four tests in the final battery. If, for example, the r of reliability of each of six tests is about .60, the r of reliability of the battery of six tests is about .90. The coefficients of reliability of a battery of tests are, approximately, in accordance with the Spearman-Brown Prophecy Formula (see Sec. 686).

105. Validity. Invalid methods of measurement should be eliminated. The validity may be determined by a correlation of the measurements with the criterion. In order to be retained for the final battery of tests, the test should have a statistically significant coefficient of correlation with the criterion.

106. Practicability. Methods of measurement that have been indicated to be impracticable should be eliminated.

107. ESTABLISHMENT OF FINAL BATTERY

The tests that have been retained as a result of the preliminary trial discussed in Sections 102 to 106, and the tests that make up the criterion should then be administered to a group of at least one hundred persons, and up to three hundred if possible.[6] The composite score that represents the criterion should be determined, and the coefficient of correlation between those scores and the scores of each of the other tests should be computed. Then the coefficient of correlation between the scores of each of the tests retained from the preliminary trial and the scores of each of the other tests should be computed.[7] All the coefficients of correlation should then be listed in order of value. One of the tests of every pair of tests that have a high correlation with each other may be eliminated. The

---

[6] The number of one hundred is acceptable if the subjects are well disciplined, if they endeavor to put forth their best efforts, if they do not have quite different physical-activity and athletics backgrounds, if there are no discordant elements (e.g., no cripples, and no persons recently ill or just recovering from operations), and if the conditions for accurate testing are exceptionally good.

[7] The total number of r's is $N(N - 1) \div 2$, N representing the number of variables; if nineteen measurements and a criterion are involved, 190 r's need to be computed.

decision of whether or not to eliminate a test is usually made by applying the methods of partial and multiple correlation. If a given test adds nothing statistically significant to the coefficient of multiple correlation, or if it is "partialed out" by another test, it may be eliminated. For example, if Test 1 correlates .80 with the criterion and Test 2 correlates .76 with the criterion, and the two tests correlate .84 with each other, then $r_{02.1} = .250$ and $R_{0.12} = .814$. This R is very little better than $.80\,(r_{01})$; hence it may be considered wise to drop Test 2 from the battery.

The validity of the tests retained as a result of the coefficients of intercorrelation of the tests described in the preceding paragraph may be determined by a coefficient of multiple correlation of those tests with the criterion. This validity is, of course, no higher than the validity of the criterion, and hence needs to be interpreted in terms of the validity of the criterion. Teachers' ratings of intelligence, for example, have an average r of only .36 with intelligence tests. Hence if teachers' ratings of intelligence were used as a criterion and an intelligence test had an r of .5 or .6 with them, the validity of the intelligence test would be only apparently high; that is, the test could be no more valid than the criterion, which was shown to be of low validity.

After some of the tests have been eliminated (as indicated in the first paragraph in this section), the coefficients of correlation of the remaining tests should be arranged in order of value with respect to the coefficients of correlation of the various tests with the criterion. The coefficient of multiple correlation should be computed between the criterion and all the remaining tests, except the test with the lowest coefficient of correlation, in the list just made. If this combination yields almost as high a coefficient of correlation as the combination with all the tests, the test with the lowest coefficient of correlation with the criterion may well be eliminated from the final battery. This procedure should be continued until the elimination of a test causes a statistically significant decrease in the value of the coefficient of multiple correlation. This procedure is facilitated if the Doolittle method is utilized (see Sec. 677).

The last step in the establishment of a battery of tests is the determination of the weighting of each test by means of a multiple regression equation.

The coefficient of reliability of the final battery may be computed mathematically on the basis of the coefficient of reliability of each measurement,[8] or on the basis of the coefficient of correlation between the results of two administrations of the battery to the same group.

108. NORMS

Norms may be in the form of T-scores or in the form of averages, or they may be based on an index obtained by the division of the score by the value derived from the multiple regression equation.

[8] Truman L. Kelley, *Statistical Method*, p. 198.

If a battery of tests is to be used for boys up to seventeen years of age, norms should be computed on the basis of age, height, and weight in terms of a classification index (see Sec. 136). Norms for girls up to the age of fourteen years may be computed on the basis of age alone. One set of norms is adequate for each of the following three groups: senior-high-school girls, college women, and college men.

109. MANUAL

A manual for the administration of a battery of tests should include the following items of information about the battery: (1) purpose, (2) field of usefulness, (3) limitations, (4) method of validation, and the coefficient of correlation with the criterion, and (5) the coefficient of reliability. It should include complete directions for the administration of the battery of tests, together with the apparatus and the space needed, and norms.

If the battery of tests is published only in the manual, a presentation of the underlying research should appear probably in an appendix. If the study is published elsewhere, the scientific aspect of the investigation may well be omitted in the manual.

CHAPTER 7

SCORING TABLES

110. PASS OR FAIL

A PERFORMER is "passed" if he achieves a predetermined standard, and "failed" if he does not achieve a predetermined standard.

111. Achievement or nonachievement of a skill. A standard is established in terms of a definition concerning the requirements for the successful execution of a skill. The requirements for a successful execution of a handspring, for example, might be that the performer execute a handspring in a straight-forward direction (i.e., that the performance not resemble the turning of a cartwheel), and that he alight upon his feet only. If the performer fulfills these requirements in turning a handspring, he receives a score of "passed"; if he does not fulfill these requirements, he receives a score of "failed." This method of scoring is especially useful for stunts, and for exercises in tumbling and on apparatus.

112. Achievement or nonachievement of a record. A standard is established in terms of a record. In the standing broad jump, for example, the standard for a given group may be decided to be 6.5 feet. Performers who execute a standing broad jump of that distance or farther receive a score of "passed"; those who do not, a score of "failed."

113. SCORES IN THREE OR FIVE CATEGORIES

The expected range of the performances of a group is divided into three or five categories. If three categories are used, the lower limits of these categories may be records that may be exceeded by 8, 50, and 92 per cent of the performers. If five categories are used, the lower limits of these categories may be records that may be exceeded by 8, 24, 50, 76, and 92 per cent of the performers. The performance is scored, then, in terms of the number of the category in which it falls. This type of test is illustrated by the California Physical-efficiency Test (see Sec. 370).

114. SCORING TABLES WITH EQUAL INTERVALS

The upper limit of a range of performances is set at a record that probably will not be exceeded by any one in the group to be tested, and the lower limit of the range is set at a record that will probably be exceeded by 90 per cent of the group to be tested. The range is then divided into equal intervals, frequently one hundred in number, and scores are assigned according to the number of the interval in which the performance falls.

A scoring table with equal intervals may be devised as follows. A large group is tested. A score of 50 is assigned to the mean of the performances, and scores of 100 and 0 are assigned to performances that are three standard deviations above and below the mean, respectively. The performances between the mean and 0 are divided into fifty equal intervals, and the performances between the mean and 100 into fifty equal intervals. Scores are then assigned according to the interval (0 to 100) in which the performance falls.

115. SCORING TABLES WITH UNEQUAL INTERVALS FOR TRACK-AND-FIELD EVENTS

116. Universal Scoring Tables.[1] The Universal Scoring Tables include track-and-field events for men[2] and for women. The range of scores in these tables is one thousand points. The world's record for each event, or in the absence of a world's record the best record available, is set at 900 points, and a record that probably could not be exceeded by a performer eight years old is set at 25 points.[3]

The Universal Scoring Tables have been so devised that the number of points assigned to a performance corresponds to the amount of power, relative to the weight of the performer and of the implement used, that is required for the performance. The theory underlying this type of scoring table is that the closer a performer approaches the world's record, the more difficult it is for him to increase his record. A performer can, for example, improve his record in the 100-yard dash from 15 seconds to 14 seconds much more easily than he can improve it from 11 seconds to 10 seconds. For the former improvement he receives 52 points in the Universal Scoring Tables, and for the latter improvement he receives 191 points.

This type of scoring table may be utilized for all performers of different ages, heights, and weights. Since the scores are absolute evaluations of a performer's ability in an event, the score of one performer is comparable with that of every other performer. This type of scoring table

---

[1] Charles H. McCloy, *The Measurement of Athletic Power* (out of print).

[2] Condensations of these scoring tables for men may be found in Tables 87 and 88 (pp. 198-202).

[3] The world's record was set at 900 points in order to allow one hundred points for increases in world's records. The lower limit was set at 25 points in order to allow a few points for a few unpredictably poor records. The world's record may change to such an extent that the one hundred points are inadequate. Such a change, however, is usually due to so great a change in the rules, in the implement, or in the method of the performance of the event itself that the event really becomes a new one; for example: the introduction of the bamboo pole to the pole vault; the change, in the discus throw, of the diameter of the circle from 7 ft. to 2.5 m.; and, in the high hurdles, the change from the glide form to the straight-over form, with the rear leg swung rapidly forward.

may also be utilized in the comparison of performances in one event with those in other events; that is, the scores in one performance are equivalent to those in other performances. For example, 11 seconds in the 100-yard dash (552 points) is almost equivalent to 55.5 seconds in the 440-yard dash, to 5 feet 5 inches in the running high jump, to 10 feet 1 inch in the pole vault, and to 43 feet in the twelve-pound shot-put.

The following formulas were used in the computation of the Universal Scoring Tables, and may be used in the computation of comparable scoring tables for events not included in those tables:

(1) For track events in which the record is in terms of the amount of time taken to walk, run, or skate a distance

$$\text{Points} + 25^4 = \frac{925 \ (\text{world's record})^n}{(\text{time for which points are to be computed})^n}$$

(2) For field events in which the record is in terms of the height or the distance covered

$$\text{Points} + 25^4 = \frac{925 \ (\text{height or distance for which points are to be computed})^n}{(\text{world's record})^n}$$

The values of the n's in these formulas are as follows: running, walking, and skating events, 3.00; high hurdles, 2.5; low hurdles, 2.6; running broad jump, 1.66; running hop-step-jump, 1.74; standing broad jump, 2.17; standing hop-step-jump, 2.17; running high jump, 2.24; standing high jump, 2.5; pole vault, 1.45; fence vault, 2.7; shot-put, 1.5; discus throw, 1.35; javelin throw, 1.23; hammer throw, 1.00; baseball throw, 1.5; basketball, football, and soccerball throw, 2.00; rope climb, 1.00.

In the computation of a scoring table for any event in which the exponent is neither the square nor the cube, the logarithmic method must be used. In computing a scoring table for the shot-put, for example, for which the exponent is 1.5, the following formula is used:

$$\log \ (\text{points} + 25) = \log 925 + 1.5 \ (\log \text{records for which points are to be computed}) - 1.5 \ (\log \text{world's record})$$

Attention is called to the fact that records in such standard track-and-field events as the 100-yard dash and the 220-yard dash and records in such less widely used events as the 20-yard dash, the 35-yard dash, and the 60-yard dash are not always quite comparable. In the former events many more performers have every year tried to break the records than in the latter events. Theoretical world's records in seconds for 20- to 120-yard dashes are as follows (the present records in seconds are given in parentheses): 20 yards, 2.8 seconds (2.8 seconds); 35, 4.0 (4.0); 40,

---

[4] The world's record is represented by 900 points by the subtraction of the 25 from the computed points.

4.4 (4.4) ; 45, 4.8 (4.9) ; 50, 5.2 (5.2) ; 60, 6.0 (6.2) ; 70, 6.8 (7.0) ; 75, 7.3 (7.4) ; 80, 7.7 (8.0) ; 90, 8.6 (8.8) ; 100, 9.4 (9.4) ; 110, 10.2 (10.2) ; 120, 11.0 (11.6).

A theoretical world's record may be computed as follows. The records of a group of superior athletes in the event for which a scoring table is desired and in a related standard event are obtained. If, for example, a theoretical world's record is desired for an 80-yard low-hurdle race, the records of about fifty superior runners, well practiced in this event and in such a standard running event of a similar distance as the 100-yard dash on an outdoor track, are obtained. Both races are administered three or four times on different days, and the best record of each performer in each run is used. The average record for the hurdle race and the average record for the 100-yard dash are computed. The theoretical world's record may be computed by the following formula:

$$\frac{W^{2.6} \text{ for 80-yard hurdles}}{W^3 \text{ for 100 yards}} = \frac{A^{2.6} \text{ for 80-yard hurdles}}{A^3 \text{ for 100 yards}}$$

Solving by logarithms:

$$\log W_{\text{hurdles}} = (3 \log W_{100} + 2.6 \log A_{\text{hurdles}} - 3 \log A_{100}) \div 2.6$$

Similar formulas, with the selection of the appropriate exponents, may be used for the computation of world's records in field events.[5]

117. Scoring tables comparable to the Universal Scoring Tables may be prepared for runs and for dashes in terms of distances run in a given length of time.[6] The method of computing such tables is based on the assumption that the performers run at full speed, and hence the method is not entirely applicable to distances of more than 150 yards. The method is as follows. (1) The distance (d) in yards of the run is determined. (2) The time (t) in seconds in fewer than which no runner is likely to run that distance is determined. (3) The distances (d') in yards to correspond to other times (t') is computed by the following formula:

$$d' = \frac{t(d + 15)}{t'} - 15^7$$

[5] If all exponents are the same, as would be the case, for example, if all events were runs with the exponent 3, the exponents could all be omitted from the formula.

[6] The timing of a large number of runners individually by one timer is, of course, a slow process. The method herewith suggested has been devised to overcome that difficulty.

[7] After a runner has accelerated to his greatest speed, his average velocity is not the distance of the entire run divided by the time for the entire run, for in such a velocity the time required from which the runner starts until he has accelerated to his greatest speed is not taken into account. In the "noteworthy performances" in *Athletic Almanacs*, records for 20, 35, and 50 yards are 2.8, 4, and 5.2 seconds, respectively. The difference between the times for the 50 and the 35 yards, and between the 35 and the 20 yards is 1.2 seconds, which time represents the amount of time required for running the last 15 yards at full speed with a running start. Hence the average velocity for running 15 yards at full speed with a running start is 12.5 yards

For example, if the distance (d) is 100 yards and the time (t) of the criterion record for that distance is 10 seconds, other distances (d') corresponding with other times (t') may be computed by the following formula:

$$d' = \frac{10(100 + 15)}{t'} - 15$$

Distances in yards run in 10 seconds that would correspond to the times required to run 100 yards are as follows: 100 yards, 10 seconds; 97.7, 10.2;

Table 3*

DETROIT PENTATHLON SCORING TABLES (GIRLS)

50-Yard Dash (sec.)		Dash and Throw (sec.)		Obstacle Race (sec.)		Running Broad (ft.-in.)		Baseball Throw (ft.)	
1000	6.0	1000	15.0	1000	10.6	1000	15-8	1000	183
993	6.2	994	15.4	993	11.0	998	15-6	995	175
978	6.4	983	15.8	980	11.4	992	15	986	167
953	6.6	964	16.2	958	11.8	979	14-6	972	159
913	6.8	936	16.6	924	12.2	960	14	950	151
855	7.0	895	17.0	873	12.6	930	13-6	920	143
775	7.2	838	17.4	804	13.0	889	13	878	135
677	7.4	766	17.8	717	13.4	833	12-6	824	127
565	7.6	678	18.2	616	13.8	763	12	759	119
435	7.8	582	18.6	500	14.2	680	11-6	681	111
323	8.0	468	19.0	384	14.6	587	11	596	103
225	8.2	368	19.4	283	15.0	477	10-6	500	95
145	8.4	276	19.8	196	15.4	381	10	404	87
87	8.6	196	20.2	127	15.8	291	9-6	319	79
47	8.8	132	20.6	76	16.2	212	9	241	71
22	9.0	83	21.0	42	16.6	147	8-6	176	63
7	9.2	48	21.4	20	17.0	96	8	122	55
0	9.4	25	21.8	7	17.4	59	7-6	80	47
		11	22.2	0	17.8	33	7	50	39
		3	22.6			16	6-6	28	31
		0	22.8			6	6	14	23
						0	5-6	5	15
								0	7

Score for gold medal....... 3850
Score for silver medal..... 2600
Score for bronze medal..... 1700

*Reproduced by permission of V. S. Blanchard, Director of Health and Physical Education, Detroit Public Schools.

per second (i.e., 15 ÷ 1.2). Hence a runner can run 65 yards with a running start in the same time it takes him to run 50 yards from a standing start. In the formula presented above, the *15* in the $d + 15$ is the allowance made for the distance that, in the time allowed, the runner could run from a running start. The $d + 15$ is multiplied by the time of the world's record for 50 yards, and the product is divided by the time for running 50 yards. The distance in yards for time t' is the result just obtained minus 15 yards. The times instead of the distances may be computed by a similar formula, that is,

$$t' = \frac{t(d + 15)}{d' + 15}.$$

In this case d' is the distance for which each time is computed.

95.6, 10.4; 93.4, 10.6; 91.5, 10.8; 89.5, 11.0; 87.7, 11.2; 85.9, 11.4; 84.1, 11.6; 82.4, 11.8; 80.8, 12.0; 79.3, 12.2; 77.7, 12.4; 76.3, 12.6; 74.8, 12.8; and 73.4, 13.00. These distances and times correspond to a best record of 10 seconds, not 9.4 seconds, for the 100-yard dash. (4) The distances (d') are marked across the lanes. (5) As many runners run as there are lanes and observers. If six lanes and six observers are available, the performances of forty-two boys may be timed in five minutes. Each observer records, when the whistle is blown, the distance that his runner has run. This distance is converted, by the appropriate formula above (3), into a time comparable for running 100 yards, or the distance is converted into points by Table 87 or 88 (pp. 198-202).

Table 4*

DETROIT DECATHLON SCORING TABLES (BOYS)

Events	Points	Chin	Stand. Broad Jump	Overhead Shot	100-Yd. Dash	Sit Up	Run. Broad Jump	Run. High Jump	S. Hop Step Jump	R. Hop Step Jump	Shot-put	Dip
Chin	1000	28	10-2	50	10.0	100	23	6	30	50	50	60
	990	26	9-9	48	10.2	90	21	5-8	28	45	48	55
Stand. Broad J.	980	24	9-6	46	10.6	80	19	5-4	27	42	46	50
	970	22	9-3	44	11.0	70	17	5	26	40	44	45
Overhead Shot	960	20	9	42	11.4	60	16-6	4-10	25	38	42	40
	950	18	8-9	40	11.6	50	16	4-8	24	36	40	35
100-Yard Dash	940	16	8-6	38	11.8	40	15-6	4-6	23	34	38	32
	930	14	8-3	36	12.0	35	15	4-4	22	32	36	29
Sit Up	920	13	8	34	12.2	30	14-6	4-2	21-6	31	34	26
	910	12	7-10	32	12.4	28	14	4-1	21	30	32	23
Run. Broad J.	860	11	7-8	30	12.6	26	13-6	4	20-6	29	30	20
	800	10	7-6	29	12.8	24	13	3-11	20	28	29	18
Run. High J.	730	9	7-4	28	13.0	22	12-6	3-10	19-6	27	28	16
Stand. Hop Step J.	650	8	7-2	27	13.2	20	12	3-9	19	26	27	14
	560	7	7	26	13.4	18	11-6	3-8	18-6	25	26	12
Run. Hop Step J.	460	6	6-9	25	13.6	16	11	3-7	18	24	25	10
	370	5	6-6	24	13.8	14	10-8	3-6	17-6	23	24	9
Shot-put	290	4	6-3	23	14.0	12	10-4	3-5	17	22	23	8
	220	3	6	22	14.2	10	10	3-4	16-6	21	22	7
Dip	160	2	5-9	21	14.4	8	9-8	3-3	16	20	21	6
	110	1	5-6	20	14.6	6	9-4	3-2	15-6	19	20	5
	70		5-3	19	14.8	5	9	3-1	15	18	19	4
	40		5	18	15.0	4	8-8	3	14-6	17	18	3
	20		4-9	17	15.2	3	8-4	2-11	14	16	17	2
Total Points	10		4-6	16	15.4	2	8	2-10	13	15	16	1

Score for gold medal..... 8600
Score for silver medal... 7300
Score for bronze medal... 6500

*Reproduced by permission of V. S. Blanchard, Director of Health and Physical Education, Detroit Public Schools.

118. Scoring tables for Detroit Pentathlon and Decathlon. Excellent scoring tables (Tables 3 and 4, pp. 41 and 42) with unequal intervals are those used by the Detroit Public Schools for their pentathlons and decathlons. The events in these tables are scored on the basis of one thousand points, with the greatest increases in points coming between 460 and 560 points (Table 4). In the running broad jump, for example, one hundred points are given for the improvement from 11 to 11.5 feet, while only ten points are given for the improvement from 8 to 8½ feet or from 21 to 23 feet. The purpose of this type of scoring table is to motivate all-round participation instead of specialism. If a performer is better in some events than in others, he is encouraged to practice the events in which he is poor because his reward for improvement is greater in those events than in events in which he already performs well.

119. STANDARD SCORES

Standard scores for athletics performances, like the scores discussed in the preceding section, are usually based on unequal intervals, for distributions of athletics performances are usually not normal, but systematically skewed; that is, the same number of points is usually not assigned to each unit of performance. Standard scores, unlike the points in the Universal Scoring Tables, which may be used for performers of all ages and of all degrees of training and experience, are comparable only for performers of the same age, training, and experience. Standard scores, also unlike the points in the Universal Scoring Tables, which are applicable only to events of power and to events in which performances are continuous variables, are applicable to all types of performances.

120. Z-scores. A Z-score is the distance of a record from the mean of the records. It is expressed in terms of the standard deviation of the records. If, for example, one record lies .6 standard deviation above the mean, and another record lies 1.2 standard deviations below the mean, the Z-scores are +.6 and −1.2, respectively, for, in this method of scoring, the mean is considered to be 0. The range of Z-scores is usually from + 3 to −3, but may be from +5 to −5 if there is a large number of performers.

121. T-scores.[8] T-scores are variations of Z-scores. They may be computed by the following formulas if the performances vary in accordance with the curve of probability: (1) For events in which the bigger record is the better score

$$\text{T-score} = 50 + \left(\frac{10 \text{ (record} - \text{mean of records)}}{\text{standard deviation of records}} \right)$$

(2) For events in which the smaller record (e.g., times) is the better score

$$\text{T-score} = 50 - \left(\frac{10 \text{ (record} - \text{mean of records)}}{\text{standard deviation of records}} \right)$$

[8] William A. McCall, *How to Measure in Education.*

If the record is equal to the mean of the records, the T-score is equal to 50. If the performances are considered to fall within five standard deviations above and below the mean, then each standard deviation is equal to 10, and hence T-scores of 100 and 0 are five standard deviations above and below the mean, respectively.

If the performances do not vary in accordance with the curve of prob-

Table 5

T-SCORES: PERCENTAGES

Per cent	T-score	Per cent	T-score	Per cent	T-score	Per cent	T-score
99.999971	0	99.38	25	50.00	50	0.62	75
99.999963	0.5	99.29	25.5	48.01	50.5	0.54	75.5
99.999952	1	99.18	26	46.02	51	0.47	76
99.999938	1.5	99.06	26.5	44.04	51.5	0.40	76.5
99.99992	2	98.93	27	42.07	52	0.35	77
99.99990	2.5	98.78	27.5	40.13	52.5	0.30	77.5
99.99987	3	98.61	28	38.21	53	0.26	78
99.99983	3.5	98.42	28.5	36.32	53.5	0.22	78.5
99.99979	4	98.21	29	34.46	54	0.19	79
99.99973	4.5	97.98	29.5	32.64	54.5	0.16	79.5
99.99966	5	97.72	30	30.85	55	0.13	80
99.99957	5.5	97.44	30.5	29.12	55.5	0.11	80.5
99.99946	6	97.13	31	27.43	56	0.097	81
99.99932	6.5	96.78	31.5	25.78	56.5	0.082	81.5
99.99915	7	96.41	32	24.20	57	0.069	82
99.9989	7.5	95.99	32.5	22.66	57.5	0.058	82.5
99.9987	8	95.54	33	21.19	58	0.048	83
99.9983	8.5	95.05	33.5	19.77	58.5	0.040	83.5
99.9979	9	94.52	34	18.41	59	0.034	84
99.9974	9.5	93.94	34.5	17.11	59.5	0.028	84.5
99.9968	10	93.32	35	15.87	60	0.023	85
99.9961	10.5	92.65	35.5	14.69	60.5	0.019	85.5
99.9952	11	91.92	36	13.57	61	0.016	86
99.9941	11.5	91.15	36.5	12.51	61.5	0.013	86.5
99.9928	12	90.32	37	11.51	62	0.011	87
99.9912	12.5	89.44	37.5	10.56	62.5	0.009	87.5
99.989	13	88.49	38	9.68	63	0.007	88
99.987	13.5	87.49	38.5	8.85	63.5	0.0059	88.5
99.984	14	86.43	39	8.08	64	0.0048	89
99.981	14.5	85.31	39.5	7.35	64.5	0.0039	89.5
99.977	15	84.13	40	6.68	65	0.0032	90
99.972	15.5	82.89	40.5	6.06	65.5	0.0026	90.5
99.966	16	81.59	41	5.48	66	0.0021	91
99.960	16.5	80.23	41.5	4.95	66.5	0.0017	91.5
99.952	17	78.81	42	4.46	67	0.0013	92
99.942	17.5	77.34	42.5	4.01	67.5	0.0011	92.5
99.931	18	75.80	43	3.59	68	0.0009	93
99.918	18.5	74.22	43.5	3.22	68.5	0.0007	93.5
99.903	19	72.57	44	2.87	69	0.0005	94
99.886	19.5	70.88	44.5	2.56	69.5	0.00043	94.5
99.865	20	69.15	45	2.28	70	0.00034	95
99.84	20.5	67.36	45.5	2.02	70.5	0.00027	95.5
99.81	21	65.54	46	1.79	71	0.00021	96
99.78	21.5	63.68	46.5	1.58	71.5	0.00017	96.5
99.74	22	61.79	47	1.39	72	0.00013	97
99.70	22.5	59.87	47.5	1.22	72.5	0.00010	97.5
99.65	23	57.93	48	1.07	73	0.00008	98
99.60	23.5	55.96	48.5	0.94	73.5	0.000062	98.5
99.53	24	53.98	49	0.82	74	0.000048	99
99.46	24.5	51.99	49.5	0.71	74.5	0.000037	99.5
						0.000029	100

ability, and usually athletics performances do not, they may be converted into percentiles, which then may be translated into T-scores by the use of Table 5 (p. 44). Methods for the computation of T-scores for two types of performance that do not vary in accordance with the curve of probability follow.

122. **T-scores for performances scored "pass or fail"** (e.g., stunts). The percentage of the performers who are successful is determined, and this percentage is translated into a T-score. If 82 per cent of the performers are successful, the T-score is 41; if 11 per cent of the performers are successful, the T-score is 62. Hence, according to the T-scores, the second performance is much more difficult than the first performance.

123. **T-scores for performances scored as continuous variables** (e.g., high jump). An example of computing T-scores for performances scored as continuous variables is presented in Table 6 (p. 45).

Table 6

T-SCORES AND P-SCORES: COMPUTATION

I	II	III	IV	V	VI	VII	VIII
Running High Jump (ft.-in.)	Fre- quen- cy	Performers Exceeding Each Record (no.)	Fre- quen- cy/2	III + IV	Vx100 N	T- score	P- score
5-0	1	0	.5	.5	.38	77	94
4-11	3	1	1.5	2.5	1.92	71	85
4-10	6	4	3	7	5.38	66	77
4-9	8	10	4	14	10.77	62	71
4-8	16	18	8	26	20.00	58	64
4-7	19	34	9.5	43.5	33.46	54	57
4-6	24	53	12	65	50.00	50	50
4-5	18	77	9	86	66.15	46	43
4-4	18	95	9	104	80.00	42	36
4-3	9	113	4.5	117.5	90.38	37	28
4-2	4	122	2	124	95.38	33	22
4-1	2	126	1	127	97.69	30	17
4-0	1	128	.5	128.5	98.85	27	12
3-11	1	129	.5	129.5	99.62	23	6
	N = 130						

In Column I are presented the class intervals into which the range of records has been divided. The best score is at the top of the column. (In the case of a time, the record of the smallest numerical value appears at the top of the column.) In Column II is presented the number of performers making records in each of the class intervals. Since a T-score represents the mid-point of a class interval, and since it is assumed that half the performances in each interval are above the mid-point of that interval and that half are below it, the frequency for each interval is divided by 2 (Column IV).

The range of the T-scores in Table 6 is from 23 to 77. T-scores for records of more than 5 feet and less than 3 feet 11 inches may be determined by the following method. (1) The records in Column I are plotted against the T-scores in Column VII. (2) A best-fitting line is drawn through the dots of the plotting. (3) The best-fitting line is extended to T-scores of 0 and 100.[9] Such an extrapolation is illustrated in Figure II (p. 46). The only alternative to this method, which is an inaccurate one, is to secure additional records. More than a million records would be needed to obtain T-scores ranging from 0 to 100.

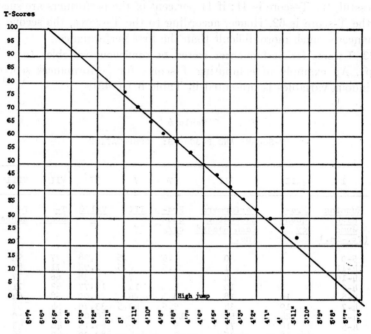

FIGURE II. Extension of T-scores from 0 to 100

Since T-scores are based on a standard deviation of 10, and since most scores fall within three standard deviations above and below the mean, most records receive T-scores ranging from 20 to 80. If the standard deviation is assigned a value of 16.66, the resulting scores range from 0 to 100. Scores based on a standard deviation of 16.66 are here called P-(performance) scores. P-scores are computed in the same way that T-scores are computed, except that the percentages in Column VI of Table 6 (p. 45) are translated into P-scores by the use of Table 7 (p. 47).

124. All T-scores[10] should be plotted against the records from which the T-scores were made in order to determine whether the records repre-

---

[9] Records of 3 feet 6.5 inches and 5 feet 5.5 inches are equivalent to T-scores of 0 and 100, respectively.

[10] From here to the end of the chapter *P-score* may be substituted for *T-score*.

sent a normal or a skewed distribution. If a straight line can be drawn through the dots of the plotting (Fig. II, p. 46), the records may be considered to be normally distributed.

If a straight line cannot be drawn through the dots of the plotting, the records may be considered to be skewed. For example, the plotting of

Table 7

P-SCORES: PERCENTAGES

P-score = $\pm$ 3 SD

Per cent	P-score	Per cent	P-score	Per cent	P-score	Per cent	P-score
99.87	0	93.32	25	50	50	6.68	75
99.851	.5	92.922	25.5	48.803	50.5	6.301	75.5
99.84	1	92.51	26	47.61	51	5.94	76
99.819	1.5	92.073	26.5	46.414	51.5	5.591	76.5
99.80	2	91.62	27	45.22	52	5.26	77
99.781	2.5	91.149	27.5	44.038	52.5	4.947	77.5
99.76	3	90.66	28	42.86	53	4.65	78
99.736	3.5	90.147	28.5	41.683	53.5	4.363	78.5
99.71	4	89.62	29	40.52	54	4.09	79
99.683	4.5	89.065	29.5	39.358	54.5	3.836	79.5
99.65	5	88.49	30	38.21	55	3.59	80
99.621	5.5	87.900	30.5	37.070	55.5	3.362	80.5
99.59	6	87.29	31	35.94	56	3.14	81
99.547	6.5	86.650	31.5	34.827	56.5	2.938	81.5
99.51	7	85.99	32	33.72	57	2.74	82
99.461	7.5	85.314	32.5	32.636	57.5	2.559	82.5
99.41	8	84.61	33	31.56	58	2.39	83
99.361	8.5	83.891	33.5	30.503	58.5	2.222	83.5
99.31	9	83.15	34	29.46	59	2.07	84
99.245	9.5	82.381	34.5	28.434	59.5	1.923	84.5
99.18	10	81.59	35	27.43	60	1.79	85
99.111	10.5	80.785	35.5	26.435	60.5	1.659	85.5
99.04	11	79.95	36	25.46	61	1.54	86
98.956	11.5	79.103	36.5	24.510	61.5	1.426	86.5
98.87	12	78.23	37	23.58	62	1.32	87
98.778	12.5	77.337	37.5	22.663	62.5	1.222	87.5
98.68	13	76.42	38	21.77	63	1.13	88
98.574	13.5	75.490	38.5	20.897	63.5	1.044	88.5
98.46	14	74.54	39	20.05	64	.96	89
98.341	14.5	73.565	39.5	19.215	64.5	.889	89.5
98.21	15	72.57	40	18.41	65	.82	90
98.077	15.5	71.566	40.5	17.619	65.5	.755	90.5
97.93	16	70.54	41	16.85	66	.69	91
97.778	16.5	69.497	41.5	16.109	66.5	.639	91.5
97.61	17	68.44	42	15.39	67	.59	92
97.441	17.5	67.364	42.5	14.686	67.5	.539	92.5
97.26	18	66.28	43	14.01	68	.49	93
97.062	18.5	65.173	43.5	13.350	68.5	.453	93.5
96.86	19	64.06	44	12.71	69	.41	94
96.638	19.5	62.930	44.5	12.100	69.5	.379	94.5
96.41	20	61.79	45	11.51	70	.35	95
96.164	20.5	60.642	45.5	10.935	70.5	.317	95.5
95.91	21	59.48	46	10.38	71	.29	96
95.637	21.5	58.317	46.5	9.853	71.5	.264	96.5
95.35	22	57.14	47	9.34	72	.24	97
95.053	22.5	55.962	47.5	8.851	72.5	.219	97.5
94.74	23	54.78	48	8.38	73	.20	98
94.408	23.5	53.586	48.5	7.927	73.5	.181	98.5
94.06	24	52.39	49	7.49	74	.16	99
93.699	24.5	51.197	49.5	7.078	74.5	.149	99.5
						.13	100

records in squat jumps against the T-scores for these records (Table 8, p. 48) does not result in an arrangement of dots through which a straight line can be drawn (Fig. III, p. 49). The records in the squat jumps, then, may be considered to be skewed.

If the plotting of records against T-scores indicates that the distribution of records is skewed, a curved line should be fitted to the dots. Several methods for fitting such a curve follow.

(1) The records are plotted against the T-scores on a very large sheet of graph paper. By means of a "spline," a long flexible ruler, which can be held in place with weights designed for that purpose, a curve is fitted, by eye, to the dots, and the curve is drawn with a hard pencil. The scores are read off the curve.

Table 8

SQUAT JUMPS: T-SCORES (UNITED STATES NAVY)

Squat Jumps (no.)	Frequency	T-score
76	1	81
72	1	78
68	0	77
64	0	77
60	8	73
56	5	70
52	7	68
48	38	64
44	15	61
40	70	58
36	47	54
32	99	50
28	107	45
24	49	40
20	36	35
16	8	30
12	4	27
8	3	23
	498	

(2) The logarithms of the T-scores are plotted against the logarithms of the records, or the T-scores against the logarithms of the records, or the logarithms of the T-scores against the records.[11] If a straight line can be drawn through the dots of the plotting, the scores can then be determined by equations for straight lines, which equations can be computed by means of simultaneous equations. (If a straight line is not obtained by one of these methods, more complicated methods of mathematical curve-fitting must be used).

The plotting of the logarithms of the records for the squat jumps (Table 8, p. 48) against the T-scores of those records appears in Figure IV (p. 50). A straight line can be drawn through the dots of this plot from the

---

[11] If records for runs are in terms of times, the times are converted into velocities by dividing the distance plus fifteen yards by the time (see Sec. 117).

frequency for the highest record to the third frequency from the lowest record. The lowest three frequencies were discarded, for the chief specialists, athletics, of the Navy should have performed more squat jumps than these frequencies indicate. A straight line goes through the intersection of the logarithm 1.85 and the T-score 78, and also through the

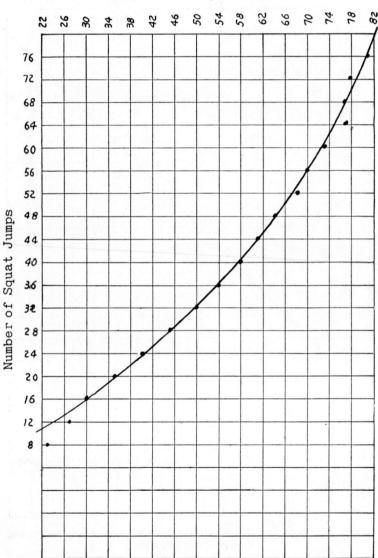

FIGURE III. Curvilinear Relationship of Squat Jumps and T-scores for Squat Jumps

logarithm 1.20 and the T-score 26. The method of fitting the line by simultaneous equations is shown in the lower right-hand quadrant of Figure IV (p. 50). The final scoring tables may be computed from the following equation: T-score = 80 (log squat jumps) − 70.

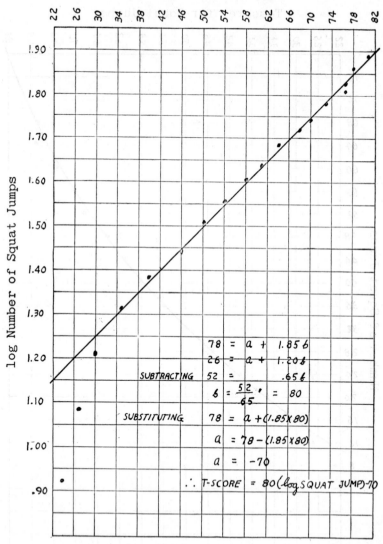

FIGURE IV. Rectilinear Relationship of Logarithms of Squat Jumps and T-scores for Squat Jumps

PART III

Motor Capacity

CHAPTER **8**

SIZE AND MATURITY

125. AGE, HEIGHT, WEIGHT, and body build influence physical performance. Furthermore, persons—young and adult, male and female—of the same age vary in height, in weight, and in body build; of the same height, in age, in weight, and in body build; of the same weight, in age, in height, and in body build; and of the same body build, in age, in height, and in weight. Hence no one of these factors is an adequate basis for classifying performers in physical activities into homogeneous groups; rather a combination of two or more of these factors needs to be used.

126. THEORETICAL CONSIDERATIONS

Classification by means of age, height, and weight is based on the influence of those three variables only; it is not based on innate motor capacity (see Chap. 12). Persons of the same age, height, and weight vary in innate motor capacity. Furthermore, classification on the basis of age, height, and weight is in terms of persons who are in good "condition"; that is, the purpose of classification is not to give handicaps to the lazy, the fat, and the untrained.

127. Theoretical influence of weight. In an adult male of good muscular development, the muscles constitute approximately 40 to 45 per cent (35 to 40 per cent in an adult female) of the weight of the body. An increase, due to training, in the weight of the body of a person *not increasing in height* is not, however, so distributed to the muscles, for the muscles increase in weight faster than the bones and the viscera. Hence the muscles receive more than 40 per cent of the increase in weight. Muscular strength, if other physiological factors and psychological factors are equal, varies about in proportion to the cross-sectional area of the muscles. Therefore,

51

in a person not increasing in height, the cross-sectional area of the muscles increases more rapidly than the weight of the body as a whole, and hence muscular strength increases faster than the load (i.e., the weight of the body as a whole). As a result, an increase in weight is accompanied by an increase in performance ability because the increase in muscular strength is disproportionate to the increase of the load. For example, if a man who weighs 150 pounds has 40 per cent of his weight comprised of muscle, he has 60 pounds of muscle. If he increased in weight to 180 pounds, and if all this increase were muscular weight, his increase in muscular weight, and hence in muscular strength, would be 30 pounds (i.e., 60 + 30), or an increase of 50 per cent. The increase in the load would be 30 pounds (i.e., from 150 to 180), or an increase of 20 per cent. Hence the increase in muscular strength would be proportionately greater than that demanded by the increased load. In this connection it is interesting to note that for North American boys of the ages of ten to sixteen years, inclusive, the regression line between weight and athletics performance is, according to the usual mathematical criteria, within the limits of rectilinearity.

Coefficients of correlation between strength and weight follow:

Age (yr.)	Boys	Girls	Age (yr.)	Boys	Girls
11	.637	.539	15	.709	.460
12	.680	.630	16	.651	.345
13	.803	.560	17	.640	.506
14	.775	.495	18	.653	

These coefficients are for persons homogeneous only in age and in sex. Differences in such items as body build, physical development, motivation, and nutritional status have not been taken into consideration. If such items were held constant, the coefficients for boys would probably run at least 10 per cent higher than the ones given for boys, and those for girls would probably run as much as 20 per cent higher than the ones given for girls.

128. Theoretical influence of height. When a person grows in height, he increases the distances (lengths of limbs) over which his muscular force is applied. If a person could grow in height without increasing his load and without decreasing his muscular strength, his muscular strength, then, would be more effective with the longer limbs than with the shorter limbs. In running, in throwing, and in jumping, the increase in velocity due to increased lengths of limbs would be according to the following formulas: (1) $Fd = .5mV^2$ (F = the force used, d = the distance over which the force is applied, m = the mass, and V = the velocity); and (2) $R = (V^2 \sin 2\theta) \div g$ (R = the range of a body thrown by a force; V = the velocity of the body in the line of flight; θ = the angle of incidence with the horizon, and g = the force of gravity). From the first formula it may be seen that the distance over which the force is applied varies with the square of the velocity. From the second formula it may be seen that the range also varies with the square of the velocity. Consequently, *other factors being equal*, the range increases with an increase in the distance over which the force is applied. Thus distances in running, in throwing, and in jumping are increased—again other factors being equal—by an increase in the height of the performer. It must be remembered, however, that in actual situations the other factors are *not* equal.

If the height increased without a change in the cross-sectional area of the muscles, the weight would increase about in proportion to the increase in height; that is, an increase of 10 per cent in height would be accompanied by approximately a 10 per-cent increase in the weight to be handled, and hence the increase in height would be of no advantage. Hence, theoretically, height *alone* would seem, on the basis of principles of mechanics, to have little influence on performance.

Physiological elements, however, may cause height to have an important effect on physical performance. Since there is for every person, regardless of how strong his muscles may be, a limit to the speed with which he can contract his muscles, a person may have more muscular strength than he can utilize. If a person with an excess of muscular strength increases in height, he can then utilize some of the excess of muscular strength, and hence can increase in velocity, for he then has a greater distance over which he can apply his muscular strength. The longer the limb, the farther the end of the limb moves in a given time with a given angular velocity, and the farther a limb moves in a given time, the greater the linear velocity at the end of the limb.

The amount of force needed to overcome internal resistance is another physiological factor[1] that is of influence in the effect of height on physical performance. If a muscle contracts at high speed, a much smaller proportion of its force is available for the accomplishment of work than if the muscle contracts slowly. The Hill Formula, which is in terms of work, may be translated into terms of force as follows:

$$F_a = F_m \left(1 - \frac{V}{V_m} \right)$$

The F_a is the force available for external work at a particular speed of movement. The F_m is the maximum force that the muscle could exert at zero velocity of contraction, that is, the maximum force that could be exerted by a muscle if a person exerted maximum effort in attempting to lift an immovable object. The V_m is the maximum speed of contraction of which the muscle would be capable if it contracted against no load (not even the weight of the limb). The V in the numerator is the speed of

[1] A. V. Hill, *Muscular Movement in Man: The Factors Governing Speed and Recovery from Fatigue.*

contraction of the muscle. If, for example, one person's legs were two feet long and another person's legs were three feet long, and the legs of both persons moved *through an arc of the same angle in the same time,* the feet at the ends of the longer legs would travel 33 per cent farther than would those at the ends of the shorter legs. Hence the person with the longer legs moving his legs a little more slowly (in terms of angular velocity or in terms of the angle subtended by the limb) would be able to apply a greater proportion of his maximum force to the task. If, in the Hill Formula, 100 per cent were substituted for F_m and various percentages were substituted for V_m, the percentage values for F_a, the force available for external work, for different values of V would be as follows:

V	F_a
Velocity in Terms of Percentage of Maximum Velocity	Force Available for Work (%)
0	100
20	80
40	60
60	40
80	20
100	0

Thus if a muscle were contracting at 20 per cent of its maximum velocity, 20 per cent of its force would be utilized in overcoming internal resistance, and 80 per cent of its force would be available for external work.

One other physiological factor that might be of influence in the effect of height on physical performance is the fact that there is an optimum load for every muscle,[2] and that a muscle does not function at its best either above or below this optimum load. Hence if the weight becomes too great for the cross-sectional area of a muscle (e.g., an excess of height for a given weight), there might be a physiological overload on the muscle with a corresponding reduction in the physiological efficiency of the muscle. The optimum height, however, would probably be near the mean rather than at either of the extremes of the heights for the person's weight (Fig. XXI, p. 165).

Height is directly advantageous in such events as the high jump and the high-hurdle race, for the center of the weight of a tall performer is raised higher from the ground to begin with than is that of a short person, and the tall performer has only to lift his legs out of the way in order to gain this advantage. In events like the shot-put, height is an advantage because the shot in the hands of a tall performer starts from a higher point than a shot in the hands of a short person, and hence the former shot travels farther than the latter shot before it reaches the ground, even if no factors other than height are involved.

[2] William H. Howell, *A Textbook of Physiology*[14], p. 27.

Theoretically, then, performance varies directly with weight, but an increase in height has little influence on performance unless there is an excess of force over the amount that can be used up to the limit of the speed of contraction except for events in which height itself is advantageous. If there is such an excess, performance theoretically varies directly with height up to the point at which there is no such excess of force available.

129. Theoretical influence of age. There is undoubtedly a causal relationship between chronological age (up to a certain maximum) and excellence of athletics performance. There may be, with the increase in chronological age, a greater "muscular maturity," and a stronger will to use complete

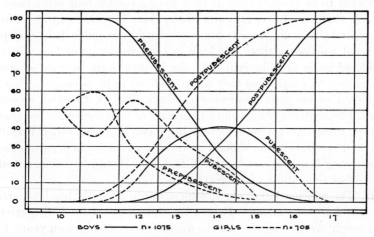

FIGURE V. Stages of Pubescence, Junior-high-school Boys and Girls

effort. Such factors, however, are difficult to analyze. The influence of physiological age on performance, on the other hand, is supported by much evidence. In track-and-field events, postpubescent boys have been found to exceed prepubescent boys of the same age, height, and weight; and in strength the former have been found to exceed the latter by as much as 20 per cent.[3] It is quite possible that the element of pubescence is the major element involved in the influence exerted by age on motor performance. From the curve for postpubescence and chronological age in Figure V (p. 55) it may be seen that from the ages of thirteen to fifteen years, inclusive, the increase in the number of boys becoming postpubescent is practically rectilinear. Below and above these years the curve resembles, in general, an ogive curve. Hence if one is dealing with the averages of

[3] Rowlen B. Keithly, "The Relationship between Physiological Age and Motor and Physical Development" (M.A. Thesis, State University of Iowa, 1939).

Hedley S. Dimock, *Rediscovering the Adolescent*, Chap. 28.

John E. Nevers, "The Effects of Physiological Age on Motor Achievement," *Research Quarterly*, May, 1948.

the performances of large numbers of boys, there is a definite increase, and, from the ages of twelve to sixteen years, inclusive, almost a linear increase in the influence of age on performance although physiological age, and not chronological age, is the factor involved.

130. The best method for accurately measuring physiological age, which may better be called "maturational age," is to X-ray a number of bones, especially the bones of the hands and the wrists, and then to compare the epiphyses of these bones with standard illustrations[4] of epiphyses of bones of persons of different maturational ages.

131. Maturational age[5] may be practicably assessed in three catagories on the basis of physical changes that accompany pubescence. Boys are considered to be prepubescent if they have no pubic hair other than fine hair like that present on all parts of the skin. They are considered to be pubescent as soon as there is pigmentation in the pubic hair, and postpubescent as soon as there is a kink or twist in the pubic hair. Girls are considered to be prepubescent until the breasts begin to show secondary sex changes, at which time they are considered to be pubescent. They are considered to be postpubescent with the arrival of the first menstrual period. The beginnings of each of the stages of pubescence are not sharply marked; rather the stages of pubescence blend into each other. Prepubescents and postpubescents should, however, participate in separate groups if such classifications can be made, and then should be subclassified on bases other than those of pubescence.

132. The relationship of chronological age to strength[6] has been arrived at in the following manner. Regression equations for predicting strength from weight were computed for the ages of eleven to nineteen years. From these regression equations were computed for each age the predicted strength of the preceding and of the following age from the average weight of the preceding and of the following age. For example, the regression equation for the twelve-year-old group was used to compute the predicted strength for the eleven-year-old group from the average weight for the eleven-year-old group, and to compute the predicted strength for the thirteen-year-old group from the average weight of the thirteen-year-old group. If age itself had an effect over and above that involved in weight, the value for the strength of the eleven-year-old group as computed from the formula for the twelve-year-old group should have been greater than the average strength for the eleven-year-old group; likewise the value for the strength of the thirteen-year-old group as computed from the formula for the twelve-year-old group should have been less than the average strength for the thirteen-year-old group. The value that was adopted to

[4] Thomas W. Todd, *Atlas of Skeletal Maturation.*
[5] Charles H. McCloy, *Appraising Physical Status: Methods and Norms,* Chap. 10.
[6] McCloy, "The Influence of Chronological Age on Motor Performance," *Research Quarterly,* May, 1935.

represent the average strength for each year of age was the average of the difference between the average strength of that age and the amount of strength predicted for the average weight of that group from the regression equations for the preceding and the succeeding age. Average increases in strength due to chronological age follow.

| Age (yr.) | Boys | | Girls | |
	Raw Value (lb.)	Smoothed Value (lb.)	Raw Value (lb.)	Smoothed Value (lb.)
11-12	20	20	15	15
12-13	29	30	34	34
13-14	52	55	109	109
14-15	98	100	77	77
15-16	108	105	-3	0
16-17	39	70	-10	0
17-18	59	50	-7	0
18-19	-16	0		

It may be noted in the tabular material that for boys there is a rapid increase in the amount of strength for each year of age from thirteen to sixteen, a sharp decline after seventeen, and no further increase after eighteen. The first period corresponds to the period of active pubescence in the male. For girls the rapid increase in strength comes from the ages of twelve to fourteen years, which period corresponds to the onset of puberty; and strength declines abruptly at the age of fifteen years.

133. The relationship of chronological age to performance in track-and-field athletics[7] has been arrived at in the following manner. Four track-and-field events were used for boys, and three for girls. All the events were scored according to the McCloy Universal Scoring Tables. For boys at the elementary-school level the regression equation was based on weight; and at the high-school level, height, which seemed to be important at that level, was used as the independent variable. For girls the regression equation was based on height and weight. The results follow.

| Age (yr.) | BOYS | | | | GIRLS | |
| | Elementary School | | High School | | Elementary School | |
	Raw Value*	Smoothed Value	Raw Value**	Smoothed Value	Raw Value***	Smoothed Value
10-11	34	34	--	--	50	50
11-12	41	41	--	--	56	56
12-13	44	53	--	--	59	59
13-14	65	65	71	73	-23	33
14-15	67	67	94	77	63	7
15-16	--	--	19	71	0	0
16-17	--	--	159	64	--	--
17-18	--	--	4	38	--	--
18-19	--	--	0	0	--	--

*Computed from weight.
**Computed from height.
***Computed from both height and weight.

[7] Ibid.

134. The results of the study of the influence of chronological age on performance in track-and-field events were somewhat more conflicting than were those of the study relative to age and strength. There were, in track-and-field events, an increase in the number of points scored for each year of age as the boys approached puberty, and a decrease after the adolescence period had been passed. For girls, on the other hand, the maximum increase in points in track-and-field activities was at the period from twelve to thirteen years of age, one year earlier than was the case with strength. In track-and-field events as in strength, however, this increase ceased at the age of fifteen years.

Hence the facts indicate with high probability not only that the relationship between age and motor performance is not a linear one, but that the relationships between height and performance and between weight and performance are also not linear.[8] The facts indicate that the whole problem of the relationship of age, height, and weight to motor performance needs to be studied with sufficiently large numbers of cases to minimize errors due to sampling.

135. LIMITATIONS OF AGE, HEIGHT, AND WEIGHT AS CLASSIFIERS

Age, height, and weight are not entirely adequate bases for classifying pupils for participation in motor activities. As has been pointed out, chronological age is only an approximation of maturational age, and some persons are as old, physiologically, at fifteen years of age as others are at twenty years of age. Even though the correlation between weight and strength is high, weight does not necessarily denote strength. This fact may be partly due to wide variations in ability to contract muscular tissue; that is, some persons are able to "throw" a larger proportion of their muscle fibers into contraction at the same time than are other persons. It is probably also partly due to wide differences in the relative amounts of muscle and fat,[9] which factor, particularly in girls, constitutes a real limitation to the usefulness of weight as a classifier. The problem of the optimum loading of muscles is a further complicating factor. A method of classification that would be very useful in gymnasium classes might not be satisfactory in situations in which maximum efforts were required. Problems introduced by differences in body build are only beginning to be adequately studied. It is probable, however, that the solution of the problem of body build relative to classification will be useful primarily for purposes of research, and not for routine procedures involving classification, although some types of body build may be more amenable than others to classification by formulas based on age, height, and weight.

---

[8] McCloy, *The Measurement of Athletic Power.*
[9] McCloy, *Appraising Physical Status: The Selection of Measurements,* Chaps. **5** and **6.**

Table 9

CLASSIFICATION INDICES: PROPOSED DIVISIONS

CLASSIFICATION INDEX--ELEMENTARY SCHOOL

Range 515-875

Class	For a small group	Class	For a larger group
A	800 and over	A	800 and over
B	770	B	775
C	740	C	750
D	710	D	725
E	680	E	700
F	650	F	675
G	620	G	650
H	619 and under	H	625
		I	600
		J	599 and under

CLASSIFICATION INDEX--JUNIOR HIGH SCHOOL

Range 540-900

Class	
A	875 and over
B	845
C	815
D	785
E	755
F	725
G	695
H	665
I	664 and under

CLASSIFICATION INDEX--HIGH SCHOOL

Range 685-955

Class	For a small group	Class	For a larger group
A	890 and over	A	900 and over
B	860	B	875
C	830	C	850
D	800	D	825
E	770	E	800
F	740	F	775
G	739 and under	G	750
		H	725
		I	724 and under

CLASSIFICATION INDEX--COLLEGE

Range 700-975

Class	For a small group	Class	For a larger group
A	910 and over	A	925 and over
B	890	B	900
C	860	C	875
D	830	D	850
E	800	E	825
F	799 and under	F	800
		G	775
		H	750
		I	749 and under

In spite of their limitations, age, height, and weight are, because of their convenience, and because of their high coefficients of correlation with valid criteria, decidedly useful for classifying persons for competitive sports.

136. In an early statistical study[10] age, height, and weight were combined into what were called "classification indices." The following combination was found to be useful for males of elementary-school, high-school, and college ages:

> Classification Index = 20 age (yr.) + 6 height (in.) + weight (lb.) *or* 20 age (yr.) + 2.5 height (cm.) + 2 weight (kg.) − 12

It was found that age ceased to make a contribution at seventeen years; hence ages of eighteen years and over are scored in the formula as seventeen years. Standards for using these formulas may be found in Table 9 (p. 59).

Table 10

CLASSIFICATION INDICES (NEILSON-COZENS):
STANDARDS (BOYS AND GIRLS)*

Exponent	Height in inches	Age in years	Weight in pounds
1	50 to 51	10 to 10-5	60 to 65
2	52 to 53	10-6 to 10-11	66 to 70
3		11 to 11-5	71 to 75
4	54 to 55	11-6 to 11-11	76 to 80
5		12 to 12-5	81 to 85
6	56 to 57	12-6 to 12-11	86 to 90
7		13 to 13-5	91 to 95
8	58 to 59	13-6 to 13-11	96 to 100
9		14 to 14-5	101 to 105
10	60 to 61	14-6 to 14-11	106 to 110
11		15 to 15-5	111 to 115
12	62 to 63	15-6 to 15-11	116 to 120
13		16 to 16-5	121 to 125
14	64 to 65	16-6 to 16-11	126 to 130
15	66 to 67	17 to 17-5	131 to 133
16	68	17-6 to 17-11	134 to 136
17	69 and over	18 and over	137 and over

Sum of exponents	Class	Sum of exponents	Class
9 and below	A	25 to 29	E
10 to 14	B	30 to 34	F
15 to 19	C	35 to 38	G
20 to 24	D	39 and above	H

*Reproduced with permission from N. P. Neilson and Frederick W. Cozens, Achievement Scales in Physical Education Activities for Boys and Girls in Elementary and Junior High Schools.

[10] McCloy, *The Measurement of Athletic Power.*

137. The Neilson-Cozens Classification Indices,[11] if converted to terms comparable to the McCloy Classification Index, are as follows: (1) 20 age (yr.) + 4.33 height (in.) + weight (lb.) *and* (2) 20 age (yr.) + 5.5 height (in.) + 1.1 weight (lb.). A chart for the easy computation of the second Neilson-Cozens Classification Index is given in Table 10 (p. 60).

An *r* of .98 has been obtained between the second Neilson-Cozens Classification Index and the McCloy Classification Index, and the following *r*'s have been obtained between these two devices and total points in track-and-field athletics:

	Elementary School	*High School*
McCloy Classification Index	.606	.579
Neilson-Cozens Classification Index	.592	.554

The differences are probably due to the fact that the values derived from the Neilson-Cozens Formula are rounded off by the use of the computation chart (Table 10). It may be seen, however, by the coefficients of correlation given immediately above that it is of little importance whether, for purposes of classification only, the Neilson-Cozens or the McCloy Classification Index is used. (Hereafter in this textbook the term "classification index" unqualified refers to the McCloy Classification Index.)

138. A simplified set of standards[12] for classifying men of the college level by height and weight has been reported. College men are divided into the following nine groups according to body build: (1) tall-slender, (2) tall-medium, (3) tall-heavy, (4) medium-slender, (5) medium-medium, (6) medium-heavy, (7) short-slender, (8) short-medium, (9) short-heavy. The bases for the classifications follow.

	Height (ft. - in.)	Slender (lb.)	Medium (lb.)	Heavy (lb.)
	4-11	Up to 93	94-100	111 up
	5-0	Up to 98	99-115	116 up
	5-1	Up to 103	104-120	121 up
Short	5-2	Up to 107	108-126	127 up
	5-3	Up to 109	110-126	127 up
	5-4	Up to 115	116-133	134 up
	5-5	Up to 116	117-134	135 up
	5-6	Up to 121	122-139	140 up
	5-7	Up to 125	126-143	144 up
Medium	5-8	Up to 128	129-147	148 up
	5-9	Up to 131	132-150	151 up
	5-10	Up to 135	136-154	155 up
	5-11	Up to 138	139-158	159 up
	6-0	Up to 139	140-162	163 up
Tall	6-1	Up to 144	145-165	166 up
	6-2	Up to 150	151-172	173 up
	6-3	Up to 156	157-178	179 up
	6-4	Up to 162	163-184	185 up

[11] N. P. Neilson and Frederick W. Cozens, *Achievement Scales in Physical Education Activities for Boys and Girls in Elementary and Junior High Schools.*

[12] Frederick W. Cozens, *Achievement Scales in Physical Education Activities for College Men.* The tabular material in this section has been reproduced by the permission of the author and the publishers, Lea and Febiger.

It was found that the tall men as a group were superior in motor performance to the short men, the "medium" as a group were superior to the short, the heavy as a group were superior to the slender, and the "medium" as a group were superior to the slender. The points scored on standardized tests by performers with the nine types of body build follow.

Build Type	Points
Medium-heavy	366
Tall-medium	359
Medium-medium	353
Tall-heavy	344
Short-heavy	343
Tall-slender	339
Short-medium	333
Medium-slender	327
Short-slender	306

Hence it may be seen that the heavy and the "medium" men decidedly outscored the slender ones, especially if they were also tall or "medium" in height. This scheme of classification has been elaborated, and scoring tables for thirty-five events[13] have been provided for it.

139. Many studies concerning the relationship of the classification index to various abilities have been conducted. An r of .574 [14] has been obtained between the classification index and a general rating of sports skills, which r was smaller than it was with track-and-field activities (.815). Evidently factors of skill weigh far more heavily in sports than do factors of size. This finding is surprising because, in the study reported, the age range was fairly large.

140. In a study of the use of age, height, and weight as classifiers for basketball,[15] it was found that weight seemed to be the most important factor of the three. In this study the r's between basketball ability (0) as rated by competent judges, and age (1), height (2), and weight (3) were as follows:

r_{01}	.451	$r_{01.23}$	.242	$R_{0.13}$	.653
r_{02}	.495	$r_{02.13}$	-.112	$R_{0.123}$	.654
r_{03}	.651	$r_{03.12}$	.471		
		$r_{01.3}$	.229		
		$r_{02.3}$	-.067		
		$r_{03.1}$	.628		
		$r_{03.2}$	.490		

It may be noted that the R of the three variables with basketball ability was .654, and with age and weight, .653. Since the r between basketball

---

[13] *Ibid.*

[14] Joy W. Kistler, "A Comparative Study of Methods of Classifying Pupils into Homogeneous Groups for Physical Education," *Research Quarterly*, March, 1934.

[15] H. D. Schrock and C. H. McCloy, "A Study of the Best Combination of Age, Height and Weight for Basketball Classification," *Journal of Physical Education*, October, 1929.

ability and weight alone was .651, it seems of no value to add age or height to weight for the prediction of basketball ability. The number of cases (43) studied, however, was small. Although the coefficients of validity were high, and the r of reliability of the three judges was about .90, it is possible that studies made with a larger number of cases would show that height is a more important factor than it appeared to be in this study. In view of the high correlation between age and experience in basketball, it is rather surprising that higher coefficients of correlation with the classification index were not obtained.

141. In a study[16] which was conducted on seventy high-school boys concerning the use of age, height, and weight as classifiers for football ability (0), the r's were as follows: age (1), .452; height (2), .105; weight (3), .106; classification index (4), .260; $R_{0.1234}$, .455.

142. In view of the widely publicized emphasis upon the value of the strength score (see Chap. 15) as a classifier for competition, attention is called to the fact that in a number of studies, the coefficients of correlation of the classification index with valid criteria for competitive ability have been as high as or higher than those for competitive ability with the strength score (see Sec. 617). In any case if *tentative* classifications that can be made rapidly are desired, the classification index serves as well as many of the more complicated devices, and in no case should a single device be relied upon for permanent classifications.

143. In studies of age, height, and weight as predictors of motor ability in girls the results have been much less satisfactory than those in similar studies with boys. In one study[17] conducted on 699 girls in two elementary schools, one junior-high school, and one senior-high school, the r's of performances in track-and-field athletics (0) with age (1), height (2), and weight (3) were as follows:

	Elementary school	Junior high school	Senior high school
r_{01}	.549	.255	.027
r_{02}	.398	.160	.094
r_{03}	.342	.043	.051
$r_{01.2}$	.412	.222	
$r_{03.2}$	.027	-.068	
$r_{02.1}$	.021	.094	
$r_{03.1}$	-.058	-.049	
$r_{01.23}$	.420	.243	
$r_{02.13}$	.078	.147	
$r_{03.12}$	-.095	-.123	
$R_{0.123}$	.555	.297	
$R_{0.12}$	.549	.271	

[16] Personal communication from George Wells.
[17] A study conducted in the Des Moines, Iowa, Public Schools.

Since the coefficients of zero-order correlation for the senior-high-school girls were approximately zero, coefficients of partial and multiple correlation were not computed for that group.

The data on the 699 girls were further studied to determine at which ages the curvilinear regression lines "leveled off." In the elementary-school group, which included ages from 9.5 to 13.5 years, inclusive, the regression lines of total points with age increased steadily and linearly; and the regression lines of height with weight also increased steadily, although the slope in terms of standard deviations was smaller than that for total points with age. In the junior-high-school group, which included the ages from 12 to 15.5 years, the regression line of total points with age increased exactly as had that of the elementary-school group up to the age of 13.5 years, after which age it leveled off to a horizontal to the age of 15.5 years. The regression line of total points with weight and that of total points with height were horizontal throughout. In the senior-high-school group all the regression lines of total points with age from the age of 14.5 to 20.5 years were horizontal, as were those of height with weight. In other words, it is apparent that age is of some importance as a classifier for girls up to and including 13.5 years, after which time it seems to level off; in the junior-high school from the age of 13.5 years and in the senior-high school, age, height, and weight may be disregarded as classifiers for girls.

144. While the classification index has been found to be of small value with high-school girls, this is not true with elementary-school girls. For boys and girls of the first three grades, an r of .668 [18] has been obtained between the McCloy Classification Index and total points computed from eight track-and-field tests; hence this index is of value in classifying younger children. It gets decreasingly effective with girls from the beginning of the fourth grade.

In one study[19] of height-weight classifications of high-school girls, the groups were ranked as follows: tall-slender build, 79.6 average points; short-medium build, 78.6; medium-medium build, 72.3; short-slender build, 72.2; tall-medium build, 70.0; medium-slender build, 68.4; medium-heavy build, 63.1; tall-heavy build, 62.6; and short-heavy build, 57.5. The slender and the "medium" girls had the advantage in every case over the heavier girls. As of the present, this study is more suggestive than definitive because of the fact that standards for use with these groups are not available. This study would seem to point, however, to the fact that there might be, for girls, a high correlation between body build and athletics performance. The whole problem is complicated by the fact that

[18] Aileen Carpenter, "The Measurements of General Motor Capacity and General Motor Ability in the First Three Grades," *Research Quarterly*, December, 1942.

[19] Karl W. Bookwalter, "An Assessment of the Validity of Height-Weight Class Divisions for High School Girls," *Research Quarterly*, May, 1944.

there is a heterogeneity of athletics ambition upon the part of girls of senior-high-school age and above. In most senior-high schools and colleges, the performance of the girls gets poorer from year to year. In some schools, however, in which the programs are strenuous ones, and in which a great deal of thought is given to motivation of the girls, the reverse is true, and the girls improve steadily from junior-high school on through college. Hence the probability is that some of the findings presented are more functions of program and of motivation than they are functions of sex differences only.

145. In summary relative to the methods of classification for girls, it seems wise to conclude, at least tentatively, that the classification index and similar classifying devices are of no greater value than age alone, and age is of value as a classifier only up to and including 13.5 years.

146. USES OF MEASUREMENTS OF SIZE AND MATURITY

With boys it has been seen that the classification index or, in some sports, weight alone gave satisfactory correlations with strength, with classifications made by the subjective judgments of experts, with track-and-field ability, and, to a lesser extent, with sports skills. Hence the classification index (or weight in the sports indicated) may be used advantageously in many cases as a classifier for motor performance, particularly in the type of athletics competition in which, if such a dynamic test as the strength test were used, there might be malingering. The classification index is probably the best device available for *quickly* classifying new groups of boys. In any situation in which maturity and size are of importance, age, height, and weight may be used for purposes of classification within the limitations that have been indicated. Maturity is determined largely by age: there is usually a high correlation between age and experience as well as between age and physiological maturity. Size is determined by height and weight.

It is emphasized that classifications made by the use of the classification index are based only on size and maturity. Subclassifications need to be made on the basis of such items as speed, motor educability, knowledge of the event, interest, persistence, and courage. For such further classification devices, see Chapter 12.

CHAPTER 9

POWER

147. ALL MOTOR performances that involve the element of velocity (V) are "power" events, for power (P) is the rate at which work (W), which is the product of the force (F) and the distance (d) over which the force is applied, is performed; that is, power is the amount of work done divided by the time (t) in which the work is done. Thus, if a person projects his body or an external object through space, power, which is the product of force (strength) and velocity, is involved.[1]

148. In athletics performances that do not involve the use of an implement, the amount of force needed is relative to the weight of the body. In athletics performances that involve the use of an implement, the amount of force needed is relative both to the weight of the body and to that of the implement.

149. Although in theoretical physics there is no limitation to either force or velocity, in the human body velocity is limited by the resistance of muscular tissue and by the fact that the speed of relaxation of muscles functioning antagonistically is less than the speed of contraction of muscles functioning agonistically. Up to the limit imposed by these restraining factors, increases in strength result in increases in velocity. Beyond this limit, an increase in strength results in little or no increase in velocity.

150. Most performers probably have not attained their maximum velocity, and can therefore increase their velocity by increasing their strength. The records made in power events by weight-training groups and by control groups at the beginning and at the end of an experiment period of three months follow.[2] The control groups were required classes in physical education. Their programs were strenuous but they did not include any weight training.

---

[1] $W = Fd$; $P = W \div t$; hence $P = Fd \div t$; $d \div t = V$; hence $P = FV$.

[2] Edward Chui, "The Effect of Systematic Weight Training on Athletic Power," *Research Quarterly*, October, 1950.

Edward K. Capen, "The Effect of Systematic Weight Training on Power, Strength, and Endurance," *Research Quarterly*, May, 1950.

The items not underscored represent the average gain (or loss) of the weight-training group. The underscored items represent the average gain (or loss) of the control group.

	Study by Chui	Study by Capen
Standing vertical jump	7.2 cm.	6.36 cm.
	slight loss	5.07 cm.
Running vertical jump	7.6 cm.	7.74 cm.
	slight loss	4.59 cm.
Standing broad jump	3.6 in.	
	slight loss	
Sixty-yard dash	33.0 sec.	
	slight loss	
Eight-pound shot-put	2.99 ft.	2 ft. 7 in.
	.42 ft.	1 ft. 3.4 in.
Twelve-pound shot-put	2.32 ft.	
	.58 ft.	
Strength		4.6%
		1.9%
Sum of T-scores of power events		14.9%
		6.3%

151. METHODS OF MEASURING POWER

The power that a performer can develop relative to the weight of his body and to the weight of an implement that he may be using can be measured by a vertical jump. In such a jump, the performer, starting in a crouched position, does enough work rapidly enough to extend the body completely, and develops enough momentum to project the body upward in space.

152. The **Sargent Physical Test of a Man**[3] consists of jumping as high as possible, with the record of the jump being the difference between the standing height and the height reached by the crown of the head during the jump. Three formulas for the conversion of the records into terms of athletic or physical ability were proposed by Sargent but none of them proved to be valid.

153. In a statistical study of the Sargent Physical Test of a Man,[4] which test came to be called the "Sargent Jump," no significant relationships between various anthropometric measurements and performance in the Sargent Jump were found. An r of .39 between age (up to 16 or 17 years) and performance in the Sargent Jump was obtained.

154. In a study on a group of college students of a high degree of athletics heterogeneity,[5] an r of .55 was obtained between four athletic events (running high jump, standing broad jump, rope climb for speed, and 980-yard run) and the Sargent Jump, and a very small coefficient of correlation was obtained between the Sargent Jump and age. The reliability of the Sargent Jump, expressed in terms of an r, was found to be .61.

[3] Dudley A. Sargent, "The Physical Test of a Man," *American Physical Education Review*, April, 1921.

[4] L. W. Sargent, "Some Observations on the Sargent Test of Neuromuscular Efficiency," *American Physical Education Review*, February, 1924.

[5] J. F. Bovard and F. W. Cozens, *The Leap-meter*.

155. The **Sargent Jump** has been restudied [6] on the basis of the following ideas. If the Sargent Jump is to be correlated with athletic activities, the athletic activities should be practiced until all the performers have had an opportunity to become proficient in them. (If a verbal intelligence test is to be correlated with achievement tests in school subjects, the subjects involved in the achievement tests should be studied until all

Table 11

SARGENT JUMP: SCORING TABLES (BOYS 9 TO 15
AND UP, GIRLS 9 TO 13 AND UP)

Cm.	BOYS						GIRLS			
	9-10	11	12	13	14	15 & up	9-10	11	12	13 & up
76										
74										
72										
70						73				
68						71				
66					76	69				
64					74	67				
62					72	65				
60				75	70	63				
58				73	68	61				
56				71	67	59				
54				69	65	57				
52				67	63	55				
50			76	65	61	53		75	76	73
48			73	63	58	51		74	74	70
46			70	61	55	49		72	72	67
44	75	74	66	59	53	47		70	66	64
42	73	72	62	56	50	45		68	61	60
40	71	69	60	53	47	43	77	64	56	57
38	68	66	55	50	45	41	73	60	52	54
36	65	61	51	48	42	39	69	57	49	51
34	59	55	46	45	40	36	65	53	45	47
32	54	51	44	43	37	34	61	49	42	44
30	50	47	42	40	35	32	57	45	38	40
28	48	43	40	38	33	30	53	41	35	35
26	45	41	37	35	31	28	48	38	32	30
24	42	37	35	32	29	25	44	35	30	25
22	40	36	32	29	27	23	40	33	28	20
20	37	34	30	26	24	21	36	30	27	15
18	35	33	28	24			33	27	26	
16	34	31	25	21			30	24	24	
14	33	28	22				26			
12	32	26					23			
10	30	24					20			
8	28	21								
6	26									
4	24									
2	22									

the students have had an opportunity to become proficient in them.) Also, the technique for performing the Sargent Jump satisfactorily should be taught. (The students taking verbal intelligence tests need to have been taught how to read.) While track-and-field activities are power events and hence usable as a criterion for power, such events as the

[6] Charles H. McCloy, "Recent Studies in the Sargent Jump." *Research Quarterly,* May. 1932.

980-yard run, in which courage and endurance are primary factors, and a rope climb, which involves groups of muscles not commonly used by the average student and which depends more upon strength than upon velocity, are not satisfactory events for a criterion for power.

The criterion for the restudy of the Sargent Jump was the total-point score for the following events: (1) 100-yard dash, (2) running high jump, (3) standing broad jump, and (4) eight-pound shot-put. The r of reliability for the track-and-field events was, on the basis of one thousand cases, .890. The r of reliability for the Sargent Jump was, on the basis of the best jump of each of two series of three jumps performed without previous practice, .770; and, on the basis of the r between the best jump of each of two series of three jumps performed on different days and the best jump of another two series of three jumps performed on different days, .854. (In one study an r of .958 was obtained for the Sargent Jump performed after the amount of practice recommended.[7]

156. In a number of studies the r's between the Sargent Jump and track-and-field events were, for boys, from .65 to .86, and, for girls, from .60 to .73. The r's between track-and-field events and a combination of the Sargent Jump and the classification index[8] were, for boys, from .72 to .93; for girls similar increases in these r's were not found. An r of .88 was obtained between track-and-field events and a combination of the Sargent Jump and arm strength.

In Table 11 (p. 68) may be found T-scores for the Sargent Jump for boys of ages nine to fifteen years and for girls of ages nine to thirteen years.

157. In several studies[9] the effect of overweight on performance in the Sargent Jump has been indicated. The subjects first practiced the Sargent Jump until they could execute it in satisfactory form, and records were obtained for their performances. Then, wearing weighted jackets or weighted belts, the subjects executed the Sargent Jump again, and records were obtained for their performances. For each per cent that the weight of the body was increased by the jacket or the belt, the height of the jump decreased approximately 1 per cent; that is, if a performer weighing 150 pounds jumped wearing a jacket that weighed 30 pounds, he jumped 20 per cent less high than when he did not wear the jacket.[10]

[7] James W. Coleman, "The Differential Measurement of the Speed Factor in Large Muscle Activities," *Research Quarterly*, October, 1937.

[8] Height and weight, if age was held constant, had little effect on the Sargent Jump.

[9] Frances H. Carter, "A Mechanical Analysis of the Relationships of Positive and Negative Loads to Performance in the Vertical Jump" (M.A. Thesis, State University of Iowa, 1945).

Donald D. Klotz, "A Mechanical Analysis of the Vertical Jump as Affected by Variations in Weight and Strength" (Ph.D. Dissertation, State University of Iowa, 1948).

Lenel Mason, unpublished study.

[10] If a person by adding fat increases his weight by 20 per cent, he develops, during the period of the increase, some additional strength to help carry the increase in

158. For purposes of classification the Sargent Jump and the McCloy Classification Index may be combined as follows: (1) 10 Sargent Jump (cm.) + McCloy Classification Index *or* (2) 25 Sargent Jump (in.) + McCloy Classification Index.

159. The Sargent Jump should not be used as a test until it can be executed according to the following directions. Stand in an eighteen-inch circle. Swing the arms downward and backward, inclining the body slightly forward and forming approximately a ninety-degree angle between the upper and lower legs. Pause momentarily in this position. (The purpose of the pause is to eliminate the possibility of a double jump.) Jump upward as high as possible, swinging the arms vigorously forward and upward to the vertical. Just before the highest point of the jump is reached, swing the arms forward and downward to the sides. (The end of the downward movement of the arms should be timed to coincide exactly with the end of the upward movement of the body. At this time the body is straight, and the crown of the head is extended upward as high as possible.)

The swinging of the arms in the Sargent Jump is exceedingly important, and may make as much as 10 to 15 per cent of difference in the height of the jump. According to one of the Newton Laws, action and reaction are equal and opposite. If the arms are swung vigorously upward *before* the performer has left the floor, the accumulated momentum of the arms aids in raising the body. Before the body has reached the end of the upward movement, the arms are swung vigorously downward in order that their downward action may produce an equally vigorous reaction of the body upward. Since this kind of arm movement is involved in jumps, and analogous arm movements are involved in running, it is proper that this type of movement should be included in the Sargent Jump.

160. Two difficulties relative to the execution of the Sargent Jump beset many performers, especially girls who have not been trained in the standing broad jump. The first difficulty concerns keeping the lower legs extended during the jump and projecting the body straight upward. Many subjects tend to dorsiflex the feet and to flex the legs, as though lifting them over an obstacle, at the beginning of the upward movement of the body. The downward reaction of this movement of the feet and legs lessens the height of the jump. The fault may be quite easily corrected by telling the performer to imagine that he is being projected upward like an arrow, and by having him try to project the top of his head as high as possible. The image of the arrow helps him keep the trunk and the legs in a straight line with each other after he has left the ground.

The second common difficulty is not swinging the arms downward from

weight. Hence the relationships expressed in the text above are not necessarily the same for the situation presented here. It is probable, however, that if an overweight person decreased his weight, he would also increase the height of his jump proportionate'

the upward position just before the highest point of the jump is reached. This fault may be corrected, although with difficulty, by having the performer jump upward repeatedly, swinging the arms upward to a point about level with the face, and when he is in the air by having him swing the arms downward and backward, and by having him jump again immediately after alighting. After the subject has learned to swing the arms downward from this shortened upward swing, he should practice the correct form with the full arm swing to the vertical, but without having to jump upward again after alighting.

161. In an unpublished study[11] to determine how much time was required for senior-high-school girls to learn the form of the Sargent Jump, it was found that the girls did not increase the height of their performances after the fifth day in a series of practice periods of ten or fifteen minutes each over a period of ten days. The results of other unpublished studies conducted on boys are in agreement with these findings for girls. Hence the Sargent Jump should not be used as a test until after it has been practiced for ten to fifteen minutes on each of four to six days. Trials should be continued until two trials are not so good as the best trial.

162. Mechanical devices in which a rope extends from the performer's head to a lever or a pulley overhead have been unsatisfactory for measuring the height jumped, for performers usually jump slightly forward, and hence the rope does not remain vertical throughout the jump.

163. The following **method, which is a** simple one, is recommended **for the measuring of the height of the jump.** On a sheet of heavy paper about two feet wide and five or six feet long are drawn horizontal lines one centimeter apart. Lines 1, 2, 3, 4, 6, 7, 8, and 9 are drawn in black; Line 5 in red; Line 10 in blue; Lines 11 to the top of the chart are drawn similarly to the first ten lines. The paper is fastened to the wall at such a height that the 0 line of the chart is just below the point that represents the standing height of the shortest performer. The performer, with a large handkerchief wrapped over the top of his head, stands with his back to the chart, and the level on the chart reached by the top of the head is recorded to the nearest centimeter. Then the performer, with one side toward the wall and with the corresponding shoulder about six inches from the wall, executes a practice jump. The observer, standing on a chair or table twelve to fifteen feet from the performer, adjusts the level of his eye to two or three centimeters higher than the height reached by the performer's head in the practice jump. In the official trials the observer records the highest line on the chart passed by the top of the jumper's head.

CHALK JUMP

164. The chalk jump is a variation of, but *not* a substitute for, the Sargent Jump. The performer reaches upward as far as possible, and with

[11] By Theresa Anderson.

a piece of chalk makes a mark on the wall. He then jumps upward as far as possible, and makes a mark on the wall as near the peak of his jump as possible. Instead of using chalk, the performer may—and this method is probably better than the preceding one—make the marks with wet fingers. The distance of the jump is the distance between the marks. The asymmetrical co-ordination involved in the chalk jump makes the chalk jump more difficult than the Sargent Jump; that is, in the chalk jump, the performer has to learn how to swing one arm instead of two arms downward just before he reaches the peak of his jump.

165. In one study[12] an r of .810 was obtained between the Sargent Jump and four track-and-field events, and an r of .776 was obtained between the chalk jump and four track-and-field events. These findings, together with similar findings in other studies, indicate that the Sargent Jump rather than the chalk jump should be used for measuring power.

POWER QUOTIENT

166. In two studies[13] on the use of the standing broad jump for the prediction of power, higher coefficients of correlation were obtained when the event was practiced than when it was not. The findings of the studies follow.[14]

	Track-and-field Events (0) (Total Points)
Sargent Jump (1)	.552
Standing broad jump (2)	.674
	<u>.8280</u>
Eight-pound shot-put (3) (from a stand)	.632
	<u>.7861</u>
$R_{0.13}$	.716
$R_{0.23}$	.795
	<u>.8975</u>

167. The following multiple regression equation was computed for the prediction of power for boys from the eight-pound shot-put and the standing broad jump: **Stansbury Power Score** = 1.5 eight-pound shot-put (ft.) + standing broad jump (in.). Norms for power relative to the classification index are presented in Table 12 (p. 73). A power quotient, which is the total points divided by the norm, of 100 is average for the classification index.

[12] Deobold Van Dalen, "New Studies in the Sargent Jump," *Research Quarterly,* May, 1940.

[13] Frederick T. Lindenmeyer, "The Physical Efficiency Index as a Measure of Athletic Development" (M.A. Thesis, State University of Iowa, 1947).

Edgar B. Stansbury, "A Simplified Method of Classifying Junior and Senior High School Boys into Homogeneous Groups for Physical Education Activities," *Research Quarterly,* December, 1941.

[14] The values not underscored are from Lindenmeyer's study. The underscored values are from Stansbury's study.

168. A formula for the prediction of power for girls from the six-pound shot-put and the standing broad jump is as follows: **Anderson-McCloy Power Score** = 2 six-pound shot-put (ft.) + standing broad jump (in.).[15] The r of this regression equation was, in a study conducted on senior-high-

Table 12

POWER TEST (STANSBURY): NORMS
(JUNIOR- AND SENIOR-HIGH-SCHOOL BOYS)

Power quotient = 100(power score/norm for classification index)

CI	0	10	20	30	40	50	60	70	80	90

.1587 Classification Index - 5.74

	0	10	20	30	40	50	60	70	80	90
500	74	75	77	78	80	82	83	85	86	88
600	89	91	93	94	96	97	99	101	102	104
700	105	107	109	110	112	113	115	116	118	120
800	121	123	124	126	128	129	131	132	134	136
900	137	139	140	142	143	145	147	148	150	151
1000	153	156	157	158	159	161	162	164	166	167
1100	169	170	172	174	175	176	178	180	182	183
1200	185	186	188	189	191	193	194	196	197	199

school girls, .85. Norms for power relative to weight may be found in Table 13 (p. 73).

169. The **MacCurdy Physical-capacity Test**[16] was formulated on the basis that power is the result of force multipled by velocity. The total strength of the back and of the legs as measured by dynamometers (see Secs. **292-**

Table 13

POWER TEST (McCLOY-ANDERSON): NORMS
(JUNIOR- AND SENIOR-HIGH-SCHOOL GIRLS)

Power quotient = 100(power score/norm for weight)

Weight	0	2	4	6	8

.2646 Weight + 84.3459

	0	2	4	6	8
70	103	103	104	104	105
80	106	106	107	107	108
90	108	109	109	110	110
100	111	111	112	112	113
110	113	114	115	115	116
120	116	117	117	118	118
130	119	119	120	120	121
140	121	122	122	123	124
150	124	125	125	126	126
160	127	127	128	128	129
170	129	130	130	131	131
180	132	133	133	134	134

[15] Theresa Anderson and C. H. McCloy, unpublished study.
[16] Howard L. MacCurdy, *A Test for Measuring the Physical Capacity of Secondary School Boys.*

93) is multiplied by the pulling-and-pushing force of the arms measured by dynamometers. This product in pounds is multiplied by the Sargent Jump in inches. An *r* of .93 was obtained between this score and track-and-field events. Standards were provided for the senior-high school, with the assumption that the same standards would be valid for the junior-high school and college.

170. The Sargent Jump as a test has been studied much more extensively than has any of the other devices of measurement discussed in this chapter. Theoretically, height should influence performance in the standing broad jump, and both height and weight should strongly influence performance in the shot-put. These considerations are partially cared for by interpreting the combination of the shot-put and the standing broad jump in terms of the power quotient. It should be emphasized, however, that the Sargent Jump and the standing broad jump are valid methods for measuring power only if the events have been adequately practiced.

CHAPTER **10**

AGILITY

171. AGILITY IS here defined as the ability to change the direction of the body or of parts of the body rapidly. It may involve small ranges of movement, as in typing and in playing the piano, or it may involve large ranges of movement, as in a zigzag run. Each of the following tests is a method of measuring some aspect of the type of agility that involves large ranges of movement.

172. Squat thrust.[1] The directions for the execution of the squat thrust are as follows. Lower the body to a squat-rest position, leaning forward, and placing the hands on the floor in front of the feet. Thrust the legs backward to the front leaning-rest position. Return almost to the squat-rest position, and then to the standing position. Repeat the movements as rapidly as possible until the command to stop is given.

The test is scored in terms of the number of performances completed in ten seconds. A complete performance is scored as 1. Scores for a partial performance are as follows: $\frac{1}{4}$ for first touching the hands to the floor, $\frac{1}{2}$ for thrusting the legs backward, and $\frac{3}{4}$ for returning to a squat-rest position with the hands still on the floor.

The two requirements as to form in the execution of the squat thrust are the following. (1) The legs must be thrust backward until the lower and upper legs are completely extended. (2) In the return position the trunk and the legs must be in a straight line with each other, although this line does not need to be vertical. The fastest performers start to thrust the feet backward just as the hands touch the floor, and they squat only until the angle behind the knees is about 130 degrees. As they thrust the legs backward, the shoulders are three to six inches in front of a perpendicular plane passing through the hands. (Slow performers thrust the legs backward so far that the shoulders are over, or slightly behind, the hands.)

173. In a study[2] of the effects of practice on the performance of senior-

---

[1] The squat thrust, which has been used as a calisthenic exercise for a long time, was, to the best of the authors' knowledge, first presented as a test by Royal H. Burpee. This test came to be called the Burpee Test. Since, however, Burpee has developed a test that should be known by his name, the term *squat thrust*, which was used in the testing programs of the Army and the Navy during World War II, is used in this edition of this book to designate the exercise described in this section.

[2] Theresa Anderson, unpublished study.

high-school girls in the squat thrust it was found that in a period of ten days half the girls had achieved their best scores by the fifth day, that the median score for the group had been reached by the third day, and that the mean of the scores of the group was highest on the tenth day. Hence it would seem that, for girls, practice should be given in the squat thrust for at least five periods on different days before the event is used as a test.

In the administration of the squat thrust the performers should be arranged in pairs in order that they may perform, and score the performances of each other, alternately. Adequate practice in scoring should be given. The best score made in three trials should be recorded.

174. T-scores for the squat thrust for boys and for girls of the elementary school, the junior-high school, and the senior-high school are given in Table 14 (p. 76).

Table 14

SQUAT THRUSTS: SCORING TABLES (ELEMENTARY-SCHOOL AND JUNIOR- AND SENIOR-HIGH-SCHOOL BOYS AND GIRLS)

Squat Thrusts	Boys			Girls				
	Elem. S.	Jr. H.S.	Sr. H.S.	Elem. S.	Jr. H.S.	Sr. H.S.	%	T
11	82	82	87					
10-3/4	80	80	85					
10-1/2	79	79	83					
10-1/4	77	77	80					
10	76	76	78				%	T
9-3/4	74	74	75					
9-1/2	73	73	73	75	88		98	71
9-1/4	71	72	71	72	86			
9	70	71	69	70	85		95	66
8-3/4	68	69	67	68	83			
8-1/2	67	68	65	66	82	86	90	63
8-1/4	65	66	62	64	80	83		
8	64	65	60	63	78	80	80	58
7-3/4	62	63	58	61	75	77		
7-1/2	61	62	56	60	72	74	60	53
7-1/4	59	60	53	58	69	71		
7	58	58	51	57	66	68	40	47
6-3/4	56	55	49	55	63	65		
6-1/2	55	53	47	54	60	62	20	42
6-1/4	53	51	44	52	57	59		
6	52	49	42	51	54	56	10	37
5-3/4	50	46	39	49	50	53		
5-1/2	48	44	37	48	47	50	5	34
5-1/4	45	41	34	46	44	46		
5	43	39	32	45	41	42	2	29
4-3/4	40	37	30	42	38	38		
4-1/2	37	35	28	40	36	34		
4-1/4	34	32	25	37	33	29		
4	32	30	23	35	31	25		
3-3/4	30	27	20	32	29	21		
3-1/2	28	25	18	30	27	18		
3-1/4	26	22		27	25			
3	25	20		25	23			
2-3/4	23	17		22	21			
2-1/2	21	15		20	20			
2-1/4	19	12						
2	18	10						

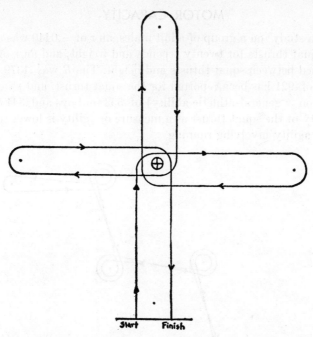

FIGURE VI. Right-boomerang Test: Floor Markings

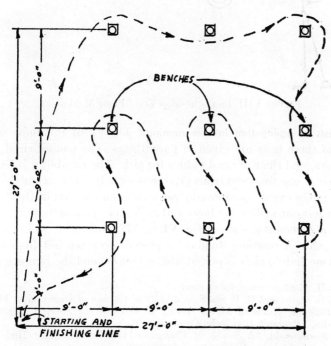

FIGURE VII. Forty-yard Maze-run Test: Floor Markings

175. In a study[3] on a group of adult males, an r of $-.0440$ was obtained between squat thrusts for twenty seconds and weight, and an r of $-.1379$ was obtained between squat thrusts and height. The R was .1379. An r of reliability of .921 has been reported for the squat thrust, and r's of validity (criterion = general-athletic ability) of .553 for boys and .341 for girls. The validity of the squat thrust as a measure of agility is lower than that of tests of agility involving running.

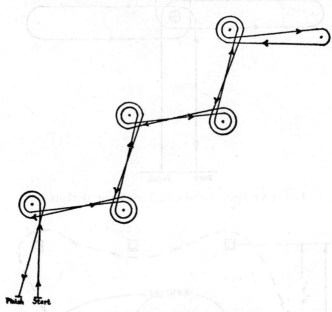

FIGURE VIII. Loop-the-loop Test: Floor Markings

176. Tests of agility that involve running.[4] The r's of reliability and of validity of these tests are given in parentheses. The nonitalicized values are for boys, and the italicized values for girls. The reliability is based on trials given at one time and trials given a week later. The validity is based on scores in the event under consideration and on the sum of the T-scores in sixteen tests of agility for boys and in fifteen tests of agility for girls.

177. *Right-boomerang run* (Fig. VI, p. 77) (val., $r = .823$, *.715;* rel., $r = .925$, *.923*). A jumping standard is placed seventeen feet from a starting line. One Indian club is placed fifteen feet beyond the jumping stand-

[3] Charles H. McCloy, unpublished study.
[4] Donald D. Gates and R. P. Sheffield, "Tests of Change of Direction as Measurements of Different Kinds of Motor Ability in Boys of the Seventh, Eighth, and Ninth Grades," *Research Quarterly,* October, 1940.

Frances Sierakowski, "A Study of Change-of-Direction Tests for High School Girls" (M.A. Thesis, State University of Iowa, 1940).

Kathryn E. Young, "An Analytic Study of the Tests of Change of Direction" (M.A. Thesis, State University of Iowa, 1937).

ard. One Indian club is placed fifteen feet on each side of the jumping standard (seventeen feet from the starting line). The performer follows the course indicated in Figure VI. He makes quarter-right turns at the jumping standard, and half-right turns at the Indian clubs. His score is the time required to run the course. The average score for a group of junior-high-school boys was 13.35 seconds, with a range of 11.2 to 18.3 seconds. For a group of girls the scores ran from 11 to 14.9 seconds.

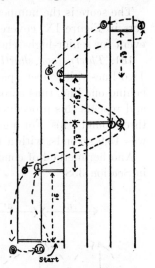

178. *Forty-yard maze run* (Fig. VII, p. 77) (val., $r = .823$; rel., $r = .954, .849$). Nine small boxes are placed on the floor in three rows, which are nine feet apart. The performer follows the course indicated in Figure VII, which course is indicated on the floor by arrows made with chalk. The score is the time required to run the course.[5]

179. *Loop-the-loop run* (Fig. VIII, p. 78) (val., $r = .774, .709$; rel., $r = .970, .956$). Indian clubs are placed nine feet apart. The performer follows the course indicated by the

FIGURE IX. Zigzag-run Test: Floor Markings

arrows, which are marked on the floor with chalk. The score is the time required to run the course. For a group of junior-high-school boys the median time was 23.2 seconds, with a range of 20.1 to 30.8 seconds.

Table 15

ZIGZAG RUN (JOHNSON): SCORING TABLES (SENIOR-HIGH-SCHOOL BOYS)*

Zone	T-score	Zone	T-score	Zone	T-score
32	109	21	31	11	10
31	97	20	27	10	9
30	87	19	24	9	8
29	77	18	22	8	7
28	69	17	19	7	6
27	61	16	17	6	6
26	55	15	15	5	5
25	49	14	14	4	4
24	43	13	12	3	4
23	39	12	11	2	3
22	34			1	3

*These T-scores are based on data collected by L. William Johnson on senior-high-school boys.

[5] Reliability and validity r's of .68 and .69, respectively, have been reported for performances in this event by college women. See: Florence D. Alden and Others, "A Motor Ability Test for University Women for the Classification of Entering Students into Homogeneous Groups," *Research Quarterly*, March, 1932.

180. *Zigzag run* (Fig. IX, p. 79) (val., $r = .775, 533$; rel., $r = .968$, $.920$). The directions for conducting the zigzag run are given in Section 553. The performer follows the course indicated in Figure IX.

The score is the number of zones, which are indicated with small numbers in Figure IX, covered in thirty seconds. Smoothed T-scores for this event for senior-high-school boys may be found in Table 15 (p. 79).

181. *Thirty-foot shuttle run* (val., $r = .829, .479$; rel., $r = .932, 893$). Two lines thirty feet apart are drawn on the floor. The performer starts behind one line, runs across the other line, returns to the starting position, and repeats this procedure three times. The score is the time required for three round trips. For a group of junior-high-school boys the median time was 15.9 seconds, with a range of 13.7 to 21.5 seconds.

Another method of conducting the thirty-foot shuttle run may be found in Section 358.

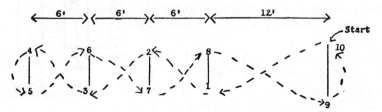

FIGURE X. Dodging-run Test: Floor Markings

182. *Dodging run* (Fig. X, p. 80) (val., $r = .820$, rel., $r = .934, .802$). A starting line six feet long is drawn on the floor. One hurdle is placed twelve feet in front of the starting line. A second hurdle is placed six feet in front of the first hurdle, a third hurdle six feet in front of the second hurdle. The performer follows the course indicated in Figure X. The score is the time required to run the complete course. For a group of junior-high-school performers the median time was 10.55 seconds, with a range of 8.5 to 13 seconds.

183. *Sidestep test*[6] (val., $r = .704$; rel., $r = .982$). Three parallel lines four feet apart are drawn on the floor. The performer stands astride the middle line. He sidesteps to the right until his right foot has crossed the line to the right. He then sidesteps to the left until his left foot has crossed the second line to the left. He repeats these movements as rapidly as possible for ten seconds. Each trip from the center line to an outside line and back to the center line counts *1*.

Performance in the sidestep test has a high correlation with the prediction of basketball potentiality. It may, although the fact has not

---

[6] The sidestep test was first proposed by H. D. Edgren in "An Experiment in the Testing of Ability and Progress in Basketball" in the *Research Quarterly* of March, 1932. A modification of that test is presented here

been demonstrated, also be highly correlated with ability in tennis, hockey, soccer, speedball, and football.

184. A modification[7] of the sidestep test, which provides for the use of the foul lines of a basketball court, is described in Section 553. Smoothed T-scores for this variation of the sidestep test are given in Table 16 (p. 81).

Table 16

SIDESTEP TEST (JOHNSON): SCORING TABLES
(SENIOR-HIGH-SCHOOL BOYS)

Zone	T-score	Zone	T-score	Zone	T-score
39	101	27	66	16	34
38	98	26	63	15	32
37	95	25	61	14	29
36	92	24	58	13	26
35	90	23	55	12	23
34	87	22	52	11	20
33	84	21	49	10	17
32	81	20	46	9	14
31	78	19	43	8	11
30	75	18	40	7	8
29	72	17	37	6	5
28	69			5	3

185. *Auto-tire test* (Fig. XI, p. 81) (val., $r = .691, 593$; rel., $r = .974, .910$). A starting line about six feet long is drawn on the floor. Five auto tires with their centers six feet apart are placed in each of the two columns four feet apart. The center of the first tire in the column at the left is six feet from the starting line, and the center of the first tire in the column at the right is three feet from the starting line. The performer begins behind the starting line, steps with his right foot into the first tire in the right

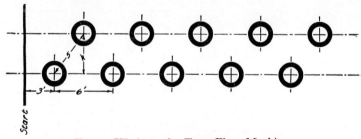

FIGURE XI. Auto-tire Test: Floor Markings

column, then with his left foot into the first tire in the left row, and similarly until he has stepped into all the tires. He then turns to the left, and returns similarly to the starting line. The score is the time required to make the round trip.

[7] By L. William Johnson.

The reliability for the auto-tire test is adequately high, but the validity is questionable. Since the test is widely used in the conditioning of football players, however, it has been included here.

186. BATTERIES OF TESTS OF AGILITY

The following batteries[8] of tests of agility have been proposed for boys.

Gates-Sheffield Agility Score I (for the seventh grade) = forty-yard maze run + zigzag sidestep test (a variation of the zigzag run) + thirty-foot shuttle run. $R = .959$.[9]

Gates-Sheffield Agility Score II (for the eighth grade) = loop-the-loop run + thirty-foot shuttle run + zigzag sidestep test. $R = .946$.[9]

Gates-Sheffield Agility Score III (for the ninth grade) = zigzag run + right-boomerang run + thirty-foot shuttle run. $R = .918$.[9]

The following multiple regression formula[10] has been proposed for the measurement of agility in high-school girls.

Sierakowski Agility Score = 3.3639 loop-the-loop run − 6.9586 right-boomerang run − 2.2213 auto-tire run + 205.35. $R = .916$.[11]

The tests of agility that involve running appear to be especially useful for a quick classification of performers into homogeneous groups and for the prediction of certain aspects of athletic ability.

[8] Gates and Sheffield, *loc. cit.*
[9] The criterion was the sum of the T-scores for sixteen tests of agility.
[10] Sierakowski, *loc. cit.*
[11] The criterion was the sum of the T-scores for fifteen tests of agility.

CHAPTER 11

MOTOR EDUCABILITY

187. ALMOST NO relationship has been found between intelligence quotients and measurements of physical ability. This lack of relationship exists even if intelligence quotients are correlated with motor quotients.[1] For an indication of ability in physical skills intelligence quotients are useless scores, at least within the zone of intellectual normality that is maintained in the public schools.[2]

The lack of relationship between intelligence quotients and motor quotients may be clarified somewhat by a discussion of the measurement of intelligence. Intelligence may be defined as educability, that is, the *ability to learn.*

188. By means of factorial analyses[3] the following factors of intelligence have been identified: (1) number facility, or the ability to "handle" numbers readily, (2) verbal fluency, or the ability to speak fluently and to express oneself adequately, (3) inductive reasoning, (4) deductive reasoning, (5) verbal reasoning, or the ability to express in verbal symbols the results of reasoning clearly, (6) memory, (7) perceptual speed or the ability to apperceive the essential elements of a situation quickly, (8) ability to visualize spatial relationships, and (9) restrictive thinking or the ability to think adaptively in terms of new concepts.

189. Educability re the understanding and the utilization of general ideas and principles. This kind of educability is usually termed "intelligence," and is what is measured by the ordinary intelligence tests used in the schools. It is, however, only one kind of intelligence. Items from class-

---

[1] If quotients are correlated with raw scores, the coefficients of correlation are usually small; for example, the strength quotient (see Secs. 284-85) correlates about .40 with the strength score, which is a raw score. The raw intelligence score has a fairly high correlation with motor abilities, but this is a spurious correlation, resulting from the common factor of age. Up to about sixteen years of age, the older the child, the higher is his intelligence *score* (corresponding to his mental age). Similarly, the older child is better in athletics performance than is the younger child. If age is held constant to both intelligence scores and athletics performance, the relationship is zero.

[2] Within the range of subnormality in intelligence, however, the higher the intelligence quotient, the more quickly a motor skill is learned (from an unpublished study by Kathryn Simmons and the senior author).

[3] L. L. Thurstone, *Primary Mental Abilities.*
——, "The Perceptual Factor," Psychometrika, March, 1938.
——, *A Factorial Study of Perception.*
——, *Mechanical Aptitude III*, Analysis of Group Tests.
—— and Thelma G. Thurstone, *Factorial Studies of Intelligence.*

room subjects, together with similar but somewhat artificial items of the same general type, comprise the majority of such intelligence test items. Items based on memory and on solving problems involving different kinds of relationships comprise another kind of intelligence test (such as many of the items in the Stanford-Binet Test). There is little relationship between intelligence, as measured by these types of tests, and performance in motor skills.

190. Educability re **the solution of mechanical or manipulative problems.** This kind of intelligence is possessed by the motor mechanic who quickly finds out what is wrong with an engine. It might be called "a kind of scientific imagination" that enables a person to visualize the inner workings of a mechanism. It is not necessarily significantly associated with the kind of intelligence involved in the understanding and the utilization of general ideas and principles, the average r between the two kinds of intelligence being lower than .3.

191. Educability re **the making of acceptable responses in social situations.** The measurement of this kind of intelligence has not advanced very far, but the r's between this kind of intelligence and the understanding and the utilization of general ideas and principles average about .26.

192. Educability re **the appreciation and the expression of the aesthetic.** For a further discussion of this topic, see Sections 240 to 242.

193. Common sense is probably one form of intelligence. Observation would indicate that it is not necessarily highly correlated with the types of intelligence indicated in Sections 189 to 192.

194. Motor educability is the ability to learn motor skills easily and well. It corresponds, in the area of general-motor skills, to intelligence in the area of classroom subjects. Most of the measurement of motor educability to date has been of a "shotgun" variety; that is, the attempts have been to measure motor educability with one general type of test.

195. Twenty-five factors in motor educability and eleven prerequisites for sucessful learning were discussed in Chapter 2 (see Secs. 19-37). While the prerequisites are not factors of motor educability, they contribute to the ability to utilize these factors. Some of the twenty-five factors of motor educability can undoubtedly be cultivated or learned, while others are probably as innate as is color blindness.

196. Attention is called to the fact that ability in one factor of motor educability may be negated by lack of ability in another factor; for example, the first factor of sensory co-ordination—the eye-hand type of motor co-ordination—may be related to the factor of general-kinesthetic sensitivity and control, which factor may, in turn, fail to function in such an activity as throwing at a target or throwing free throws in basketball if there is a deficiency in the factor of depth perception or in the factor of arm control. Both activities may be further complicated by ability or lack of ability in eye-motor timing. This analysis indicates that the problem of motor educability is just beginning to be defined.

TESTS OF GENERAL-MOTOR EDUCABILITY

197. The following tests will undoubtedly be supplanted in another decade by tests devised to measure single factors or sets of related factors of motor educability.

198. Brace Test.[4] The Brace Test of Motor Ability (Tests 1 to 20, Sec. 201) was the first published test of general-motor achievement. It is believed that this excellent test can be validly used to measure some aspects of motor educability.[5] Like the Stanford-Binet Intelligence Test the Brace Test includes skills that range from easy to difficult ones. Since the Brace Test was not designed to be a test of motor educability, it includes some stunts that depend, for their execution, primarily upon strength.

199. Iowa-Brace Test.[6] The Iowa Revision of the Brace Test, commonly referred to as the "Iowa-Brace Test," resulted from an attempt to design a test primarily for the measurement of motor educability. Of the forty stunts studied, twenty-one stunts,[7] each of which meets the following criteria, were retained for the Iowa-Brace Test.

(1) The percentage of persons who executed a stunt correctly increased with each year of age; for example, a stunt executed successfully by 80 per cent of the thirteen-year-old performers but by only 45 per cent of the fourteen-year-old performers was eliminated.

(2) The stunt had a low correlation with the strength test, with the classification index, and with the Sargent Jump; in other words, it was not a significant measurement of strength, size and maturity, and/or power.

(3) The stunt had a high correlation with track-and-field athletics when the classification index (or age alone for girls), the Sargent Jump, and the strength score were held constant to the athletic events but not to the stunt. The assumption upon which this criterion was based is that persons who, in track-and-field events, are better than the average of those having the same age, size, speed, and strength, are better primarily because they have greater skills or a greater degree of motor educability.

200. Since the formulation of the Brace Test and of the Iowa-Brace Test, numerous studies have been conducted to investigate the efficacy of these tests for the measurement of general-motor educability. The results obtained in these studies have been conflicting. Low coefficients of correla-

---

[4] David K. Brace, *Measuring Motor Ability.*

[5] Brace does not consider this test to be a test of motor educability. The present authors, however, think that this excellent test does function to a large degree as a test of motor educability.

[6] Charles H. McCloy, "An Analytical Study of the Stunt Type Test as a Measure of Motor Educability," *Research Quarterly*, October, 1937.

[7] This number includes ten stunts of the Brace Test.

tion have been obtained between tests of general-motor educability made up of artificial activities, and the Brace Test and the Iowa-Brace Test.[8] These low coefficients of correlation may be due to the neglect of such variables as the background of the performers, methods of teaching, and motivation.

The validity of the stunt type of test for the measurement of general-motor educability is supported by the following findings.

(1) The high correlation obtained between stunt types of tests (Brace Test and Iowa-Brace Test) and athletic events when strength, speed, and size and maturity were held constant (Table 17, p. 86).

Table 17

STUNT-TYPE TESTS; SPORTS RATINGS, SPORTS INTELLIGENCE:
CORRELATION COEFFICIENTS

	Sports Ratings	Sports Intelligence	
Brace Test	.706	.671	
	.521*	.507*	.448**
Brace Test modified (two trials allowed for each stunt)	.668	.668	
Iowa-Brace Test	.682	.618	
	.540*	.509*	.478**
Hill Test	.690		
Johnson Test	.678	.661	
	.473*	.493*	.337**

*Sargent Jump held constant.

**Sargent Jump and two of the Thurstone tests of spatial relationships held constant.

(2) The finding in a study[9] on 155 senior-high-school girls who were rated on their skills in sports (reliability of rating, $r = .95$) and on "sports intelligence" (the quickness with which appropriate sports strategy is devised). The coefficients of correlation between these ratings and stunt types of tests are presented in Table 17 (p. 86).

(3) The findings in a study[10] on eight-grade boys who had not practiced tumbling previous to the administration of the tests. The criterion

[8] Brace, "Studies in the Rate of Learning Gross Bodily Motor Skills," *Research Quarterly*, May, 1941.

———, "Studies in Motor Learning of Gross Bodily Motor Skills," *Research Quarterly*, December, 1946.

Eugenia Gire and Anna Espenschade, "The Relationship between Measures of Motor Educability and the Learning of Specific Motor Skills," *Research Quarterly*, March, 1942.

[9] Theresa Anderson and C. H. McCloy, "The Measurement of Sports Ability in High School Girls," *Research Quarterly*, March, 1947.

[10] Kenneth Hill, "The Formulation of Tests of Motor Educability for Junior High School Boys" (M.A. Thesis, State University of Iowa, 1935).

was the sum of the T-scores of ten tumbling stunts, which ranged from easy ones to difficult ones. For each stunt twenty-five trials were given, with a score of 1 for success on the first trial, 2 for success on the second trial . . . 25 for success on the twenty-fifth trial, and 26 if the stunt had not been mastered by the twenty-fifth trial. A coefficient of biserial correlation was obtained between performances in fifty-five stunts and the criterion score. An *r* of .624 was obtained between the sums of the scores of the twelve best performances in the stunts and the T-scores for tumbling.

(4) The findings in a study[11] on eighth-, ninth-, and tenth-grade boys. The major difference between this study and the one discussed under item 3 is that sixteen, instead of ten, tumbling stunts were used. An *r* of reliability (by the split-half method) of .885 was obtained for the Brace Test, and a coefficient of validity of .606 was obtained between the records for the twelve best performances in the stunts and the sum of the T-scores for tumbling.

201. The stunts used in the Brace Test,[12] in the Iowa-Brace Test, and in the Hill Test are the following.

(1) *Straight-line-walk test.* Place heel of left foot in front of toes of right foot. Then place heel of right foot in front of toes of left foot. Take a total of ten steps in this manner. It is a failure: (a) to lose the balance; (b) to fail to place heel so that it touches toes.

(2) *Single-heel-click test.* Jump into the air, click heels together once, and land with feet apart. Failure: (a) not to click heels together once; (b) not to land with feet apart.

(3) *Sit-up test.* Lie on back, with arms folded on chest. Sit up without raising feet from the floor. Failure: (a) to unfold arms; (b) to raise feet from the floor.

(4) *Kneel-and-up test.* Standing, fold arms behind back. Kneel on both legs. Get up without losing the balance or without moving feet. Failure: (a) to lose the balance; (b) to move feet after standing up; (c) to unfold arms.

(5) *Three-dip test.* Take a front leaning-rest position. Bend arms, touching chest to the floor, and push body up again until forearms are in a straight line with upper arms. Execute three performances in succession. Do not touch the floor with legs or with abdomen. Failure: (a) not to push body up three times; (b) not to touch chest to the floor; (c) to touch the floor with any part of body other than hands, feet, and chest.

(6) *Heel-jump test.* Squat on heels, touching the floor in front of feet with fingers. Jump to the side-straddle position, standing on heels with toes raised, and with arms raised sideways. Execute three performances in succession. Failure: (a) to lose the balance; (b) not to land on heels.

(7) *Full-left-turn test.* Stand with feet together. Jump upward, making a full

---

[11] Don W. Harshbarger, "The Brace Test and Elements Selected from the Brace Test as a Measure of Motor Skills Educability" (M.A. Thesis, State University of Iowa, 1936).

[12] The first twenty items make up the Brace Test. The authors are indebted to the publishers, A. S. Barnes and Company, and to David K. Brace for permission to republish these stunts. The word "test" has been added to the title of each stunt, and the directions have been somewhat reworded to conform with the wording of the directions for Tests 21 to 39.

turn to the left. Land at approximately the same place from which the test was started. (Feet may be separated when landing.) Do not lose the balance, or move feet after they have touched the floor. Failure: (a) not to make a full turn to the left; (b) to move feet after they have returned to the floor; (c) to lose the balance.

(8) *Double-heel-click test.* Jump upward, clap feet together twice, and land with feet apart (any distance). Failure: (a) not to clap feet together twice; (b) to land with feet touching each other.

(9) *Knee-dip test.* Stand on right foot. Grasp left foot with right hand behind back. Bend trunk forward, and touch the floor with left knee. Return to the standing position. Failure: (a) to lose the balance; (b) not to return to the standing position.

(10) *Jump-foot test.* Hold toes of one foot in opposite hand. Jump upward, with free foot jumping over foot that is held. Do not release the hold of foot. Failure: (a) to release foot that is held; (b) not to jump through the loop made by foot and arm.

(11) *Heel-slap test.* Jump upward, and slap both heels with hands behind body. Failure: (a) not to slap both heels; to move feet or to lose the balance after landing.

(12) *High-kick test.* Kick right foot to the level of shoulders. Failure: (a) not to kick foot to level of shoulders; (b) to lose the balance.

(13) *One-foot-touch-head test.* Stand on left foot. Bend trunk forward, and place both hands on the floor. Raise right leg, and extend it backward. Touch head to the floor, and return to the standing position without losing the balance. Failure: (a) not to touch head to the floor; (b) to lose the balance.

(14) *Grapevine test.* Stand with heels together. Bend trunk forward, extend both arms down between legs and behind ankles, and hold fingers of hands together in front of ankles. Hold this position for five seconds. Failure: (a) to lose the balance; (b) not to hold fingers of both hands together; (c) not to hold the position for five seconds.

(15) *Full-right-turn test.* Stand with feet together. Jump upward, making a full turn to the right. Land at approximately the same place from which the test was started. (Feet may be separated when landing.) Do not lose the balance or move feet after they have touched the floor. Failure: (a) not to make a full turn to the right; (b) to move feet after they have returned to the floor; (c) to lose the balance.

(16) *Kneel-jump-to-feet test.* Kneel on both knees. Rest backs of toes on the floor. Swing arms, and jump to the standing position. Do not rock backward on toes, or lose the balance. Failure: (a) to curl toes and to rock backward on them; (b) not to execute the jump, and not to stand still after the standing position has been reached.

(17) *Cross-leg-squat test.* Fold arms across chest. Cross feet and sit down. Get up without unfolding arms and without moving feet about to regain the balance. Failure: (a) to unfold arms; (b) to lose the balance; (c) not to get up.

(18) *Stork-stand test.* Stand on left foot. Hold the bottom of right foot against the medial side of left knee. Place hands on hips. Shut eyes, and hold the position for ten seconds, without moving left foot. Failure: (a) to lose the balance; (b) not to hold right foot against left knee; (c) to open eyes, or to remove hands from hips.

(19) *Tip-up test.* Squat, and place hands on the floor between and close to feet. Bend arms slightly, keeping knees over elbows. Rock forward upon hands, raising feet from the floor and supporting body on hands. Hold the position for

five seconds. Failure: (a) not to keep the position and not to keep body off the floor for five seconds.

(20) *Single-leg-squat test.* Stand on left foot, with right foot in front of left foot. Sit down on left heel, with right leg raised forward, and stand up without touching the floor or losing the balance. Failure: (a) to lose the balance; (b) not to be able to get up.

(21) *Side-leaning-rest test.* Sit on the floor, with lower legs extended, and feet together. Put right hand on the floor behind body. Turn to the right, and take a side leaning-rest position, resting the body on right hand and right foot. Raise left arm and left leg, and hold this position for five counts. Failure: (a) not to take the proper position; (b) not to hold the position for five counts.

(22) *One-knee-balance test.* Right face. Kneel on one knee, with other leg raised from the floor and with arms raised sideward to the level of shoulders. Hold the position for five counts. Failure: (a) to touch the floor with any other part of body than one lower leg; (b) to fall over.

(23) *One-knee-head-to-the-floor test.* Kneel on one knee, with other leg raised behind body and not touching the floor, and with arms raised sideward to the level of shoulders. Bend trunk forward, touching head to the floor, and raise head from the floor without losing the balance. Failure: (a) to lose the balance; (b) not to touch the floor with head; (c) to touch the floor with any part of body other than head, and leg supporting the weight of body.

(24) *Hop-backward test.* Stand on either foot. Close eyes, and take five hops backward. Failure: (a) to open eyes; (b) to touch the floor with foot not supporting the weight of body.

(25) *Forward-hand-kick test.* Jump upward, swinging legs forward. Bend trunk forward, and touch toes with both hands before landing. Keep lower legs in as straight a line as possible with upper legs. Failure: (a) not to touch toes with both hands before landing; (b) to bend lower legs more than forty-five degrees.

(26) *Full-squat-arm-circles test.* Take a full-squat position, with arms raised sideward to the level of shoulders. Wave arms so that each hand makes a circle of about one foot in diameter, and at the same time jiggle body up and down. Continue the performance for ten counts. Failure: (a) to move feet; (b) to lose the balance: (c) to touch the floor with any other part of body than feet; (d) not to move hands in a circle; (e) not to jiggle up and down.

(27) *Half-turn-jump-left-foot test.* Stand on left foot, and jumping, make a one-half turn to the left. Keep the balance. Failure: (a) to lose the balance; (b) to fail to complete the half turn; (c) to touch the floor with right foot.

(28) *Side-kick test.* Swing left leg sideways to the left, jumping upward with right leg. Strike feet together in the air, and land with feet apart. Feet should strike together in a line that would go to the left of left shoulder. Failure: (a) not to swing leg enough to the side; (b) not to strike feet together in the air, to the left of the line of left shoulder; (c) not to land with feet apart.

(29) *Russian-dance test.* Squat. Raise one leg forward. Perform a Russian-dance step by extending legs alternately while in a squat position. Perform four such steps, that is, two with each leg. Heel of forward foot may touch the floor. Heel of rear foot should strike hip on that side. Failure: (a) to lose the balance; (b) not to do the stunt twice with each leg.

(30) *Top test.* Sit, with lower legs flexed, on the floor. Put arms between legs, and under and behind knees, and grasp ankles. Roll rapidly around to the right, with the weight first over right knee, then over right shoulder, then on back, then on left shoulder, and then on left knee. Sit up, facing in the opposite direction from which the test was started. Repeat the movements from this position, and

finish facing in the same direction from which the test was started. Failure: (a) to release the hold of ankles; (b) not to complete the circle.

(31) *Single-squat-balance test*. Squat on either foot. With hands on hips, raise one leg forward. Hold this position for five counts. Failure: (a) to remove hands from hips; (b) to touch the floor with raised leg; (c) not to hold the balance for five seconds.

(32) *Face-to-knee test*. With hands on hips, stand on foot of one leg, extending other leg backward. Bend trunk forward, and touch, with face, knee of leg that is supporting body. Return to the standing position without losing the balance. Failure: (a) to take hands off hips; (b) to fall over; (c) not to touch knee with face.

(33) *Free-seat-support test*. Sit on the floor. Place hands on the floor halfway between hips and knees, and support the weight of body on hands, holding, for three counts, entire body except hands off the floor. Failure: (a) to support body with any part of body other than hands; (b) to fail to hold the position for three counts.

(34) *Stiff-leg-bend test*. Place a paper on the floor near left heel. Stand with lower legs completely extended, bend trunk forward, grasp right toes with right fingers, and pick up the paper with left fingers. At no time must lower legs be allowed to bend. Failure: (a) not to pick up the paper; (b) to release the hold of right toes; (c) to bend legs at knees.

(35) *Hitch-kick test*. Kick, lifting body with a half kick (fake kick) with one foot and then with a higher kick with other foot while first foot is still off the floor. The higher kick should go to the level of shoulders. Failure: (a) not to kick while first foot is off the floor; (b) not to kick to the height of shoulders.

(36) *Mouth-dive test*. Kneel on knee of one leg, with other leg and foot entirely off the floor. Bending trunk forward, pick up with teeth a paper which has one corner turned up and which is on the floor directly in front of knee that is supporting the weight of body. Failure: (a) to lose the balance; (b) to touch the floor with free foot or with hands; (c) not to pick up the paper.

(37) *Crane-drive test*. Place on the floor a folded sheet of paper about six inches high. Pick up the paper with teeth by bending trunk forward from a position of standing on one foot. Foot not in use is, for balance, extended behind body. It is difficult to bend trunk beyond the position where chest strikes knee. Failure: (a) not to pick up the paper; (b) to lose the balance; (c) to touch the floor with free foot.

(38) *Seal-slap test*. From a front leaning-rest position push body up from the floor with hands, clap hands in front of chest, and land with arms apart in the front leaning-rest position. Failure: (a) not to clap hands; (b) not to have hands apart; (c) to touch the floor with any part of body other than hands and feet.

(39) *Crawl-up test*. Lie, face down, on the floor. Clasp hands behind back; roll over on one shoulder, and come to a standing position on both feet. Failure: (a) not to reach the standing position; (b) to loosen hands from behind back.

The *Brace Test* is made up of Tests 1 to 20, inclusive. The tests are administered in two groups: (1) Tests 1 to 10 and (2) Tests 11 to 20. They are for boys and for girls of all ages.[13] The *Iowa-Brace Test* is made up of Tests 5, 7, 8, 10, 13, 14, 15, 16, 17, 18, 21, 22, 23, 24, 25, 26, 27, 28, 29, 30, and 31 (Table 18, p. 91).

[13] An interesting modification of the Brace Test for young children has been presented by Vernette S. Vickers and Others in "The Brace Scale Used with Young Children" in the *Research Quarterly* for October, 1942.

202. In a factorial analysis of the Iowa-Brace Test[14] the following six factors were identified: (1) dynamic energy, (2) flexibility, (3) balance, (4) semicircular-canal balance, (5) insight into the nature of the stunt, and (6) arm control.

203. The Hill Test is made up of two parts: the first half consists of Tests 2, 35, 39, 36, 30, and 21; and the second half consists of Tests 32, 38, 25, 34, 19, and 37. These batteries have been designed for boys of junior-high-school age, but they are probably satisfactory for boys of senior-high-school age and for boys of upper-elementary-school age.

Table 18

IOWA-BRACE TEST: STUNTS USED (ELEMENTARY-SCHOOL AND JUNIOR- AND SENIOR-HIGH SCHOOL BOYS AND GIRLS)

Elementary School		Junior-high School		Senior-high School	
1st half	2nd half	1st half	2nd half	1st half	2nd half
BOYS					
24	21	13	21	13	14
22	14	5	14	25	5
27	17	27	26	16	28
25	16	30	16	18	29
7	29	8	29	31	10
GIRLS					
24	13	21	13	14	21
15	14	26	27	25	15
7	16	28	25	17	16
30	28	30	16	29	23
25	8	29	31	30	31

204. Carpenter Stunt Tests for first three grades.[15] Tests 14, 22, 17, 7 or 15, 24, and 16 have, if given in this order, been found to be effective for use in the first three grades. If the performer succeeds in executing the stunt on the first trial, he receives two points; if he fails on the first trial but succeeds on the second trial, he receives one point; if he fails on both trials, he receives zero points.

205. *Administration of stunt types of tests.* Performance in stunt types of tests is greatly affected by the practice of stunts. Hence stunts included in the Brace Test, in the Iowa-Brace Test, and in the Hill Test should not be included in the physical-activity program. Performers should probably not be tested in these stunts more than once every three years.

[14] Esther E. Cope, "A Study of the Component Factors of the Iowa Revision of the Brace Motor Ability Test" (M.A. Thesis, State University of Iowa, 1938).

[15] Aileen Carpenter, "The Measurement of General Motor Capacity and General Motor Ability in the First Three Grades," *Research Quarterly*, December, 1942.

206. The following directions, which are in general those suggested by Brace, should be followed in the administration of stunt types of tests:[16]

(1) Arrange the performers six to eight feet apart in double lines about ten feet apart.

(2) Provide each performer with a pencil and a score blank (Fig. XII, p. 92). Have each performer fill out his blank and then exchange it with that of the performer opposite him in the other line.

(3) Explain the test and how to score it as follows: "We are going to take a test that is made up of ten stunts (twenty for the Brace Test, twelve for the Hill

Stunt number *	1st trial	2nd trial	Score
1			
2			
3			
4			
5			
6			
7			
8			
9			
10			
		Total score	
		T-score	

* Renumber the appropriate stunts for the group so they will be consecutive.

FIGURE XII. Iowa-Brace Test: Score Card

Test). Some of these stunts are very easy and some are more difficult. Probably none of you will be able to do all of them. You will score the performances of each other. The persons in one line will do five stunts (ten for the Brace Test, six for the Hill Test), and the persons in the other line will indicate whether their partners succeeded or failed in the performances. Performers and scorers will be alter-

[16] These directions are for the administration of the Iowa-Brace Test. The adaptations necessary for the administration of the Brace Test and the Hill Test are indicated in parentheses.

nated until everyone has performed ten stunts (twenty for the Brace Test, twelve for the Hill Test). Two trials (one for the Brace Test) will be given for each stunt. If your partner does the stunt correctly on the first trial, put an *X* in the first square; if he fails, a *0* in the first square. If he fails on the first trial, he is given a second trial (only one trial for the Brace Test). If he does the stunt correctly on the second trial, put an *X* in the second square; if he fails, a *0* in the second square. Do not permit your partner to practice the stunt. In some of the stunts you will have to count the time. Do not count 'one, two, three,' but count 'one thousand and ONE, one thousand and TWO, one thousand and THREE.' (Let them practice counting this way.) As soon as you have done a stunt correctly

Table 19

BRACE TEST: SCORING TABLES
(BOYS AND GIRLS 11 TO 16 AND COLLEGE WOMEN)

	T-score*	
Tests Passed	Boys and Girls	College Women
1	21	11
2	23	14
3	27	18
4	29	22
5	32	26
6	35	30
7	37	34
8	40	37
9	43	41
10	46	45
11	48	48
12	51	52
13	54	56
14	58	60
15	61	63
16	64	67
17	68	71
18	72	75
19	76	78
20	80	80

EXAMPLES:

    Age: 14 years
          T-score for 12
          tests passed = 51

    Age: College
          T-score for 12
          tests passed = 52

*T-scores adjusted by curve fitting.

or have had two trials at it, sit down on the floor so that I will know when everyone is ready for the next stunt. When you are scoring the performance of your partner, do not practice the stunt, but sit or lie on the floor. Watch the person whose performance you are scoring and pay no attention to anyone else. Do not talk to the others. Are there any questions about what you are to do?" Then have the performers in one line put aside their pencils and papers, and stand facing the scorers.

(4) Demonstrate the first stunt, using the standard instructions given in the description of the tests. It is convenient to have each stunt written on a separate

card, which can be held in one hand and read while the stunt is being demonstrated. Read slowly, indicating the parts of the body referred to and taking the correct positions as you read. Then read what constitutes a failure, and where it seems desirable illustrate by saying: "This would be a failure and should be scored *0*." Then do the stunt correctly, saying: "This would be correct and should be scored *X*."

(5) Have the first line perform the first stunt. After each person has had an

Table 20

IOWA-BRACE TEST: SCORING TABLES (ELEMENTARY-SCHOOL
AND JUNIOR- AND SENIOR-HIGH-SCHOOL BOYS AND GIRLS)

Test Score Points	T-scores					
	BOYS			GIRLS		
	Elementary School	Junior-High School	Senior-High School	Elementary School	Junior-High School	Senior-High School
20	69	66	71	67	64	71
19	66	63	65	65	61	66
18	63	60	60	62	58	63
17	60	57	56	60	56	60
16	57	54	53	58	53	57
15	54	51	50	56	50	55
14	51	48	47	54	47	53
13	48	45	44	52	45	51
12	45	42	41	50	43	49
11	43	39	38	48	41	47
10	41	36	35	45	39	45
9	39	34	33	42	37	43
8	37	32	31	39	35	41
7	35	30	29	36	32	39
6	33	28	--	33	30	37
5	31	26	--	30	26	34
4	29	24	--	28	--	32
3	27	22	--	26	--	30
2	25	20	--	24	--	28
1	23	19	--	--	--	--

opportunity for two trials (unless everyone succeeded on the first trial), demonstrate the second stunt, and so on through the list of the first five stunts (ten for the Brace Test, six for the Hill Test).

(6) After the first line has tried the first five stunts (ten for the Brace Test, six for the Hill Test), have the second line try all ten stunts (twenty for the Brace Test, twelve for the Hill Test).

(7) After the second line has tried all ten stunts (twenty for the Brace Test, twelve for the Hill Test), have the first line try the second five stunts (ten for the Brace Test, six for the Hill Test).

207. *Scoring of Brace Test* (Table 19, p. 93). If a performer executes a stunt correctly on the first trial, he receives one point; if he fails, he receives zero points. The maximum score is 20.

208. *Scoring of Iowa-Brace Test* (Table 20, p. 94). If the performer succeeds in executing a stunt on the first trial, he receives two points; if he fails on the first trial but succeeds on the second trial, he receives one point; if he fails on both trials, he receives zero points. The maximum score is 20.

209. *Scoring of Hill Test* (Table 21, p. 95). The Hill Test is scored in the same way as is the Iowa-Brace Test.

Table 21

HILL TEST: SCORING TABLES
(JUNIOR-HIGH-SCHOOL BOYS)

Points	T-score	Points	T-score	Points	T-score
24	75	16	59	8	44
23	72	15	57	7	42
22	71	14	56	6	41
21	69	13	54	5	39
20	67	12	52	4	37
19	65	11	50	3	35
18	63	10	48	2	33
17	61	9	46	1	31

210. The **Johnson Test**[17] was designed for sectioning classes into homogeneous units. Further studies have indicated that the Johnson Test is probably the most valid test of general-motor educability that has been published to date. In one study[18] an *r* of .9687 was obtained between the Johnson Test and the time required to learn ten tumbling stunts. Compared with the stunt tests described previously, the Johnson Test requires more time for administration and is more difficult to score. Approximately twenty students can be tested by an expert administrator of the test in a forty-minute period.

The Johnson Test is administered on a sheet of ten-ounce canvas, eight feet wide and twenty feet long, marked off according to the design in Figure XIII (p. 96). The pattern is a rectangle 4.5 feet wide and 15 feet long, divided into squares 1.5 feet on a side. This makes three lanes 1.5 feet wide down the length of the chart. The main outline of the rectangle and the lines marking the lanes are painted in black ⅜ inch wide. The second, fourth, sixth, eighth, and tenth squares in the two outside lanes are painted black. The center lane is not marked off in squares, but the first, third, fifth, seventh, and ninth spaces in this lane each contains a "target" twelve inches by three inches in the center. There is an additional target placed outside the main pattern on the finish end. There is another lane two feet wide marked in red down the center of the canvas, divided

[17] Granville B. Johnson, "Physical Skill Tests for Sectioning Classes into Homogeneous Units," *Research Quarterly*, March, 1932.

[18] Clarence G. Koob, "A Study of the Johnson Skills Test as a Measure of Motor Educability" (M.A. Thesis, State University of Iowa, 1937).

halfway by a crossline of red; this is used only for the rolling exercises. It is advisable to have grommets inserted along the edge of the canvas and about two feet apart. After the canvas has been folded under the mats upon which it is stretched, it should be laced together underneath the mats in order that it may be pulled taut and smooth.

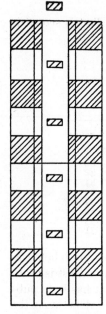

Figure XIII. Johnson Physical-skill Test: Diagram of Mat

211. The Johnson Test consists of the following exercises:[19]

(1) *Straddle-jump test.* Stand, with hands on hips and with feet together, on the first target in the center lane. Jump forward, straddling, with feet on the first two black squares. Jump forward, landing with feet together on the second target. Proceed similarly to the last (sixth) target. You must maintain a regular rhythm.

(2) *Stagger-skip test.* Stand, with hands on hips and with feet together, behind the right lane. Step, with left foot, on the first target in the center lane; hop, with left foot, to the first black square in the left lane. Step, with right foot, to the second target in the center lane; hop, with right foot, to the second black square in the right lane. Proceed similarly to the last (sixth) target. You must maintain a regular rhythm.

(3) *Stagger-jump test.* Stand, with hands on hips and with feet together, behind the right lane. Jump obliquely to the left, landing with feet together on the first white square in the left lane. Jump obliquely to the right, landing with feet together on the first black square in the right lane. Proceed similarly across the mat, finishing on the sixth target. Throughout the test keep hands on hips and feet together, and jump rhythmically.

(4) *Forward-skip test.* Stand, with feet together, behind either the right or the left lane. Hop forward, with right foot, to the first white square; at the same time raise left foot behind body, and grasp left foot, with right hand, behind right thigh. Continuing to hold left foot with right hand, hop forward, with right foot, to the first black square. Release left foot. Hop forward, with left foot, to the second white square; at the same time raise right foot behind body, and grasp it, with left hand, behind left thigh. Continuing to hold right foot with left hand, hop forward, with left foot, to the second black square. Proceed similarly across the mat, finishing on the sixth target. You must maintain a regular rhythm.

(5) *Front-roll test.* Stand in front of the red lane. Perform one front roll in the first half of the red lane. Perform another front roll in the second half of the red lane.

(6) *Jumping-half-turn test A.* Stand, with feet together, on the first target. Keeping feet together, and executing a half turn to either the right or the left,

---

[19] The authors are indebted to Granville B. Johnson and to the editor of the *Research Quarterly* for permission to reproduce these tests. The word "test" has been added to the title of each stunt, and the directions have been somewhat reworded to conform with the wording of the directions for the stunt tests described earlier in this chapter.

jump to the second target. Body now faces the starting line. Keeping feet together, and executing a half turn in the same direction as the first half turn was executed, jump to the third target. Body now faces the finishing line. Proceed similarly to the sixth target where body faces the starting line.

(7) *Back-roll test.* Stand behind the red lane and with back toward the red lane. Perform one back roll in the first half of the red lane. Perform another back roll in the second half of the red lane.

(8) *Jumping-half-turn test B.* Stand, with feet together, on the first target. Keeping feet together, and executing a half turn to either the right or the left, jump to the second target. Body now faces the starting line. Keeping feet together, and executing a half turn in the opposite direction from which the first half turn was executed, jump to the third target. Body now faces the finishing line. Proceed similarly to the sixth target where body faces the starting line.

(9) *Front-and-back-roll test.* Start behind the red lane. Perform a front roll in the first half of the red lane. Finish with legs crossed at ankles. Executing a two-foot pivot, turn body to either the right or the left. Perform a back roll in the second half of the red lane.

(10) *Jumping-full-turn test.* Stand, with feet together, in front of either the right or the left lane. Keeping feet together and executing a full turn to either the right or the left, jump to the first black square in the same lane in front of which the start was made. Land on both feet. Proceed similarly to the fifth black square. Execute all the turns in the same direction.

212. *Scoring of Johnson Test.* The maximum score for each exercise is 10. When a step, skip, or jump is made into any white or black square with one or both feet, the feet must land entirely within the limits of that square. If the heel is lifted, it may project over the edge of the square, but no part of the foot may touch outside the square. When a step, skip, or jump is made to any target with one or both feet, the feet must land touching the target, and not touching the side lines or the outside lanes.

Test 1. One point is deducted for each of the following failures: to land within an indicated square or within an indicated target, for feet to land at the same time, to keep hands on hips throughout the exercise, to maintain throughout the test the rhythm of about two jumps a second.

Test 2. Same as for Test 1 except that feet do not land at the same time.

Test 3. Same as for Test 1.

Test 4. One point is deducted for each of the following failures: to land within an indicated square and/or to take and maintain the indicated position for held hand and foot (only one point for each square is deducted for these failures), to maintain throughout the test the rhythm of about two jumps a second.

Test 5. The maximum score for each roll is 5. Two points for each roll are deducted for each of the following failures: to perform the roll within the left boundary of the red lane, and to perform the roll within the right boundary of the red lane. One point for each roll is deducted for the failure to complete the roll within the indicated half of the red lane. Five points are deducted for the failure to execute a "true" roll. If the subject fails to execute the first roll, he may attempt to execute the second roll in the second half of the red lane.

Test 6. Two points are deducted for each of the following failures: to land with both feet on the indicated target and to turn body in the indicated direction (only two points for each target are deducted for these failures). The turn does not need to be exactly 180 degrees.

Test 7. Same as for Test 5.

Test 8. Same as for Test 6 except that one point is deducted for the failure to make a turn of 180 degrees. (This scoring is different from the Johnson method of scoring.)

Test 9. Same as for Test 5 except that one point is deducted for the failure to execute the turn correctly.

Test 10. Same as for Test 6 except that, if the only failure is that of not making a 360-degree turn, but if a turn of more than 270 degrees is made, only one point is deducted. (This scoring is different from the Johnson method of scoring.)

213. *Administration of Johnson Test.* The following directions, which are in general those suggested by Johnson, should be followed in the administration of the Johnson Test.

(1) Explain the purpose of the test, and point out the markings on the mat.

(2) Give explicit directions for Test 1, and perform the exercise once. Explain the method of scoring, and demonstrate the errors for which points are deducted. Have all the subjects perform Test 1.

(3) Proceed similarly with Tests 2 to 10.

(4) In order to lessen as much as possible the disadvantage of coming first and the advantage of coming last in the group, start the different tests with different subjects. If, for example, there are twenty subjects in the group, have the first subject be the first to perform Test 1, the third subject be the first to perform Test 2, the fifth subject be the first to perform Test 3, etc.

214. Performance in the Johnson Test is subject to improvement on retesting; pupils who have engaged in tumbling and in mat work have a slight advantage over those who have not practiced such exercises. Specific exercises, however, are not commonly practiced; hence practice in tumbling and in mat work does not have a significant effect on the score

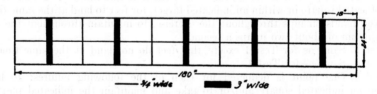

FIGURE XIV. Metheny Mat Diagram

in the whole Johnson Test. Such practice is not as serious as the effect of practice on scores in the stunt tests in school systems where stunts are taught. Like the stunt-type tests, however, the Johnson Test may best be used at three-year intervals.

215. Metheny Test.[20] For boys, r's of .977 and .934 have been obtained between Johnson Tests 5-7-8-10 and the total Johnson Test and a cri-

[20] Eleanor Metheny, "Studies of the Johnson Test as a Test of Motor Educability," *Research Quarterly*, December, 1938.

terion, respectively. For girls, an r of .868 has been obtained between Johnson Tests 5-7-8 and the total Johnson Test.

In the Metheny Tests an undue amount of emphasis is put on the front and the back roll; hence performances are influenced by activities practiced in tumbling classes. In a program in which no great amount of emphasis has been placed upon tumbling activities, the Metheny Tests may well be used, particularly for purposes of screening. The Metheny Mat Diagram (Fig. XIV, p. 98), which is a decided simplification of the Johnson Mat Diagram, is one that can be easily drawn on mats with chalk.

216. Scores for six tests of motor educability for college women have been equated so that equivalents can be obtained if it is desired to substitute one of these tests for another in a test battery.[21]

217. In a factorial analysis[22] of eighteen Johnson-type Tests, including the ten tests devised by Johnson, the following factors were identified.

Factor I or strength, which was not of great importance in these tests.

Factor II, which included only those tests that consisted of forward and backward rolls, probably represents a phase of body control in turns about a transverse axis (an R of .817 was obtained between this factor and Tests 5-7-9).

Factor III, which seems to be more general in nature than the other factors, is probably the ability to solve new motor-skill co-ordinations quickly, or is what has been called "insight into the skill" (an R of .758 was obtained between this factor and Tests 3-4-8).

Factor IV was represented by only the two tests in which the trunk is horizontal and the orientation of the head is different from the usual orientation, and in which the arms are used as organs of locomotion (the R, .557, that was obtained between this factor and the two tests was too low to be used for predictive purposes).

218. Carpenter Mat Tests.[23] The Carpenter Mat was devised for use in the first three grades. The mat is ten feet long and three feet wide, with the squares each one foot square and with the center zone one foot wide. The targets, which are placed as in the Johnson design (Fig. XIII, p. 96), are eight inches long and two inches wide.

(1) *Single-hop-left test.* Stand, with hands on hips and with feet together, behind the first white square in the left lane. Hop forward, with left foot, to the first white square. Hop forward, with left foot, to the first black square. Proceed similarly the length of the mat.

(2) *Diagonal-jump test.* Stand, with feet together, on the first target. Keeping feet together, jump to the first black square in the right lane. Jump to the second

---

[21] S. Lucille Hatlestad, "Motor Educability Tests for Women College Students," *Research Quarterly,* March, 1942.

[22] Carpenter, "Factors in Motor Educability," *Research Quarterly,* December, 1943.

[23] Carpenter, "Tests of Motor Educability for the First Three Grades," *Child Development,* December, 1940.

target. Jump to the next black square at the left. Proceed similarly the length of the mat.

(3) *Backward-hop-right test*. Stand, with hands on hips and with feet together, behind the first white square in the left lane and with back toward the mat. Hop backward, with right foot, to the first white square. Hop backward, with right foot, to the next black square. Proceed similarly the length of the mat.

(4) *Left-sideward-hop test*. Stand, with left side toward the mat and with left foot on the first target. Hop diagonally backward, with left foot, to the first black square in the left lane. Hop diagonally forward, with left foot, to the second target. Hop diagonally forward with left foot to the second black square in the right lane. Proceed similarly the length of the mat.

(5) *Right-sideward-hop test*. This test is the same as Test 4 except that it is performed on right foot and with right side toward the finish target.

219. The Carpenter Tests are scored according to the directions for scoring the Johnson Tests. For each test, the maximum score is 10 from which are subtracted one point if the performer breaks his rhythm, one point if he takes his hands off his hips, one point for every time he steps over a line or fails to touch the designated square or the designated center target. In Tests 4 and 5, one point is subtracted if the performer hops forward instead of sideward. If the performer makes ten errors in any one test, his score is 0 for that test.

The highest coefficients of multiple correlation with the general factor of motor educability were obtained from the following formulas: for boys, $1(1) + 2(2) + 1(3) + 1(4) + 1(5)$; for girls, $1(3) + 2(2) + 1.75(5) + 1(4) + .25(1)$.

TESTS TO MEASURE SPECIFIC ASPECTS OF MOTOR EDUCABILITY

220. Tests of insight into nature of skill. It has been well established in a number of unpublished studies that a thorough understanding of a skill aids a performer greatly in his learning the skill accurately and quickly. Such an understanding on the part of a performer depends largely upon an adequate knowledge and understanding upon the part of the teacher and upon the teacher's ability to impart that knowledge and understanding to the performer. Tests that assist in measuring this aspect of educability consist primarily of tests of knowledge (see Chap. 24). Such tests need to be designed for each teaching situation by the teacher in charge. Such tests of knowledge are concerned with knowledge of the techniques used in learning the skills and not in the knowledge of the rules and of general strategy.

221. Tests of eye-hand co-ordination. The following semisubjective tests have been found to have a high correlation with general-motor educability and with eye-hand co-ordination.

222. Wendler Test for Fielding Ground Balls.[24] A standard softball diamond is used, with the fielder approximately eighty-five feet from the home base, and standing (if a right-handed thrower) about where the shortstop would normally play, slightly closer to second than to third base. Left-handed players play on the opposite side of the diamond between the first and the second base. The players are allowed to use gloves, and are told that they will be scored on the manner in which they field and throw the ground balls that are hit to them. The experimenter should attempt to have the grounders hit the ground a short distance (ten to twelve feet) away from the batter, five balls going to the right and five balls going to the left of the fielders, in such a manner that the balls bounce at least twice before reaching the fielder. The balls should be hit rather sharply. Only attempts made on balls so hit are scored. If (1) the fielder meets the ball properly, (2) fields cleanly, and (3) maintains such a position as to make efficient throwing possible, he is given three points. If he fails in any of these three items, a point is deducted for each failure. The maximum score is 30.

There have been obtained r's of .466 and .577 between the Wendler Test for Fielding Ground Balls and what the experimenter considered to be general-motor educability and eye-hand co-ordination, respectively.

223. Wendler Test for Throwing a Softball.[25] Immediately upon catching the ball, the fielder, if a right-handed thrower, turns, and throws sharply and as accurately as possible to the first base, and if a left-handed thrower, to the third base. If the fielder gets his throw away in good form, he receives one point; if he throws accurately, one point; and if he throws with reasonable speed, one point. The maximum score is 30.

An r of .404 has been obtained between the Wendler Test for Throwing the Softball and a factor of general-motor educability, and an r of .565 between this test and eye-hand co-ordination.

224. Wendler Test for Throwing a Soccer Ball.[26] A center, standing fifteen feet from the passer, passes the ball back to the passer. The potential catcher stands fifteen feet at the right of the center. When the ball is passed, the catcher runs in a path approximately forty-five degrees at the left of straight forward. The passer attempts to pass the ball to the catcher so that the catcher may receive the ball about fifteen feet in front of the center and somewhat at the left. If the thrower leads the catcher properly, he receives one point; if the thrower throws the ball at such a height that the catcher has to raise his arms above his head to catch the ball, he receives one point; if the thrower throws the ball at such a speed that the

[24] Arthur J. Wendler, "A Critical Analysis of Test Elements Used in Physical Education," *Research Quarterly,* March, 1938.

[25] *Ibid.*

[26] *Ibid.*

throw results in a "zip" rather than in a "floating" ball, he receives one point. The passer throws ten times to the catcher.

An r of .452 has been obtained between the Wendler Test for Throwing a Soccer Ball and general-motor educability, and an r of .340 between this test and eye-hand co-ordination.

225. Wendler Test for Catching a Fly Ball.[27] The player stands at a point in the center field (on a softball field) behind the second base and approximately 130 feet from the home base. The experimenter hits five fly balls to the right and five fly balls to the left of the fielder, but with no regular pattern; hence the player needs to move reasonably fast and directly after each hit in order to make the catch. Only attempts to catch balls so hit are scored, and ten such attempts are scored. The results are scored as follows: two points for a catch, one point if the ball is only touched. The maximum score is 20.

An r of .440 has been obtained between the Wendler Test for Catching a Fly Ball and general-motor educability, and an r of .551 with eye-hand co-ordination.

In view of the r's obtained between eye-hand co-ordination and each of the four Wendler Tests, the R between these four tests and eye-hand co-ordination would probably be about .80.

226. Target-throwing tests. A standardized target with a bull's-eye and with numerous concentric rings equally spaced is used.[28] The throwing is usually done with a twelve-inch softball. However, if the target is small and the distance of the throw is short, darts may be used instead of balls. The distance of the throw is in accordance with the age and the size of the performers. The size of the target is in accordance with the distance of the throw. The coefficients of reliability that have been obtained for this test are exceedingly low unless at least twenty-five trials have been given.

In a test of target-throwing by college women[29] the r's of reliability increased as follows with the number of trials (fifty subjects): ten trials, r = .724; twenty, .833; thirty, .894; forty, .953; and fifty, .970. Four concentric circles, six, twenty-two, forty-two, and sixty-six inches in diameter, were used.

227. Collins-Howe Test of Accurate Lunging.[30] In this test a triangular target is used. The subject lunges, with a fencing foil, toward the target from a standard distance. The target consists of three copper discs, four inches in diameter, and a fencing foil so wired that contact with the discs rings a

[27] *Ibid.*

[28] The reliability of target-throwing, which is scored by passed and failed (throwing strikes), is very low. If concentric rings are used, the closer they are together (though not closer than the diameter of the ball used), the higher the reliability of the test.

[29] Kathleen Brophy, "A New Target for Testing Accuracy in Throwing," *Spalding's Athletic Library*, 121 R.

[30] Vivian D. Collins and Eugene C. Howe, "A Preliminary Selection of Tests of Fitness," *American Physical Education Review*, December, 1924.

bell. The subject makes one hundred lunges at the target, aiming at the three discs in clockwise rotation. The time taken to make one hundred lunges and the number of hits are considered in scoring.

228. Miles Pursuitmeter Test.[31] The pursuitmeter is an expensive electrical instrument with which can be tested the ability to follow with considerable accuracy a moving object that changes direction. It requires five minutes to test a subject, following a short practice trial.

229. Miles Pursuit-pendulum Test.[32] A swinging pendulum, which contains water, swings back and forth over a considerable arc. The subject endeavors on each swing to catch the water in a cup having an opening only ¾ inch in diameter. The apparatus is relatively inexpensive, can be made in one's own laboratory, and is rather interesting to use.

230. Koerth Pursuitmeter Test.[33] A small metal spot about the size of a twenty-five cent piece is placed about halfway from the center to the rim of a turntable, which turns at the speed of one rotation a second. The subject attempts to maintain contact with this metal disc by means of a metal rod with which he is unable to exert pressure. An automatic counter records the time that contact is maintained. For a small group of gymnasts an r of .41 has been obtained between the Koerth Pursuitmeter Test and ability in apparatus work.

231. Tests of balance. Two categories of tests of balance are available. These two categories may be called, for convenience, "static balance" and "dynamic balance." Both types are probably compounded of the same elements but in widely different degrees. There is evidence available that indicates that balance, as it is used in physical activities, is dependent upon at least the following items (see also Sec. 23).

(1) Kinesthetic responses, both sensory and motor. These responses are probably compounded physiologically of both joint sense and muscle sense. Since they seem always to work together, however, they appear in analyses as one element.

(2) Visual response, or the aid that is obtained from the eyes.

(3) The semicircular-canal system. The part that the semicircular canals play in the finer forms of balance is still an unanswered question. There is some statistical evidence to indicate that these canals, with the ampullae, function separately as well as together in certain forms of balance.

232. The term "static balance" has been chosen to indicate the kind of balance in which the movement is not great and in which the adjustments are, relative to the range of movement, small. This is the type of

---

[31] Walter R. Miles, "The Pursuitmeter," *Journal of Experimental Psychology*, April, 1921.

[32] Miles, "Pursuit Pendulum," *Psychological Review*, September, 1920.

[33] Robert H. Seashore, "Stanford Motor Skills Unit," *Psychological Monographs* XXXIX (1928).

balance required, for example, in walking the tight wire or the balance beam.[34]

233. Balance-beam test of static balance.[35] For years the balance beam has been used for the purpose of both developing static balance and testing it. The tests suggested were not usually validated. The r's of reliability that have been obtained for this type of test are, on the whole, low, seldom running above .5. The reason for the low coefficients is probably that it is difficult to standardize such a test, for such a test involves speed of locomotion as well as balance. The major difficulty is that it requires so much time to administer the test that the experimenters usually give each performer too few trials. If one wishes to use the balance beam as a test of balance, however, it is best to have several beams end to end (four is a common number) in order to lengthen the test and increase the reliability, and to give the performer an opportunity to walk a long distance. If he falls off the balance beam, he should step up on the beam again and continue to walk the beam. The distance traveled and the number of times the performer loses his balance should both count in the final score.

234. Springfield Beam-walking Test of Static Balance.[36] This test, details of which are given in the reference cited, uses nine oak beams each ten feet in length, of widths ranging from 4 inches to $\frac{1}{4}$ inch. The scoring method used greatly increases the validity of the beam-walking test. Because of the amount of specialized equipment needed, the test is useful largely for purposes of research.

235. The Bass Stick Tests of Static Balance[37] were devised for the testing of large numbers of performers at one time. The directions for the administration of the tests are as follows. A stick one inch wide, one inch high, and twelve inches long is needed for each performer. Arrange the performers in two lines. Have each performer in one line stand with the foot lengthwise on a stick. Count aloud for sixty seconds. Have each observer in the other line note the time when the performer opposite him steps off the stick. Then have each performer stand with the foot crosswise on the stick. Count and have the observers record the time as before. Have all the performers execute each of the two tests six times, and use for the score of each test the sum of the times for all six trials.

The r's of reliability that have been obtained for the Bass Stick Tests run from .8 to .9. The r's that have been obtained between the Bass Stick Tests and ratings of general-motor ability in women, and between the Bass Stick Tests and ratings of rhythm are about .5. These coefficients are

[34] The term "static balance" should be confined to the type of balance required in such tests as the stick tests (see Sec. 235). It has, however, been extended to include the type of balance required in tests involving a small amount of movement.

[35] Ruth I. Bass, "An Analysis of the Components of Tests of Semicircular Canal Function and of Static and Dynamic Balance," *Research Quarterly,* May, 1939.

[36] Harold G. Seashore, "The Development of a Beam-Walking Test and Its Use in Measuring Development of Balance in Children," *Research Quarterly,* December, 1947.

[37] Bass, *loc. cit.*

surprisingly high in view of the large number of elements of which general-motor ability is composed.

The Bass Sticks Tests may be used to measure the kinesthetic aspects of balance by having the performers execute the tests with their eyes closed. The difficulty of the test may be increased by the use of sticks the tops of which are $\frac{1}{2}$ inch in width. It is suggested that sticks two feet long, with the first foot 1 inch square, and with the second foot 1 inch wide on the bottom and $\frac{1}{2}$ inch wide on the top, be provided.

236. Collins-Howe Test of Static Balance.[38] In this test a balance board resembling a short seesaw with two side boards, which run from the ends of this board upward to another board pivoted above the subject's head, is used. These side boards are about three feet apart. Two handles, about two feet apart and hanging downward for about four feet, are hinged to this top board. The same effect can be obtained by having ropes run upward from the two ends of the board, and tied to the ends of a stick three feet long, which stick is, in turn, suspended from the middle by a rope from a rafter. A work adder is attached to one end of the board so that all fluctuations in one direction are added cumulatively. In the original presentation, there were two work adders, one attached to each end. This seems, however, an unnecessary refinement. As the individual stands on this board and attempts to maintain his balance, every fluctuation is recorded on the work adder. The more steadily the individual stands, the less is the recorded movement. The setup of this apparatus is indicated in Figure XV (p. 105).[39]

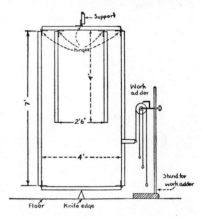

FIGURE XV. Collins-Howe Balance Beam

For the Collins-Howe Test, two variations of standing position may be used: (1) astride the fulcrum of the board, so that the maximum fluctuations are in the vertical semicircular-canal systems; (2) astride the fulcrum, bent forward ninety degrees, so that the major disturbances are in the horizontal canal systems.

This method of testing static balance is an excellent laboratory method, but is adapted primarily to research purposes because it is very slow of administration. At the present time, coefficients of correlation between the results of this test and those of the Bass Sticks Test described in Section 235 are not available.

---

[38] Collins and Howe, *loc. cit.*

[39] The work adder may be purchased from the Harvard Apparatus Company, Back Bay Post Office, Boston, Massachusetts.

237. Bass Test of Dynamic Balance.[40] The term "dynamic balance" has been chosen to indicate steadiness and stability in leaping from one spot on the floor to another. It is the kind of balance that is required when one crosses a brook, leaping from stone to stone, with the stones not in a straight line. This type of balance is used in apparatus work, in the dance, and in tumbling. There is evidence that the component elements determining success in this type of balance are the eyes and the sensory-motor-kinesthetic response.

238. The directions for the administration of the Bass Test of Dynamic Balance are as follows.

Circles, eleven in number and 8½ inches[41] in diameter, are drawn on the floor (Fig. XVI, p. 106). The performer stands with his right foot on the starting circle, *leaps* (not steps) into the first circle with the left foot, leaps into the second circle with the right foot, and so on, from circle to circle, alternating the feet. The performer must leave the floor entirely in leaping from one circle before alighting in another, must alight upon the ball of the foot, and must not touch the heel to the floor. He should remain stationary in each circle for five seconds. The score for the trip is 50, plus the number of seconds taken to negotiate the test, minus three times the "errors." The "errors" are as follows: (1) touching the heel to the floor, (2) moving the foot while standing in the circle, (3) hopping upon the supporting foot, (4) touching the floor outside the circle, (5) touching the floor with the other foot, (6) touching the floor with any other part of the body. Each error counts one penalty point; thus if the performer, in endeavoring to maintain the balance in any one circle, hops four times, this is counted as four separate errors.

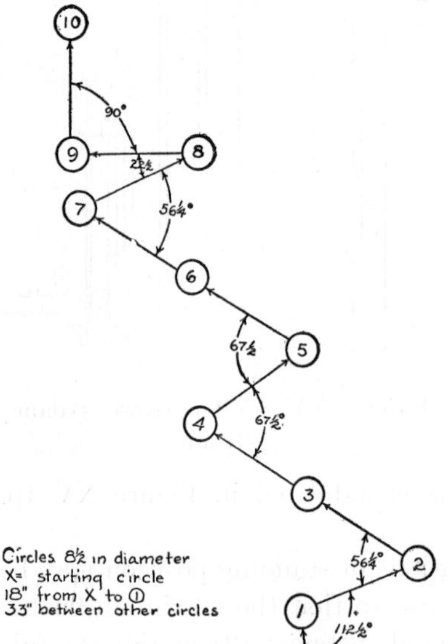

The test should be explained and demonstrated by the teacher or by a leader, and one or two practice trials should be permitted. This practice may be conducted without the use of the circles, the students choosing spots on the floor and leaping to them. In giving the test, the timer counts the seconds, beginning the count as the performer alights in each circle.

Circles 8½ in diameter
X= starting circle
18" from X to ①
33" between other circles

FIGURE XVI. Bass Dynamic-balance Test: Pattern

[40] Bass, *loc. cit.*
[41] For senior-high-school boys and college men the circles are 9½ inches in diameter; for all other persons. 8½ inches.

For example, after the performer jumps into the first circle, the timer, who has already started the watch, counts 1, 2, 3, 4, 5, beginning the count again on each subsequent circle. If the performer leaps to the next circle before the count of 5, the count begins anew. If he remains in the circle more than five seconds, the extra time is deducted from the total time. The instructor accompanies the performer, and counts the errors silently and cumulatively. Three trials should be given, and the average of the three taken as the score. A minus score should be recorded as 0.

An r of reliability of .95 was obtained for this test when three trials were used. An r of .74 has been obtained between this test and ratings of general-motor ability in a group of college women, and an r of .69 with ratings of ability in rhythms and in dancing.

239. Rhythm. The following tests of rhythm are primarily instruments of research.

240. The **Seashore Sensory-rhythm Tests** consist of a number of phonograph records, which are played and scored under standard conditions. Only two of these records are of value in physical education, the one on the sense of time (Catalogue No. QC-8706-1D8) and the one on the sense of rhythm (Catalogue No.QC-8708-1D8).[42] The sense-of-time record has a series of three clicks, which mark off two intervals of time, either the first or the second being the longer interval. The subject records "l" (for longer) if the second interval is shorter than the first, and "s" (for shorter) if the second interval is longer than the first. In the sense-of-rhythm record, two rhythmic patterns are given in succession. The second rhythmic pattern is either the same as the first or different from the first, and the subject records either "s" or "d."

The r of reliability of each of these tests if the tests are administered only once is about .5, but it may be increased to a satisfactory level by repeating each test three times, and taking the sum of the scores of the three trials as the official score. The r's with teachers' ratings of rhythmic ability and of ability to dance run from .12 to .45. An r of .392 was obtained between the Seashore Sensory-rhythm Test and gymnastics ability.[43] The usefulness of this type of test of rhythm in other types of athletics performance is exceedingly questionable.

241. Seashore Motor-rhythm Test.[44] In this test a rotating turntable clicks off a series of four clicks a second, always in the same rhythm. The subject taps a telegraph key, and attempts to tap in exact rhythm with the clicking. If he taps within .025 second either way from the click, the tap is recorded on an adder.

---

[42] These records, together with a manual giving directions for their use, are obtainable from the Psychological Corporation, 522 Fifth Avenue, New York 18, New York. It should be noted that the records must be ordered by the school, not by individuals.

[43] Eugene Wettstone, "Tests for Predicting Potential Ability in Gymnastics and Tumbling," *Research Quarterly*, December, 1938.

[44] Robert H. Seashore, *loc. cit.*

The r's of this test with teachers' estimates of rhythm have varied. from .10 to .46. With a small number of gymnasts, an r of .42 between motor rhythm and apparatus-work ability was obtained. The test is an individual test, and requires, in addition to an expensive piece of apparatus, much time for administration.

242. The **Muzzey Motor-rhythm Test**,[45] which is better for measuring rhythm in athletics performance and in the dance than the Seashore Rhythm Test, requires complicated and expensive apparatus. The rhythm of the feet of six performers may be tested at one time.

243. Tests of athletics intelligence. Four closely related factors, which have been isolated by Thurstone (see Sec. 25), seem to be closely related to "athletics intelligence." These factors are two related factors of the ability to visualize spatial relationships, and two factors of the function that is called "closure." The tests[46] for the measurement of these factors are all paper-and-pencil tests, and hence can be administered to a large group at one time. Norms for the tests may be obtained from the publishers of the tests.

244. The factor of visualization of spatial relationships is one that is important in various aspects of team and individual sports. For example, a broken-field runner in football needs to be able to visualize not only how he can evade the first potential tackler, but where he will be immediately after that evasion, *where the next two or three potential tacklers should be by that time,* and, in general, what he should plan to do not only to evade the first tackler but also to be in a favorable position to evade the next two tacklers. This type of ability to visualize spatial relationships is present to a high degree in "smart" athletes—the ones who readily outwit their opponents. An r of .70 [47] has been obtained between a battery of

[45] Dorothy M. Muzzey, "Group Progress of White and Colored Children in Learning a Rhythm Pattern," *Research Quarterly,* October, 1933.

[46] These tests are published by Science Research Associates, 57 West Grand Avenue, Chicago 10. The order numbers and the titles of the Thurstone Space Tests follow.

Order No.	Title of Test
7-261	SRA Primary Mental Abilities, for Ages 5 to 7
7-251	SRA Primary Mental Abilities, for Ages 7 to 11
7-231	SRA Primary Mental Abilities, for Ages 11 to 17
7-351	Chicago Tests of Primary Mental Abilities, for Ages 11 to 17, Single Booklet Edition
7-631	Three Thurstone Space Tests published in a separate booklet in the Chicago Tests of Primary Mental Abilities, for Ages 11 to 17, Separate Booklet Edition

The order numbers and the titles of three experiment tests highly loaded with the closure factor follow.

Order No.	Title of Test
7-811	Gottschaldt Figures
7-821	Designs
7-691	Mutilated Words

[47] Jake H. Moser, "An Attempt to Devise a Simple Method of Measuring Potential Football Intelligence" (M.A. Thesis, State University of Iowa, 1938).

tests devised to measure the ability to visualize spatial relationships and coaches' estimates of the athletics intelligence of their football players. The factor of closure is that factor that enables the performer to see relationships quickly, put them together, and act upon the situation as

Table 22

BLOCKS TEST (McCLOY):
NUMBER AND COLOR IDENTIFICATIONS

Top		Bottom	
Number	Color	Color	Number
1	Red	Blue	1
2	White	Any color	
3	Blue	Green	4
4	Green	Red	2
5	Red	White	5
6	White	White*	3
7	Blue	Green	6
8	Green	Red	8
9	Red	Blue*	7
10	White	White	9
11	Blue	Red	10
12	Green	Green	12
13	Red	White	13
14	White	Blue*	11
15	Blue	Green	14
16	Green	Any color	
17	Red	White	15
18	White	Blue	17
19	Blue	Red*	16
20	Green	Green	18
21	Red	White	19
22	White	Blue	21
23	Blue	Red*	20
24	Green	Any color	22

*A black dot about 3/4 inch in diameter is painted in the middle of the block, or a black rim is painted around the outside of the block (not around the edge of the block where it can be seen before the block is turned over).

observed. This factor has not been studied carefully in relationship to athletics intelligence, but there seems little reason to doubt that it will prove to be of high value.[48]

245. The **McCloy Blocks Test of Multiple Response**[49] was devised to measure the ability to respond quickly and adaptively to changing situations. The equipment consists of twenty-four wooden blocks about 3 inches square and ¾ inch thick. The tops of six of the blocks are painted red; six, white; six, blue; and six, green. The bottoms of the blocks are painted in the same four colors according to Table 22 (p. 109). The numbers indicated in the last column in Table 22 represent the order in which the blocks are picked up. The two blocks without numbers are not picked up at all.

[48] Since a considerable amount of continuing research is going on in these fields, individuals desiring to conduct research in the area may well be advised to correspond with the author of the tests, Dr. L. L. Thurstone, Department of Psychology, University of North Carolina, Chapel Hill, North Carolina.

[49] McCloy, "'Blocks Test' of Multiple Response," *Psychometrika*, September, 1942.

The blocks are arranged about three inches apart in two rows on a table, with the odd-numbered blocks in the first row, and the even-numbered blocks in the second row.

246. *Standardized directions for blocks test.* While giving the directions, perform the indicated actions.

"This is a test of how rapidly you can make decisions that involve intelligent choice, and act upon them. You will note that these blocks are arranged in two rows, and that going in this order (point), the colors on the tops are red, white, blue, green, red, white, etc. The bottom of each block is painted one of these four colors, also, but it may be any one of the four colors, regardless of the color on the top. On some of the blocks, in addition to the color on the bottom, there is a black dot.

"In taking this test, pick up this first (red) block (pick it up), raise it, and look at the bottom. Then put it back again, and pick up the block beyond, that is, one color *beyond* the color on the bottom of the block in the red, white, blue, green, red sequence; for example, the bottom of the first block is blue, so you pick up the next block with a green top; if the bottom of the block is green, pick up the next block whose top is *red* in color. *If*, however, the bottom of the block has a black dot on it, pick up the next color in the sequence, but *before* the block you have picked up; for example, if I pick up this block (pick up No. 9), you note that the bottom is blue with a black dot. You would then pick up this one (No. 8), whose top is green—the next color in the sequence.

"Now let us try one or two. If I pick up this one (pick up No. 11, turn it over, and show that the bottom is red), which one should I pick up next? That is correct, I should pick up this one (No. 14). If I pick up this one (pick up No. 19) that has a red bottom with a black dot, which should I pick up next? That is correct; it would be this one (No. 18).

"Is the method clear now? All right, begin with this one (No. 1), and continue to the end on the right."

(Note: Continue with the demonstration until the subject gives evidence that he understands the procedure. Pick the blocks for the demonstration at random, not in order. This prevents learning the sequence before taking the test. The experimenter may need to tell the subject to put the blocks down again with the bottoms down.)

The subject, being timed in seconds, should be allowed one practice trial and two test trials. If he makes an error, he must correct it before going on.[50]

247. An r of .510 was obtained between the blocks test and composite ratings of the abilities of three hundred senior-high-school girls in basketball, volleyball, diving, and the dance.[51] For high-school basketball players whose "basketball smartness" was rated by two coaches, the uncorrected r between the sum of the ratings of the two raters and the score

---

[50] To aid the examiner, it is well to have the color of the bottom (with black dot where indicated), together with a number indicating the order in which the block will be picked up, marked on the block. This order is indicated in the first column of Table 23 (p. 111). This information can be marked on a small white label and pasted on the edge of the block away from the subject.

If the subject makes an error, say "Stop: what block do you pick up after ——?" (naming the color on the bottom); or "What block do you pick up after —— with a black dot?"

[51] Anderson and McCloy, *loc. cit.*

Table 23

BLOCKS TEST (McCLOY): SEQUENCE

Block Number	Color on Top	Color on Bottom	Block Number	Color on Top
Pick up 1	red	blue	go to 4	green
Pick up 4	green	red	go to 6	white
Pick up 6	white	white*	go to 3	blue
Pick up 3	blue	green	go to 5	red
Pick up 5	red	white	go to 7	blue
Pick up 7	blue	green	go to 9	red
Pick up 9	red	blue*	go to 8	green
Pick up 8	green	red	go to 10	white
Pick up 10	white	white	go to 11	blue
Pick up 11	blue	red	go to 14	white
Pick up 14	white	blue*	go to 12	green
Pick up 12	green	green	go to 13	red
Pick up 13	red	white	go to 15	blue
Pick up 15	blue	green	go to 17	red
Pick up 17	red	white	go to 19	blue
Pick up 19	blue	red*	go to 18	white
Pick up 18	white	blue	go to 20	green
Pick up 20	green	green	go to 21	red
Pick up 21	red	white	go to 23	blue
Pick up 23	blue	red*	go to 22	white
Pick up 22	white	blue	go to 24	green

*This block has a black dot.

Table 24

BLOCKS TEST (McCLOY): NORMS
(BOYS AND GIRLS 13 TO 19)

These norms were computed from data from 283 senior-high-school girls and 84 high-school boys, with ages ranging from thirteen to nineteen years. The r with age was about .17. The norms are in the form of T-scores, extrapolated. The relationship was somewhat curvilinear. The score is the best in three trials.

Score on Blocks Test (sec.)	T-score	
	Girls	Boys
6	99	
10	89	
14	82	
18	77	
22	72	100
26	68	75
30	64	68
34	61	63
38	58	59
42	55	57
46	52	54
50	49	53
54	46	50
58	44	48
62	41	47
66	39	46
70	37	44
74	34	43
78	32	42
82	30	41
86	28	40
90	26	39
94	25	38
98	23	37
102	21	36
106	20	35

obtained with the blocks test was .651.[52] Norms for the blocks test may be found in Table 24 (p. 111).

248. Tests of kinesthetic sense. Kinesthesis has been defined as "the process of cognizing bodily tension and/or movement on the basis of what one is doing, or in terms of their (tension and movement) relation to some contemplated mode of behavior, sensations of which are received through any or all of the mechanical senses."[53] Relative to physical activities, kinesthesis might be considered to include at least the three following aspects: (1) ability to distinguish position accurately; that is, ability to place the arms, the legs, the trunk, and the head and the neck in designated positions; (2) control of force in movement; for example, ability in a free throw to throw a basketball with just enough force to reach the center of the basket (this ability also involves the ability to judge distance); and (3) ability to perform movements accurately, as distinguished from ability to take a given position.

249. The *Phillips Test of Kinesthesis*[54] consists of tests that are based primarily upon the control of force in relation to movement. An attempt was made to predict, through these tests, skill in putting a golf ball and in driving a golf ball. The r's of reliability for putting and driving were .64 and .85, respectively. The r's of reliability of the five tests studied were from .59 to .84. The R of four of these tests with putting was .505, and with driving, .422. While these coefficients are low, it is surprising that they are as high as they are in view of the numerous other aspects of motor educability that would apply to these two skills.

250. The *Young Test of Kinesthesis*[55] includes, primarily, tests of position such as raising the arms to ninety degrees sideward, to ninety degrees forward, etc. It also includes two balance exercises and six exercises requiring a considerable amount of skill (over-arm throw and point, under-arm throw and point, throw at target, kick at target, hitting ball, and squeezing a dynamometer. In squeezing a dynamometer the performer is supposed to repeat a given sequence of strengths achieved while watching the dial). The criterion for the Young Test was a general-motor-ability test consisting of a basketball throw for distance, a dash, a standing broad jump, and passing the basketball against the wall for speed —a criterion that would depend upon so many other things than kinesthesis that it is surprising that as high a coefficient of correlation was obtained as was. Three of the test elements—raising the arms sideward to ninety degrees, lying on the side and raising the leg sideward twenty degrees, and stick balance lengthwise—gave an R of .984 with eighteen

[52] Stanley M. Smith, "The 'Blocks Test' as a Measurement of Adaptive Athletic Response" (M.A. Thesis, State University of Iowa, 1943).

[53] Bernath E. Phillips, "The Relationship between Certain Phases of Kinesthesis and Performance during the Early Stages of Acquiring Two Perceptuo-Motor Skills," *Research Quarterly*, October, 1941, p. 572.

[54] *Ibid.*

[55] Olive G. Young, "A Study of Kinesthesis in Relation to Selected Movements," *Research Quarterly*, December, 1945.

different items of which these three were a part. With two of the items, namely raising the arms sideward forty-five degrees and crosswise balance, an R of .522 was obtained with the general-motor-ability criterion.

251. The *Wiebe Test of Kinesthesis*[56] consists of a battery of six tests of which the individual r's of validity with total scores of fifteen tests ranged from .420 to .540, and of which the r's of intercorrelation ranged from −.148 to .488. An r of .808 was obtained between the battery of six tests and the total score. A description of the Wiebe Test follows. The subject is blindfolded for each of the tests.

On side, leg raise twenty degrees. The subject is instructed to lie on his nondominant side. He is shown a stick-figure drawing with the leg raised at a twenty-degree angle. He is instructed to duplicate the angle seen. The deviation from twenty degrees is measured with a goniometer. The score is the total of three trials.

Pedestrial kinesthesis of size. The subject is instructed to stand erect with the heels touching, and to separate the heels so that the medial sides of the heels are twelve inches apart. The deviation from the preferred score is measured to the nearest one-fourth inch with a yardstick. The score is the total of three trials.

Basketball pass, forty-five degrees to dominant side. The subject's toes are placed against a toeboard (base of quadrant) with the medial line at the axis of the quadrant. The subject is instructed to attempt to pass the basketball (two-handed chest pass) forty-five degrees toward the dominant side. A fishline, attached at the quadrant axis, is placed over the place of impact, and the degrees are read from the quadrant. The score is the total of three trials.

Baseball throw, forty-five degrees to nondominant side. The subject's toes are placed against a toeboard (base of quadrant), with the shoulder joint of the dominant side over the axis of the quadrant. The subject is instructed to attempt to throw the baseball (overhead) forty-five degrees toward the nondominant side. A fishline is placed over the place of impact, and the degrees are read from the quadrant. The score is the total of three trials.

"Baseball fielding." Apparatus: bulletin board, targets with eight concentric circles, the first being one-half inch in radius and each succeeding one a half inch larger; a pointer made of a nail driven through a piece of beaver board $2\frac{1}{2}$ inches by $\frac{1}{2}$ inch by $\frac{1}{4}$ inch. The center of the target is placed at the belt line of the subject. The pointer is fastened to the subject's dominant hand by means of rubber bands. The subject is blindfolded, and the arm is positioned so that the pointer touches the distal edge of the largest circle. The subject is guided to sense the position of his arm when the pointer is directly in the center circle. He is then instructed to become erect and to touch the sensed position with the pointer. The smallest circle counts one point with a successive increase of one point for each ring. Missing the target counts nine points. The score is the total of three trials.

Pedestrial kinesthesis of vertical linear space. The subject is shown a line drawn fourteen inches above the floor, and is instructed to estimate the height of the line. He is then blindfolded and instructed to place the bottom of his sole on the top of the line (i.e., step upon the "step"). The deviation from the preferred score is recorded to the nearest one-fourth inch. The score is the total of three trials.

252. Further tests which are indirectly related to motor educability will be found in Chapter 19.

[56] Vernon R. Wiebe, "A Study of Tests of Kinesthesis" (M.A. Thesis, State University of Iowa, 1951).

CHAPTER 12

GENERAL-MOTOR CAPACITY

253. JUST AS there are tests for measuring intelligence (see Secs. 188-89), which is largely innate, so there should be tests for measuring general-motor capacity, which is largely innate. *General* is used to indicate the type of motor capacity that is basic to all motor performance that involves large ranges of movement; it is used in contrast to specific types of motor capacities required for the execution of specific skills. *Motor* is used primarily for *neuromuscular,* and secondarily for *psychomotor. Capacity* is used to indicate potentiality in contrast to achievement.

Both in the construction of a test of intelligence and in the construction of a test of general-motor capacity, certain skills, regardless of their state of development in the persons to be tested, must be utilized. In the construction of a test of intelligence for persons of a given age, an effort is made to utilize items of information that have been presented previously to either all or none of the persons tested. In a test of intelligence for persons of high-school age, for example, items of information that have been presented to all persons in elementary schools may be used; or such items as nonsense syllables, which have not been presented to any of the subjects before, may be used. In the construction of a test of general-motor capacity, the first method cannot be used validly, for the curricula in physical and health education in this country are not standardized. The second method may be used.

254. As a basis for the measurement of general-motor capacity, the following items were established: (1) items of known validity, (2) items that had been unpracticed so that equal opportunities for learning could be given to all performers, and (3) items with provision for standard amounts of practice. The general-motor-capacity test that was devised was, in the absence of any other such tests that might be used as criteria, validated against a battery of motor tests and against the ratings of competent teachers.

255. The criterion for general-motor capacity for boys was arbitrarily made up of the sum of the T-scores for the following items: (1) McCloy Classification Index, (2) McCloy Pull-up-strength Score (see Chap. 14), (3) sixty-yard dash, (4) standing broad jump, (5) running high jump, (6) eight-pound shot-put, (7) Sargent Jump, (8) McCloy Pull-up-strength

Quotient (see Chap. 14), (9) ten-second squat-thrust test, (10) Brace Test, and (11) intelligence quotient derived from the Otis Self-administering Test.

256. The criterion for general-motor capacity for girls was made up of the sum of the T-scores for the following items: (1) number of pull-ups performed according to the Rogers technique (see Chap. 14), (2) McCloy Pull-up-strength Score (see Chap. 14), (3) sixty-yard dash, (4) standing broad jump, (5) indoor baseball throw for distance, (6) Sargent Jump, (7) McCloy Pull-up-strength Quotient, (8) ten-second squat-thrust test, (9) Brace Test, and (10) intelligence quotient derived from the Otis Self-administering Test.

257. The McCloy General-motor-capacity Test[1] that was developed includes the following items: (1) McCloy Classification Index (size and maturity, see Sec. 136), (2) Sargent Jump (power, see Sec. 159), (3) ten-second squat-thrust test (agility, see Sec. 172), and (4) Iowa-Brace Test (motor educability, see Sec. 199). The multiple regression equations follow.

Elementary-school boys: .181 McCloy Classification Index + .769 Sargent Jump (cm.) + .510 Brace Test (T-score) + 2.187 squat-thrust test − 62.

Junior- and senior-high-school boys: .329 McCloy Classification Index + 1.446 Sargent Jump (cm.) + .926 Brace Test (T-score) + 3.973 squat-thrust test − 202.

Elementary-school girls:[2] 3.576 Sargent Jump (cm.) + 2.20 Brace Test (T-score) + 19.12 squat-thrust test + 29.

Junior- and senior-high-school girls:[2] 3.576 Sargent Jump (cm.) + 2.20 Brace Test (T-score) + 19.12 squat-thrust test + 119.

258. An *r* of .512 for boys and an *r* of .734 for girls were obtained between the batteries given in Section 257 and ratings made by competent teachers. An *r* of .969 for boys and an *r* of .921 for girls were obtained between these batteries and the criterion scores. The coefficients of correlation of the batteries with the criterion scores are spuriously high because some of the same elements were included both in the batteries and in the criteria. On the other hand, the coefficients of correlation of the batteries with the teachers' rating are undoubtedly low. In one study[3] an *r* of .812 was obtained between general-motor-capacity scores and teachers' ratings of ability in sports. Since the ratings were made before the general-motor-capacity test was administered, the raters were not influenced by performance in the test.

[1] Charles H. McCloy, "The Measurement of General Motor Capacity and General Motor Ability," *Supplement to Research Quarterly*, March, 1934.

[2] Since the classification index was found to be of little value in the measurement of the general-motor capacity of girls, it was eliminated from the battery.

[3] Theresa Anderson and Charles H. McCloy, "The Measurement of Sports Ability in High School Girls," *Research Quarterly*, March, 1947.

259. Interesting findings relative to the general-motor-capacity test were obtained in a comprehensive study[4] conducted at the junior-high-school level. The criterion was composed of the sum of the T-scores for two sprints, two shuttle runs, a fifty-yard pick-a-back run, a standing broad jump, three standing broad jumps, a running broad jump, a running broad jump with a thirty-foot start, an eight-pound shot-put, and two obstacle races. Coefficients of correlation between these events and the

Table 25

TOTAL POINTS AND TESTS OF PHYSICAL FITNESS,
GENERAL-MOTOR CAPACITY, STRENGTH, ENDURANCE:
CORRELATION COEFFICIENTS

Total Points	Variable Held Constant	Correlation Coefficients
General-motor-capacity score		.8679
Total points for endurance events (pull-ups, push-ups, sit-ups, sixty-second thrusts)		.7759
Endurance ratio (time for 200-yard run ÷ time for 60-yard dash)		.3911
Strength score		.6990
General-motor-capacity score	Sprint speed (60-yard dash)	.8061
Endurance events	Sprint speed	.6628
Endurance ratio	Sprint speed	.5597
Strength score	Sprint speed	.6543
General-motor-capacity score	Strength score	.7115
Endurance events	Strength score	.7929
Endurance ratio	Strength score	.3397
General-motor-capacity score	Classification index	.8753
Endurance events	Classification index	.7316
Endurance ratio	Classification index	.4050
Strength score	Classification index	.4868
Endurance events	General-motor-capacity score	.7222
Endurance ratio	General-motor-capacity score	.2903
Strength score	General-motor-capacity score	.0253

general-motor-capacity score, a set of endurance tests, a test that was called the "endurance ratio" (see Sec. 338), and a strength test are given in Table 25 (p. 116). An *r* of .8679 was obtained between the general-motor-capacity score and the criterion, and this coefficient remained high when the influence of speed, of strength, and of size and maturity was held constant. When the general-motor-capacity score itself was held constant, the influence of the strength score was eliminated. The coefficient of

[4] Raymond M. Fritsch, "An Evaluation of Fitness Tests for Junior High School Boys" (M.A. Thesis, State University of Iowa, 1947).

correlation that was obtained between the muscular-endurance events and the criterion, and that between the criterion and the endurance ratio were about the same whether or not the influence of speed, of strength, and of size and maturity was held constant.

It should be noted that events that require specialized ability have a lower correlation with the general-motor-capacity score than do events that require motor ability of a general nature. Hence, in contrast to football and basketball ability,[5] track-and-field ability is highly correlated with performance in the general-motor-capacity test.

260. The effect of over- and underweight upon performance in the general-motor-capacity test is shown in Table 26 (p. 117).[6] The normal weights involved were assessed according to the McCloy method (see Chap. 28). Those persons whose weights ranged from 95 to 105 per

Table 26

GENERAL-MOTOR-CAPACITY SCORES RELATIVE TO WEIGHT
(COLLEGE MEN)

	Under-weight (N = 40)	Of Normal Weight (N = 87)	Over-weight (N = 31)
Classification index	893.8	905.2	927.8
Sargent Jump	50.65	53.20	48.73
Squat-thrust test	5.49	5.55	5.31
Iowa-Brace Score	12.98	12.45	11.10
General-motor-capacity score	228.0	236.4	228.6
Motor quotient	96.3	98.0	91.0

cent of their normal weights were considered to be of normal weight. The range of weights extended from 75 to 120 per cent of normal weights. Relative to the findings presented in Table 26 the following items should be kept in mind. Persons who are underweight may have lost weight because of illness and hence are not "up to par," or they may be lacking in fat and still be in good physical condition. Persons who are overweight may frequently be athletic in type although possessing an excessive amount of "dead" weight.

According to the findings indicated in Table 26, the performers who were underweight and of normal weight obtained better scores in motor educability as measured by the Iowa-Brace Test and in power as measured by the Sargent Jump than did the performers who were overweight. The three groups did not vary greatly in general-motor-capacity scores; the larger classification indices of the persons who were overweight com-

[5] An r of .7 has been obtained between the general-motor-capacity score and ratings of the football and the basketball ability of high-school players.

[6] Lyle E. Felderman, "The Effect of Variations in Body Weight on the Scores of the General Motor Capacity Test" (M.A. Thesis, State University of Iowa, 1948).

pensated for the lower scores of these persons in the Iowa-Brace Test, the squat-thrust test, and the Sargent Jump. The performers who were over-weight were, in motor quotients, 7 per cent under those who were of normal weight. These findings indicate that the effects of overweight on general-motor-capacity scores should be kept in mind.

261. The **general-motor-capacity score,** which is the motor analogue of

Table 27

GENERAL–MOTOR-CAPACITY SCORE: POINTS FOR
CLASSIFICATION INDEX (ELEMENTARY-SCHOOL BOYS)

.181 (Classification Index) - 62.4

CI	00	10	20	30	40	50	60	70	80	90
			Points							
400						19.05	20.86	22.67	24.48	26.29
500	28.10	29.91	31.72	33.53	35.34	37.15	38.96	40.77	42.58	44.39
600	46.20	48.01	49.82	51.63	53.44	55.25	57.06	58.87	60.68	62.49
700	64.30	66.11	67.92	69.73	71.54	73.35	75.16	76.97	78.78	80.59
800	82.40	84.21	86.02	87.83	89.64	91.45	93.26	95.07	96.88	98.69

Interpolation table

1	.181
2	.362
3	.543
4	.764
5	.905
6	1.086
7	1.267
8	1.448
9	1.629

Table 28

GENERAL–MOTOR-CAPACITY SCORE: POINTS FOR
CLASSIFICATION INDEX (HIGH-SCHOOL BOYS)

.3287 (Classification Index) - 172

CI	00	10	20	30	40	50	60	70	80	90
		Points								
500				2.21	5.50	8.79	12.07	15.36	18.65	21.93
600	25.22	28.5	31.8	35.08	38.37	41.66	44.94	48.23	51.52	54.80
700	58.09	61.38	64.66	67.95	71.24	74.53	77.81	81.10	84.39	87.67
800	90.96	94.25	97.53	100.82	104.11	107.40	110.68	113.97	117.26	120.54
900	123.83	127.12	130.40	133.69	136.98	140.27	143.55	146.84	150.13	153.41
1000	156.70	159.99	163.27	166.56	169.85	173.14	176.42	179.71	183.00	186.28

Interpolation table

1	.329
2	.657
3	.986
4	1.315
5	1.644
6	1.972
7	2.301
8	2.630
9	2.958

the raw score of the intelligence test is, **for boys,** the sum of the points obtained as follows:

(1) The McCloy Classification Index is converted into points for elementary-school boys by Table 27 (p. 118) and for high-school boys by Table 28 (p. 118). Note: Ages over seventeen years are represented by seventeen years in the classification index.

Table 29

GENERAL-MOTOR-CAPACITY SCORE: POINTS FOR
SARGENT JUMP (ELEMENTARY-SCHOOL BOYS)

.7962 (Sargent Jump)

SJ	0	1	2	3	4	5	6	7	8	9
0			Points			3.98	4.78	5.57	6.37	7.17
10	7.96	8.76	9.55	10.35	11.15	11.94	12.74	13.54	14.33	15.13
20	15.92	16.72	17.52	18.31	19.11	19.91	20.70	21.50	22.29	23.09
30	23.89	24.68	25.48	26.27	27.07	27.87	28.66	29.46	30.26	31.05
40	31.85	32.64	33.44	34.24	35.03	35.83	36.63	37.42	38.22	39.01
50	39.81	40.61	41.40	42.20	42.99	43.79	44.59	45.38	46.18	46.98
60	47.77	48.57	49.36	50.16	50.96	51.75	52.55	53.35	54.14	54.94

(2) The score for the Sargent Jump is converted into points for elementary-school boys by Table 29 (p. 119) and for high-school boys by Table 30 (p. 119).

(3) The score for the squat-thrust test is converted into points for elementary-school boys by Table 31 (p. 120) and for high-school boys by Table 32 (p. 120).

Table 30

GENERAL-MOTOR-CAPACITY SCORE: POINTS FOR
SARGENT JUMP (HIGH-SCHOOL BOYS)

1.446 (Sargent Jump) - 15

SJ	0	1	2	3	4	5	6	7	8	9
10	Points		.91	2.35	3.80	5.24	6.69	8.14	9.58	11.03	12.47
20	13.92	15.37	16.81	18.26	19.70	21.15	22.60	24.04	25.49	26.93
30	28.38	29.83	31.27	32.72	34.16	35.61	37.06	38.50	39.95	41.39
40	42.84	44.29	45.73	47.18	48.62	50.07	51.52	52.96	54.41	55.85
50	57.30	58.75	60.19	61.64	63.08	64.53	65.98	67.42	68.87	70.31
60	71.76	73.21	74.65	76.10	77.54	78.99	80.44	81.88	83.33	84.77
70	86.22	87.67	89.11	90.56	92.00	93.45	94.90	96.34	97.79	99.23

(4) The score for the Iowa-Brace Test is converted into points for elementary-school boys by Table 33 (p. 120), for junior-high-school boys by Table 34 (p. 120), and for senior-high-school boys by Table 35 (p. 121).

262. The **general-motor-capacity score for girls** is the sum of the points obtained as follows:

Table 31

GENERAL-MOTOR-CAPACITY SCORE: POINTS FOR
SQUAT THRUSTS (ELEMENTARY-SCHOOL BOYS)

2.187 (Squat-thrust test)

ST	0	1/4	1/2	3/4
	Points			
0		.55	1.09	1.64
1	2.19	2.73	3.28	3.83
2	4.37	4.92	5.47	6.01
3	6.56	7.11	7.65	8.20
4	8.75	9.29	9.84	10.39
5	10.94	11.48	12.03	12.58
6	13.12	13.67	14.22	14.76
7	15.31	15.86	16.40	16.95
8	17.50	18.04	18.59	19.14
9	19.68	20.23	20.78	21.32
10	21.87	22.42	22.96	23.51
11	24.06	24.60	25.15	25.70
12	26.24	26.79	27.34	27.88
13	28.43	28.98	29.52	30.07
14	30.62	31.16	31.71	32.26
15	32.81	33.35	33.90	34.45

Table 32

GENERAL-MOTOR-CAPACITY SCORE: POINTS FOR
SQUAT THRUSTS (HIGH-SCHOOL BOYS)

3.973 (Squat-thrust test)

ST	0	1/4	1/2	3/4
	Points			
0		.99	1.99	2.98
1	3.97	4.97	5.96	6.95
2	7.95	8.94	9.93	10.93
3	11.92	12.91	13.91	14.90
4	15.89	16.89	17.88	18.87
5	19.87	20.86	21.85	22.84
6	23.84	24.83	25.82	26.82
7	27.81	28.80	29.80	30.79
8	31.78	32.78	33.77	34.76
9	35.76	36.75	37.74	38.74
10	39.73	40.72	41.72	42.71
11	43.70	44.70	45.69	46.68
12	47.68	48.67	49.66	50.66
13	51.65	52.64	53.64	54.63
14	55.62	56.62	57.61	58.60
15	59.60	60.59	61.58	62.57

Table 33

GENERAL-MOTOR-CAPACITY SCORE: POINTS
IOWA-BRACE TEST (ELEMENTARY-SCHOOL BO

.5095 (Brace score)

Score	Points
1	11.72
2	12.74
3	13.76
4	14.78
5	15.79
6	16.81

Table 34

GENERAL-MOTOR-CAPACITY SCORE: POINTS
IOWA-BRACE TEST (JUNIOR-HIGH-SCHOOL BO

.9258 (Brace T-score) - 15

Score	Points
1	2.59
2	3.52
3	5.37
4	7.22
5	9.07
6	10.92
7	12.77
8	14.63
9	16.48
10	18.33
11	21.11
12	23.88
13	26.66
14	29.44
15	32.22
16	34.99
17	37.77
18	40.55
19	43.33
20	46.10

(1) The score for the Sargent Jump is converted into points by Table 36 (p. 121).

(2) The score for the squat-thrust test is converted into points by Table 37 (p. 122).

(3) The score for the Iowa-Brace Test is converted into points for elementary-school girls by Table 38 (p. 122), for junior-high-school girls by Table 39 (p. 122), and for senior-high-school girls by Table 40 (p. 122).

Table 35

GENERAL-MOTOR-CAPACITY SCORE: POINTS FOR
IOWA-BRACE TEST (SENIOR-HIGH-SCHOOL BOYS)

.9258 (Brace T-score) - 15

Score	Points
1	.73
2	2.59
3	4.44
4	6.29
5	8.15
6	10.00
7	11.85
8	13.70
9	15.55
10	17.40
11	20.18
12	22.96
13	25.74
14	28.51
15	31.29
16	34.07
17	36.84
18	40.55
19	45.18
20	50.73

Table 36

GENERAL-MOTOR-CAPACITY SCORE: POINTS FOR
SARGENT JUMP (GIRLS)

3.576 (Sargent Jump) + 119.27

SJ	0	1	2	3	4	5	6	7	8	9
					Points					
10	155.03	158.61	162.18	165.76	169.33	172.91	176.49	180.06	183.64	187.21
20	190.79	194.37	197.94	201.52	205.09	208.67	212.25	215.82	219.40	222.97
30	226.55	230.13	233.70	237.28	240.85	244.43	248.01	251.58	255.16	258.73
40	262.31	265.89	269.46	273.04	276.61	280.19	283.77	287.34	290.92	294.49
50	298.07	301.65	305.22	308.80	312.37	315.95	319.53	323.10	326.68	330.25
60	333.83	337.41	340.98	344.56	348.13	351.71	355.29	358.86	362.44	366.01

Table 37

GENERAL-MOTOR-CAPACITY SCORE: POINTS FOR
SQUAT THRUSTS (GIRLS)

19.12 (Squat-thrust test)

ST	0	1/4	1/2	3/4
	Points			
0	19.12	4.78	9.56	14.34
1	38.24	23.90	28.68	33.46
2	57.36	43.02	47.80	52.58
3	76.48	62.14	66.92	71.70
4		81.26	86.04	90.82
5	95.60	100.38	105.16	109.94
6	114.72	119.50	124.28	129.06
7	133.84	138.62	143.40	148.18
8	152.96	157.74	162.52	167.30
9	172.08	176.86	181.64	186.42
10	191.20	195.98	200.76	205.54
11	210.32	215.10	219.88	224.66
12	229.44	234.22	239.00	243.78

Table 39

GENERAL-MOTOR-CAPACITY SCORE: POINTS FO
IOWA-BRACE TEST (JUNIOR-HIGH-SCHOOL GIRL

2.20 (Brace T-score)

Score	Points
1	37.4
2	44.0
3	48.4
4	52.8
5	57.2
6	66.0
7	70.4
8	77.0
9	81.4
10	85.8
11	90.2
12	94.6
13	99.0
14	103.4
15	110.0
16	116.6
17	123.2
18	127.6
19	134.2
20	140.8

Table 38

GENERAL-MOTOR-CAPACITY SCORE: POINTS FOR
IOWA-BRACE TEST (ELEMENTARY-SCHOOL GIRLS)

2.20 (Brace T-score)

Score	Points
1	46.2
2	52.8
3	57.2
4	61.6
5	66.0
6	72.6
7	79.2
8	85.8
9	92.4
10	99.0
11	105.6
12	110.0
13	114.4
14	118.8
15	123.2
16	127.6
17	132.0
18	136.4
19	143.0
20	147.4

Table 40

GENERAL-MOTOR-CAPACITY SCORE: POINTS FOF
IOWA-BRACE TEST (SENIOR-HIGH-SCHOOL GIRLS

2.20 (Brace T-score)

Score	Points
1	57.2
2	61.6
3	66.0
4	70.4
5	74.8
6	81.4
7	85.8
8	90.2
9	94.6
10	99.0
11	103.4
12	107.8
13	112.2
14	116.6
15	121.0
16	125.4
17	132.0
18	138.6
19	145.2
20	156.2

Table 41

GENERAL-MOTOR-CAPACITY TEST: NORMS
(ELEMENTARY-SCHOOL BOYS)

Norm = .2327 (Classification Index) - 29.9

Motor quotient = 100(general-motor-capacity score/norm for classification index)

CI	0	10	20	30	40	50	60	70	80	90
400			Norms			74.82	77.14	79.47	81.80	84.12
500	86.45	88.78	91.10	93.43	95.76	98.09	100.41	102.74	105.07	107.39
600	109.72	112.05	114.37	116.70	119.03	121.36	123.68	126.01	128.34	130.66
700	132.99	135.32	137.64	139.97	142.30	144.63	146.95	149.28	151.61	153.93
800	156.26	158.59	160.91	163.24	165.57	167.90	170.22	172.55	174.88	177.20

Interpolation table

1	.23
2	.46
3	.70
4	.93
5	1.16
6	1.40
7	1.63
8	1.86
9	2.09

Table 42

GENERAL-MOTOR-CAPACITY TEST: NORMS
(HIGH-SCHOOL BOYS)

Norm = .4316 (Classification Index) - 149.31

Motor quotient = 100(general-motor-capacity score/norm for classification index)

CI	0	10	20	30	40	50	60	70	80	90
500			Norms			88.07	92.39	96.70	101.02	105.33
600	109.65	113.97	118.28	122.60	126.91	131.23	135.55	139.86	144.18	148.49
700	152.81	157.13	161.44	165.76	170.07	174.39	178.71	183.02	187.34	191.65
800	195.97	200.29	204.60	208.92	213.23	217.55	221.87	226.18	230.50	234.81
900	239.13	243.45	247.76	252.08	256.39	260.71	265.03	269.34	273.66	277.97
1000	282.29	286.61	290.92	295.23	299.55	303.87	308.19	312.50	316.82	321.13
1100	325.45	329.77	334.08	338.40	342.71	347.03	351.35	355.66	359.98	364.29

Interpolation table

1	.43
2	.86
3	1.29
4	1.72
5	2.16
6	2.59
7	3.02
8	3.45
9	3.88

263. The **motor quotient,** which is the motor analogue of the intelligence quotient in the mental field, is the motor capacity of a person relative to his size and maturity. Thus a boy with a motor quotient of 100 is average in motor capacity for his age and size, while a boy with a motor quotient of 120 is superior and a boy with a motor quotient of 80 is inferior in the respect indicated. The motor quotient for boys is the general-motor-capacity score divided by the norm for general-motor capacity (Table 41, p. 123, for elementary-school boys, and Table 42, p. 123, for high-school boys), which norm is in terms of the McCloy Classification Index.

Table 43

GENERAL-MOTOR-CAPACITY TEST: NORMS
(GIRLS)

Norm = 19.8732 (age) + 236.05

Motor quotient = 100(general-motor-capacity score/norm for age)

Elementary-school girls		Junior- and senior-high-school girls
Age	Norm	
8	395.04	For all ages, use
8½	404.97	470 as the norm.
9	414.91	
9½	424.85	
10	434.78	
10½	444.72	
11	454.66	
11½	464.59	
For over 11½ years of age, use 465 as the norm.		

The motor quotient for girls is the general-motor-capacity score divided by the norm for general-motor capacity (Table 43, p. 124), which norm is in terms of age.

264. The T-scores for the Iowa-Brace Test (Table 20, p. 94), for the Sargent Jump (Table 11, p. 68), and for the squat-thrust test (Table 14, p. 76) may be interpreted in the form of a profile. For example, a performer with a large classification index, a high T-score in the Sargent Jump, a low T-score in the squat-thrust test, and a low T-score in the Iowa-Brace Test should, with practice and experience, become proficient in power events although he would probably always be somewhat clumsy and would learn motor skills slowly. On the other hand, a performer with an average classification index, a low T-score in the Sargent Jump, an average T-score in the squat-thrust test, and a high T-score in the Iowa-Brace Test should learn motor skills quickly but would probably reach the peak of his achievement early.

265. ADMINISTRATION OF GENERAL-MOTOR-CAPACITY TEST

(1) Have the performers practice the Sargent Jump and the squat thrusts for at least five class periods. In no case administer the tests until the performers have learned how to execute the events correctly.

(2) Record the age of each performer, preferably from school records.

(3) In one period measure the height and the weight of each performer, and administer the Sargent Jump. (In the upper grades trained student leaders may obtain the records for the Sargent Jump. The Sargent Jump may be administered while regular class activities are going on under the direction of student leaders.) Have the performer execute the Sargent Jump until his records in two successive trials are lower than his previous best record for that day.

Table 44

GENERAL-MOTOR-CAPACITY TEST: SAMPLE SCORE CARD
(SENIOR-HIGH-SCHOOL BOY)

Age	16	
Height	65	
Weight	122	
McCloy Classification		
Index	.832	101.48 (Table 28)
Sargent Jump	57	67.42 (Table 30)
Squat-thrust test	5-3/4	22.84 (Table 32)
Iowa-Brace Test	16	34.07 (Table 35)
General-motor-capacity		
score		225.81
Norm for general-motor		
capacity		209.78 (Table 42)
Motor quotient		
$\dfrac{\text{GMCS}}{\text{Norm for GMC}}$		107.64

(4) In another period administer the squat-thrust test and the Iowa-Brace Test. Have the performer execute the squat-thrust test until his records in two successive trials are lower than his previous record.

(5) If any performers appear not to be doing their best in the Sargent Jump or in the squat thrusts, have them practice further, and retest them in these events in another period.

A sample score card for the general-motor-capacity test is shown in Table 44 (p. 125).

266. Measurement of general-motor capacity for the first three grades. Between the batteries that follow and the sum of the T-scores of eight tests of motor ability r's of approximately .83 [7] have been obtained.

For boys

Carpenter General-motor-capacity Score I = 1.3577 Sargent Jump + 5.0006 squat-thrust test + .8731 Iowa-Brace Test (modified, see Sec. 218)

[7] Aileen Carpenter, "The Measurement of General Motor Capacity and General Motor Ability in the First Three Grades," *Research Quarterly,* December, 1942.

$+ .2730$ McCloy Classification Index $- 43.95$. Norm $= .4055$ McCloy Classification Index $- 49.24$.

Carpenter General-motor-capacity Score II $= 1.3292$ Sargent Jump $+ 3.4095$ squat-thrust test $+ .4353$ Johnson Test (modified, see reference) $+ .2507$ McCloy Classification Index $- 27.87$. Norm $= .4073$ McCloy Classification Index $+ 48.47$.

For girls

Carpenter General-motor-capacity Score I $= .1058$ Sargent Jump $+ .9862$ squat-thrust test $+ .6151$ Iowa-Brace Test (modified, see Sec. 218) $+ .0776$ McCloy Classification Index $+ 9.45$. Norm $= .0968$ McCloy Classification Index $+ 11.27$.

Carpenter General-motor-capacity Score II $= .1476$ Sargent Jump $+ 1.1243$ squat-thrust test $+ .1042$ Johnson Test (modified, see reference) $+ .0846$ McCloy Classification Index $+ 6.85$. Norm $= .1064$ McCloy Classification Index $+ 6.83$.

Scoring tables for the Carpenter General-motor-capacity Tests may be found in the reference cited in footnote 7.

PART **IV**

Present Status

CHAPTER **13**

INTRODUCTION

267. IN PART IV are discussed methods of measuring physical achievement relative to physical education. Chapter 25 on the "Measurement of Potentiality for Different Sports" belongs in Part III as much as it does in Part IV; it has been included in Part IV, however, because many of the methods of measurement suggested for that purpose are discussed in other chapters of Part IV.

In both Part IV and Part V are discussed methods of measuring physical fitness, the type of fitness that is produced primarily by physical *training.* Although many physical educators deplore the use of the term "physical fitness" on the basis that fitness cannot be achieved by the development of any one of its components but rather can be achieved only by a simultaneous development of all its components, *physical fitness* is used in this discussion to imply the following two items.

268. (1) *Alleviation of hereditary or of acquired physical ailments.* There is little that can be done to remedy many hereditary shortcomings. Persons who inherit hearts or kidneys that are defective, or of poor quality are likely to die of "heart disease" or of "kidney disease" at an early age in spite of all that can be accomplished by medical science. Persons who acquire disabilities can, however, frequently be helped by medical science. Tests that are related primarily to the health examinations are discussed in Part V.

269. (2) *Development of physical efficiency.* Persons can be free from organic disabilities and yet be low in functioning ability. Persons who function physically at a high level of efficiency are said to be "in good condition," "in excellent training," or "physically fit." Methods of measuring this type of efficiency are discussed in Part IV, especially in Chapters 14 to 18.

CHAPTER 14

STRENGTH

270. THE ORIGINAL Intercollegiate Strength Test consisted of the following items: (1) the strength of the expiratory muscles, (2) the gripping strength of the hands, (3) the strength of the back, (4) the strength of the legs, and (5) the strength of the arms. The strength of the expiratory muscles was represented by the record made by a subject in blowing against a manometer (something like a steam gauge), which registered the maximum pressure exerted by the lungs.[1] Gripping strength, and the strength of the back and of the legs were measured by dynamometers. The strength of the arms was represented by one tenth of the subject's weight multiplied by the sum of the pull-ups and the parallel-bar dips that the subject could execute. The total strength was represented by the sum of the five items in metric units.

271. The **Rogers Strength Test**[2] includes the same items as the Intercollegiate Strength Test, but it is different from that test in the following respects.

(1) English units of measurements are used.

(2) Breathing capacity is in terms of cubic inches.

(3) Arm strength is determined by the formula

[pull-ups + dips (no.)] [(weight (lb.) / 10) + height (in.) − 60].

(4) In the Rogers method of push-ups for girls[3] the hands are so placed on a stall-bar bench, thirteen inches high, that when the girl is in the front leaning-rest position, the hands are just below and slightly behind the shoulders.

(5) In the Rogers method of pull-ups for girls[4] a pair of rings is hung from a low horizontal bar at such a height that the bottom of the rings

---

[1] Because of the fact that a contestant, in blowing against the manometer, developed a lung hemorrhage, one twentieth of the breathing capacity in deciliters was substituted for the measurement by the manometer. Hence, breathing capacity, which is not a measurement of strength, came to be included in some of the modern strength tests. Truly the strength of tradition is often stronger than that of scientific insight!

[2] Frederick R. Rogers, *Physical Capacity Tests in the Administration of Physical Education.* Norms for the Rogers Strength Test may be found in: H. Harrison Clarke, *Application of Measurement to Health and Physical Education*[2], pp. 440-43.

[3] Rogers, *Tests and Measurement Programs in the Redirection of Physical Education.*

[4] *Ibid.*

is four feet from the floor. From a half-fall-hanging position, the feet are far enough under the bar so that when the girl pulls herself up, the rings are just in front of the shoulders.

272. The Rogers Strength Test has three shortcomings.

(1) Breathing capacity, although an important anthropometric measurement, is not a measurement of strength, and hence should not be included in a strength test.[5]

(2) The Rogers Pull-up-dip-strength Score unduly penalizes the person who is small and whose ability in pull-ups and in dips is not well developed, while it unduly rewards the person whose ability in pull-ups and in dips is above the average.[6]

(3) In the Rogers method of pull-ups for girls short girls are kept so erect by the prescribed position that they can pull themselves up an undue number of times (one girl pulled herself up over a hundred times!).

273. The **McCloy Strength Test** differs from the Rogers Strength Test in the following respects.

(1) Breathing capacity is not included.

(2) In pull-ups for girls the horizontal bar is used instead of the rings, and the height of the bar is adjusted to within half an inch of the bottom of the sternum.

(3) Arm strength[7] is determined by the following formulas:

Boys: pull-up-(or dip)-strength score I (lb.) = 1.77 weight (lb.) + 3.42 pull-ups or dips (no.) − 46 (Table 45, p. 130)

pull-up-dip-strength score I (lb.) = 3.42 (pull-ups + dips) (no.) + 3.54 weight (lb.) − 92 (Table 46, p. 130)

Girls: pull-up-strength score (lb.) = .67 weight (lb.) + 1.2 pull-ups (no.) + 52 (Table 47, p. 131)

push-up-strength score (lb.) = .78 weight (lb.) + 1.1 push-ups (no.) + 74 (Table 48, p. 131)

[5] Deobold Van Dalen, "The Contribution of Breathing Capacity to the Physical Fitness Index," *Research Quarterly*, December, 1936.

[6] A boy ten years of age, 53 inches tall, and weighing 60 pounds executed seven pull-ups and five dips. According to the Intercollegiate Strength Test the boy's pull-up-dip-strength score was 72 pounds $\left[\text{ i.e., } \left(\frac{60}{10}\right)(7+5) \right]$. According to the Rogers Strength Test the boy's pull-up-strength score was −12 pounds $\left[\text{i.e., } (7+5)\left(\frac{60}{10} + 53 - 60\right) \right]$. In other words, the boy was penalized for each pull-up and dip. It is obvious that this boy had enough strength to pull sixty pounds up to the bar and to push sixty pounds up from a bent-arm rest on the parallel bars. This arm strength as tested by a dynamometer was 137 pounds.

An adult 69 inches tall and weighing 142 pounds executed forty pull-ups and twenty-seven dips. According to the Intercollegiate Strength Test the performer's pull-up-dip-strength score was 952 pounds. According to the Rogers Strength Test the pull-up-dip-strength score was 1,554 pounds, or three fourths of a ton! The arm strength as tested by a dynamometer was 632 pounds.

[7] Charles H. McCloy, "A New Method of Scoring Chinning and Dipping," *Research Quarterly*, December, 1931.

Table 45

STRENGTH IN POUNDS FOR NUMBER OF PULL-UPS OR DIPS (BOYS):
3.42 PULL-UPS OR DIPS + 1.77 WEIGHT (LB.) - 46

Weight	0	1	2	3	4	5	6	7	8	9
					1.77 Weight - 46					
50	42.5	44.3	46.0	47.8	49.6	51.4	53.1	54.9	56.7	58.4
60	60.2	62.0	63.7	65.5	67.3	69.1	70.8	72.6	74.4	76.1
70	77.9	79.7	81.4	83.2	85.0	86.8	88.5	90.3	92.1	93.8
80	95.6	97.4	99.1	100.9	102.7	104.5	106.2	108.0	109.8	111.5
90	113.3	115.1	116.8	118.6	120.4	122.2	123.9	125.7	127.5	129.2
100	131.0	132.8	134.5	136.3	138.1	139.9	141.6	143.4	145.2	146.9
110	148.7	150.5	152.2	154.0	155.8	156.6	159.3	161.1	162.9	164.6
120	166.4	168.2	169.9	171.7	173.5	175.3	177.0	178.8	180.6	182.3
130	184.1	185.9	187.6	189.4	191.2	193.0	194.7	196.5	198.3	200.0
140	201.8	203.6	205.3	207.1	208.9	210.7	212.4	214.2	216.0	217.7
150	219.5	221.3	223.0	224.8	226.6	228.4	230.1	231.9	233.7	235.4
160	237.2	239.0	240.7	242.5	244.3	246.1	247.8	249.6	251.4	253.1
170	254.9	256.7	258.4	260.2	262.0	263.1	265.5	267.3	269.1	270.8
180	272.6	274.4	276.1	277.9	279.7	281.5	283.2	285.0	286.8	288.5
190	290.3	292.1	293.8	295.6	297.4	299.2	300.9	302.7	304.5	306.2
200	308.0	309.8	311.5	313.3	315.1	316.9	318.6	320.4	322.2	323.9

Pull-ups or Dips	0	1	2	3	4	5	6	7	8	9
					3.42 Pull-ups or Dips					
0	0.0	3.4	6.8	10.3	13.7	17.1	20.5	23.9	27.4	30.8
10	34.2	37.6	41.0	44.5	47.9	51.3	54.7	58.1	61.6	65.0
20	68.4	71.8	75.2	78.7	82.1	85.5	88.9	92.3	95.8	99.2
30	102.6	106.0	109.4	112.0	116.3	119.7	123.1	126.5	130.0	133.4

Table 46

STRENGTH IN POUNDS FOR NUMBER OF PULL-UPS AND DIPS (BOYS):
3.42 (PULL-UPS + DIPS) + 3.54 WEIGHT (LB.) - 92

Weight	0	1	2	3	4	5	6	7	8	9
					3.54 Weight - 92					
50	85.00	88.54	92.08	95.62	99.16	102.70	106.24	109.78	113.32	116.86
60	120.40	123.94	127.48	131.02	134.56	138.10	141.64	145.18	148.72	152.26
70	155.80	159.34	162.88	166.42	169.96	173.50	177.04	180.58	184.12	187.66
80	191.20	194.74	198.28	201.82	205.36	208.90	212.44	215.98	219.52	223.06
90	226.60	230.14	233.68	237.22	240.76	244.30	247.84	251.38	254.92	258.46
100	262.00	265.54	269.08	272.62	276.16	279.70	283.24	286.78	290.32	293.86
110	297.40	300.94	304.48	308.02	311.56	315.10	318.64	322.18	325.72	329.26
120	332.80	336.34	339.88	343.42	346.96	350.50	354.04	357.58	361.12	364.66
130	368.20	371.74	375.28	378.82	382.36	385.90	389.44	392.98	396.52	400.06
140	403.60	407.14	410.68	414.22	417.76	421.30	424.84	428.38	431.92	435.46
150	439.00	442.54	446.08	449.62	453.16	456.70	460.24	463.78	467.32	470.86
160	474.40	477.94	481.48	485.02	488.56	492.10	495.64	499.18	502.72	506.26
170	509.80	513.34	516.88	520.42	523.96	527.50	531.04	534.58	538.12	541.66
180	545.20	548.74	552.28	555.82	559.36	562.90	566.44	569.98	573.52	577.06
190	580.60	584.14	587.68	591.22	594.76	598.30	601.84	605.38	608.92	612.46
200	616.00	619.54	623.08	626.62	630.16	633.70	637.24	640.78	644.32	647.86

Pull-ups and Dips	0	1	2	3	4	5	6	7	8	9
					3.42 (Pull-ups + Dips)					
0	0.0	3.4	6.8	10.3	13.7	17.1	20.5	23.9	27.4	30.8
10	34.2	37.6	41.0	44.5	47.9	51.3	54.7	58.1	61.6	65.0
20	68.4	71.8	75.2	78.7	82.1	85.5	88.9	92.3	95.8	99.2
30	102.6	106.0	109.4	112.0	116.3	119.7	123.1	126.5	130.0	133.4
40	136.80	140.22	143.64	147.06	150.48	153.90	157.32	160.74	164.16	167.58
50	171.00	174.42	177.84	181.26	184.68	188.10	191.52	194.94	198.36	201.78
60	205.20	208.62	212.04	215.46	218.88	222.30	225.72	229.14	232.56	235.98

Table 47

STRENGTH IN POUNDS FOR NUMBER OF PULL-UPS (GIRLS):
1.2 PULL-UPS + .67 WEIGHT (LB.) + 52

Weight	0	1	2	3	4	5	6	7	8	9

.67 Weight + 52

Weight	0	1	2	3	4	5	6	7	8	9
50	85.50	86.17	86.84	87.51	88.18	88.35	89.52	90.19	90.86	91.53
60	92.20	92.87	93.54	94.21	94.88	95.55	96.22	96.89	97.56	98.23
70	98.90	99.57	100.24	100.91	101.58	102.25	102.92	103.59	104.26	104.93
80	105.60	106.27	106.94	107.61	108.28	108.95	109.62	110.29	110.96	111.63
90	112.30	112.97	113.64	114.31	114.98	115.65	116.32	116.99	117.66	118.33
100	119.00	119.67	120.34	121.01	121.68	122.35	123.02	123.69	124.36	125.03
110	125.70	126.37	127.04	127.71	128.38	129.05	129.72	130.39	121.06	131.73
120	132.40	133.07	133.74	134.41	135.08	135.75	136.42	137.09	137.76	138.43
130	139.10	139.77	140.44	141.11	141.78	142.45	143.12	143.79	144.46	145.13
140	145.80	146.47	147.14	147.81	148.48	149.15	149.82	150.49	151.16	151.83
150	152.50	153.17	153.84	154.51	155.18	155.85	156.52	157.19	157.86	158.53
160	159.20	159.87	160.54	161.21	161.88	162.55	163.22	163.89	164.56	165.23
170	165.90	166.57	167.24	167.91	168.58	169.25	169.92	170.59	171.26	171.93

1.2 Pull-ups

Pull-ups	0	1	2	3	4	5	6	7	8	9
0	0.0	1.2	2.4	3.6	4.8	6.0	7.2	8.4	9.6	10.8
10	12.0	13.2	14.4	15.6	16.8	18.0	19.2	20.4	21.6	22.8
20	24.0	25.2	26.4	27.6	28.8	30.0	31.2	32.4	33.6	34.8
30	36.0	37.2	38.4	39.6	40.8	42.0	43.2	44.4	45.6	46.8
40	48.0	49.2	50.4	51.6	52.8	54.0	55.2	56.4	57.6	58.8
50	60.0	61.2	62.4	63.6	64.8	66.0	67.2	68.4	69.6	70.8
60	72.0	73.2	74.4	75.6	76.8	78.0	79.2	80.4	81.6	82.8
70	84.0	85.2	86.4	87.6	88.8	90.0	91.2	92.4	93.6	94.8

Table 48

STRENGTH IN POUNDS FOR NUMBER OF PUSH-UPS (GIRLS):
1.1 PUSH-UPS + .78 WEIGHT (LB.) + 74

Weight	0	1	2	3	4	5	6	7	8	9

.78 Weight + 74

Weight	0	1	2	3	4	5	6	7	8	9
50	113.00	113.78	114.56	115.34	116.12	116.90	117.68	118.46	119.24	120.02
60	120.80	121.58	122.36	123.14	123.92	124.70	125.48	126.26	127.04	127.82
70	128.60	129.38	130.16	130.94	131.72	132.50	133.28	134.06	134.84	135.62
80	136.40	137.18	137.96	138.74	139.52	140.30	141.08	141.86	142.64	143.42
90	144.20	144.98	145.76	146.54	147.32	148.10	148.88	149.66	150.44	151.22
100	152.00	152.78	153.56	154.34	155.12	155.90	156.68	157.46	158.24	159.02
110	159.80	160.58	161.36	162.14	162.92	163.70	164.48	165.26	166.04	166.82
120	167.60	168.38	169.16	169.94	170.72	171.50	172.28	173.06	173.84	174.62
130	175.40	176.18	176.96	177.74	178.52	179.30	180.08	180.86	181.64	182.42
140	183.20	183.98	184.76	185.54	186.32	187.10	187.88	188.66	189.44	190.22
150	191.00	191.78	192.56	193.34	194.12	194.90	195.68	196.46	197.24	198.02
160	198.80	199.58	200.36	201.14	201.92	202.70	203.48	204.26	205.04	205.82
170	206.60	207.38	208.16	208.94	209.72	210.50	211.28	212.06	212.84	213.62

Push-ups	0	1	2	3	1.1 Push-ups 4	5	6	7	8	9
0	0.0	1.1	2.2	3.3	4.4	5.5	6.6	7.7	8.8	9.9
10	11.0	12.1	13.2	14.3	15.4	16.5	17.6	18.7	19.8	20.9
20	22.0	23.1	24.2	25.3	26.4	27.5	28.6	29.7	30.8	31.9
30	33.0	34.1	35.2	36.3	37.4	38.5	39.6	40.7	41.8	42.9
40	44.0	45.1	46.2	47.3	48.4	49.5	50.6	51.7	52.8	53.9
50	55.0	56.1	57.2	58.3	59.4	60.5	61.6	62.7	63.8	64.9

Table 49

STRENGTH IN POUNDS FOR NUMBER OF PULL-UPS OR DIPS:

1.27 (PULL-UPS OR DIPS)$^{.133}$ x WEIGHT

Pull-ups	1	2	3	4	5	6	7	8	9

1.27 (Pull-ups or Dips)$^{.133}$ x Weight

	1	2	3	4	5	6	7	8	9
1	1.2697	2.5394	3.8091	5.0788	6.3485	7.6182	8.8879	10.1576	11.4273
2	1.3924	2.7848	4.1772	5.5696	6.9620	8.3544	9.7468	11.1392	12.5316
3	1.4697	2.9394	4.4091	5.8788	7.3485	8.8182	10.2879	11.7576	13.2273
4	1.5268	3.0536	4.5804	6.1072	7.6340	9.1608	10.6876	12.2144	13.7412
5	1.5730	3.1460	4.7190	6.2920	7.8650	9.4380	11.0110	12.5840	14.1570
6	1.6110	3.2220	4.8330	6.4440	8.0550	9.6660	11.2770	12.8880	14.4990
7	1.6450	3.2900	4.9350	6.5800	8.2250	9.8700	11.5150	13.1600	14.8050
8	1.6744	3.3488	5.0232	6.6976	8.3720	10.0464	11.7208	13.3952	15.0696
9	1.7010	3.4020	5.1030	6.8040	8.5050	10.2060	11.9070	13.6080	15.3090
10	1.7250	3.4500	5.1750	6.9000	8.6250	10.3500	12.0750	13.8000	15.5250
11	1.7468	3.4936	5.2404	6.9872	8.7340	10.4808	12.2276	13.9744	15.7212
12	1.7664	3.5328	5.2992	7.0656	8.8320	10.5984	12.3648	14.1312	15.8976
13	1.7862	3.5724	5.3586	7.1448	8.9310	10.7172	12.5034	14.2896	16.0758
14	1.8032	3.6064	5.4096	7.2128	9.0160	10.8192	12.6224	14.4256	16.2288
15	1.8210	3.6420	5.4630	7.2840	9.1050	10.9260	12.7470	14.5680	16.3890
16	1.8352	3.6704	5.5056	7.3408	9.1760	11.0112	12.8464	14.6816	16.5168
17	1.8513	3.7026	5.5539	7.4052	9.2565	11.1078	12.9591	14.8104	16.6617
18	1.8648	3.7296	5.5944	7.4592	9.3240	11.1888	13.0536	14.9184	16.7832
19	1.8741	3.7482	5.6223	7.4964	9.3705	11.2446	13.1187	14.9928	16.8669
20	1.8900	3.7800	5.6700	7.5600	9.4500	11.3400	13.2300	15.1200	17.0100
21	1.9047	3.8094	5.7141	7.6188	9.5235	11.4282	13.3329	15.2376	17.1423
22	1.9162	3.8324	5.7486	7.6648	9.5810	11.4972	13.4134	15.3296	17.2458
23	1.9274	3.8548	5.7822	7.7096	9.6370	11.5644	13.4918	15.4192	17.3466
24	1.9369	3.8738	5.8107	7.7476	9.6845	11.6214	13.5583	15.4952	17.4321
25	1.9500	3.9000	5.8500	7.8000	9.7500	11.7000	13.6500	15.6000	17.5500
26	1.9578	3.9156	5.8734	7.8312	9.7890	11.7468	13.7046	15.6624	17.6202
27	1.9683	3.9366	5.9049	7.8732	9.8415	11.8098	13.7781	15.7464	17.7147
28	1.9768	3.9536	5.9304	7.9072	9.8840	11.8608	13.8376	15.8144	17.7912
29	1.9865	3.9730	5.9595	7.9460	9.9325	11.9190	13.9055	15.8780	17.8785
30	1.9950	3.9900	5.9850	7.9800	9.9750	11.9700	13.9650	15.9600	17.9550
31	2.0057	4.0114	6.0171	8.0228	10.0285	12.0342	14.0399	16.0456	18.0513
32	2.0128	4.0256	6.0384	8.0512	10.0640	12.0768	14.0896	16.1024	18.1152
33	2.0229	4.0458	6.0687	8.0916	10.1145	12.1374	14.1603	16.1832	18.2061
34	2.0298	4.0596	6.0894	8.1192	10.1490	12.1788	14.2086	16.2384	18.2682
35	2.0370	4.0740	6.1110	8.1480	10.1850	12.2220	14.2590	16.2960	18.3330
36	2.0448	4.0896	6.1344	8.1792	10.2240	12.2688	14.3136	16.3584	18.4032
37	2.0535	4.1070	6.1605	8.2140	10.2675	12.3210	14.3745	16.4280	18.4815
38	2.0596	4.1192	6.1788	8.2384	10.2980	12.3576	14.4172	16.4768	18.5364
39	2.0670	4.1340	6.2010	8.2680	10.3350	12.4020	14.4690	16.5360	18.6030
40	2.0760	4.1520	6.2280	8.3040	10.3800	12.4560	14.5320	16.6080	18.6840

Example

Number of pull-ups $= 8$; weight $= 129$ lb., which $= 100 + 20 + 9$

For 8 pull-ups

$1 = 1.6744$, which is multiplied by 100, which $= 167.44$

$2 = 3.3488$, which is multiplied by 10, which $= 33.488$

$9 = 15.0696$, which is multiplied by 1, which $= \underline{15.0696}$

Pull-up-strength score $= \overline{215.9976} = 216$

274. Coefficients of correlation of about .95 have been obtained between arm strength for boys as measured by a dynamometer and the McCloy Pull-up-dip-strength Scores. The formula for boys is quite accurate within limits of "normality." For boys of exceptional endurance, however, it is somewhat inaccurate at the upper extreme. Also, it slightly rewards the

Table 50*

PULL-UP-DIP-STRENGTH EQUIVALENTS FOR
PUSHING-AND-PULLING STRENGTH (BOYS)

Push and Pull	0	1	2	3	4	5	6	7	8	9
				Pull-up and Dip Equivalents						
50	424	426	427	429	430	431	433	434	436	437
60	439	440	442	443	445	446	448	449	451	452
70	454	455	456	458	459	461	462	464	465	467
80	468	470	471	473	474	476	477	478	480	481
90	483	484	486	487	489	490	492	493	495	496
100	498	499	501	502	503	505	506	508	509	511
110	512	514	515	517	518	520	521	523	524	525
120	527	528	530	531	533	534	536	537	539	540
130	542	543	545	546	548	549	550	552	553	555
140	556	558	559	561	562	564	565	567	568	570
150	571	572	574	575	577	578	580	581	583	584
160	586	587	589	590	592	593	595	596	597	599
170	600	602	603	605	606	608	609	611	612	614
180	615	617	618	619	621	622	624	625	627	628
190	630	631	633	634	636	637	639	640	642	643
200	644	646	647	649	650	652	653	655	656	658
210	659	661	662	664	665	667	668	669	671	672
220	674	675	677	678	680	681	683	684	686	687
230	689	690	691	693	694	696	697	699	700	702
240	703	705	706	708	709	711	712	714	715	716
250	718	719	721	722	724	725	727	728	730	731
260	733	734	736	737	738	740	741	743	744	746
270	747	749	750	752	753	755	756	758	759	761
280	762	763	765	766	768	769	771	772	774	775
290	777	778	780	781	783	784	785	787	788	790
300	791	793	794	796	797	799	800	802	803	805
310	806	808	809	810	812	813	815	816	818	819
320	821	822	824	825	827	828	830	831	833	834
330	835	837	838	840	841	843	844	846	847	849
340	850	852	853	855	856	857	859	860	862	863
350	865	866	868	869	871	872	874	875	877	878
360	880	881	882	884	885	887	888	890	891	893
370	894	896	897	899	900	902	903	904	906	907
380	909	910	912	913	915	916	918	919	921	922

*If this table is used to convert pushing-and-pulling strength into pull-up-dip strength in the short form of the athletic-strength index, the result should be multiplied by 1.5. This table should not be used for that purpose unless the boy cannot perform even one pull-up or dip.

small boys and slightly penalizes the large ones. The following formula is more accurate, although less convenient to use, than the preceding one: McCloy Pull-up-(or dip)-strength Score II (lb.) = 1.27 (pull-ups or dips)$^{.133}$ × weight (lb.) (Table 49, p. 132). A coefficient of curvilinear correlation of .965[8] has been obtained between arm strength as measured

[8] *Ibid.*

by a dynamometer and the McCloy Pull-up-(or dip)-strength Score II. For the range of three to twenty pull-ups or dips about the same pull-up-(or dip)-strength scores are obtained from both formulas.

275. For girls, a sufficiently high coefficient of correlation between arm strength as measured by a dynamometer and the pull-up-push-up-strength score has not been obtained for pull-ups and push-ups to be

Table 51

PULL-UP-PUSH-UP-STRENGTH EQUIVALENTS FOR
PUSHING-AND-PULLING STRENGTH (GIRLS)

Push and Pull	0	1	2	3	4	5	6	7	8	9
				Pull-up and Push-up Equivalents						
10	229	230	231	232	232	233	234	235	236	237
20	237	238	239	240	240	241	242	243	244	244
30	245	247	247	248	248	249	250	251	252	253
40	253	254	255	256	257	257	258	259	260	261
50	261	262	263	264	265	265	266	267	268	269
60	269	270	271	271	273	274	274	275	276	277
70	278	278	278	280	281	282	282	283	284	285
80	286	286	287	288	289	290	290	291	292	292
90	294	295	295	296	297	298	299	299	300	301
100	302	303	303	304	305	306	307	307	308	309
110	310	311	312	312	313	314	315	316	316	317
120	318	319	320	320	321	322	323	324	324	325
130	326	327	328	328	329	330	331	332	333	333
140	334	335	336	337	337	338	339	340	341	341
150	342	343	344	345	345	346	347	348	349	349
160	350	351	352	353	354	354	355	356	357	358
170	358	359	360	361	362	362	363	364	365	366
180	366	367	368	369	370	370	371	372	373	374
190	375	375	376	377	378	379	379	380	381	382
200	383	383	384	385	386	387	387	388	389	390
210	391	391	392	393	394	395	396	396	397	398
220	399	400	400	401	402	403	404	404	405	406
230	407	408	408	409	410	411	412	413	413	414
240	415	416	417	417	418	419	420	421	421	422
250	423	424	425	425	426	427	428	429	429	430
260	431	432	433	434	434	435	436	437	438	438
270	439	440	441	442	442	443	444	445	446	446
280	447	448	449	450	450	451	452	453	454	455
290	455	456	457	458	459	459	460	461	462	463
300	463	464	465	466	467	467	468	469	470	471

considered valid tests of strength.[9] In a study[10] on college women, in which pushing-and-pulling strength measured by means of a grip dynamometer with a push-and-pull attachment was substituted for the pull-up-push-up-strength score, it was found that the measurement of strength by means of the dynamometer was somewhat more accurate than the pull-up-push-up-strength score. The measurements of strength obtained by these two methods do not, however, represent entirely the strength of the same groups of muscles. With a group of high-school girls, an r of .63 was obtained be-

[9] Unpublished studies, State University of Iowa.

[10] Aileen Carpenter, "A Critical Study of the Factors Determining Effective Strength Tests for Women," *Research Quarterly*, December, 1938.

tween pushing-and-pulling strength measured by a dynamometer with a push-and-pull attachment and the pull-up-push-up-strength score. Evidence from a factorial analysis, however, indicates that much more pulling-and-pushing strength appears in the measurement by the dynamometer with the push-and-pull attachment than in the pull-up-push-up-strength score.

276. The following formulas may be used for the conversion of pushing-and-pulling strength into a score somewhat comparable to the McCloy Pull-up-push-up-strength Score.

Boys: 1.469 pushing-and-pulling strength + 351 (Table 50, p. 133)

Girls: .808 pushing-and-pulling strength + 221 (Table 51, p. 134)

277. The following items are included in the McCloy Strength Test for boys, the general-strength score being the sum of the strengths represented by the following six items: (1) right grip, (2) left grip, (3) back lift, (4) leg lift, (5) pull-ups, and (6) parallel-bar dips. Breathing capacity is not included. The strengths represented by the first four items are in terms of pounds of strength as registered on dynamometers. The strengths represented by the fifth and sixth items are determined from Table 45 (p. 130) or 49 (p. 132), or 46 (p. 130). Norms for the general-strength scores for boys may be found in Table 52 (pp. 136-38). The following items are included in the McCloy Strength Test for girls: (1) right grip, (2) left grip, (3) back lift, (4) leg lift, (5) pulling strength, and (6) pushing strength. The strengths represented by the first four items are in terms of pounds of strength as registered on dynamometers. The fifth and sixth items as registered on the dynamometer are converted into a pull-up-push-up-strength score (Table 51, p. 134). The general-strength score, then, is the sum of the strengths represented by these six items. Norms for strength scores for girls may be found in Table 53 (pp. 139-41).

278. **Uses.** Only the amount of strength possessed by a person is measured by the strength tests that have been described. Neither the potentiality of a person to develop strength nor the motor educability of a person is measured by this type of test. Although strength has in many recent studies been shown to be the most important item in all motor performances, and, on the average, to contribute more than twice as much to motor achievement as does velocity, and more than ten times as much as does motor educability, motor performance is not measured by strength tests except in so far as motor performance depends upon strength. The value of measurements of strength and the contribution of strength to motor performance should be differentiated. Velocity, for example, is increased considerably by an increase in strength.[11] This increase is

[11] Edward K. Capen, "The Effect of Systematic Weight Training on Power, Strength, and Endurance," *Research Quarterly*, May, 1950.

Edward Chui, "The Effect of Systematic Weight Training on Athletic Power," *Research Quarterly*, October, 1950.

PRESENT STATUS

Table 52

STRENGTH TEST (McCLOY): NORMS (BOYS)

Strength quotient = 100(strength score/norm for age and weight)

Weight	11	11½	12	12½	13	13½	14	14½	15	15½	16	16½	17	17½
200							1989	2019	2049	2096	2143	2174	2204	2230
198						1905	1970	2000	2030	2077	2124	2155	2185	2211
196						1886	1951	1981	2011	2058	2105	2136	2166	2192
194						1867	1932	1962	1992	2039	2086	2116	2146	2172
192						1848	1913	1945	1974	2021	2067	2097	2127	2153
190					1763	1828	1894	1926	1955	2002	2048	2078	2108	2134
188					1746	1811	1875	1907	1936	1983	2029	2059	2089	2116
186					1728	1792	1856	1888	1917	1964	2010	2040	2069	2096
184					1710	1774	1837	1869	1898	1945	1991	2020	2050	2077
182				1614	1692	1756	1818	1850	1879	1926	1972	2002	2031	2058
180				1597	1674	1738	1799	1831	1860	1907	1953	1982	2011	2038
178				1580	1656	1718	1780	1812	1841	1888	1934	1963	1992	2019
176				1563	1638	1700	1761	1793	1822	1869	1915	1944	1973	2000
174			1473	1547	1620	1681	1742	1774	1804	1850	1896	1925	1954	1981
172			1457	1530	1602	1663	1723	1755	1785	1831	1877	1906	1934	1961
170			1442	1513	1584	1644	1704	1736	1766	1812	1858	1887	1915	1942
168			1427	1497	1567	1626	1684	1718	1747	1793	1839	1868	1896	1923
166		1367	1411	1480	1549	1607	1665	1699	1728	1774	1820	1844	1877	1914
164		1352	1396	1464	1531	1589	1646	1680	1709	1755	1801	1824	1857	1885
162		1337	1381	1447	1513	1570	1627	1661	1690	1736	1782	1805	1838	1856
160		1321	1365	1430	1495	1552	1608	1642	1671	1717	1763	1786	1819	1837
158	1261	1306	1350	1414	1477	1533	1589	1621	1653	1699	1744	1772	1799	1826
156	1248	1291	1334	1396	1459	1515	1570	1602	1634	1680	1725	1753	1780	1808
154	1234	1277	1319	1380	1441	1496	1551	1583	1615	1661	1706	1734	1761	1789
152	1220	1262	1304	1364	1423	1478	1532	1564	1596	1641	1686	1714	1742	1770
150	1207	1248	1288	1344	1405	1459	1513	1545	1577	1622	1667	1694	1722	1750
148	1193	1233	1273	1331	1388	1441	1494	1526	1558	1603	1648	1676	1703	1731
146	1179	1219	1258	1314	1370	1423	1475	1507	1539	1584	1629	1657	1684	1712
144	1166	1204	1242	1297	1352	1404	1456	1488	1520	1565	1610	1637	1664	1693
142	1152	1190	1227	1281	1334	1386	1437	1470	1502	1547	1591	1618	1645	1674
140	1138	1175	1211	1264	1316	1367	1418	1441	1483	1528	1572	1599	1626	1655
138	1125	1161	1196	1247	1298	1349	1399	1432	1464	1509	1553	1580	1607	1636
136	1111	1146	1181	1231	1280	1330	1380	1413	1445	1490	1534	1561	1587	1616
134	1097	1131	1165	1213	1262	1312	1361	1394	1426	1471	1515	1542	1568	1597
132	1084	1117	1150	1197	1244	1293	1342	1375	1407	1452	1496	1523	1549	1578
130	1070	1102	1134	1180	1226	1274	1323	1356	1388	1433	1477	1503	1529	1558
128	1056	1088	1119	1164	1209	1257	1304	1337	1369	1414	1458	1484	1510	1539
126	1043	1073	1104	1148	1191	1238	1285	1318	1350	1395	1439	1465	1491	1520
124	1029	1050	1088	1131	1173	1220	1266	1299	1332	1376	1420	1446	1472	1501
122	1015	1044	1073	1114	1155	1201	1247	1280	1313	1357	1401	1427	1452	1482
120	1001	1027	1058	1098	1137	1183	1228	1261	1294	1338	1382	1408	1433	1463
118	988	1014	1042	1081	1119	1164	1208	1242	1275	1319	1363	1389	1414	1444
116	974	1000	1027	1059	1101	1145	1189	1223	1256	1300	1344	1370	1395	1425
114	960	986	1011	1047	1083	1127	1170	1204	1237	1281	1325	1350	1375	1405
112	947	972	996	1031	1065	1108	1151	1185	1218	1262	1306	1331	1356	1386
110	933	957	981	1014	1047	1090	1132	1166	1199	1243	1287	1312	1337	1367

Table 52 (continued)

Weight	Age													
	11	11½	12	12½	13	13½	14	14½	15	15½	16	16½	17	17½
108	919	941	965	998	1030	1072	1113	1147	1181	1225	1268	1293	1317	
106	906	928	950	981	1012	1053	1094	1128	1162	1206	1249	1274	1298	
104	892	916	935	965	994	1035	1075	1109	1143	1187	1230	1254	1278	
102	878	899	919	948	976	1016	1056	1090	1124	1167	1210	1235	1260	
100	865	885	904	931	958	998	1037	1071	1105	1148	1191			
98	851	870	888	914	940	979	1018	1052	1086	1129	1172			
96	837	855	873	898	922	961	999	1033	1067	1110	1153			
94	824	836	858	881	904	942	980	1014	1048	1091	1134			
92	810	826	842	864	886	924	961	997	1030					
90	796	812	827	848	868	905	942	977	1011					
88	783	807	811	831	851	887	923	958	992					
86	769	793	796	815	833	869	904	939	973					
84	755	767	781	798	815	850	885	920						
82	742	754	765	781	797	832	866	901						
80	728	739	750	765	779	813	847							
78	714	725	735	748	761	795	828							
76	701	710	719	730	743	777								
74	687	696	704	715	725	759								
72	673	678	688	698	707									
70	659	666	673	681	689									
68	646	652	658	664										
66	632	637	642	650										
64	618	623	627											
62	605	609	612											
60	591													
Multiplier	6.85	7.30	7.70	8.35	8.95	9.25	9.50	9.45	9.40	9.60	9.55	9.56	9.63	9.60

Weight	Age												
	18	19	20	21	22	23	24	25	26	27	28	29	30
218	2428	2508	2525	2525	2525	2477	2477	2452	2428	2379	2331	2301	2282
216	2408	2480	2504	2504	2504	2456	2456	2432	2408	2360	2312	2288	2264
214	2389	2461	2485	2485	2485	2437	2437	2413	2389	2341	2293	2270	2246
212	2370	2441	2465	2465	2465	2417	2417	2394	2370	2323	2275	2252	2228
210	2351	2422	2445	2445	2445	2398	2398	2375	2351	2304	2257	2233	2210
208	2332	2402	2425	2425	2425	2379	2379	2355	2332	2285	2239	2215	2192
206	2313	2382	2406	2406	2406	2359	2359	2336	2313	2267	2220	2197	2174
204	2294	2363	2386	2386	2386	2340	2340	2317	2294	2248	2202	2179	2156
202	2275	2343	2366	2366	2366	2321	2321	2298	2275	2230	2184	2161	2139
200	2257	2325	2347	2347	2347	2302	2302	2280	2257	2212	2167	2144	2122
198	2237	2304	2326	2326	2326	2282	2282	2259	2237	2192	2148	2125	2103
196	2217	2284	2306	2306	2306	2261	2261	2239	2217	2173	2128	2106	2084
194	2198	2264	2286	2286	2286	2242	2242	2220	2198	2154	2110	2088	2066
192	2179	2244	2266	2266	2266	2223	2223	2201	2179	2135	2092	2070	2048
190	2160	2225	2246	2246	2246	2203	2203	2182	2160	2117	2074	2052	2030
188	2141	2205	2227	2227	2227	2184	2184	2162	2141	2098	2055	2034	2013
186	2122	2186	2207	2207	2207	2164	2164	2143	2122	2080	2037	2016	1995
184	2103	2166	2187	2187	2187	2145	2145	2124	2103	2061	2019	1998	1977
182	2084	2147	2167	2167	2167	2126	2126	2105	2084	2042	2001	1980	1959
180	2065	2127	2148	2148	2148	2106	2106	2086	2065	2024	1982	1962	1941

Table 52 (continued)

Weight	Age												
	18	19	20	21	22	23	24	25	26	27	28	29	30
178	2046	2107	2128	2128	2128	2087	2087	2066	2046	2005	1964	1944	1923
176	2026	2087	2107	2107	2107	2067	2067	2046	2026	1985	1945	1925	1904
174	2007	2067	2087	2087	2087	2047	2047	2027	2007	1967	1927	1907	1887
172	1988	2048	2068	2068	2068	2028	2028	2008	1988	1948	1908	1889	1869
170	1969	2028	2048	2048	2048	2008	2008	1989	1969	1930	1890	1871	1851
168	1950	2009	2028	2028	2028	1989	1989	1970	1950	1911	1872	1853	1833
166	1931	1989	2008	2008	2008	1970	1970	1950	1931	1892	1854	1834	1815
164	1912	1969	1988	1988	1988	1950	1950	1931	1912	1874	1836	1816	1797
162	1893	1950	1969	1969	1969	1931	1931	1912	1893	1855	1817	1798	1779
160	1874	1930	1949	1949	1949	1911	1911	1893	1874	1837	1799	1780	1762
158	1855	1911	1929	1929	1929	1892	1892	1874	1855	1818	1781	1762	1744
156	1835	1890	1908	1908	1908	1872	1872	1853	1835	1798	1762	1743	1725
154	1816	1870	1889	1889	1889	1852	1852	1834	1816	1780	1743	1725	1707
152	1797	1851	1869	1869	1869	1833	1833	1815	1797	1761	1725	1707	1689
150	1778	1831	1849	1849	1849	1814	1814	1796	1778	1742	1707	1689	1671
148	1759	1812	1829	1829	1829	1794	1794	1777	1759	1724	1689	1671	1653
146	1740	1792	1810	1810	1810	1775	1775	1757	1740	1705	1670	1653	1636
144	1721	1773	1790	1790	1790	1755	1755	1738	1721	1687	1652	1635	1618
142	1702	1753	1770	1770	1770	1736	1736	1719	1702	1668	1634	1617	1600
140	1683	1733	1750	1750	1750	1717	1717	1700	1683	1649	1616	1599	1582
138	1664	1714	1731	1731	1731	1697	1697	1681	1664	1631	1597	1581	1564
136	1644	1693	1710	1710	1710	1677	1677	1660	1644	1611	1578	1562	1545
134	1625	1674	1690	1690	1690	1658	1658	1641	1625	1593	1560	1544	1528
132	1606	1654	1670	1670	1670	1638	1638	1622	1606	1574	1542	1526	1510
130	1587	1635	1650	1650	1650	1619	1619	1603	1587	1555	1524	1508	1492
128	1568	1615	1631	1631	1631	1599	1599	1584	1568	1537	1505	1490	1474
126	1549	1595	1611	1611	1611	1580	1580	1564	1549	1518	1487	1472	1456
124	1530	1576	1591	1591	1591	1561	1561	1545	1530	1499	1469	1454	1438
122	1511	1556	1571	1571	1571	1541	1541	1526	1511	1481	1451	1435	1420
120	1492	1537	1552	1552	1552	1522	1522	1507	1492	1462	1432	1417	1402
118	1473	1517	1532	1532	1532	1502	1502	1488	1473	1444	1414	1399	1385
116	1453	1497	1511	1511	1511	1482	1482	1468	1453	1424	1395	1380	1366
114	1434	1477	1491	1491	1491	1463	1463	1448	1434	1405	1377	1362	1348
112	1415	1457	1472	1472	1472	1443	1443	1429	1415	1387	1358	1344	1330
110	1396	1438	1452	1452	1452	1424	1424	1410	1396	1368	1340	1326	1312
Multiplier	9.56	9.83	9.93	9.93	9.93	9.77	9.77	9.67	9.57	9.37	9.20	9.10	9.00

Table 53

STRENGTH TEST (McCLOY): NORMS (GIRLS)

Strength quotient = 100(strength score/norm for age and weight)

Weight	11	11½	12	12½	13	13½	14	14½	15	15½	16	16½	17	17½
176							1339	1370	1401	1430	1458	1495	1532	1517
174							1329	1361	1392	1420	1448	1485	1522	1507
172							1319	1351	1383	1411	1439	1476	1512	1497
170							1309	1342	1374	1402	1429	1466	1502	1487
168							1299	1332	1365	1393	1420	1456	1492	1477
166						1258	1289	1322	1355	1383	1410	1446	1482	1467
164						1248	1280	1313	1346	1374	1401	1437	1472	1458
162						1238	1270	1304	1337	1364	1391	1427	1462	1448
160						1228	1260	1294	1328	1355	1382	1417	1452	1438
158						1218	1250	1285	1319	1346	1372	1407	1442	1428
156					1176	1208	1240	1275	1310	1337	1363	1398	1432	1418
154					1166	1198	1230	1265	1300	1327	1353	1388	1422	1408
152					1155	1188	1220	1256	1292	1318	1344	1378	1412	1398
150				1105	1145	1178	1211	1247	1282	1308	1334	1368	1402	1388
148				1096	1135	1168	1201	1237	1273	1295	1325	1359	1392	1378
146				1086	1125	1158	1191	1228	1264	1290	1315	1349	1382	1368
144				1077	1115	1148	1181	1218	1255	1281	1306	1339	1372	1359
142			1027	1067	1105	1138	1171	1209	1246	1271	1296	1329	1362	1349
140			1018	1057	1095	1128	1161	1199	1237	1262	1287	1320	1352	1339
138			1008	1047	1085	1118	1151	1190	1228	1253	1277	1310	1342	1329
136			1001	1038	1075	1109	1142	1181	1219	1244	1268	1300	1332	1319
134		999	991	1028	1065	1099	1132	1171	1209	1234	1258	1290	1322	1309
132		981	983	1019	1055	1089	1122	1161	1200	1224	1248	1280	1311	1298
130		983	974	1010	1045	1079	1112	1152	1191	1215	1239	1270	1301	1288
128		974	965	1000	1035	1069	1102	1142	1182	1206	1229	1260	1291	1278
126	939	948	956	991	1025	1059	1092	1133	1173	1197	1220	1251	1281	1268
124	930	939	947	941	1015	1049	1082	1123	1164	1187	1210	1241	1271	1258
122	920	929	938	972	1005	1039	1073	1115	1155	1178	1201	1232	1261	1248
120	911	921	930	962	994	1029	1063	1107	1146	1169	1191	1222	1251	1238
118	902	912	921	953	984	1019	1053	1097	1137	1160	1182	1212	1241	1228
116	892	902	912	943	974	1009	1043	1085	1127	1150	1172	1202	1231	1218
114	883	893	903	934	964	999	1033	1076	1118	1141	1163	1192	1221	1209
112	874	884	894	924	954	989	1023	1066	1109	1131	1153	1182	1211	1199
110	864	875	886	905	944	979	1013	1057	1100	1122	1144	1173	1201	1189
108	855	866	877	906	934	969	1004	1048	1091	1113	1134	1163	1191	1179
106	845	857	868	896	924	959	994	1038	1082	1104	1125	1154	1181	1169
104	836	848	859	887	914	949	984	1029	1073	1094	1115	1144	1171	
102	827	839	850	877	904	939	974	1019	1064	1085	1106	1134	1161	
100	817	829	841	868	894	929	964	1009	1054	1075	1096	1124	1151	
98	808	821	833	859	884	919	954	1000	1045	1066	1087	1114	1141	
96	798	811	824	849	874	909	944	990	1036	1057	1077	1104	1131	
94	789	802	815	840	864	899	935	981	1027	1047	1068	1095	1121	
92	780	793	806	830	854	889	925	972	1018	1038	1058	1085	1111	
90	770	784	797	821	844	879	915	962	1009	1029	1049	1075	1101	
88	761	775	789	812	834	869	905	953	1000	1020	1039			
86	752	766	780	802	823	859	895	943	991	1011	1030			
84	742	757	771	792	813	849	885	933	981	1001	1020			
82	733	748	762	783	803	839	875	924	972	991	1010			
80	723	739	753	773	793	829	865	914	963	982				

Table 53 (continued)

Weight						Age								
	11	11½	12	12½	13	13½	14	14½	15	15½	16	16½	17	17½
78	714	729	744	764	783	820	856	905	954	973				
76	705	721	736	755	773	810	846	896	945					
74	695	711	727	745	763	800	836	886	936					
72	686	703	718	736	753	790	826	870						
70	677	693	709	726	743	780	816	866						
68	667	684	700	717	733	770	806							
66	658	675	692	708	723	760	796							
64	648	666	683	698	713	750								
62	639	657	674	689	703	740								
60	630	648	665	679	693									
58	620	638	656	670	683									
56	611	629	647											
Multi-plier	4.67	4.53	4.40	4.67	5.03	5.00	4.93	4.43	4.57	4.67	4.77	4.87	5.03	5.00

Weight						Age							
	18	19	20	21	22	23	24	25	26	27	28	29	30
176	1501	1471	1440	1409	1379	1348	1325	1310	1287	1272	1272	1256	1241
174	1492	1461	1431	1400	1370	1339	1317	1301	1278	1263	1263	1248	1233
172	1482	1452	1421	1391	1361	1331	1308	1293	1270	1255	1255	1240	1225
170	1472	1442	1419	1382	1352	1322	1299	1284	1262	1247	1247	1232	1217
168	1462	1432	1402	1373	1343	1313	1291	1276	1253	1238	1238	1223	1209
166	1452	1423	1393	1363	1334	1304	1282	1267	1245	1230	1230	1215	1200
164	1443	1413	1384	1354	1325	1295	1273	1259	1236	1222	1222	1207	1192
162	1433	1404	1374	1345	1316	1287	1265	1250	1228	1213	1213	1199	1184
160	1423	1394	1365	1336	1307	1278	1256	1241	1220	1205	1205	1191	1176
158	1413	1384	1355	1327	1298	1269	1247	1233	1211	1197	1197	1182	1168
156	1403	1375	1346	1317	1289	1260	1239	1224	1203	1189	1189	1174	1160
154	1394	1365	1337	1308	1280	1251	1230	1216	1194	1180	1180	1166	1152
152	1384	1356	1327	1299	1271	1243	1221	1207	1186	1172	1172	1158	1144
150	1374	1346	1318	1290	1262	1234	1213	1199	1178	1164	1164	1150	1136
148	1364	1336	1308	1281	1253	1225	1204	1190	1169	1155	1152	1141	1128
146	1354	1327	1299	1271	1244	1216	1195	1182	1161	1147	1147	1133	1124
144	1345	1317	1290	1262	1235	1207	1187	1173	1152	1139	1139	1125	1111
142	1335	1308	1280	1253	1226	1199	1178	1165	1144	1130	1130	1117	1103
140	1325	1298	1271	1244	1217	1190	1169	1156	1136	1122	1122	1109	1095
138	1315	1288	1261	1235	1208	1181	1161	1147	1127	1114	1114	1100	1087
136	1305	1279	1252	1225	1199	1172	1152	1139	1119	1106	1106	1092	1079
134	1296	1269	1243	1216	1190	1163	1144	1130	1110	1097	1097	1084	1071
132	1285	1259	1232	1206	1180	1154	1134	1121	1101	1088	1088	1075	1062
130	1275	1249	1223	1197	1171	1145	1125	1112	1093	1080	1080	1067	1054
128	1265	1239	1214	1188	1162	1136	1117	1104	1084	1072	1072	1059	1046
126	1255	1230	1204	1179	1153	1127	1108	1095	1076	1063	1063	1050	1038
124	1246	1220	1195	1169	1144	1118	1099	1087	1068	1055	1055	1042	1030
122	1236	1211	1185	1160	1135	1110	1091	1078	1059	1047	1047	1034	1021
120	1226	1201	1176	1151	1126	1101	1082	1070	1051	1038	1038	1026	1013

Table 53 (continued)

Weight	Age												
	18	19	20	21	22	23	24	25	26	27	28	29	30
118	1216	1191	1167	1142	1117	1092	1073	1061	1042	1030	1030	1018	1005
116	1206	1182	1157	1133	1108	1083	1065	1053	1034	1022	1022	1009	997
114	1197	1172	1148	1123	1099	1074	1056	1044	1026	1013	1013	1001	989
112	1187	1163	1138	1114	1090	1066	1048	1035	1017	1005	1005	993	981
110	1177	1153	1129	1105	1081	1057	1039	1027	1009	997	997	985	973
108	1167	1143	1120	1096	1072	1048	1030	1018	1000	989	989	977	965
106	1157	1134	1110	1087	1063	1039	1022	1010	992	980	980	968	957
Multi-plier	4.93	4.83	4.73	4.60	4.53	4.43	4.33	4.03	4.02	4.02	4.02	4.01	4.01

explained by the fact that power is force multiplied by velocity, and hence an increase in force results in an increase in power, which increase results in an increase in the speed of muscular contraction. The appropriate method of measuring power, however, is not by means of a strength test but by a direct measurement of power (see Chap. 9).

279. There are two general ways in which the results of the strength tests may be used: (1) as a measure of absolute or "raw" strength (strength score) and (2) in relation to norms of strength according to sex, age, and weight (strength quotient).[12]

280. Strength scores on an absolute basis (i.e., not relative to sex, age, and weight) are here expressed both in terms of unweighted items—unweighted-strength score—and weighted items—general-strength score and athletic-strength score. (The term "athletic strength" is a questionable one, and is meaningful only in connection with the definitions presented for it.)

281. The McCloy **Unweighted-strength Score,** which is the sum of the six items of the test, represents with a high degree of accuracy the total strength of the skeletal musculature with the exception of that of the muscles that flex the trunk and the thighs. It is useful for classification for performance in such events as football.

282. In the McCloy **Athletic-strength Score** the various items are weighted to give the maximum degree of correlation with performances in athletic events; hence, in so far as strength is important, this score may be used for the prediction of athletic ability. Either of the two following formulas[13] may be used for the computation of the McCloy Athletic-strength Score:

[12] Since Rogers' first publication on strength tests in 1925 the term here called "strength quotient" has been called the "physical-fitness index." The strength quotient is, actually, an achievement quotient. Also, the term "strength index" has been changed to "strength score."

[13] McCloy, "The Apparent Importance of Arm Strength in Athletics," *Research Quarterly,* March, 1934.

PRESENT STATUS

Table 54

ATHLETIC-STRENGTH TEST (LONG FORM): NORMS (BOYS)

Athletic-strength quotient = 100(athletic-strength score/norm for age and weight)

Weight	11	11½	12	12½	13	13½	14	14½	15	15½	16	16½	17	17½	18
218									819	822	825	830	835	833	831
216									811	815	818	824	829	827	825
214								806	804	808	812	817	823	821	819
212								798	797	801	805	811	816	815	813
210								791	789	794	798	804	810	809	808
208								783	782	787	792	798	804	803	802
206							776	775	775	780	785	792	798	797	796
204							768	768	768	773	778	785	791	791	790
202							760	760	760	766	772	779	785	785	785
200							752	753	753	759	765	772	779	779	779
198						729	744	745	746	752	758	766	773	773	773
196						721	736	737	739	745	751	759	766	767	767
194						713	728	730	731	738	745	753	760	761	762
192						705	720	722	724	731	738	746	754	755	756
190					684	697	712	714	717	724	731	740	748	749	750
188					676	689	704	707	709	716	725	733	741	743	744
186					668	681	696	699	702	710	718	727	735	737	739
184					660	673	688	691	695	703	711	720	729	731	733
182				623	652	665	680	684	687	696	705	714	723	725	727
180				615	644	657	672	676	680	689	698	707	716	719	721
178				608	636	649	663	668	673	682	691	701	710	713	716
176				601	628	641	655	661	666	675	684	694	704	707	710
174			567	593	620	633	647	653	658	668	678	688	698	701	704
172			560	586	612	626	639	645	651	661	671	682	692	695	699
170			553	579	604	618	631	638	644	654	664	675	685	689	693
168			546	571	596	610	623	630	636	647	658	669	679	683	687
166		491	539	564	589	602	615	622	629	640	651	662	673	677	681
164		485	532	556	581	594	607	615	622	633	644	656	666	671	676
162		479	525	549	573	586	599	607	614	626	638	649	660	665	670
160		473	518	541	565	578	591	599	607	619	631	643	654	659	664
158	422	467	511	534	557	570	583	592	600	612	624	636	648	653	658
156	417	461	504	526	549	562	575	584	593	605	617	630	642	647	653
154	412	455	497	519	541	554	567	576	585	598	611	623	635	641	647
152	407	449	490	511	533	546	559	569	578	591	604	617	629	635	641
150	402	443	483	504	525	538	551	561	571	584	597	610	623	629	635
148	398	437	476	497	517	530	543	554	563	577	591	604	617	623	630
146	393	431	468	489	510	522	535	546	556	570	584	597	610	617	624
144	388	425	461	482	502	514	527	538	549	563	577	591	604	611	618
142	383	419	454	474	494	506	519	531	541	556	571	584	598	605	612
140	378	413	447	467	486	498	511	523	534	549	564	578	592	599	607

(1) Right grip + left grip + .1 back lift + .1 leg lift + 2 pull-up-strength score[14] + dip-strength score[14] −3 weight

(2) Right grip + left grip + 2 pull-up-strength score[14] + dip-strength score[14] − 3 weight

An r of .914 has been obtained between the athletic-strength score computed according to the first formula and a valid measure of general-athletic ability, and an r of .911 between the athletic-strength score computed according to the second formula and a valid measure of

[14] (1) Table 54 (pp. 142-43). (2) Table 55 (pp. 144-45).

Table 54 (continued)

Weight	11	11½	12	12½	13	13½	14	14½	15	15½	16	16½	17	17½	18
138	373	407	440	459	478	490	503	515	527	542	557	572	585	593	601
136	368	401	433	452	470	482	495	508	519	535	550	565	579	587	595
134	363	395	426	444	462	474	487	500	512	528	544	559	573	581	589
132	358	389	419	437	454	466	479	492	505	521	537	552	567	575	584
130	353	383	412	429	446	458	471	485	498	514	530	546	560	569	578
128	349	377	405	422	438	450	463	477	490	507	524	539	554	563	572
126	344	371	398	414	431	442	455	469	483	500	517	533	548	557	567
124	339	365	391	407	423	434	447	462	476	493	510	526	542	551	561
122	334	360	384	400	415	427	439	454	468	486	504	520	536	545	555
120	329	354	377	392	407	419	431	446	461	479	497	513	529	539	549
118	324	348	370	385	399	411	423	439	454	472	490	507	523	533	544
116	319	342	363	377	391	403	415	431	447	465	483	500	517	527	538
114	314	336	356	370	383	395	407	423	439	458	477	494	511	521	532
112	309	330	349	362	375	387	399	416	432	451	470	487	504	515	526
110	304	324	342	355	367	379	391	408	425	444	463	481	498	509	521
108	300	318	335	347	359	371	383	400	417	437	457	474	492	503	
106	295	312	328	340	352	363	375	393	410	430	450	468	486	497	
104	290	306	321	332	344	355	367	385	403	423	443	462	479		
102	285	300	314	325	336	347	359	377	395	416	437	455	473		
100	280	294	307	317	328	339	351	370	388	409	430	449			
98	275	288	300	310	320	331	343	362	381	402	423	442			
96	270	282	293	303	312	323	335	354	374	395	416				
94	265	276	286	295	304	315	327	347	366	388	410				
92	260	270	279	288	296	307	319	339	359	381					
90	255	264	272	280	288	299	311	331	352	374					
88	251	258	265	273	281	291	303	324	345						
86	246	252	258	265	273	283	295	316	337						
84	241	246	251	258	265	275	287	308							
82	236	240	244	250	257	267	279	301							
80	231	234	237	243	249	259	271								
78	226	228	230	235	241	251	263								
76	222	222	223	228	234	243									
74	217	216	216	220	226	235									
72	212	210	209	213	218										
70	207	204	202	205	210										
68	202	198	195	198											
66	197	192	188	190											
64	192	186	181												
62	187	180	174												
60	182	175													
Multiplier	2.45	2.98	3.51	3.73	3.95	3.98	4.01	3.83	3.65	3.50	3.35	3.235	3.12	3.00	2.87

general-athletic ability. Hence, for the prediction of athletic ability, the shorter formula (the second) is almost as accurate as the longer formula (the first).

283. McCloy General-strength and Pure-strength Scores. In factorial analyses of strength tests two elements have been identified: (1) "pure" strength and (2) strength dependent upon the size of the body. Pure strength may be computed from the following formula for males only: .5 (left grip + right grip) + .1 back lift + .1 leg lift + McCloy Pull-up-

Table 55

ATHLETIC–STRENGTH TEST (SHORT FORM): NORMS (BOYS)

Athletic–strength quotient = 100 (athletic–strength score/norm for age and weight)

Weight	Age, Years														
	11	11½	12	12½	13	13½	14	14½	15	15½	16	16½	17	17½	18
218									703	706	710	714	719	722	725
216									696	700	704	709	714	716	720
214								692	690	694	698	703	708	711	715
212								685	683	688	692	697	703	705	709
210								678	677	681	687	692	697	700	704
208								671	671	675	681	686	692	695	699
206							666	665	664	669	675	680	686	689	693
204							659	658	658	663	669	674	681	684	688
202							652	651	651	657	663	669	675	678	683
200							645	645	645	651	657	663	670	673	677
198						625	638	638	639	645	651	657	664	668	672
196						618	631	631	632	638	645	652	659	662	667
194						611	624	625	626	632	639	646	653	657	662
192						604	617	618	620	626	633	640	648	651	656
190					584	597	610	611	613	620	628	635	642	646	651
188					577	590	602	604	607	614	622	629	637	641	646
186					570	583	595	598	600	608	616	623	631	635	640
184					563	576	588	591	594	601	610	617	626	630	635
182				529	556	569	581	584	588	595	604	612	620	624	630
180				522	549	562	574	578	581	589	598	606	615	619	624
178				516	542	555	567	571	575	583	592	600	609	614	619
176				510	535	548	560	564	568	577	586	595	604	608	614
174			478	503	528	541	553	557	562	571	580	589	598	603	609
172			472	497	521	534	546	551	556	565	574	583	593	597	603
170			466	490	514	527	539	544	549	558	569	578	587	592	598
168			460	484	507	520	532	537	543	552	563	572	582	587	593
166		409	454	477	500	513	525	530	536	546	557	566	576	581	587
164		404	448	471	494	506	518	524	530	540	551	560	571	576	582
162		399	442	464	487	499	511	517	524		545	555	565	570	577
160		393	436	458	480	492	504	510	517	528	539	549	560	565	571
158	347	388	430	451	473	485	497	504	511	522	533	543	554	560	566
156	343	383	424	455	466	478	490	497	504	515	527	538	549	554	561
154	339	378	418	438	459	471	483	490	498	509	521	532	543	549	556
152	335	373	412	432	452	464	476	483	492	503	515	526	538	543	550
150	331	368	406	425	445	457	469	477	485	497	510	521	532	538	545

strength Score + McCloy Dip-strength Score. If strength is used as a measure of general-motor achievement, the formula for the pure-strength score is probably more useful than either of the formulas for the athletic-strength score. The measurement of pure strength is especially useful for certain types of research in motor activities. No norms are available for the pure-strength score.

284. Strength relative to sex, age, and weight may be expressed in terms of a general-strength quotient or an athletic-strength quotient (males only).

285. The **general-strength quotient** is obtained by the division of the unweighted-strength score by the norm for strength according to sex, age, and weight (Table 52, pp. 136-38 or Table 53, pp. 139-41)[15] and by the

[15] If the leg lift is executed according to Rogers' directions, the methods and the norms for the Rogers Test should be used (footnote 2).

Table 55 (continued)

Weight	Age, Years														
	11	11½	12	12½	13	13½	14	14½	15	15½	16	16½	17	17½	18
148	327	363	400	419	438	450	462	470	479	491	504	515	527	533	540
146	322	358	393	413	431	443	455	463	472	485	498	509	521	527	534
144	318	353	387	406	425	436	448	457	466	478	492	503	516	522	529
142	314	348	381	400	418	429	441	450	460	472	486	498	510	516	524
140	310	343	375	393	411	422	434	443	453	466	480	492	505	511	518
138	306	338	369	387	404	415	426	436	447	460	474	486	499	506	513
136	302	333	363	380	397	408	419	430	440	454	468	481	494	500	508
134	298	327	357	374	390	401	412	423	434	448	462	475	488	495	503
132	294	322	351	367	383	394	405	416	428	442	456	469	483	489	497
130	290	317	345	361	376	388	398	410	421	435	451	464	477	484	492
128	286	312	339	354	369	381	391	403	415	429	445	458	472	479	487
126	281	307	333	348	362	374	384	396	408	423	439	452	466	473	481
124	277	302	327	341	356	367	377	389	402	417	433	446	461	468	476
122	273	297	321	335	349	360	370	383	396	411	427	441	455	462	471
120	269	292	315	328	342	353	363	376	389	405	421	435	450	457	465
118	265	287	309	322	335	346	356	369	383	399	415	429	444	452	460
116	261	282	303	315	328	339	349	362	376	392	409	424	439	446	455
114	257	277	296	309	321	332	342	356	370	386	403	418	433	441	450
112	253	272	290	302	314	325	335	349	364	380	397	412	428	435	444
110	249	266	284	296	307	318	328	342	357	374	392	407	422	430	439
108	245	261	278	289	300	311	321	336	351	368	386	401	417	425	
106	240	256	272	283	293	304	314	329	344	362	380	395	411	419	
104	236	251	266	276	287	297	307	322	338	355	374	389	406		
102	232	246	260	270	280	290	300	315	332	349	368	384	400		
100	228	241	254	263	273	283	293	309	325	343	362	378			
98	224	236	248	257	266	276	286	302	319	337	356	372			
96	220	231	242	251	259	269	279	295	313	331	350				
94	216	226	236	244	252	262	272	289	306	325	344				
92	212	221	230	238	245	255	265	282	300	319					
90	208	216	224	231	238	248	258	275	293	312					
88	204	211	218	225	232	241	251	268	287						
86	199	206	212	218	225	234	244	262	281						
84	195	201	206	212	218	227	237	255							
82	191	196	200	205	211	220	230	249							
80	186	191	194	199	204	213	223								
78	183	186	188	192	197	206	216								
76	179	181	182	186	191	199									
74	174	176	176	179	184	192									
72	170	170	170	173	177										
70	166	165	164	166	170										
68	162	160	157	160											
66	158	155	151	153											
64	154	150	145												
62	150	145	139												
60	146	140													
Multiplier	2.05	2.54	3.03	3.24	3.45	3.49	3.52	3.36	3.20	3.07	2.95	2.85	2.75	2.70	2.65

multiplication of this value by 100. Thus, a person with a strength quotient of 100 is average in strength for his sex, age, and weight, while a person with a strength quotient of 120 is, in respect to strength, 20 per cent above average for his sex, age, and weight.

286. The McCloy Athletic-strength Quotient is obtained by the division of the McCloy Athletic-strength Score by the norm for strength according to age and weight (Table 54, pp. 142-43 or Table 55, pp. 144-45), and by the multiplication of this value by 100.

In view of the fact that pull-up strength alone is very highly correlated

PRESENT STATUS
Table 56
PULL–UP–STRENGTH TEST: NORM BOYS

Pull–up–strength quotient = 100 (pull–up–strength/norm for age and weight)

Weight	11	11½	12	12½	13	13½	14	14½	15	15½	16	16½	17	17½	18
218									357	357	355	355	355	355	354
216									353	353	352	352	352	352	351
214									351	350	349	349	349	349	348
212								348	347	346	345	345	346	346	345
210								344	343	343	342	342	343	343	342
208								341	340	340	339	339	340	340	339
206							339	337	336	336	336	336	337	337	336
204							335	334	333	333	333	333	333	333	333
202							332	330	330	330	329	329	330	330	330
200							328	327	326	326	326	326	327	327	327
198						322	325	324	323	323	323	323	324	324	324
196						319	321	321	320	320	320	320	321	321	321
194						315	318	317	316	316	317	317	318	318	318
192						312	314	314	313	313	313	314	315	315	315
190					306	308	310	310	310	310	310	311	312	312	312
188					302	304	307	307	306	306	307	308	309	309	309
186					299	301	303	303	303	303	304	305	306	306	306
184					295	297	300	300	300	300	301	302	303	303	303
182				288	292	294	296	296	296	296	297	298	300	300	300
180				284	288	290	292	292	293	293	294	295	297	297	297
178				281	285	287	289	289	289	290	291	292	293	293	294
176				277	281	283	285	285	286	287	288	289	290	290	291
174			270	274	278	280	282	282	283	284	285	286	287	287	288
172			267	270	274	276	278	278	279	280	281	282	284	284	285
170			263	267	271	273	275	275	276	277	278	279	281	281	282
168			260	263	267	269	271	272	273	274	275	277	278	278	279
166		251	257	260	264	266	268	268	269	270	272	273	275	275	276
164		248	253	256	260	262	264	265	266	267	269	270	272	272	273
162		245	250	253	257	259	261	262	263	264	265	267	269	269	270
160		241	246	249	253	255	257	258	259	260	262	264	266	266	267
158	233	238	243	246	250	252	254	255	256	257	259	261	263	263	264
156	230	235	240	243	246	248	250	251	252	254	256	258	260	260	261
154	227	231	236	239	243	245	247	248	249	251	253	254	256	257	258
152	224	228	233	236	239	241	243	244	246	247	249	251	253	254	255
150	221	225	230	233	236	238	240	241	242	244	246	248	250	251	252

with performance in athletic sports, norms for pull-up strength are given in Table 56, pp. 146-47.

287. In an unpublished study[16] it was found that physicians' estimates of the health status of children were markedly influenced by the appearance of strength; that is, if the physician found minor or no defects in the person being examined, he was likely to rate the child's health as superior, average, or inferior according to the child's appearance in strength. These ratings, then, were highly correlated with strength quotients. In another unpublished study[17] the strength quotients of one hundred boys without any medical defects listed in their medical examination records were compared with the strength quotients of one hundred boys having moderate or serious medical defects. The average strength

[16] By McCloy.
[17] Ibid.

Table 56 (continued)

Weight	Age, Years														
	11	11½	12	12½	13	13½	14	14½	15	15½	16	16½	17	17½	18
148	218	222	226	229	232	234	236	237	239	241	243	245	247	248	249
146	214	219	223	226	229	231	233	234	236	238	240	242	244	245	246
144	211	215	219	222	225	227	229	230	232	234	237	239	241	242	243
142	208	212	216	219	222	224	226	227	229	231	233	235	238	239	240
140	205	209	213	215	218	220	222	224	226	228	230	232	235	236	237
138	202	205	209	212	215	217	219	220	222	224	227	229	232	233	234
136	199	202	206	208	211	213	215	217	219	221	224	226	229	230	231
134	195	199	203	205	208	210	212	214	216	218	221	223	226	227	228
132	192	195	199	201	204	206	208	210	212	214	217	220	223	224	225
130	189	192	196	198	201	202	204	206	209	211	214	217	220	221	222
128	186	189	192	194	197	199	201	203	205	208	211	213	216	217	219
126	183	186	189	191	194	195	197	199	202	205	208	210	213	214	216
124	180	183	186	188	190	192	194	196	199	202	205	207	210	211	213
122	176	179	182	184	187	188	190	192	195	198	201	204	207	208	210
120	173	176	179	181	183	185	187	189	192	195	198	201	204	205	207
118	170	172	175	177	180	181	183	186	189	192	195	198	201	202	204
116	167	169	172	174	176	178	180	182	185	188	192	195	198	199	201
114	164	166	169	171	173	174	176	179	182	185	189	192	195	196	198
112	161	163	165	167	169	171	173	176	179	182	185	188	192	193	195
110	158	160	162	164	166	167	169	172	175	178	182	185	189	190	192
108	154	156	159	160	162	164	166	169	172	175	179	182	186	187	
106	151	153	155	157	159	160	162	165	168	172	176	179	183	184	
104	148	150	152	153	155	157	159	162	165	169	173	175	179		
102	145	146	148	150	152	153	155	158	162	165	169	172	176		
100	142	143	145	146	148	149	152	155	158	162	166	169			
98	139	140	142	143	145	146	148	151	155	159	163	166			
96	136	137	139	140	142	142	144	148	152	156	160				
94	133	133	135	136	138	139	141	144	148	152	157				
92	130	130	132	133	135	135	137	141	145	149					
90	126	127	128	129	131	132	134	137	142	146					
88	123	124	125	126	128	128	130	134	138						
86	120	120	122	122	124	125	127	130	135						
84	117	117	119	119	121	121	123	127							
82	114	113	115	115	117	118	120	123							
80	111	110	112	112	114	114	116								
78	107	107	108	108	110	111	113								
76	104	104	105	105	107	107									
74	101	100	102	101	103	104									
72	98	97	98	98	99										
70	95	94	95	94	96										
68	92	90	92	91											
66	88	87	88	88											
64	85	84	85												
62	82	81	81												
60	79	77													
Multiplier	1.58	1.64	1.69	1.72	1.75	1.76	1.76	1.72	1.68	1.64	1.60	1.57	1.54	1.52	1.50

quotient of the boys with defects was slightly higher than that of the boys with no defects, and the distributions were almost identical. The differences between the strength quotients of the two groups were not statistically significant. By such findings, doubt is cast upon certain conclusions arrived at in other studies[18] to the effect that strength and health are highly correlated.

[18] Carl G. Chamberlain and Dean F. Smiley, "Functional Health and the Physical Fitness Index," *Research Quarterly*, March, 1931, Part II.

V. F. Hernlund, "The Selection of Physical Tests for Measuring Y.M.C.A. Secretaries," *Supplement to Research Quarterly*, March, 1935. The findings in this study were re-analyzed by McCloy.

288. Since strength is one of the most important elements in motor performance, the strength quotient is an excellent measure of a person's general ability to work. A person who is deficient in strength, whether this deficiency is due to overweight or to insufficient muscle, or to both conditions, is affected by chronic fatigue, and hence probably has an increased susceptibility to common infections. Therefore strength tests, which are excellent motivators for the improvement of physical condition, should be used, both for young people and for adults, as a routine measure of general-physical status.[19]

289. The following formula[20] has been devised for the prediction of the probable maximum strength that a person can develop: **Lookabaugh Potential-strength Score** = 20.02 chest circumference (cm.) + 176.88 elbow width (cm.) + 85.9 knee width (cm.) − 1529.[21] Such a score is useful for predictive purposes in such sports as football and wrestling.

290. Administration. The necessary instruments are arranged around the room in the order in which they will be used. At the first station is a

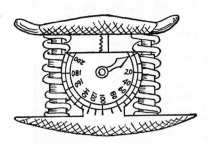

FIGURE XVII. Grip Dynamometer

beam scale or a spring scale. At the second station[22] is a grip dynamometer. At the third station is a back-and-leg dynamometer. At the fourth station are parallel bars (boys) or a stall-bar bench (girls) or any stool thirteen inches high, twenty inches long, and fourteen inches wide (girls). At the fifth station is a horizontal bar. The fourth station and the fifth station may be reversed. There should be a five-minute rest period between the pull-ups and the push-ups. There should be a trained assistant and a recorder at each station. It is possible to test about forty persons in one class period.

291. *Grip.* Magnesium carbonate should be rubbed on the hands. The grip dynamometer (Fig. XVII, p. 148), with the indicator toward the palm (to prevent the finger tips from stopping the indicator), should be placed in the hand. The edge of the dynamometer with the ends curved upward should be against the fingers and the rounded edge against the base of the hand. With the body in any

[19] McCloy, "How about Some Muscle?" *Journal of Health and Physical Education,* May, 1936.

―――, *Philosophical Bases for Physical Education,* Chap. 4.

[20] Guy Lookabaugh, "The Prediction of Total Potential Strength of Adult Males from Skeletal Build," *Research Quarterly,* May, 1937.

[21] Detailed descriptions of the technique of taking these measurements may be found in: McCloy, *Appraising Physical Status: The Selection of the Measurements.* See also Chapter 28.

[22] If breathing capacity is included in the test, a spirometer is located at the second station, and the instruments designated for the second, third, and fourth stations are located at the third, fourth and fifth stations, respectively.

desired position, the subject should grip the dynamometer as vigorously as possible. The hand and fingers must not rest against the body or against any object. A second trial is permitted if it is desired.

292. Back lift. For the sake of convenience in reading the record registered on the dial, the back-and-leg dynamometer (Fig. XVIII, p. 149) should be placed on a small elevated platform. The dynamometer should in no case be attached to the

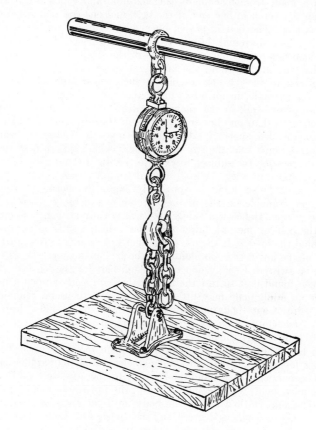

FIGURE XVIII. Back-and-leg Dynamometer

platform. The subject stands at attention with the center of the feet opposite the chain[23] and with the hands on the fronts of the thighs. The tester then hooks the handle into the chain so that the top of the bar is just below the tips of the subject's fingers. The subject is instructed as follows. Bend the trunk forward at the hips, and, with one palm facing forward and one palm facing backward, grasp the bar at the ends. Wrap the hands partially around the bar in order to gain as much aid from the friction of the skin of the hands as possible. Lift steadily (without a jerk) but as vigorously as possible. After having exerted a

---

[23] If the subject stands too far forward, he tips backward, and if he stands too far backward, he can increase the leverage by swaying backward and hence "make" a spuriously large lift.

maximum lift, release the pull rather slowly. The amount of the lift is read on the dial of the dynamometer. Since the first trial is usually better than subsequent ones, it is usually unnecessary to give more than one trial.

293. *Leg lift.* The subject stands at attention with the center of the feet opposite the chain. The bar is placed across the fronts of the subject's thighs in the angle formed by the thighs and the trunk. It is strapped in place with a belt, which is made from machine-belting material and which is 2.5 to 3 inches wide. A loop is riveted in one end of the belt, and one end of the bar is slipped through this loop. The belt is passed over the sacrum to the other end of the bar where it is looped around the end of the bar and pulled tight. The bar should be long enough not to slip out of the loops of the strap. The chain should be so adjusted that the angle behind the knee is as near 120 degrees as possible. A variation of ten to twenty degrees in the angle causes the lift to be changed markedly; for example, in an adult male, the difference in the angle resulting from the use of one link in the chain instead of an adjacent link may cause a difference of more than one hundred pounds in the lift. This direction concerning the recommended angle of 120 degrees behind the knee is in conflict with the recommendation[24] that the size of the angle behind the knee be just enough under 180 degrees for the subject to execute the lift without completely extending the lower and upper legs. A lift executed from a position in which the angle behind the knee is so large is spuriously high. Furthermore, most of the dynamometers available on the market stretch considerably when pulled by a very strong person. Hence if a subject is exceptionally strong, it is usually best to adjust the belt to one link lower than that which results in an angle of 120 degrees behind the knee.[25] If the use of another link results in too great a change in the size of the angle (e.g., in children), the higher link may be used and the chain may be twisted. Usually one trial is sufficient for the leg lift.

It has been found best to rest the bar on the bare skin or upon a pad of soft cloth. Since an adult male may lift as much as two thousand pounds with his legs (a pressure of one thousand pounds on each thigh), a slight slipping of the bar over coarse cloth, such as khaki trousers, may tear the surface of the skin. No back or leg lift should be administered to any subject who has a heart defect or a hernia, or who has been operated upon recently.

294. *Dips for boys.* The subject stands at one end of the parallel bars, grasps the bars, one bar with each hand, and jumps to the cross-rest position. At the end of this movement, which counts one dip, the forearms should be completely extended. The subject then lowers the body until the angle in front of each of the elbows is less than ninety degrees, and then pushes the body up until the forearms are again completely extended. These movements should be repeated as many times as possible. The trunk should be approximately in a straight line with the legs, and under no circumstances should a jerk or kick be permitted, although a moderate flexion of the thighs may be permitted. The subject may do the exercise as rapidly as he wishes. If he does not go down to the prescribed position, or all the way up to a straight-arm position, only half a credit is given. After four successive half credits the exercise is stopped, and the subject retested later.

295. *Push-ups for girls.* The subject is instructed to flex the forearms and,

[24] Edgar W. Everts and Gordon J. Hathaway, "The Use of a Belt to Measure Leg Strength Improves the Administration of Physical Fitness Tests," *Research Quarterly,* October, 1938.

[25] A back-and-leg dynamometer that stretches very little has been devised by the C. H. Stoelting Company, 424 North Homan Avenue, Chicago 24. With this dynamometer the 120-degree angle may be used for all subjects.

keeping the trunk straight, to lower the body until the upper part of the chest touches the edge of the stall-bar bench; and then to raise the body until the forearms are completely extended. In no case should the subject be permitted to raise and lower the hips out of line with the shoulders and the feet. If the body sways or arches, or if the subject does not go down to the prescribed position or does not raise the body until the forearms are completely extended, only half a credit is given.

296. *Pull-ups for boys.* At least five minutes should elapse between the dips and the pull-ups. Either a horizontal bar or a pair of small rings attached to a horizontal bar may be used. The subject is instructed to hang, by the hands, from the bar or the rings, using either the forward or the reverse grasp, and to pull the body upward until the chin is even with the hands or over the bar, and then to lower the body until the arms are straight. The subject is not permitted to kick, jerk, or use a "kip" motion. Any such maneuver or the failure to go down until the arms are straight or up to the prescribed position counts half a movement. After four consecutive half movements the exercise is stopped, and the subject retested later. The subject is permitted to do the exercise as rapidly or as slowly as he desires. Strong boys usually prefer to perform quite rapidly at the beginning of the exercise. In both pull-ups and dips the counting should be aloud, and the subject should be encouraged both before beginning the exercise and during the exercise to continue as long as possible.

297. *Pull-ups for girls.* The horizontal bar or the rings should be adjusted to about the height of the bottom of the sternum. The subject is instructed to grasp the bar with the palms upward and to slide the feet under the bar until the legs and the trunk are completely extended and until the arms are ninety degrees from the chest. The weight of the body should rest on the heels. It is well to have someone place a foot sidewise under the subject's insteps to prevent the subject's feet from sliding on the mat. Keeping the trunk extended, the subject pulls the body upward to the bar or the rings as many times

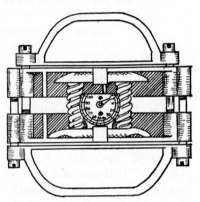

FIGURE XIX. Grip Dynamometer with Push-and-pull Attachment

as possible. If the hips sag or rise during the performance, the movement counts half a credit.

298. *Pushing strength.* The hand dynamometer is placed between the jaws of the push-and-pull attachment (Fig. XIX, p. 151). With the palms of the hands facing each other and at the height of the chest and with the forearms almost horizontal, the subject is instructed to grasp the handles of the push-and-pull attachment and to push on the handles as vigorously as possible.

299. *Pulling strength.* The positions for pulling strength are the same as those for pushing strength. The subject is instructed to pull on the handles as vigorously as possible.[26]

[26] Purchasers of strength-testing equipment should note that inaccurate calibration of dynamometers is very common. All dynamometers used should be carefully tested about every second year.

To test the back-and-leg dynamometer, the instrument is suspended by the bottom, usually from a horizontal bar. Different weights are then hung from the chain. It is usually satisfactory to use weights of approximately 100 lbs., 300 lbs., 500 lbs., 800

300. *Scoring.* A recommended type of score card, together with directions for the scoring, may be found in Figure XX (p. 152).

		Pounds
Name	John E. Davis	
Date	February 23, 1951	
Age	´16 years, 8 months	
Weight	133 pounds	

		Pounds
Right grip		105
Left grip		100
Back lift		325
Leg lift with belt		880
Pull-ups	Number = 12 (Table 45, p. 130)*	230
Dips	Number = 9 (Table 45, p. 130)**	220
		———
Strength score		1860
Norm	(Table 52, pp. 136-38)***	1533
Strength quotient		121

  * For girls, Table 51, p. 134 (Pulling strength)
 ** For girls, Table 51, p. 134 (Pushing strength)
*** For girls, Table 53, pp. 139-41

FIGURE XX. Strength Test: Sample Score Card
(Senior-high-school Boy)

Age. An age of 16 years and 1 to 5 months is recorded as 16 years. An age of 16 years and 6 to 11 months is recorded as 16.5 years.

Grips, leg lift, back lift. The strengths for these three items are recorded to the nearest pound from the readings on the dials of the dynamometers.

Pull-ups, dips, push-ups. If the pulling-and-pushing strengths are used instead of pull-ups and dips (push-ups for girls), the pulling-strength score and the pushing-strength score are, for boys, converted into the McCloy Pull-up-dip-strength Score by the use of Table 50 (p. 133), and, for girls, by the use of Table 51 (p. 134). If, for example, the pulling-strength score for a boy is 67 pounds and the pushing-strength score is 84 pounds, the McCloy Pull-up-dip-strength Score is 572 pounds.

If, in pull-ups, the subject cannot flex his (or her) forearms at all, the pull-up-strength score is taken to be half of the subject's weight. If the weight is 133 pounds, the McCloy Pull-up-strength Score is 66.5 pounds. If the subject can flex the forearms even slightly, the pull-up-strength score is the same as the subject's weight (for girls, .67 the weight). If the

---

lbs., 1200 lbs., and 1600 lbs. The weights are carefully weighed on an accurate scale and the forces registered on the dynamometer noted. The actual weights are plotted against the registered weights on a graph, and a curve is fitted to the results. A conversion chart is then readily prepared for dynamometers with systematic errors.

The grip dynamometer may be calibrated by placing it in the push-and-pull attachment, tying one handle to the horizontal bar, and hanging known weights varying from 10 lbs. to about 170 lbs. at twenty-pound intervals. The results are plotted and a conversion chart prepared.

weight is 133 pounds, the pull-up-strength score for boys is 133 pounds. If the subject can flex his forearms ninety degrees, the pull-up-strength score is 1.77 times the subject's weight minus 46 pounds. If the weight is 133 pounds, the pull-up-strength score is 189.4 pounds (for girls, .67 weight + 52).

If, in dips, the subject is unable to raise the body at all, the dip-strength (push-up-strength score for girls) score is that for half of the subject's weight. If the weight is 133 pounds, the dip-strength score is 66.5 pounds. If the subject can push the body up at all, the dip-strength score is the same as the subject's weight. If the weight is 133 pounds, the dip-strength score is 133 pounds. (If a girl can lift her chest away from the stall-bar bench, but cannot completely extend the forearms, the push-up-strength score is .78 of the girl's weight.) If the subject can raise the body half of the way, the dip-strength score is 1.77 times his weight minus 46 pounds. If the weight is 133 pounds, the dip-strength score is 143.4 pounds (for girls, .78 weight + 74).

301. OTHER TYPES OF STRENGTH TESTS

The strength tests that are discussed in this section concern primarily the measurement of the strength of muscles that have atrophied as a result of injuries to the nerves (e.g., the effects of poliomyelitis) or as a result of disuse (e.g., the effects of long bedrest during an illness). Hence these tests will be of interest primarily to persons working in remedial programs in the schools and in reconditioning or corrective-therapy programs in hospitals.

These strength tests may be divided into two types, "active" or pulling strength, and "breaking" strength. The strength tests of the active or pulling type are those, like the Intercollegiate, the Rogers, and the McCloy Tests, in which the subject attempts to contract his muscles to move or overcome the resistance of the dynamometer. In the "breaking" strength type, the tester exerts a force while the subject resists the pull as much as possible until his strength is overcome by the force, and he "breaks" or gives way. This breaking strength is registered automatically on a dial on the dynamometer.

302. TESTS OF ACTIVE OR PULLING STRENGTH

303. Manual testing.[27] The subject tries to perform a designated movement against strong resistance offered by the tester and against gravity. If he succeeds, the function of the muscle group is considered to be "normal." The subject tries to perform a designated movement against moderate resistance offered by the tester, and against gravity. If he succeeds, the function of the muscle group is considered to be "good." The subject tries to perform a designated movement against gravity only. If

[27] Lucille Daniels and Others, *Muscle Testing, Techniques of Manual Examination.*

he succeeds, the function of the muscle group is considered to be "fair." The subject tries to perform a designated movement with the influence of gravity eliminated by the tester. If he succeeds, the function of the muscle group is considered to be "poor." If he cannot perform the movement but there is some hardening of the muscles, the function of the muscle group is indicated by "trace." If there is no hardening of the muscles, the function of the muscle group is indicated by "zero."

304. Progressive resistance.[28] A type of test frequently used by orthopedic surgeons is the number of times a weight can be moved by a group of muscles. Not infrequently the effort is made to determine what amount of weight can be moved ten times, which amount is about three fourths of that which can be moved once. Such a method devised by DeLorme[29] involves the use of a complicated table with various pulleys and weights that can be adapted to the testing of almost any group of muscles that function together. With a little ingenuity, the tester can usually obtain equally good results with adjustable dumbbells, iron boots, and barbells.

305. The **Kellogg Strength Test**[30] is one of the most complete tests of strength available. By means of the Kellogg Dynamometer the strength of almost any group of muscles can be measured. Since the dynamometer costs over four hundred dollars and since about half an hour is required for the administration of the test to one person, the Kellogg Test is not discussed further in this book.[31]

306. The **Clarke Test**[32] utilizes a "tensiometer," an instrument used in measuring cable tension in airplane cables. In the reference cited, directions for measuring the strengths of thirty-eight groups of muscles are given. In order to decrease the amount of fatigue of such testing on the tester, there has been devised a table, together with numerous hooks, so positioned as to simplify the procedure of the testing. This apparatus is illustrated in a separate publication.[33] No standards for the strengths of various groups of muscles have been published. The method of securing such standards given in Table 57 (p. 160) may well be used in connection with the testing discussed in this section.

307. Tests of Breaking Strength. The breaking strength of a group of

[28] Thomas L. DeLorme and Arthur L. Watkins, *Progressive Resistance Exercise.*

[29] *Ibid.*

[30] J. H. Kellogg, "The Value of Strength Tests in the Prescription of Exercise," *Modern Medicine Library, II.*

[31] Details concerning the Kellogg Test, and norms for adults may be obtained from the Battle Creek Sanitarium, Battle Creek, Michigan.

[32] Clarke, "Objective Strength Tests of Affected Muscle Groups Involved in Orthopedic Disabilities," *Research Quarterly,* May, 1948.

———, *Cable-Tension Strength Tests.*

The tensiometer is obtainable from the Pacific Scientific Company, 1430 Grande Vista Avenue, Los Angeles 23, California.

[33] Clarke and Others, "Relationship between Body Position and the Application of Muscle Power to Movements of the Joints," *Archives of Physical Medicine,* February, 1950.

muscles that function together is usually 25 per cent greater than the pulling strength of the same group of muscles.[34]

308. The **Martin Test**[35] is the best known of the tests used for measuring such breaking strength. For administering this test an inexpensive dynamometer[36] that resembles spring scales for weighing ice is used. A leather loop is fastened to one end of the dynamometer, and a handle to the other end. The leather loop is placed around the limb of the subject to be tested. The tester pulls on the handle until the subject, who resists as much as possible the pull of the tester, gives way or "breaks." This "breaking" strength is registered automatically on a dial on the dynamometer. A grip dynamometer (see Sec. 291) with a push-and-pull attachment may be used instead of the Martin Dynamometer. A strap is fastened to one handle of the attachment, and the other handle is pulled. The Clarke Cable Tensiometer (see Sec. 306) may also be used for measuring breaking strength.

Two persons administer the Martin Test: the adjuster and the operator. The duties of the adjuster are to place the loop in the designated position about the arm or the leg, support the loop with one hand, and, if necessary, support the arm or the leg of the subject with the other hand. The adjuster gives the command "Hold back," to mark the beginning of the pull, and "Stop," to mark the end. The operator holds the handle of the dynamometer in his right hand, and the body of the dynamometer in his left hand.

After the loop has been adjusted, the adjuster gives the command "Hold back." At this command, the subject contracts as vigorously as possible the group of muscles being tested, and simultaneously the operator pulls upon the dynamometer. Tension must be developed as rapidly as possible *without jerking,* and must be increased until the resistance of the subject is actually overcome. At the command "Stop," the pull is immediately discontinued. The scale is read at once, and the reading is recorded by an assisting clerk. The sliding indicator of the scale is then returned to the 0 position. Great care should be taken not to continue the pull after the muscles have actually yielded.

No group of muscles that are reported by the subject to be sore should be tested.

(1) *Muscles that plantarflex the foot.* The subject lies on his back on a smooth table. To serve as a foot brace, a stout transverse cleat about three inches high is firmly fixed to the foot of the table The subject steadies himself by holding to the edges of the table with both hands and by firmly pressing, against the foot brace, the heel of the foot not being tested. The foot to be tested

[34] Albrecht Bethe, "Aktive und passive Kraft menschlicher Muskeln," *Ergebnisse der Physiologie,* 1925.

[35] E. G. Martin, "Tests of Muscular Efficiency," *Physiological Reviews,* July, 1921.

[36] Obtainable (stock number 100A) from John Chatillon and Sons, 85 Cliff Street, New York City 38.

is pressed with the ball resting against a pad, which is exactly one third of the distance up an upright lever about two feet long; the fulcrum of the lever is at the level of the table. A stout stick about 1.5 inches square makes an excellent lever. The adjustment of the lever must be such that with the foot in maximum plantarflexion, the ball of the foot rests squarely upon the pad, the lever itself making an angle of about twenty-five degrees beyond the perpendicular. This is the only test in the Martin series in which a lever is required. The dynamometer is attached to the tip of the lever. The pull is made by the operator from the head of the table. The balance is horizontal and in line with the leg being tested. The pull is increased in intensity until the muscular resistance has been overcome. To prevent slipping on the table, the shoulders of the subject are held by braces. The muscle gives at about fifteen degrees of plantarflexion, with a rather sharp break in the resistance offered to the pull.

(2) *Muscles that dorsiflex the foot.* The general position of the subject is the same as that for the preceding test. The foot should be flush with the end of the table (to give freedom of action to the operator in making the pull), and should be slightly lifted and braced by the hands of the adjuster, which encircle the ankle. The leather loop of the dynamometer is placed across the toes at the metatarsophalangeal joints. With the foot of the subject in maximum dorsiflexion, the operator makes the pull at right angles to the plantar surface of the subject's foot, lowering the scale to maintain this angle as the foot gives.

(3) *Muscles that invert the foot.* The position of the subject is the same as for the two preceding tests. The loop is across the inner surface of the metatarsophalangeal joint of the great toe. The ankle is braced by the hands of the adjuster. With the foot at right angles to the leg, the foot is inverted and adducted as far as possible without inward rotation of the leg. The pull is opposite in direction to the muscular contraction, horizontal, and in the same vertical plane as the foot. The operator swings the dynamometer in order to maintain this relationship as the foot gives.

(4) *Muscles that evert the foot.* The position of the subject is the same as for the preceding tests. The loop is at the outer surface of the distal end of the fifth metatarsal. The foot is at right angles to the leg and is everted and abducted as far as possible without outward rotation of the leg. The pull is horizontal and in the same vertical plane as the foot, with a swing of the dynamometer to maintain this position.

(5) *Muscles that adduct the thigh.* The position of the subject is the same as for the preceding tests. The adjuster stands at the foot of the table. With one hand he places the loop in the hollow just above the malleolus (an equally correct method is to have the strap just clear of the top of a man's shoe), seizes the subject's heel with the other hand, lifts the leg until the heel is just high enough to clear the toes of the other foot, and then draws the leg into extreme adduction. The foot of the leg to be tested must be kept vertical. The operator stands at the side of the table, and develops tension at the word of command. The command "Stop" should be given as soon as the leg has been drawn into line with the longitudinal axis of the body.

(6) *Muscles that abduct the thigh.* The position of the subject and that of the adjuster are the same as for the preceding test. The loop is adjusted as in the preceding test, but the direction of the pull is opposite to that used in the preceding test. The leg to be tested is drawn fifteen degrees beyond the mid-line of the body, and the effort of the subject at the command "Hold back" is to prevent the operator from drawing the leg into line with the body. The command "Stop" is given just as the leg reaches the mid-line.

(7) *Muscles that extend the thigh.* The subject lies on the side opposite to

that to be tested, with one hip directly above the other. The abdomen is braced firm in position, and, to secure steadiness, the subject pushes against the foot brace with the foot of the leg not being tested. The trunk is braced forward by the subject's holding to the edge of the table with the hands. The adjuster assists in maintaining, with one hand, the position of the abdomen, and in supporting, with the other hand, the weight of the leg to be tested, and keeps the subject's leg parallel to the table. The loop is placed across the popliteal space (behind the knee). The thigh is placed in maximum extension, and the lower leg is kept extended. The direction of pull of the balance is slightly less than ninety degrees to the thigh, being deflected toward the trunk; and it is exerted horizontally. The angle of pull must be constant throughout the movement. The adjuster signals as the thigh crosses the line of the trunk, or if the muscle gives before this, the reading is taken when the muscle yields.

(8) *Muscles that flex the thigh.* The subject lies on the side opposite that to be tested, with one hip directly above the other. To secure steadiness he pushes against the foot brace with the foot of the leg not being tested. The small of the back is braced. The subject maintains the rigidity of the trunk by pushing with the hands against a support in front of him. The adjuster supports the thigh parallel to the table, with one hand at the subject's knee and the other at the subject's ankle. The loop is placed just above the patella. The lower leg is well flexed, and the thigh is flexed more than ninety degrees. The pull is horizontal and as nearly as possible at a right angle to the thigh.

(9) *Muscles that extend the lower leg.* The subject lies prone on the table. The lower leg is flexed ninety degrees at the knee. The loop passes in front of the ankle. The operator, standing at the head of the subject, braces with one hand the subject's shoulder. The pull is horizontal, and parallel to the median plane. The adjuster, with one hand, braces the subject's knee on the table, and, with the other hand at the subject's ankle, limits the extension of the lower leg. The movement begins from the perpendicular position. The effort of the subject to extend the lower leg, and the pull of the operator must start simultaneously at the command of the adjuster. Both pulls should begin slowly: it is essential in this test that the muscle-pull and the pull of the dynamometer should develop together. The lower leg is not permitted to extend more than twenty-five degrees from the perpendicular position. Greater extension than this changes the leverage so much that inaccuracy results. The pull of the operator continues until the lower leg has been drawn back to the original position. This test is one of the most accurate of all the Martin Tests; it is, however, the most liable to error if overextension of the lower leg is permitted before the balance pull begins to draw the leg back to the vertical position.

(10) *Muscles that flex the lower leg.* The subject lies prone on the table. The operator stands at the foot of the table. The loop passes behind the ankle. The subject places the lower leg in maximum flexion. The pull is horizontal, and the rotation of the thigh should be minimized. The adjuster calls "Stop" as the lower leg crosses the perpendicular position.

(11) *Muscles that adduct the upper arm in front of the body.* The subject stands, with the middle of the back pressed firm against an upright post, and with the hand of the arm that is not being tested grasping a post. The adjuster, facing the subject, stands directly in front of the subject. He places the loop in front of and just above the elbow of the arm to be tested. With one hand the adjuster holds the loop in its position, and with the other hand grasps lightly the subject's hand or wrist. The adjuster, keeping the subject's arm straight, draws it across the subject's body as far as possible, keeping it as close to the body as possible and still giving clearance for the loop. At the command "Hold back," the

subject's effort is to hold the arm from being drawn downward, sideward, and backward. The operator holds the dynamometer in a line downward, sideward, and backward from the subject's elbow in such a position that as the arm is drawn downward, sideward, and backward, it will just clear the subject's body. At the command "Hold back," the operator develops sufficient tension to draw the arm down to the side of the body. The command "Stop" must be given, and the pulling discontinued before the arm has been drawn beyond the vertical line.

(12) *Muscles that adduct the upper arm behind the body.* The subject stands, with the middle of the abdomen pressed firm against an upright post, and with the hand of the arm that is not being tested grasping a post. With the fist closed, and with the dorsum of the hand toward the back, the arm, just clearing the trunk, is drawn as far as possible across the back of the body. The strap is placed just above the elbow, and the pull is horizontal and outward anteriorly at an angle of thirty degrees to the lateral plane.

(13) *Muscles that horizontally adduct the upper arm.* The subject stands, with the middle of the back pressed firm against an upright post, and with the hand of the arm that is not being tested grasping a support in such a way that the shoulders are not elevated. The arm being tested is raised to the level of the shoulders, and brought forward to an angle of thirty degrees from the lateral plane of the trunk. The strap is placed just above the elbow, and the pull is backward and downward, establishing an angle of sixty degrees with the upper arm. This angle is maintained until the arm gives.

(14) *Muscles that horizontally abduct the upper arm.* The position of the subject is the same as for the preceding test. The arm to be tested is raised to the level of the shoulders posteriorly at an angle of thirty degrees to the lateral plane of the trunk. The strap is placed just above the elbow, and the pull is forward and downward, establishing an angle of sixty degrees with the upper arm. This angle is maintained until the arm gives.

(15) *Muscles that extend the forearm.* The subject lies on his back. The arm to be tested is at the side of the body, and the forearm is perpendicular to the table, against which the elbow rests. The hand, with the thumb pointing to the shoulder, is closed. The loop is behind the wrist. The operator stands at the head of the table. The adjuster stands at the side of the table, and, with one hand, braces the subject's elbow on the table, and, with the other hand at the subject's wrist, limits the extension of the forearm. The pull is horizontal. At the command of the adjuster, the extension of the forearm and the pull of the operator start together slowly. Extension is permitted for from five to fifteen degrees from the perpendicular, and is overcome by the pull of the operator. The command "Stop" is given just as the forearm crosses the vertical line.

(16) *Muscles that flex the forearm.* The subject lies on his back, with his heels pressed firm against the cleat at the end of the table. The adjuster stands at the left of the subject. With his right hand he holds the subject's elbow to the table. With his left hand he flexes the subject's forearm about fifteen degrees, and adjusts the loop about the wrist so that the upper edge of the loop is at the crease in the skin at the base of the hand. The operator stands at the foot of the table, and exerts tension at the word of command. The command "Stop" should be given when the forearm reaches the vertical.

(17) *Muscles that dorsiflex the hand.* The subject stands beside an upright post. His arm is elevated forward to the level of the shoulders. The front of the distal part of the forearm is against the post with the hand extended past the post to the styloid process of the ulna. With the palmar surface of the hand vertical and the fingers extended, the hand is put in maximum dorsiflexion. The adjuster encircles the wrist with his hand, bracing the subject's arm in posi-

tion. The loop is placed across the dorsum of the hand, just distal to the metacarpals. The pull is exerted horizontally and at an angle slightly less than ninety degrees to the hand, being deflected toward the wrist. The angle of pull must be constant: to secure this the operator swings the dynamometer through an arc as the hand gives. The accuracy of the reading depends upon maintaining the indicated direction of pull and upon placing the loop correctly. Both of these items are very important in this test and in the three following tests.

(18) *Muscles that palmarflex the hand.* The position of the subject is the same as in the preceding test except that the back of the forearm is against the post, with the hand projecting past the post to the styloid process of the ulna. A folded handkerchief or towel may be interposed between the forearm and the post. The adjuster stands directly in front of the subject's palm. With one hand he holds the subject's wrist against the post, and with the other hand he adjusts and holds the loop. The loop is so placed that the middle of the loop is directly over the crease at the base of the fingers. Keeping the subject's fingers straight, the adjuster palmarflexes the subject's hand. The operator pulls at an angle just less than ninety degrees from the plane of the subject's hand. At the command "Hold back," the subject holds the hand in extreme palmarflexion. The command "Stop" must be given as soon as the hand begins to yield.

(19) *Muscles that extend the fingers.* The subject stands beside an upright post. His arm is elevated forward to the level of the shoulders. The front of the forearm is against the post. The palmar surface of the hand is vertical. The adjuster braces, against the post, the palm of the subject's hand well below the palmar crease. A small loop of cloth is placed behind the middle phalanges. The pull is horizontal, and at an angle slightly less than ninety degrees to the extended fingers. The deflection of the angle is toward the wrist.

(20) *Muscles that flex the fingers.* The position of the subject and the bracing by the adjuster are the same as for the preceding test. The small loop of cloth is placed on the palmar surface of the middle phalanges. The dorsal surface of the hand is vertical against the post. The pull is horizontal and slightly less than ninety degrees to the proximal phalanges. The deflection is toward the dorsum of the hand.

(21) *Muscles that adduct the thumb.* The hand of the subject is held in a horizontal position, with the palmar surface directed downward. The adjuster braces, with one hand, the subject's extended fingers, and, with the other hand, he braces the subject's wrist. The small loop is placed at the interphalangeal joint of the thumb. The subject adducts the thumb as far as possible under the palm. The pull is horizontal and at a right angle to the thumb joint. The call "Stop" is made by the adjuster just as the thumb appears from the hand.

(22) *Muscles that abduct the thumb.* The position of the hand and the bracing by the adjuster are the same as for the preceding test. The subject abducts the thumb in the same horizontal plane as the hand. The position of the small loop is the same as in the preceding test, but the direction of the loop is reversed. The pull deflects downward from the horizontal just enough for the loop to escape the palmar surface of the hand. It is exerted at a right angle to the thumb.

Complete, usable standards have not been developed for the Martin Test. Martin has prepared a number of standards in terms of the strengths of different groups of muscles in terms of percentages of strengths of twenty-two groups of muscles. Averages of standards for the twenty-two groups of muscles may be found in Table 57 (p. 160), and directions for the use of these standards may be found in Table 58 (p. 160).

Table 57

STRENGTHS OF SPECIFIC GROUPS OF MUSCLES IN TERMS OF PERCENTAGES
OF SUM OF STRENGTHS OF TWENTY-TWO GROUPS OF MUSCLES (MARTIN)*

Feet

Plantarflexors**	10.00***	
Dorsiflexors	2.87	
Invertors	1.93	
Evertors	1.85	

Thighs

Adductors	1.60
Abductors	1.43
Extensors	3.55
Flexors	2.95

Lower legs

Extensors	3.23
Flexors	1.53

Upper arms and shoulder girdle

Adductors (in front of body)	2.23
Adductors (behind body)	1.68
Horizontal adductors	2.28
Horizontal abductors	1.60

Forearms

Extensors	2.05
Flexors	1.40

Hands

Extensors	1.18
Flexors	1.63

Fingers 2 to 5

Extensors	.65
Flexors	3.06

Thumbs

Adductors	1.33
Abductors	Negligible

*E. G. Martin, "Tests of Muscular Efficiency," Physiological Reviews, July, 1921.
**Plantarflexors, dorsiflexors, etc., refer to the muscles that plantarflex the feet, dorsiflex the feet, etc.
***I.e., the strength of the plantarflexors of each foot is 10 per cent of the sum of the strengths of the twenty-two groups of muscles. All the numbers in the table are interpreted similarly.

Table 58

STRENGTH OF EXTENSORS OF LOWER LEGS ON BASIS OF MARTIN STANDARDS

"Normal" Muscle Group	Tested Strength (lb.)	Percentage of Normal Strength	Predicted Strength of Extensors of Lower Legs
Extensors of thighs* (Test 7)	52	$\frac{3.23}{3.55}$	47
Flexors of thighs (Test 8)	48	$\frac{3.23}{2.95}$	53
Adductors of arms in front of body (Test 11)	30	$\frac{3.23}{2.23}$	43
Adductors of upper arms behind body (Test 12)	29	$\frac{3.23}{1.68}$	$\frac{56}{199}$

Average Predicted Strength = 49.75

*Extensors, etc., refer to the muscles that extend the thighs, etc.

Table 59

STRENGTH--PHYSICAL-EFFICIENCY TEST (STANSBURY):
NORMS (JUNIOR- SENIOR-HIGH-SCHOOL BOYS)

C.I.	McCloy Classification Index									
	0	2	4	6	8	10	12	14	16	18
					Norms					
500	83	84	85	86	87	88	89	90	91	92
520	93	94	95	96	97	98	99	100	101	102
540	103	104	105	106	107	108	109	110	111	112
560	113	114	115	116	117	118	119	120	121	122
580	123	124	125	126	127	128	129	130	131	132
600	133	134	135	136	137	138	139	140	141	142
620	143	144	145	146	147	148	149	150	151	152
640	153	154	155	156	157	158	159	160	161	162
660	163	164	165	166	167	168	169	170	171	172
680	173	174	175	176	177	178	179	180	181	182
700	183	184	185	186	187	188	189	190	191	192
720	193	194	195	196	197	198	199	200	201	202
740	203	204	205	206	207	208	209	210	211	212
760	213	214	215	216	217	218	219	220	221	222
780	223	224	225	226	227	228	229	230	231	232
800	233	234	235	236	237	238	239	240	241	242
820	243	244	245	246	247	248	249	250	251
840	252	253	254	255	256	257	258	259	260	261
860	262	263	264	265	266	267	268	269	270	271
880	272	273	274	275	276	277	278	279	280	281
900	282	283	284	285	286	287	288	289	290	291
920	292	293	294	295	296	297	298	299	300	301
940	302	303	304	305	306	307	308	309	310	311
960	312	313	314	315	316	317	318	319	320	321
980	322	323	324	325	326	327	328	329	330	331
1000	332	334	335	336	337	338	339	340	341	342
1020	342	343	344	345	346	347	348	349	350	351
1040	352	353	354	355	356	357	358	359	360	361
1060	362	363	364	365	366	367	368	369	370	371
1080	372	373	374	375	376	377	378	379	380	381
1100	382	383	384	385	386	387	388	389	390	391
1120	392	393	394	395	396	397	398	399	400	401
1140	402	403	404	405	406	407	408	409	410	410
1160	411	412	413	414	415	416	417	418	419	420
1180	421	422	423	424	425	426	427	428	429	430
1200	431	432	433	434	435	436	437	438	439	440

EXAMPLE:

Age = 15 yr.
Height = 64 in.
Weight = 123 lb.
McCloy Classification Index = 807 (i.e., (20 x 15) + (6 x 64) + 123)
Eight-pound shot-put = 32.5 ft.
Standing broad jump = 94 in.
Stansbury Physical-efficiency Score = 262.5 (i.e., (1.4 x 32.5) + 94 + 123)
Norm = 236.5
Stansbury Physical-efficiency Quotient = 111 (i.e., $100 \times \frac{262.5}{236.5}$)

In the first column are four groups of muscles of normal strength. In the second column are the strengths of these muscles as measured by the Martin technique. Each of the numerators in the third column is the relation of the strength of the muscles that extend the lower legs in terms of a percentage of the sum of the strengths of twenty-two groups of muscles. The denominators in the third column are the relations of the strengths of the muscles that extend and flex the thighs, together with the strengths of the adductors of the arms in front of the body and of the adductors of the arms behind the body, in terms of percentages of the sum of the

Table 60

STRENGTH-PHYSICAL-EFFICIENCY TEST (ANDERSON-McCLOY):
NORMS (SENIOR-HIGH-SCHOOL GIRLS)

Weight (lb.)	Weight (lb.)				
	0	2	4	6	8
		NORMS			
70	120	121	121	122	123
80	124	125	125	126	127
90	128	129	130	130	131
100	132	133	134	135	135
110	136	137	138	139	139
120	140	141	142	143	144
130	144	145	146	147	148
140	149	149	150	151	152
150	153	153	154	155	156
160	157	158	158	159	160
170	161	162	163	163	164
180	165	166	167	167	168

EXAMPLE

Weight = 112 lb.
Six-pound shot-put = 20 ft.
Standing broad jump = 80 in.
Anderson-McCloy Physical-efficiency Score =
    144 (i.e., (1.8 x 20) + 80 + (.25 x 112))
Norm = 137
Anderson-McCloy Physical-efficiency Quotient = 105

strengths of twenty-two groups of muscles. The fourth column is the second column multiplied by the third column. The predicted strength of the muscles that extend the lower legs, then, is the average of the four predicted strengths (i.e., 49.75 pounds).

The administration of the Martin Strength Test requires much time and effort although the effort that needs to be exerted by the tester can be minimized by the use of a block and tackle for pulling the dynamometer. An r of .96 has been obtained between the Martin Strength Test and the McCloy Strength Test (see Sec. 274). Hence the two tests may be used interchangeably for measuring general strength, although the standards for the two tests differ. The Martin Strength Test, which was devised primarily for testing muscles that had been weakened as a result of poliomyelitis, and which is excellent for such a purpose, is not practicable

Table 61

STRENGTH--PHYSICAL-EFFICIENCY TEST (CARPENTER):
NORMS (ELEMENTARY-SCHOOL BOYS)

McCloy C.I.	0	1	2	3	4	5	6	7	8	9
					Norms					
600	115.94	116.24	116.54	116.84	117.14	117.44	117.75	118.05	118.35	118.65
590	112.93	113.23	113.53	113.83	114.13	114.44	114.74	115.04	115.34	115.64
580	109.92	110.22	110.52	110.82	111.13	111.43	111.73	112.03	112.33	112.63
570	106.91	107.21	107.51	107.82	108.12	108.42	108.72	109.02	109.32	109.62
560	103.90	104.20	104.51	104.81	105.11	105.41	105.71	106.01	106.31	106.61
550	100.90	101.20	101.50	101.80	102.10	102.40	102.70	103.00	103.30	103.60
540	97.80	98.19	98.49	98.79	99.09	99.39	99.69	99.99	100.29	100.59
530	94.88	95.18	95.48	95.78	96.08	96.38	96.68	96.98	97.28	97.59
520	91.87	92.17	92.45	92.77	93.07	93.37	93.67	93.97	94.28	94.58
510	88.86	89.16	89.46	89.76	90.06	90.36	90.66	90.97	91.27	91.57
500	85.85	86.15	86.45	86.75	87.05	87.35	87.66	87.96	88.26	88.56
490	82.84	83.14	83.44	83.74	84.04	84.35	84.65	84.95	85.25	85.55
480	79.83	80.13	80.43	80.73	81.04	81.34	81.64	81.94	82.24	82.54
470	76.82	77.12	77.42	77.73	78.03	78.33	78.63	78.93	79.23	79.53
460	73.81	74.11	74.42	74.72	75.02	75.32	75.62	75.92	76.22	76.52
450	70.81	71.11	71.41	71.71	72.01	72.31	72.61	72.91	73.21	73.51
440	67.80	68.10	68.40	68.70	69.00	69.30	69.60	69.90	70.20	70.50
430	64.79	65.09	65.39	65.69	65.99	66.29	66.59	66.89	67.19	67.50
420	61.78	62.08	62.38	62.68	62.98	63.28	63.58	63.88	64.19	64.49
410	58.77	59.07	59.37	59.67	59.97	60.27	60.57	60.88	61.18	61.48
400	55.76	56.06	56.36	56.66	56.96	57.26	57.57	57.87	58.17	58.47

Table 62

STRENGTH--PHYSICAL-EFFICIENCY TEST (CARPENTER):
NORMS (ELEMENTARY-SCHOOL GIRLS)

McCloy C.I.	0	1	2	3	4	5	6	7	8	9
					Norms					
600	125.03	125.28	125.54	125.79	126.05	126.30	126.56	126.81	127.07	127.32
590	122.48	122.74	122.99	123.25	123.50	123.76	124.01	124.26	124.52	124.78
580	119.93	120.19	120.44	120.70	120.95	121.21	121.46	121.72	121.97	122.23
570	117.38	117.64	117.89	118.15	118.40	118.66	118.91	119.17	119.42	119.68
560	114.83	115.09	115.34	115.60	115.85	116.11	116.36	116.62	116.87	117.13
550	112.29	112.54	112.79	113.05	113.30	113.56	113.81	114.07	114.32	114.58
540	109.74	109.39	110.25	110.50	110.76	111.01	111.27	111.52	111.78	112.03
530	107.19	107.44	107.70	107.95	108.21	108.46	108.72	108.97	109.23	109.48
520	104.64	104.89	105.15	105.40	105.66	105.91	106.17	106.42	106.68	106.93
510	102.09	102.34	102.60	102.85	103.11	103.36	103.62	103.87	104.13	104.38
500	99.54	99.79	100.05	100.30	100.56	100.81	101.07	101.32	101.58	101.83
490	96.99	97.25	97.50	97.76	98.01	98.27	98.52	98.78	99.03	99.29
480	94.44	94.70	94.95	95.21	95.46	95.72	95.97	96.23	96.48	96.74
470	91.89	92.15	92.40	92.66	92.91	93.17	93.42	93.68	93.93	94.19
460	89.34	89.60	89.85	90.11	90.36	90.62	90.87	91.13	91.38	91.64
450	86.80	87.05	87.30	87.56	87.81	88.07	88.32	88.58	88.83	89.09
440	84.25	84.50	84.76	85.01	85.27	85.52	85.78	86.03	86.29	86.54
430	81.70	81.95	82.21	82.46	82.72	82.97	83.23	83.48	83.74	83.99
420	79.15	79.40	79.66	79.91	80.17	80.42	80.68	80.93	81.19	81.44
410	76.60	76.85	77.11	77.36	77.62	77.87	78.13	78.38	78.64	78.89
400	74.05	74.30	74.56	74.81	75.07	75.32	75.58	75.83	76.09	76.34

for use with large groups of persons. The Intercollegiate, Rogers, and McCloy Strength Tests are more interesting to the person being tested than is the Martin Test, and are practicable for more testing situations in the schools.

309. PHYSICAL-EFFICIENCY TESTS

If the equipment needed for administering the strength tests is not available, the **Stansbury Physical-efficiency Test**[37]—1.4 eight-pound shot-put (ft.) + standing broad jump (in.) + weight (lb.)—may be used for junior- and senior-high-school boys, and the **Anderson-McCloy Physical-efficiency Test**[38]—1.8 six-pound shot-put (ft.) + standing broad jump (in.) + .25 weight (lb.)—may be used for junior- and senior-high-school girls. The shot is put from a stand, with the shot in the palm of the hand, not up in the fingers.

An r of .84 for boys and an r of .74 for girls have been obtained between the Stansbury and Anderson-McCloy Physical-efficiency Tests and the McCloy Strength Test. Norms for the physical-efficiency scores may be found for boys in Table 59 (p. 161) and for girls in Table 60 (p. 162). The physical-efficiency quotient is the physical-efficiency score divided by the norm, which for boys is based on the McCloy Classification Index, and which for girls is based on weight, and the result is multiplied by 100.

310. The **Carpenter Physical-efficiency Tests**[39] are for use in the first three grades: (1) *Boys:* .1 broad jump (in.) + 2.3 four-pound shot-put (ft.) + weight (lb.); norm = 3 McCloy Classification Index − 64.60 (Table 61, p. 163). The shot is put from a stand. An r of .63 was obtained between this regression equation and the combination of right and left grips and pushing-and-pulling strength. (2) *Girls:* .5 broad jump (in.) + 3 four-pound shot-put (ft.) + weight (lb.); norm = .255 McCloy Classification Index − 27.91 (Table 62, p. 163). The shot is put from a stand. An r of .50 was obtained between this regression and the combination of right and left grips and pushing-and-pulling strength.

[37] Edgar B. Stansbury, "A Simplified Method of Classifying Junior and Senior High School Boys into Homogeneous Groups for Physical Education Activities," *Research Quarterly*, December, 1941.

[38] Theresa Anderson and C. H. McCloy, unpublished study.

[39] Carpenter, "Strength Testing in the First Three Grades," *Research Quarterly*, October, 1942.

CHAPTER **15**

ENDURANCE

FACTORS IN ENDURANCE

311. Factors in muscular and in circulorespiratory endurance

312. *Strength of body relative to weight and to additional load.* This factor is complicated by the factor of muscular endurance. The relationship between strength and muscular endurance may be illustrated as follows. Two men of the same age, weight, and height recline on their backs and "press" toward the ceiling heavy barbells. The maximum weight that *A* can press is 150 pounds, and the maximum weight that *B* can press is only 100 pounds, and these weights can be pressed only once by *A* and by *B*, respectively. Then *A* and *B* each presses a weight of 75 pounds as many times as possible. *A* can press the weight twenty to twenty-five times, and *B* can press the weight only six or seven times. The difference is probably due to the fact that *A* uses a smaller proportion of his motor units for each press than does *B*, and can, therefore, alternate the use of these units more freely than can *B*. Hence, other factors being equal, *B* fatigues more quickly than does *A*, and reaches earlier than does *A* the point at which he can no longer press the weight.

The factor of strength is further complicated by the commonly known physiological fact illustrated in Figure XXI (p. 165). In this figure is

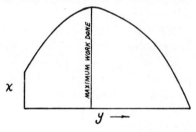

FIGURE XXI. Work Efficiency of Muscle under Different Loads

represented the total amount of work done, under electrical stimulation, by an intact gastrocnemius muscle of a frog. The ordinate (height in the illustration) represents the weight lifted multiplied by the height to which the weight was lifted. At the beginning the weight was very light, and then was increased, as represented by the abscissa (horizontal line in the illustration), until the muscle could no longer lift it. With the increase in the load, the muscle increased in efficiency (that is, in the amount of work that it did) up to a certain point, and after that point it decreased in efficiency with the increase in the load until the load became so heavy that the muscle could not lift it at all. According to this phenomenon a muscle functions most

165

efficiently if it is not too nearly loaded with the maximum load that it can manage.

313. *Muscular endurance.* The phenomenon of quick recovery or of the postponement of fatigue is due, largely, to the number of functioning capillaries. It was long ago demonstrated that in the sedentary person many of the capillaries are nonfunctioning. It has been further demonstrated that if a person once sedentary engages in an intensive program of physical training, the capillaries that were nonfunctioning begin gradually to function, and that the increase in the number of functioning capillaries may be as great as several hundred per cent. In the guinea pig the number of new capillaries that proliferate in a muscle as a result of training is equal to 50 per cent of the total number of capillaries, and these capillaries are gradually resorbed when training is discontinued.

In addition to being associated with the factor of strength, muscular recovery is probably also associated with changes in the chemical qualities of muscles. Thus if two men are unequal in respect to strength, but equal in respect to the capillary supply and the chemical condition of their muscles, and if they are performing the same task, the stronger man has more endurance than the weaker man has. Hence the speed of muscular recovery is based on the strength of the muscles *and* on the blood supply to the muscles.

314. *Circulorespiratory endurance.* This type of endurance, which is associated with "wind," and which is requisite to such performers as distance runners and quarter-mile swimmers, appears to be a function of the following items:

(1) Strength and muscular endurance of the skeletal muscles concerned (in running, for example, the muscles associated with moving the legs).

(2) Strength and muscular endurance of the heart muscle. The heart muscle increases in strength and in circulatory supply during training just as do the skeletal muscles. A hypertrophied heart is a strengthened heart (i.e., the cross-sectional area of its muscle has been increased); if trained for endurance, it develops an additional capillary supply.

(3) Increased efficiency of the lungs. Training results in an increase of about 20 per cent in the ability of the lungs to transmit oxygen and carbon dioxide. This increase may be due, in part, to the development of "partitions" in the alveoli of the lungs, which partitions increase the surface area within the alveoli and which partitions hence increase the amount of oxygen that can be absorbed from the inspired air.

(4) Improved responses of the circulatory system to stimulation by the sympathetic nervous system.

315. The factors of strength, muscular endurance, and efficiency of the heart and of the lungs are interdependent. Muscular endurance is a combination of the first two factors, and circulorespiratory endurance is a combination of all three factors. Performances in such activities as sprints and gymnastics are limited by the first two factors. If the muscles are in excellent condition, performance in such activities as distance running and distance swimming is limited by the third factor.

316. FACTORS OTHER THAN THOSE OF SKELETAL MUSCLES, HEART, AND LUNGS

317. *Adaptation of circulatory responses to stimulation by sympathetic nervous system.* Relative to performance in strenuous exercise, a chronic loss of sleep results in a decrease in strength and in endurance, and in a tendency to nausea. Such results are probably due to a lack of circulatory responses to stimulation by the sympathetic nervous system.[1] This aspect of endurance may be influenced by the application of ice packs to the abdomen.[2]

318. *Glandular effects.* The output of the glands varies in accordance with the curve of probability. The output of the thyroid gland, for example, varies from extreme hyperthyroidism to extreme hypothyroidism, but the output in most persons is between these extremes. Differences in output of the anterior pituitary gland, the adrenal glands, and the male sex glands affect the ability to resist fatigue; for example, long-continued injections of testosterone result in an increased manifestation of strength.[3] The effects of interest and excitement on manifestations of strength and endurance are common experiences. The factor of the adaptation of circulatory responses to stimulation by the sympathetic nervous system and the factor relative to glandular effects are probably interrelated.

319. *Effects of intense effort.* This factor, which is undoubtedly related to the preceding two factors, is possibly also related to the intensity of the nerve stimulus. Some weight lifters, for example, perform very much better when trying to surpass someone who has already surpassed their past records. Persons responding to such stimuli are said to be "good competitors."

320. *Skill.* The factor of skill is associated with a decrease in efforts to produce the same result. The interference of muscles irrelevant to the performance is avoided, and the desired response of the antagonistic muscles is secured.

321. TYPES OF FATIGUE TO WHICH RESISTANCE (ENDURANCE) CAN BE DEVELOPED

In addition to both acute local or muscular fatigue and acute circulo-respiratory fatigue, there is *general fatigue*. General fatigue, which is

---

[1] The feeling of a lack of strength and of endurance and the tendency to nausea experienced by a person attempting to exercise immediately upon arising in the morning are probably due to the same cause.

[2] William P. Happ and Others, "The Physiologic Effects of Abdominal Cold Packs," *Research Quarterly,* May, 1949.

[3] Personal communication from Arthur H Steinhaus.

illustrated by the effects of prolonged marching, results in a person's becoming "all in" and often nauseated, even though the muscular condition of the person is good. It is probably associated with factors of local or muscular fatigue and with factors involved in glandular and circulatory responses to stimuli from the sympathetic nervous system. It is intensified by heat and by a loss of salt through excessive perspiration, and it is lessened by cold. Tests of this type of fatigue are not so useful in the schools as they are with the Armed Services or in heavy industry or in situations in which persons must work very hard under conditions of high temperatures.

322. TESTS OF STRENGTH AS RELATED TO TESTS OF ENDURANCE

A strength quotient is probably the best practicable measurement available of strength relative to endurance. For purposes of research, tests of "breaking" strength and tests of "active" contraction of specific muscle groups as they are related kinesiologically to the endurance under consideration are recommended (see Chap. 14).

323. TESTS OF MUSCULAR ENDURANCE

The relationship between the strength and the endurance of the muscles involved in pull-ups has been demonstrated in a study[4] in which it was found that an unduly large increase in the number of pull-ups was not accompanied by an equal increment in strength (Table 49, p. 132). It has been indicated further that an increase in muscular endurance as a function of muscular strength is primarily at the lower end of the range of endurance.[5] The test items most frequently used for the measurement of muscular endurance follow.

324. TESTS FOR ENDURANCE OF MUSCLES OF ARMS AND OF SHOULDER GIRDLE: PULL-UP TYPE

Pull-ups. The performer starts by hanging, usually with the reverse grasp (i.e., with the palms facing the body),[6] from a horizontal bar, and then raises the body until the chin is over the bar, and then returns to the starting position. Standards for pull-ups may be found in Table 75 (p. 178).

[4] Charles H. McCloy, "A New Method of Scoring Chinning and Dipping," *Research Quarterly*, December, 1931.
[5] Ross Wedemeyer, "A Differential Analysis of Sit-ups for Strength and Muscular Endurance," *Research Quarterly*, March, 1946.
[6] The Armed Services have recommended the use of the grasp with the palms directed away from the body on the basis that "This is the grip used in the climbing of a fence." It might be mentioned here that the reverse grasp is the one used in the climbing of a rope! Most performers can execute about 10 per cent more pull-ups with the reverse grasp than with the grasp in which the palms are directed away from the body, and certainly the reverse grasp is the more popular with boys (few girls can execute a pull-up).

Three types of *supine pull-ups* follow.

(1) A horizontal bar is placed at the height of the bottom of the sternum. This type of pull-up, which is used only for girls, is described in Section **297**. Strength equivalents may be found in Table 47 (p. 131).

Table 63

STRADDLE PULL-UPS: SCORING TABLE (BOYS)

Pull-ups	0	1	2	3	4	5	6	7	8	9
					T-scores					
0		10	15	18	21	23	26	28	30	31
10	33	35	36	38	39	41	42	43	44	46
20	47	48	49	50	51	52	53	54	55	56
30	57	58	59	60	61	62	63	64	65	65
40	66	67	68	69	69	70	71	72	73	73
50	74	75	76	76	77	78	78	79	80	80
60	81	82	82	83	84	84	85	86	86	87
70	88	88	89	89	90	91	91	92	92	93
80	94	94	95	95	96	97	97	97	98	99
90	99	100								

EXAMPLE:

T-score for 23 straddle pull-ups = 50

(2) Another type of supine pull-ups is similar to that in *1* except that the lower legs are flexed so that the angles behind the knees are ninety degrees each. In this type of pull-up, the body must be straight from the knees to the shoulders. The bar is just high enough for the upper back to clear the floor by three or four inches.

(3) *Straddle pull-ups.* The performer starts from a supine position. An assistant, of approximately the same height as the performer, stands fac-

Table 64

STRADDLE PULL-UPS: SCORING TABLE (GIRLS)

Pull-ups	0	1	2	3	4	5	6	7	8	9
					T-scores					
0		17	23	28	32	35	39	42	44	47
10	49	51	53	55	57	59	61	63	65	66
20	68	70	71	73	74	76	77	78	80	81
30	82	83	85	86	87	88	90	91	92	93
40	94	95	96	97	98	99	100			

EXAMPLE:

T-score for 11 straddle pull-ups = 51

ing the head of the performer and straddling the chest of the performer. The performer, with his palms facing his body, raises his arms, and the assistant grasps, with his palms facing his body, the wrists of the performer. The assistant stands erect, and the performer raises his body (pulls himself up) until his chest touches the crotch of the assistant. The assistant should keep his legs well apart and maintain an erect position throughout the exercise. Standards for straddle pull-ups for boys may be found in Table 63 (p. 169) and for girls in Table 64 (p. 169).

325. TESTS FOR ENDURANCE OF MUSCLES OF ARMS AND OF SHOULDER GIRDLE: PUSH-UP TYPE

(1) *Floor push-ups.* In this type of push-up, which is used primarily for boys, the performer starts from a prone position. The fingers are directed forward, and the hands are on the mat just behind the shoulders. The performer supporting his weight on his hands and on his toes, and keeping his body straight from the shoulders to the toes, first raises his body and then lowers it until his chest touches the floor. Standards for floor push-ups may be found in Table 65 (p. 170).

Table 65

PUSH-UPS (FLOOR): SCORING TABLE (BOYS)

Push-ups	0	1	2	3	4	5	6	7	8	9
				T-scores						
0		15	16	18	19	20	22	23	25	27
10	28	30	31	33	35	36	38	40	41	42
20	44	45	46	48	49	50	52	53	54	55
30	57	58	59	60	61	62	63	64	65	66
40	67	68	69	70	71	72	73	74	75	75
50	76	77	78	78	79	80	81	82	82	83
60	84	84	85	85	86	87	88	88	89	90
70	91	92	92	93	94	95	95	96	96	97
80	97	98	98	99	99	100				

EXAMPLE:

T-score for 42 push-ups • 69

(2) *Bench push-ups.* This type of push-up, which is used primarily for girls, is described in Section 295.

(3) *Knee push-ups.* In this type of push-up, which is used only for girls, the performer starts from a prone position with the lower legs flexed so that there is an angle of ninety degrees behind each of the knees. Keeping the body straight[7] from the shoulders to the knees, the performer raises and lowers the body. Standards for knee push-ups may be found in Table 66 (p. 171).

[7] The number of performances can be doubled or tripled if the hips rise or sag.

(4) *Parallel-bar push-ups* (*dips*). This type of push-up, which is used primarily for boys, is described in Section 294.

In the execution of the tests described in Sections 324 and 325, the performer repeats the movements as many times as possible. If any movements are not performed with the body in the position indicated, these movements count half movements. If there are four half movements, the exercise is stopped, and the performer is retested later.

Table 66

PUSH-UPS (KNEE):   SCORING TABLE (GIRLS)

Push-ups	0	1	2	3	4	5	6	7	8	9
				T-scores						
0		12	22	28	32	36	38	41	43	44
10	46	47	49	50	51	52	53	54	55	55
20	56	57	58	58	59	60	60	61	61	62
30	62	63	63	64	64	64	65	65	66	66
40	66	67	67	68	68	68	69	69	69	69
50	70	70	70	71	71	71	71	72	72	72
60	72	73	73	73	73	74	74	74	74	75
70	75	75	75	75	76	76	76	76	76	77
80	77	77	77	77	77	78	78	78	78	78
90	78	79	79	79	79	79	79	80	80	80
100	80	80	80	80	81	81	81	81	81	81

EXAMPLE·   T-score for 13 knee push-ups · 50

326. TESTS FOR ENDURANCE OF ABDOMINAL MUSCLES AND OF THIGH FLEXORS

(1) *Sit-ups.* The performer sits on the floor, with the hands behind the head and the fingers interlaced. The feet, which are held down by an assistant, are about eighteen inches apart. The performer sits up, touching the right elbow to the left knee, and then returns to the starting position; he then sits up, touching the left elbow to the right knee, and then returns to the starting position.[8] Standards for boys for the number of sit-ups executed in one minute, three minutes, and five minutes may be found in Table 67 (pp. 172-73). Standards for boys for the number of sit-ups that can be executed with no time limit may be found in Table 68 (p. 173). For boys the number of sit-ups executed in two minutes is the recommended test. Standards for girls for the number of sit-ups that can be executed in two minutes may be found in Table 69 (p. 174). Standards for girls for the number of sit-ups that can be executed with no time limit may be found in Table 70 (p. 174), in Table 76 (p. 179), and in Table 77 (p. 180).

[8] Some versions of sit-ups do not include directions for touching the elbows to the opposite knees. Also some versions provide for the lower legs to be partially flexed; it is difficult for a performer with light legs and a heavy trunk to execute sit-ups in this manner unless the feet are held down.

Table 67

SIT-UPS (1, 2, 3, AND 5 MINUTES): SCORING TABLES (BOYS)

1 Min. Sit-ups	0	1	2	3	4	5	6	7	8	9
					T-scores					
20						2	5	8	11	14
30	17	20	23	25	28	31	34	37	40	43
40	46	48	51	54	57	60	63	66	69	71
50	74	77	80	83	86	89	92	94	97	100·

EXAMPLE:

T-score for 42 sit-ups = 51

2 Min. Sit-ups	0	1	2	3	4	5	6	7	8	9
20								1	3	4
30	5	6	8	9	10	11	13	14	15	16
40	17	19	20	21	22	24	25	26	27	29
50	30	31	32	34	35	36	37	38	40	41
60	42	43	45	46	47	48	50	51	52	53
70	55	56	57	58	59	61	62	63	64	66
80	67	69	70	71	72	73	74	76	77	78
90	79	80	82	83	84	85	87	88	89	90
100	92	93	94	95	97	98	99	100		

EXAMPLE:

T-score for 66 sit-ups = 50

3 Min. Sit-ups	0	1	2	3	4	5	6	7	8	9
30						1	2	3	4	4
40	5	6	7	8	9	9	10	11	12	13
50	14	14	15	16	17	18	19	19	20	21
60	22	23	24	24	25	26	27	28	29	29
70	30	31	32	33	34	34	35	36	37	38
80	39	39	40	41	42	43	44	44	45	46
90	47	48	49	49	50	51	52	53	54	54
100	55	56	57	58	59	59	60	61	62	63
110	64	64	65	66	67	68	69	69	70	71
120	72	73	74	75	75	76	77	78	79	79
130	80	81	82	83	84	84	85	86	87	88
140	89	89	90	91	92	93	94	94	95	96
150	97	98	99	99	100					

EXAMPLE:

T-score for 94 sit-ups = 50

Table 67 (continued)

5 Min. Sit-ups	0	1	2	3	4	5	6	7	8	9
						T-scores				
50				1	2	2	3	4	4	5
60	5	6	7	7	8	9	9	10	11	11
70	12	12	13	14	14	15	16	16	17	18
80	18	19	19	20	21	21	22	23	23	24
90	25	25	26	26	27	28	28	29	30	30
100	31	32	32	33	33	34	35	35	36	37
110	37	38	39	39	40	40	41	42	42	43
120	44	44	45	46	46	47	47	48	49	49
130	50	50	50	51	51	52	52	53	53	53
140	54	54	55	55	55	56	56	57	57	57
150	58	58	59	59	60	60	60	61	61	62
160	62	62	63	63	64	64	65	65	65	66
170	66	67	67	67	68	68	69	69	70	70
180	70	71	71	72	72	72	73	73	74	74
190	74	75	75	76	76	77	77	77	78	78
200	79	79	79	80	80	81	81	82	82	82
210	83	83	84	84	84	85	85	86	86	87
220	87	87	88	88	89	89	89	90	90	91
230	91	91	92	92	93	93	94	94	94	95
240	95	96	96	96	97	97	98	98	99	99
250	99	100	100							

EXAMPLE:

T-score for 130-132 sit-ups = 50

Table 68

SIT-UPS (NO TIME LIMIT):   SCORING TABLE (BOYS)

Sit-ups	0	1	2	3	4	5	6	7	8	9
						T-scores				
0								1	5	9
10	12	15	18	20	22	24	27	28	29	31
20	32	33	35	36	38	40	41	42	43	44
30	44	45	46	47	48	49	50	50	51	52
40	53	53	54	55	56	56	57	58	58	59
50	59	60	61	61	62	63	63	64	64	65
60	65	66	66	67	67	68	68	69	69	70
70	70	70	71	71	72	72	72	73	73	74
80	74	74	75	75	75	75	76	76	76	77
90	77	77	78	78	78	78	78	79	79	79
100	80	80	80	80	80	81	81	81	81	81
110	82	82	82	83	83	84	84	84	84	84
120	85	85	85	85	85	86	86	86	86	86
130	87	87	87	87	87	88	88	88	88	88
140	89					90				
150	91					92				
160	93					94				
170	95					95				
180	96					97				
190	98					98				
200	99					100				

EXAMPLE:

T-score for 36 sit-ups = 50

(2) *Hanging half-lever*. The performer starts from a position of hanging from a horizontal bar. He raises the legs, with the lower legs completely extended, until the legs are parallel to the floor, and then lowers the legs. The movement must be performed without a swing. The score is the number of such movements that can be performed continuously.

Table 69

SIT-UPS (2 MINUTES): SCORING TABLE (GIRLS)

Sit-ups	0	1	2	3	4	5	6	7	8	9
					T-scores					
0		20	25	28	31	34	36	38	40	41
10	43	44	46	47	48	49	50	51	52	53
20	54	55	56	57	58	59	59	60	61	62
30	62	63	64	65	65	66	66	67	68	68
40	69	70	70	71	71	72	72	73	73	74
50	74	75	75	76	76	77	77	77	78	79
60	79	80	80	80	81	81	82	82	83	83
70	83	84	84	85	86	86	86	87	87	88

EXAMPLE:

T-score for 16 sit-ups = 50

Table 70

SIT-UPS (NO TIME LIMIT): SCORING TABLE (GIRLS)

Sit-ups	0	1	2	3	4	5	6	7	8	9
					T-scores					
0		19	25	28	31	33	35	37	39	40
10	42	43	44	45	46	47	48	49	50	51
20	52	53	54	54	55	56	56	57	58	58
30	59	60	60	61	61	62	63	63	64	64
40	65	65	66	66	67	67	68	68	69	69
50	69	69	70	70	70	70	71	71	71	71
60	72	72	72	72	73	73	73	73	73	73
70	74	74	74	74	74	74	74	75	75	75
80	75	75	75	76	76	76	76	76	76	77
90	77	77	77	77	77	78	78	78	78	78
100	78	79	79	79	79	79	79	80	80	80
110	80	80	80	81	81	81	81	81	81	82
120	82	82	82	82	82	83	83	83	83	83
130	83	84	84	84	84	84	84	85	85	85
140	85	85	85	86	86	86	86	86	86	87
150	87	87	87	87	87	88	88	88	88	88
160	88	89	89	89	89	89	89	90	90	90
170	90	90	90	90	91	91	91	91	91	91
180	92	92	92	92	92	92	93	93	93	93
190	93	93	94	94	94	94	94	94	95	95
200	95	95	95	95	96	96	96	96	96	96
210	97	97	97	97	97	97	98	98	98	98
220	98	98	98	99	99	99	99	99	99	100
230	100	100	100	100						

EXAMPLE:

T-score for 18 sit-ups = 50

(3) *Leg lift.* The performer starts from a supine position, with the palms of the hands on the floor, at the sides of the hips. The performer raises the legs, keeping the lower legs completely extended, until the legs are vertical, and then lowers the legs, and repeats these movements as many times as possible. This test is more for the measurement of the strength and the endurance of the thigh flexors than for the measurement of the strength and the endurance of the abdominal muscles.[9] Various scoring

Table 71

BACK LIFTS OR WING LIFTS. SCORING TABLE (GIRLS)

Back Lifts	0	1	2	3	4	5	6	7	8	9
				T-scores						
0		12	16	19	22	24	26	28	30	32
10	33	35	36	37	38	40	41	42	43	44
20	45	46	47	48	49	50	51	52	52	53
30	54	55	56	56	57	58	59	59	60	61
40	62	62	63	64	64	65	65	66	67	67
50	68	69	69	70	70	71	71	72	73	73
60	74	74	75	75	76	76	77	77	77	78

EXAMPLE:

T-score for 25 back lifts • 50

tables have been devised for this test, but on the basis of inadequate re‚ search. It is recommended that a sit-up test be substituted for the leg-lift test.

327. TEST FOR ENDURANCE OF TRUNK EXTENSORS

Back lift or wing lift.[10] The performer starts in a prone position, with the hands clasped behind the head. He raises the head and the trunk upward until only the lowest portion of the rib cage is touching the floor. The height to which the performer rises may be determined as follows. An assistant of the same height as the performer lies prone on the floor, with his head opposite the head of the performer. The assistant places his right

[9] This exercise has been widely condemned on the basis that its execution causes the lumbar curvature to be increased by the contraction of the psoates majores muscles. This conclusion appears to be incorrect, for these muscles act to rotate the lumbar vertebrae clockwise, thus straightening the lumbar spine. In this exercise, the lumbar curvature is increased primarily by the contraction of the recti femorum, the sartorii, and the tensores fasciarum latarum, which contraction causes the pelvis to be rotated clockwise around a transverse axis. This clockwise rotation can readily be prevented by the contraction of the abdominal muscles; hence in the execution of this exercise the performer should attempt to keep the lumbar spine in contact with the mat.

[10] This type of exercise has appeared in tests published by the Women's Army Corps (see Sec. 333).

elbow on the floor, and looks across his clenched fist. The performer raises his body until his eyes are on the same level as those of the assistant. The score is the number of upward movements executed in one minute. Standards for back lifts or wing lifts may be found in Table 71 (p. 175) and in Table 76 (p. 179).

Table 72

SQUAT JUMPS: SCORING TABLE (BOYS)

Squat Jumps	0	1	2	3	4	5	6	7	8	9
					T-scores					
160	98	98	99	99	99	99	99	99	100	100
150	96	96	97	97	97	97	97	98	98	98
140	94	94	95	95	95	95	95	96	96	96
130	92	92	92	93	93	93	93	94	94	94
120	90	90	90	91	91	91	91	91	92	92
110	87	88	88	88	88	89	89	89	89	90
100	85	85	85	86	86	86	87	87	87	87
90	82	82	83	83	83	84	84	84	84	85
80	79	79	79	80	80	80	81	81	81	82
70	75	76	76	76	77	77	77	78	78	78
60	71	72	72	72	73	73	74	74	74	75
50	65	65	66	66	67	68	69	69	70	71
40	56	57	58	59	59	60	61	62	63	64
30	45	46	47	49	50	51	52	53	54	55
20	29	31	33	35	36	38	39	41	42	44
10	3	7	10	13	16	19	21	23	25	28

EXAMPLE:

T-score for 34 squat jumps = 50

328. TESTS FOR ENDURANCE OF MUSCLES OF LEGS

(1) *Squat jumps.* The performer stands with the hands clasped together on the top of the head, and the right foot about twelve inches in front of the left foot. He squats down until the right heel touches the right buttock. He then jumps upward until both lower legs are completely extended, and the feet have cleared the floor. Then he squats down until the left heel touches the left buttock. He then jumps upward as before, and repeats the movements as many times as possible. If the movements are not continuous (i.e., if the performer stops to rest), the exercise should be stopped, and the performer retested later. In order that the knees may become accustomed to the movements involved in the squat jump, this exercise should be preceded by exercise in the full squat for several weeks, and then the number of performances in the squat jump should be increased gradually. Standards for squat jumps may be found in Table 72 (p. 176).

(2) *Step tests.* The various forms of the Harvard Step Test (see Secs. 498-500) and the Taylor Pack Test (see Sec. 503) may be used as tests of leg endurance, although they qualify as tests of general endurance as well.

329. TESTS FOR ENDURANCE OF WHOLE BODY

(1) *Squat thrusts* (see Sec. 172) performed for ten seconds were previously presented as a measurement of agility. Squat thrusts performed for at least thirty seconds by girls and for one minute[11] by boys may be used as a measurement of endurance. Standards for twenty-second squat thrusts may be found in Table 73 (p. 177) and for one-minute squat thrusts in Table 74 (p. 178).

Table 73

SQUAT THRUSTS (20 SECONDS):   SCORING TABLE (BOYS)

Squat Thrusts	0	1/4	1/2	3/4
		T-scores		
21	97	98	100	
20	91	92	94	95
19	85	86	87	89
18	78	80	81	83
17	72	74	75	77
16	66	67	69	70
15	59	61	62	64
14	53	55	56	58
13	47	48	50	51
12	40	42	44	45
11	34	36	37	38
10	28	29	31	32
9	22	23	25	26
8	15	17	18	20
7	9	11	12	14
6	3	4	6	7

EXAMPLE:

T-score for 13½ squat thrusts in twenty seconds = 50

330. (2) The *Army Test of Endurance*[12] includes pull-ups, squat jumps, floor push-ups, sit-ups for two minutes, and a 300-yard run. The last item is a measurement of circulorespiratory endurance. Standards for pull-ups may be found in Table 75 (p. 178); for squat jumps, in Table 72 (p. 176); for floor push-ups, in Table 65 (p. 170); for sit-ups, in Table 67 (pp. 172-73); and for the 300-yard run, in Table 81 (first two columns) (pp. 186-87). The standards given in this text are T-scores ranging from five standard deviations above to five standard deviations below the mean, and do not correspond to the Army standards.

[11] A time limit of twenty seconds has been used for this test by the Armed Services. If executed for twenty seconds, the squat thrusts are an adequate measurement of agility but not of endurance.

[12] *Physical Training*, War Department Field Manual 21-20 (1950). The Army standards are based on P-scores ranging from three standard deviations above to three standard deviations below the mean. Hence in a good program of physical education many performers surpass the highest scores included in the scoring tables of the Manual.

331. (3) The *Iowa High-school Test of Endurance*[13] includes pull-ups, floor push-ups, squat jumps, sit-ups for two minutes, and squat thrusts for one minute. The standards are scores ranging from five standard deviations above to five standard deviations below the mean. Standards for pull-ups may be found in Table 75 (p. 178); for floor push-ups, in Table

Table 74

SQUAT THRUSTS (1 MINUTE): SCORING TABLE (BOYS)

Squat Thrusts	0	1	2	3	4	5	6	7	8	9
				T-scores						
0			1	2	4	5	6	7	9	10
10	12	14	15	17	19	21	23	25	27	29
20	31	33	35	37	39	42	44	46	49	51
30	53	56	58	61	63	66	68	71	74	76
40	79	82	84	87	90	92	95	98	100	

EXAMPLE:

T-score for 29 squat thrusts in one minute = 51

65 (p. 170); for squat jumps, in Table 72 (p. 176); for sit-ups, in Table 67 (pp. 172-73); for squat thrusts for twenty seconds, in Table 73 (p. 177), and for squat thrusts for one minute, in Table 74 (p. 178).

332. (4) The *Navy Test of Endurance* includes squat thrusts for one minute, sit-ups with no time limit, floor push-ups, squat jumps, and pull-ups. If sit-ups for two minutes are substituted for sit-ups with no time limit, this combination of tests appears to be the best test presented in

Table 75

PULL-UPS: SCORING TABLE (BOYS)

Pull-ups	T-scores	Pull-ups	T-scores	Pull-ups	T-scores	Pull-ups	T-scores
44	100	33	91	22	78	11	59
43	99	32	90	21	76	10	56
42	99	31	89	20	75	9	54
41	98	30	88	19	73	8	52
40	97	29	87	18	72	7	50
39	97	28	86	17	70	6	47
38	96	27	85	16	68	5	45
37	95	26	83	15	66	4	42
36	94	25	82	14	65	3	39
35	93	24	81	13	63	2	36
34	92	23	79	12	61	1	33

EXAMPLE:

T-score for 7 pull-ups = 50

[13] *The Iowa Program of Physical Education for Boys.*

TABLE 76

MUSCULAR ENDURANCE--WAC TEST: SCORING TABLES (WOMEN)

Point Scores	Push-ups	Sit-ups	Wing Lifts	Squat Thrusts
100	19 F*	91 and up	112	23
98		88-90	111	
96	18 F	85-87	109-110	
94	17 F	82-84	107-108	22
92		79-81	105-106	
90	16 F	76-78	104	
88	15 F	73-75	102-103	21
86		70-72	100-101	
84	14 F	67-69	98-99	
82	13 F	64-66	97	20
80		62-63	95-96	
78	12 F	59-61	93-94	
76	11 F	56-58	91-92	19
74		53-55	90	
72	10 F	50-52	88-89	
70	9 F	48-49	86-87	18
68		46-47	85	
66	8 F	44-45	83-84	
64	7 F	42-43	81-82	17
62		40-41	79-80	
60	6 F	38-39	77-78	
58	5 F	36-37	75-76	
56		34-35	74	16
54	4 F	32-33	72-73	
52	3 F	30-31	70-71	
50		28-29	69	15
48	2 F	26-27	67-68	
46	1 F	25	65-66	
44		23-24	63-64	14
42	10 K**	21-22	62	
40	9 K	20	60-61	
38	8 K	18-19	58-59	13
36	7 K	16-17	56-57	
34	6 K	15	54-55	
32	5 K	13-14	52-53	12
30		12	51	
28	4 K	11	49-50	
26		10	48	11
24	3 K	9	46-47	
22		8	44-45	
20	2 K	7	42-43	10
18		6	41	
16		5	39-40	9
14	1 K	4	37-38	
12		3	36	8
10		2	34-35	
8		1	32-33	7
6			30-31	6
4			28-29	5
2			25-27	4

*F = floor push-up
**K = knee push-up

this section for the measurement of muscular endurance only. It is essentially the same as the Iowa High-school Test (see Sec. 331). The Navy Test can very well be supplemented by tests of strength and of circulorespiratory endurance. For young boys squat thrusts for thirty seconds may be substituted for squat thrusts for one minute, and sit-ups for one minute may be substituted for sit-ups for two minutes. Standards for squat thrusts may be found in Table 74 (p. 178); for sit-ups, in Table 67 (pp. 172-73); for floor push-ups, in Table 65 (p. 170); for squat jumps, in Table 72 (p. 176); and for pull-ups, in Table 75 (p. 178).

TESTS OF MUSCULAR ENDURANCE FOR GIRLS

333. (1) *The WAC Test of Muscular Endurance*[14] includes push-ups, sit-ups, wing lifts (see Sec. 327), and squat thrusts for thirty seconds. The first ten push-ups are knee push-ups. The push-ups after the tenth are

Table 77

MUSCULAR ENDURANCE--NSWA PHYSICAL-PERFORMANCE LEVELS
(HIGH-SCHOOL GIRLS)

(1945 REVISION)

Scale Score	Standing Broad Jump	Basket Ball Throw	Potato Race	Pull- ups	Push- ups	Sit- ups	Squat Thrusts (10 sec.)	Squat Thrusts (30 sec.)
100	7-9	78	8.4	47	61	65	9-1	24
95	7-7	75	8.6	45	58	61	9	23
90	7-4	72	8.8	42	54	57	8-3	22
85	7-2	68	9.0	39	51	54	8-1	21
80	6-11	65	9.4	37	47	50	8	20
75	6-9	62	9.6	34	43	46	7-3	19
70	6-7	59	10.0	32	39	43	7-1	18-2
65	6-4	56	10.2	29	36	39	7	18
60	6-2	53	10.4	26	32	36	6-2	17
55	6-0	50	10.6	24	28	33	6-1	16
50	5-9	46	11.0	21	25	29	6	15
45	5-7	43	11.2	18	21	25	5-2	14-2
40	5-5	40	11.6	16	17	22	5-1	14
35	5-2	37	11.8	13	13	18	4-3	13
30	5-0	34	12.0	10	10	15	4-2	12
25	4-9	31	12.4	8	6	11	4	11
20	4-7	27	12.6	5	2	7	3-3	10
15	4-4	24	13.0	3	1	3	3-2	9
10	4-2	21	13.2	1	0	1	3	8-2
5	4-0	18	13.4	0	0	0	2-3	7-2
0	3-9	15	13.6	0	0	0	2-2	7

floor push-ups. The sit-ups are executed with the lower legs partially flexed and with the soles of the feet on the floor. The arms, which are at the sides in the starting position, are thrust forward when the sit-ups are executed. Standards may be found in Table 76 (p. 179).

334. (2) The *NSWA Physical-performance Levels for high-school*

[14] *War Department Training Circular*, No. 40, June, 1944.

girls[15] include eight items, the last five of which are the following muscular-endurance tests: modified pull-ups, modified push-ups, sit-ups, and squat thrusts for ten seconds or for thirty seconds. This test is discussed more fully in Chapter 18. Standards for these tests may be found in Table 77 (p. 180).

Tests of muscular endurance for boys and for girls can be easily constructed. For boys, for example, the following items constitute an excellent test of muscular endurance: (1) squat thrusts for thirty or sixty seconds, (2) a form of push-ups, (3) sit-ups for thirty seconds or for one or two minutes, and (4) squat jumps. For girls, the first three items constitute an excellent test of muscular endurance.

MISCELLANEOUS TABLES

335. *Full squats for girls* (Table 78, p. 181) are executed as follows. The girl flexes her legs and thighs and squats all the way down. Only the toes are in contact with the floor. The trunk and the head are held erect. The arms and fingers are thrust forward. The girl then rises to a stand-

Table 78

FULL SQUATS: SCORING TABLE (GIRLS)

Squats	0	1	2	3	4	5	6	7	8	9
					T-scores					
0							3	7	10	13
10	15	17	19	21	23	25	26	27	29	30
20	31	32	33	34	35	36	37	38	39	40
30	41	42	42	43	44	44	45	46	46	47
40	48	48	49	49	50	50	51	51	52	52
50	53	54	54	54	54	55	56	56	56	57
60	57	57	58	58	59	59	59	60	60	60
70	61	61	61	62	62	62	63	63	63	64
80	64	64	64	65	65	65	66	66	66	66
90	67	67	67	67	68	68	68	68	69	69
100	69	69	70	70	70	70	70	71	71	71
110	71	72	72	72	72	72	73	73	73	73
120	73	74	74	74	74	74	75	75	75	75
130	75	75	76	76	76	76	76	77	77	77
140	77	77	77	78	78	78	78	78	78	78
150	79	79	79	79	79	79	80	80	80	80
160	80	80	80	81	81	81	81	81	81	81
170	82	82	82	82	82	82	82	83	83	83
180	83	83	83	83	83	84	84	84	84	84
190	84	84	84	85	85	85	85	85	85	85
200	85	86	86	86	86	86	86	86	86	86
210	87	87	87	87	87	87	87	87	87	88
220	88	88	88	88	88	88	88	88	88	89
230	89	89	89	89	89	89	89	89	89	90

EXAMPLE:

T-score for 44-45 squat thrusts = 50

[15] "Physical Performance Levels for High School Girls," *Journal of Health and Physical Education*, June, 1945.

ing position with the shoulders back, the upper arms hyperextended and the forearms flexed forward, and the fingers clenched.

Equivalents of knee push-ups and floor push-ups may be found in Table 79 (p. 182).

Table 79

PUSH-UPS FROM FLOOR AND PUSH-UPS FROM KNEES:
EQUIVALENTS (GIRLS)

Knee Push-ups	Floor Push-ups	Knee Push-ups	Floor Push-ups	Knee Push-ups	Floor Push-ups
14	1	28	9	36	17
16	2	30	10	37	18
19	3	31	11	37	19
21	4	32	12	38	20
22	5	33	13	38	21
24	6	34	14	39	22
26	7	35	15	39	23
27	8	35	16	40	24

336. TESTS OF CIRCULORESPIRATORY ENDURANCE THAT INVOLVE RUNNING

337. Carlson Fatigue-curve Test.[16] The performer lifts and lowers his feet alternately, just high enough to clear the floor, as fast as he can for ten seconds. He counts the number of contacts of either the right or the left foot with the floor for ten seconds, and then rests for ten seconds. He executes ten such bouts of stationary running, with a rest of ten seconds between each two bouts of running. He should run at full speed during each inning, and not pace himself. If this rule is strictly adhered to, the number of steps taken in every bout after the first bout is smaller than the number of steps taken in the preceding bout. The score is the number of double steps performed in the ten innings of running.

Ten seconds after the completion of the tenth bout of running, and upon a signal given by the tester, the performer counts the beats of his pulse for ten seconds. Similarly at the end of two minutes, at the end of four minutes, and at the end of six minutes, he counts the beats of his pulse. The sum of the beats of the pulse (five countings) represents the "cost" (in heart beats) for the "production" (i.e., the number of steps run). In cases in which this test has been used as a conditioning exercise, it has been found that, as condition was improved, the number of steps was increased and the number of beats of the pulse was decreased. Hence this test has the advantage of being usable as a conditioning device. It has been used in many instances as one means of conditioning for basketball teams.[17]

[16] H. C. Carlson, "Fatigue Curve Test," *Research Quarterly*, October, 1945.
[17] Basketball players who have performed the Carlson Test daily have appeared to develop circulorespiratory endurance, and have appeared to be fresh at the end

338. Shuttle runs, with speed held constant. The statement that distance running has one shortcoming as an accurate measurement of circulo-respiratory endurance may be clarified by the following illustration. A can run 100 yards in 10 seconds, and B cannot run this distance in less than 15 seconds. Both A and B are in an excellent state of training. B, however, is innately slow and cannot move his limbs as fast as A can. If A and B were to run $\frac{1}{2}$ mile at top speed, A would probably run it in about 1:58, while B would run it in about 2:56. Corresponding times for running 1 mile would be 4:26 for A, and 6:38 for B; that is, on the basis of the time, B would be considered to have poor endurance, but relative to his potentiality in speed, his endurance would be as good as that of A. If A ran 1 mile in 4:50 and B in 6:40, B would really be in better circulorespiratory condition than A would be.

Circulorespiratory endurance may be measured rather accurately by the division of the time for a distance run (e.g., 200 yards, 300 yards) by the time for a sprint (e.g., 60-yard dash). The result is called an "endurance quotient."

339. In order that a large number of performers may run and be timed at one time, the following modifications are suggested for the conduct of the races. All the performers run for six seconds, and the distances run in six seconds are interpreted in terms of the times in which they would run a 60-yard dash. Then all the performers run two or three hundred yards, and are timed to the nearest half second. The endurance quotient is the time for the 200- or the 300-yard run divided by the time (obtained from the six-second run) that would correspond to the time for the 60-yard dash. The times for the 200- or the 300-yard run and for the 60-yard dash are T-scored, and the endurance quotient can be read from a two-dimensional table.

The six-second run may be a straightaway run or a shuttle run. Markers of heavy cardboard about nine inches square, with the appropriate yardages painted on them, are placed, for the straightaway run, at intervals of two yards from 34 to 56 yards and, for indoor shuttle runs (see Sec. 343), from 20 to 46 yards. (If chalk lines are drawn on the ground, the scoring is expedited.) An inspector is stationed in each lane about forty-five yards from the starting line in the case of the straightaway run, and about ten yards from the far end of the lane in the case of a shuttle run. The starter calls the usual "Get on your marks," "Get set," and "Go" signals. On the "Get-set" signal he raises his hand, with a white handkerchief in it, and on the "Go" signal waves the handkerchief downward. On the command

---

of competitive games. A track coach has reported that one year when he was unable to have his trackmen work outdoors prior to the state indoor meet, he used the Carlson Test, for purposes of conditioning, eventually increasing the number of seconds for each inning. That year his distance runners, with practically no other training, won the mile and half-mile races and the mile relay in the winter indoor championship meet in excellent times.

"Go," the starter starts his watch. He counts the third, the fourth, and the fifth second aloud, and at the end of six seconds blows the whistle. Each inspector records the distance that his runner has run. If the front of the chest of the runner is just at or past a card, the number of yards on the card is recorded; if halfway between two cards or just beyond halfway between two cards, the number of yards halfway between the two cards is recorded. Two trials, which may be very close together, should be given. There should be a five-minute rest period before the performer executes the 200- or the 300-yard run.

340. The 200-yard run for high-school boys is executed on a 100-yard straightaway (usually lengthwise on a football field). The performer runs down the straightaway, around a stake in the ground, and back to the starting line. The signals for starting are the same as those for the six-second run. As the first runner approaches the end of the 200-yard run, the starter counts the seconds aloud, with the accented syllable corresponding to the full second in the count and a hup for the half second; for example, twenty-*six*, hup, twenty-*seven*, hup. Each inspector records, to the nearest half second, the time for his runner; if the runner crosses the finish line when the timer calls "Thirty," the time is recorded as thirty seconds. If the runner crosses the finish line when the timer calls "Hup" after thirty, the time is recorded as thirty and one-half seconds (Table 80, p. 185).

341. The 300-yard run may be executed on a 60-yard course. There should be a stake in the middle of both ends of each lane around which the performer runs. The performer runs the course five times, thus finishing at the opposite end from which he started. The administration of the 300-yard run is the same as that for the 200-yard run. Running-endurance quotients for the 300-yard run may be obtained from Table 81 (pp. 186-87).

342. A 375-yard run may be executed on a 75-yard course.[18] Boards are fastened to the floor at the ends of the lanes in such a way that the angle between the board and the course is 135 degrees (the angles between the board and the floor in front of the starting line and between the board and the floor beyond the other end of the lane are 45 degrees each.) The runner starts with one foot against the board at the starting line. He runs up and down the lanes five times, using the boards at the ends of the lanes as devices for assisting him to turn. He finishes the race by jumping over the board at the end opposite from which he originally started. The administration of the 375-yard shuttle run is the same as that for the 300-yard shuttle run. Running-endurance quotients are not available for the 375-yard run.

343. The indoor short shuttle run may conveniently be executed in a gymnasium. Two lines, twenty yards apart, are marked on the floor. For the run equivalent to the six-second run, the runner starts at one end, runs to the other end, touches one foot over this end and returns to the starting

[18] Proposed by the Air Forces for an indoor course.

Table 80

SIX-SECOND- AND 200-YARD-RUN ENDURANCE TEST: SCORING TABLES (BOYS)

Time (sec.)	Pt. Score	32	33	34	35	36	37	38	39	40	41	42	43	44	45	46	47	48	49	50	51	52	53	54	55	56	57
Yds. run in →		32	33	34	35	36	37	38	39	40	41	42	43	44	45	46	47	48	49	50	51	52	53	54	55	56	57
6 sec. Pt. Score →		24	25	27	28	30	32	34	36	38	40	42	44	46	48	50	53	55	57	60	63	66	69	72	75	78	81
										Endurance Scores																
22	100	92	95	98	101	104																					
23	85	85	88	91	94	97	100	103																			
24	75	78	81	84	87	90	93	96	99	102																	
25	67	71	74	77	80	83	86	89	92	95	98	101	104														
26	60	64	67	70	73	76	79	82	85	88	91	94	97	100	103												
27	55	57	60	63	66	69	72	75	78	81	84	87	90	93	96	99	102										
28	51	50	53	56	59	62	65	68	71	74	77	80	83	86	89	92	95	98	101	104							
29	47	43	46	49	52	55	58	61	64	67	70	73	76	79	82	85	88	91	94	97	100	103					
30	44	36	39	42	45	48	51	54	57	60	63	66	69	72	75	78	81	84	87	90	93	96	99	102			
31	41	29	32	35	38	41	44	47	50	53	56	59	62	65	68	71	74	77	80	83	86	89	92	95	98	101	104
32	38	22	25	28	31	34	37	40	43	46	49	52	55	58	61	64	67	70	73	76	79	82	85	88	91	94	97
33	35	15	18	21	24	27	30	33	36	39	42	45	48	51	54	57	60	63	66	69	72	75	78	81	84	87	90
34	33	8	11	14	17	20	23	26	29	32	35	38	41	44	47	50	53	56	59	62	65	68	71	74	77	80	83
35	31	1	4	7	10	13	16	19	22	25	28	31	34	37	40	43	46	49	52	55	58	61	64	67	70	73	76
36	28				3	6	9	12	15	18	21	24	27	30	33	36	39	42	45	48	51	54	57	60	63	66	69
37	26						2	5	8	11	14	17	20	23	26	29	32	35	38	41	44	47	50	53	56	59	62
38	24								1	4	7	10	13	16	19	22	25	28	31	34	37	40	43	46	49	52	55
39	23											3	6	9	12	15	18	21	24	27	30	33	36	39	42	45	48
40	21													2	5	8	11	14	17	20	23	26	29	32	35	38	41
41	20															1	4	7	10	13	16	19	22	25	28	31	34
42	18																		3	6	9	12	15	18	21	24	27
43	17																				2	5	8	11	14	17	20
44	15																						1	4	7	10	13
45	14																									3	6
46	12																										
47	11																										
48	10																										
49	8																										

EXAMPLE:

Score for 200-yard run in 32 seconds = 38
Score for 41 yards run in 6 seconds = 40
Endurance Score = 49

Table 81

SIX-SECOND- AND 300-YARD-RUN ENDURANCE TEST:
SCORING TABLES (BOYS)

Endurance Scores

Time (sec.)	T-score	Yds. run in 32	33	34	35	36	37	38	39	40	41	42	43	44	45	46	47	48	49	50	51	52	53	54	55	56
6 sec. T-score						2	8	14	20	25	30	35	40	46	51	57	63	68	74	80	85	90	96	102	107	113
42	100	74	76	78	80	82	84	86	88	90	92	94	96	98	100	102										
43		68	70	72	74	76	78	80	82	84	86	88	90	92	94	96	98	100	102							
44		62	64	66	68	70	72	74	76	78	80	82	84	86	88	90	92	94	96	98	100	102				
45	92	56	58	60	62	64	66	68	70	72	74	76	78	80	82	84	86	88	90	92	94	96	98	100	102	
46	85	50	52	54	56	58	60	62	64	66	68	70	72	74	76	78	80	82	84	86	88	90	92	94	96	98
47	78	44	46	48	50	52	54	56	58	60	62	64	66	68	70	72	74	76	78	80	82	84	86	88	90	92
48	71	38	40	42	44	46	48	50	52	54	56	58	60	62	64	66	68	70	72	74	76	78	80	82	84	86
49	65	32	34	36	38	40	42	44	46	48	50	52	54	56	58	60	62	64	66	68	70	72	74	76	78	80
50	59	26	28	30	32	34	36	38	40	42	44	46	48	50	52	54	56	58	60	62	64	66	68	70	72	74
51	53	20	22	24	26	28	30	32	34	36	38	40	42	44	46	48	50	52	54	56	58	60	62	64	66	68
52	47	14	16	18	20	22	24	26	28	30	32	34	36	38	40	42	44	46	48	50	52	54	56	58	60	62
53	41	8	10	12	14	16	18	20	22	24	26	28	30	32	34	36	38	40	42	44	46	48	50	52	54	56
54	35	2	4	6	8	10	12	14	16	18	20	22	24	26	28	30	32	34	36	38	40	42	44	46	48	50
55	30				2	4	6	8	10	12	14	16	18	20	22	24	26	28	30	32	34	36	38	40	42	44
56	25								3	5	7	9	11	13	15	17	19	21	23	25	27	29	31	33	35	37
57	20											3	5	7	9	11	13	15	17	19	21	23	25	27	29	31
58	15														3	5	7	9	11	13	15	17	19	21	23	25
59	10																	3	5	7	9	11	13	15	17	19
60	6																				3	5	7	9	11	13
61	2																							3	5	7
62																										
63																										
64																										

Table 81 (continued)

Yds. run in 6 sec.	32	33	34	35	36	37	38	39	40	41	42	43	44	45	46	47	48	49	50	51	52	53	54	55	56
T-score					2	8	14	20	25	30	35	40	46	51	57	63	68	74	80	85	90	96	102	107	113

Time (sec.)	32	33	34	35	36	37	38	39
T-score								
65	43	38	33	28	22	15	8	3
66	38	33	28	23	17	10	3	
67	34	29	23	18	12	5		
68	30	24	18	13	7			
69	25	20	13	8	2			
70	20	15	8	3				
71	16	10	3					
72	11	5						
73	7	0						
74	2							

EXAMPLE:

T-score for 300-yard run in 55 seconds = 30
T-score for 40 yards run in 6 seconds = 25
Endurance Score = 52

line.[19] For the run that corresponds to the 200- or the 300-yard run, boys complete four round trips on the course, and girls complete three round trips on the course. The administration of the run is the same as that for the 200- or the 300-yard run. Running-endurance quotients for boys may be found in Table 82 (p. 188), and for girls, in Table 83 (p. 189).

344. Distance runs (440 yards, 880 yards, 1 mile) that are used alone for measures of endurance should be scored according to the directions for scoring them in connection with the athletics quotients (see Sec. 355).

Table 82

TWO-LAP- AND EIGHT-LAP-INDOOR-SHUTTLE-RUN ENDURANCE TEST:
SCORING TABLES (BOYS)

Yds. run in 6 sec.	20	22	24	26	28	30	32	34	36	38	40
T-score	23	27	31	35	40	45	51	56	63	70	78

Time (sec.) for Eight-lap Shuttle	T-score, Eight-lap Shuttle	20	22	24	26	28	30	32	34	36	38	40
28	86										84	80
29	77						88	84	80	77	71	65
30	68		84	83	81	79	77	73	69	66	60	55
31	60	80	78	76	74	71	68	64	61	56	52	47
32	54	75	72	70	68	64	60	56	52	49	45	42
33	50	70	67	64	62	58	53	50	46	43	41	38
34	46	65	63	60	56	52	47	44	41	39	37	35
35	42	61	59	56	52	47	43	40	38	36	34	33
36	40	58	56	52	47	43	39	36	35	34	32	31
37	38	55	52	49	43	40	36	34	33	32	30	29
38	36	51	49	45	40	37	34	32	31	30	28	27
39	34	48	45	42	37	35	32	30	29	28	26	25
40	32	45	42	39	35	33	30	28	27	26	25	24
41	31	42	39	36	33	31	28	27	26	24	23	22
42	29	39	36	34	31	29	26	25	24	23	22	21
43	28	37	34	32	29	27	25	24	23	22	21	20
44	27	35	32	30	28	26	23	22	21	21	20	
45	26	33	31	28	26	24	22	21	20	20		
46	25	31	29	27	25	23	21	20				
47	24	29	27	25	23	21	20					
48	23	28	26	24	22	20						
49	22	26	25	23	21							
50	21	25	23	21	20	Endurance T-scores						
51	20	23	21	20								
52	19	22	20									
53	18	21	19									
54	17	20										

EXAMPLE:

T-score for running eight laps in 36 seconds = 40
T-score for running two laps in 24 seconds = 31
Endurance quotient = 52

[19] A 60-yard outdoor course is used for a run to correspond to the six-second run, and a 40-yard indoor course is used for a run to correspond to the six-second run. The reason for the differences in the length of the courses is that approximately two seconds are required for making the turn on the indoor course.

345. TESTS OF CIRCULORESPIRATORY ENDURANCE THAT INVOLVE SWIMMING

346. Cureton Swimming Test for Endurance in Speed Swimming.[20] The following instructions for the administration of the Cureton Swimming Test for Endurance in Speed Swimming are quoted from the author of the test:

(1) Place the swimmer in the water, feet against the wall and holding on to the gutter with one hand, facing in the direction of the swim.

(2) Instruct the swimmer to swim as *fast as possible* for 60 feet.

Table 83

TWO-LAP- AND SIX-LAP-INDOOR-SHUTTLE-RUN ENDURANCE TEST:
SCORING TABLES (GIRLS)

Yds. run in 6 sec.	18	20	22	24	26	28	30	32	34	36	38	40
T-score	23	28	33	38	43	48	53	58	63	68	73	78

Time (sec.) for Six-lap Shuttle	T-score for Six-lap Shuttle	18	20	22	24	26	28	30	32	34	36	38	40
20	110			87	85	83	81	79	77	76	75	74	73
21	99	87	85	83	81	79	77	75	73	72	71	70	69
22	88	83	81	79	77	75	73	71	70	69	68	67	66
23	79	79	77	75	73	71	69	68	67	66	65	63	62
24	71	76	73	71	70	68	66	65	64	62	61	59	57
25	64	73	70	68	67	65	62	61	59	58	56	54	52
26	58	70	67	65	63	61	58	56	54	53	51	49	48
27	52	66	63	62	59	57	54	52	50	48	46	45	44
28	48	62	60	58	55	53	50	48	46	44	42	41	40
29	44	59	57	54	51	49	46	44	42	40	39	38	36
30	40	56	54	51	48	45	42	40	39	37	36	35	33
31	37	52	50	47	44	41	39	37	35	34	33	32	30
32	34	48	46	43	40	37	35	33	32	30	29	28	27
33	29	44	42	39	36	33	31	30	28	26	25	24	23
34	27	40	38	35	32	29	27	26	24	22	21	20	19
35	25	36	34	31	28	25	23	22	20	18	17	16	15
36	23	32	29	27	24	22	20	18	16	14	13		
37	22	28	26	23	21	18	16						
38	21	25	23	20	18								
39	20	22	20	18									

Endurance T-scores

EXAMPLE:

T-score for running six laps in 31 seconds = 37
T-score for running two laps in 20 seconds = 28
Endurance quotient   = 50

(3) Start the swimmer with a sharp command or whistle and simultaneously start a stop watch (double-hand preferred). Stop the watch when the swimmer has completed the 60-foot sprint.

(4) Rest at least 15 minutes.

(5) Instruct the swimmer to swim 100 yards by *doing the first lap as fast as possible* and then doing the best possible on the other laps. Have at hand his previous time for 60 feet at top speed so that if the time of the first lap is not

[20] Thomas K. Cureton, Jr., "A Test for Endurance in Speed Swimming," *Supplement to Research Quarterly*, May, 1935. Republished by permission of the author.

within ½ second of the previous first lap time, the swimmer can be stopped and take the rest of the test when he *can* do the first lap as fast as possible.

(6) Start the swimmer again and also the double-handed stop watch. Time each lap of the swim and record the times.

(7) Compute the time of each lap by deducting the first lap from the second, the second from the third, etc. Compute the drop-off index by deducting the time of the first lap from the second, the second from the third, the third from the fourth, and the fourth from the fifth. Add all of the differences cumulatively. An example follows:

	Cumulative Time (sec.)	Time per lap (sec.)	Drop-off (sec.)
Time at 20 yds.	9.6	9.6	
Time at 40 yds.	21.0	11.4	1.8
Time at 60 yds.	33.4	12.4	1.0
Time at 80 yds.	46.4	13.0	.6
Time at 100 yds.	59.2	12.8	-.2
		Total	3.2

Note that the drop-off index can be secured by deducting the time of the first lap from the time of the last lap. However, the intermediate drop-off times are interesting for the swimmer to see. The times should gradually increase. If there is a negative result on any lap, it indicates that the swimmer paced the race and did not "go his limit." It is true that swimmers who do this will have a better endurance index than they deserve. They should be made to repeat the test.

Note: Proceed in a similar manner for the seventy-five foot pool.

(8) Look up both the speed and drop-off endurance ratings on the performance ladders (percentile charts) and give the swimmer a rating on each ladder. How many more rungs does he have to climb on the speed ladder? On the endurance ladder?

(9) Instruct those who are relatively low in endurance or lower than their speed rating that they will have to train harder. Suggest what they may do in diet, pool dosage, stretching or relaxation drills.

(10) Show that the time in the 100-yard swim can be computed very closely:

Method: (60-foot pool)

Multiply the time of the first lap × 5 =   (× 4 for 75′ pool)
Multiply the drop-off index × 2.25 =   (× 2.6 for 75′ pool)
Constant = 5.5
Add all =   Calculated time

(11) Time the swimmer in a 100-yard swim his regular pace on another day and compare the result.

Percentile ratings and endurance scores for the Cureton Test, which has a high degree of reliability, may be found in Table 84 (p. 191). The major difficulty in the administration of the Cureton Test is in preventing the performer from pacing himself during the first lap and hence not going "all out."

347. Moyle Test for Endurance in Speed Swimming.[21] The directions for the administration of the Moyle Test, which is somewhat simpler than the Cureton Test, are as follows.

[21] William J. Moyle, "A Study of Speed and Heart Size as Related to Endurance in Swimming" (M.A. Thesis, State University of Iowa, 1936).

Table 84

SWIMMING SPEED AND ENDURANCE IN 100-YARD CRAWL STROKE (CURETON)*:
SCORING TABLE (COLLEGE MEN)

Percentile rating	Rungs to climb	TIME OF SHORT SPRINT (START IN WATER) 60 feet (seconds)	75 feet (seconds)	ENDURANCE INDEX (1st lap from last) (seconds)	Time in 100 yards (seconds)
100	0	8.8	10.8	.5	49.7
99	1	9.0	11.0	1.0	51.9
98	2	9.4	11.4	1.1	54.1
97	3	9.6	11.6	1.2	55.7
96	4	9.8	11.8	1.3	57.4
95	5	10.0	12.0	1.6	59.0
94	6	10.1	12.1	2.0	60.7
93	7	10.3	12.3	2.3	62.3
92	8	10.5	12.5	2.6	63.9
91	9	10.7	12.7	3.0	65.9
90	10	10.9	12.9	3.3	67.3
88	12	11.0	13.0	3.5	68.5
86	14	11.1	13.1	3.8	69.6
84	16	11.2	13.2	4.1	70.2
82	18	11.3	13.3	4.4	71.3
80	20	11.4	13.4	4.7	72.5
78	22	11.5	13.5	4.8	73.4
76	24	11.6	13.6	5.0	74.0
74	26	11.65	13.65	5.2	74.8
72	28	11.7	13.7	5.4	75.7
70	30	11.75	13.75	5.6	76.5
68	32	11.8	13.8	5.8	77.4
66	34	11.9	13.9	6.0	78.3
64	36	12.0	14.0	6.2	79.2
62	38	12.1	14.1	6.3	80.2
60	40	12.2	14.2	6.5	81.1
58	42	12.3	14.3	6.7	81.9
56	44	12.35	14.35	6.9	82.5
54	46	12.4	14.4	7.1	83.4
52	48	12.5	14.5	7.2	84.2
50	50	12.6	14.6	7.4	84.9
48	52	12.7	14.7	7.6	85.9
46	54	12.8	14.8	7.7	86.7
44	56	12.9	14.9	7.9	87.8
42	58	13.1	15.1	8.0	88.7
40	60	13.2	15.2	8.1	89.7
38	62	13.3	15.3	8.3	90.4
36	64	13.35	15.35	8.4	91.1
34	66	13.4	15.4	8.5	91.7
32	68	13.5	15.5	8.7	92.4
30	70	13.6	15.6	8.8	93.1
28	72	13.8	15.8	9.0	94.7
26	74	14.0	16.0	9.2	96.2
24	76	14.2	16.2	9.4	97.6
22	78	14.3	16.3	9.7	98.9
20	80	14.4	16.4	10.0	100.2
18	82	14.7	16.7	10.4	102.2
16	84	15.0	17.0	10.7	104.3
14	86	15.2	17.2	11.0	106.4
12	88	15.5	17.5	11.4	108.4
10	90	15.7	17.7	11.7	110.5
05	95	17.3	19.3	15.1	126.3
00	100	19.3	21.3	18.6	143.9

*Republished by permission of T. K. Cureton, Jr.

Two marks, five and fifteen yards, respectively, from the take-off are made on the side of the pool. The swimmer starts in the water at the take-off end and pushes off as in a turn. He swims at full speed until he has passed the 15-yard mark. He is timed from the 5- to the 15-yard mark, the watch being started and stopped as the head of the swimmer enters and leaves the zone. The swimmer is instructed to swim at top speed for this distance. Two or three trials are given, and the best time is recorded. After resting for twenty minutes or longer, the performer swims one hundred yards, pacing himself according to his judgment.

The Moyle Swimming-endurance Quotient is obtained by the division of the time for the swimming of one hundred yards by the time in seconds required for the swimming of ten yards. For varsity and freshman swimmers at the State University of Iowa an average index of 10.35 was obtained, with the best index being 9.9. Norms have not been established for the Moyle Test, nor have the results of this test been correlated with those of the Cureton Test.

348. Uses of tests of endurance that involve running and swimming. The tests that involve running measure the endurance of a performer relative to his speed. In the swimming tests a complicated problem is involved by the differences of various bodies in resistance to the water;[22] hence some performers have to use a larger percentage of their strength to attain their maximum velocity in the water than do others. The two swimming tests, however, do measure swimming endurance or, perhaps more accurately, relative racing efficiency. No matter what the reason may be for a large dropping-off in endurance over one's highest speed, the fact remains that if there be a large dropping-off, the performer does not function well as a swimmer. All the tests serve as excellent criteria of endurance for purposes of research.

[22] Peter V. Karpovich, "Water Resistance in Swimming," *Research Quarterly,* October, 1933.

CHAPTER 16

TRACK-AND-FIELD ATHLETICS

349. TRACK-AND-FIELD athletic events have for many years been given a prominent place in the testing of physical abilities. The skills involved in track-and-field athletics—running, jumping, and throwing—are fundamental to many athletic events: it has been shown that if skills in both team sports and track-and-field athletics are practiced to the point that the participants are nearing their maximum performances, the r between total points for several track-and-field events and the ratings of skills in major-sports abilities averages .80. Thus, track-and-field athletic events offer an interesting and a useful approach to the testing for general-athletic capacity.

In most track-and-field athletics tests, a battery of events, rather than one event only, is chosen. It matters little which specific events are chosen as long as they include a run, a broad jump, a high jump, and a weight throw,[1] of which events the high jump seems to be the least important. The records made in the events are converted into points by the use of scoring tables, and the sum of the points represents the track-and-field ability of the performer: hence the term "total points" has come to designate a score for track-and-field ability.

350. BADGE TEST (Table 85, pp. 194-95)

This test includes three tests for boys and three tests for girls. Each of these tests, which are graded in difficulty, includes three or four sets of events, in each of which the choice of the event to be used is usually dependent on whether the test is conducted indoors or outdoors. In order to "pass" each test, the performer must achieve a designated requirement in *each* event.

In the runs, performers usually run at one time. In some instances an inspector is assigned to each performer. At other times, the individuals who have passed the test are separated from those who have not passed the test by having two individuals, one on either side of the track upon which the run is performed, hold a small soft rope stretched tight above the track and above the heads of the runners. Upon the blowing of the whistle, this rope is quickly lowered, and the two rope-holders run with the individuals being tested. The runners who get under the rope have "passed," and those who are caught by the rope have "failed."

[1] Charles H. McCloy, *The Measurement of Athletic Power.*

193

Table 85

TRACK-AND-FIELD ATHLETICS--BADGE TEST: STANDARDS (BOYS AND GIRLS)*

Boys

First Test

1.	Pull-ups (chinning)** or	4 times
	rope climb (using hands and legs)	12 ft.
2.	Standing broad jump**	5 ft. 9 in.
3.	60-yard dash** or	9 sec.
	50-yard dash**	8 sec.
4.	Baseball throw (accuracy) or	3 strikes out of 6 throws at 40 ft.
	baseball throw (distance)**	130 ft.

Second Test

1.	Pull-ups (chinning)** or	6 times
	rope climb (using hands and legs)	16 ft.
2.	Standing broad jump** or	6 ft. 6 in.
	running broad jump**	12 ft.
3.	60-yard dash** or	8 sec.
	100-yard dash**	13-2/5 sec.
4.	Baseball throw (accuracy) or	3 strikes out of 5 throws at 45 ft.
	baseball throw (distance)**	195 ft.

Third Test

1.	Pull-ups (chinning)** or	9 times
	rope climb (using hands, not legs)	16 ft.
2.	Running high jump** or	4 ft. 4 in.
	running broad jump**	14 ft.
3.	220-yard run** or	28 sec.
	100-yard dash	12-3/5 sec.
4.	Baseball throw (accuracy) or	3 strikes out of 5 throws at 50 ft.
	baseball throw (distance)**	220 ft.
	8-pound shot-put**	28 ft.

Girls

First Test

1.	Balancing (1 deep knee bend) on balance beam**	24 ft., 2 trials
2.	Potato race or	22 sec.
	all-up Indian-club race or	30 sec.
	50-yard dash**	8 sec.
3.	Basketball throw (distance)** or	35 ft.
	12-inch indoor-baseball throw (accuracy)	2 strikes out of 5 throws at 25 ft.
4.	Volleyball serve*** or	2 in 5
	tennis serve or	3 in 6
	basketball goal throw (10-ft. line) or	2 in 5
	12-inch indoor baseball throw and catch	3 errors allowed

Table 85 (continued)

Girls

Second Test

1. Balancing (book on head; 1 deep
knee bend) on balance beam**   24 ft., 2 trials
2. Potato race or   20 sec.
all-up Indian-club race or   28 sec.
run and catch or   19 sec.
50-yard dash**   (-3/5 sec.
3. Basketball throw (distance)** or   45 ft.
12-inch indoor-baseball throw
(accuracy)   3 strikes out of 6 at 30 ft.
4. Volleyball serve*** or   3 in 6
tennis serve or   3 in 5
basketball goal throw (12-ft.
line) or   3 in 6
12-inch indoor-baseball throw and
catch   2 errors allowed

Third Test

1. Balancing (book on head, 3 deep knee
bends) on balance beam**   24 ft., 2 trials
2. Potato race or   18 sec.
run and catch or   17 sec.
50-yard dash**   7-1/5 sec.
3. Basketball throw (distance)** or   55 ft.
12-inch indoor-baseball throw
(accuracy)   3 strikes out of 5 at 36 ft.
4. Volleyball serve*** or   3 in 5
tennis serve or   3 in 4
basketball goal throw (15-ft. line)
or   3 in 5
12-inch indoor baseball throw and
catch   1 error allowed

*Republished by permission of the National Recreation Association. De-
tailed rules for conducting the events may be obtained from the Association,
the address of which is 315 Fourth Avenue, New York City.
**Events recommended by the present authors. Events involving a high
degree of accuracy should, because of their low degree of reliability,
probably not be included in a test of this type.
***None of the events listed under 4 in each test for girls is of high
validity or of high reliability; hence any item under the 4's may be
chosen, or all the items under the 4's may be omitted.

Since the basis for the formulation of standards for the badge test is
entirely arbitrary, and since the test is scored only as "passed" or "failed,"
the test is of value only for motivating large numbers of persons to participate in track-and-field events—a value not to be treated lightly.

351. PHILADELPHIA AGE AIMS (ELEMENTARY SCHOOLS) (Table 86, p. 196)

Standards are suggested according to the ages of the performers. These
standards are better graded than those of the badge test, but no allowance
is made for differences in the sizes of performers of the same age. The
standards represent the point at which 75 per cent of the performers
"pass" the tests, and are useful primarily in motivation, not as a valid
measurement of achievement.

352. COZENS ACHIEVEMENT SCALES FOR TRACK-AND-FIELD ATHLETICS [2]

Numerous standards relative to the age, the height, and the weight of the performer have been proposed for track-and-field events. Those proposed by Cozens and his collaborators and those proposed by the senior author (see Chap. 7, and Secs. 136-38), which have been demonstrated to be of high validity, are approximately equivalent in usefulness, but are based on different principles.

Table 86*

TRACK-AND-FIELD ATHLETICS--PHILADELPHIA AGE AIMS:
STANDARDS (BOYS AND GIRLS 8 TO 16)

AGE AIMS FOR TRACK-AND-FIELD EVENTS

Age	Standing broad jump (feet and inches)		Ball throw overhead (feet)		30-yard dash (seconds and fifths)		40-yard dash (seconds and fifths)		50-yard dash (seconds and fifths)		Chinning	Knee rais- ing
											(Times)	
	Boys	Girls	Boys	Girls	Boys	Girls	Boys	Girls	Boys	Girls	Boys	Girls
8	4-0	3-8	17	15	6.2	6.4	8.0	8.3	9.2	9.2		
9	4-4	3-10	19	17	6.1	6.4	7.4	8.2	9.0	9.3		
10	4-6	4-0	21	19	6.0	6.3	7.3	8.1	8.4	9.2		
11	4-10	4-2	23	21	5.4	6.2	7.2	8.0	8.3	9.1	1	16
12	5-0	4-4	25	23	5.3	6.1	7.0	7.4	8.1	9.0	2	25
13	5-2	4-6	27	25	5.2	6.0	6.4	7.3	8.0	8.4	3	28
14	5-6	4-8	30	27	5.1	5.4	6.3	7.2	7.4	8.3	4	30
15	5-10	4-10	33	28	5.0	5.3	6.2	7.1	7.3	8.2	4	32
16	6-2	5-0	36	29	4.4	5.2	6.1	7.0	7.2	8.1	5	35

*By permission of Board of Public Education, Division of Physical and Health Education, Grover W. Mueller, Director.

In the Cozens Achievement Scales, which include tables for boys and for girls of elementary-school, junior-high-school, senior-high-school, and college ages, scores equivalent to various levels of performance and to each age-height-weight classification are given. These scores are P-scores with a mean of 50, and with 0 and 100 being three standard deviations below and above the mean, respectively. Complete directions for the administration of the tests, and scoring tables for boys and for girls from ten to twenty years of age may be found in the manuals of Cozens and his collaborators.

353. The Cozens Achievement Scales for college men include standards

[2] N. P. Neilson and Frederick W. Cozens, *Achievement Scales in Physical Education Activities for Boys and Girls in Elementary and Junior High Schools.* (This book may be secured from the California State Department of Education, Sacramento, California.)

Frederick W. Cozens, *Achievement Scales in Physical Education Activities for College Men.*

―― and Others, *Achievement Scales in Physical Education Activities for Secondary School Girls and College Women.*

――, *Physical Education Achievement Scales for Boys in Secondary Schools.*

for a number of track-and-field events, which standards were derived from performances in forty-two track-and-field events. A number of batteries, including from four to seven tests each, was proposed. R's of .90 to .97 have been obtained between these batteries and excellent criteria. (Several of the batteries, which include events other than track-and-field athletics, are discussed in Chapter 18.) Perhaps the most usable of the batteries is the one composed of the baseball throw for distance, the standing broad jump, the quarter-mile run, and the 120-yard low hurdles. An R of .94 has been obtained between this battery and an excellent criterion of general-athletic ability. In studies in which the 120-yard low-hurdle race was replaced by a dodging run (like the one shown in Fig. IX, p. 79, but with the distance from the first to the second hurdle being five yards instead of three yards), approximately the same coefficients of multiple correlation have been obtained.

Since the Cozens scoring tables are out of print, it is suggested that standards be established on the basis of the sum of the T-scores for the events (four to seven) administered after the events have been practiced. This score will not be so valid a measure of track-and-field ability as if the scores for the events were weighted according to the multiple regression weights used by Cozens, but it will be a satisfactory score.

354. UNIVERSAL SCORING TABLES [3] (see Chap. 7)

The standards for boys are based on the following five levels of achievement: (1) An athletics quotient (see Sec. 355) of 90 is one probable error below the average score. At this level 75 per cent of an ordinary group succeed. (2) An athletics quotient of 100 is an average score. At this level about 50 per cent of a normal group succeed, and 50 per cent fail. (3) An athletics quotient of 112 is one standard deviation above the average. At this level approximately 16 per cent succeed. (4) An athletics quotient of 124 is two standard deviations above the average. At this level about 2.5 per cent succeed. An athletics quotient of 124 represents varsity performance in most institutions. (5) An athletics quotient of 136 is three standard deviations above the average. At this level only about 0.13 per cent usually succeed. An athletics quotient of 136 represents superior varsity performance.

355. The athletics quotient may be computed by the division of the sum of the points received in four standard events (scored on the Universal Scoring Tables) by the standard number of points for a given classification index. The result is an achievement quotient, which, when multiplied by 100, represents, in the form of a percentage, the ability of a performer in comparison with the average ability of performers of his age, height, and weight.

[3] McCloy, *The Measurement of Athletic Power*. Universal Scoring Tables may be found, in the present text, in Tables 87 and 88 (pp. 198-202).

Table 87

ATHLETICS QUOTIENT ON BASIS OF UNIVERSAL SCORING TABLES (BOYS)

	Universal Scoring Table Points	50-Yard Dash	60-Yard Dash	100-Yard Dash	6" Run for 60-Yd Dash	10" Run for 100-Yd. Dash	3 Potato Race	5 Potato Race	Standing Broad Jump	3 Standing Broad Jumps
1.	90	10.4	12.0	18.8	67-6	138-6	22.0	41.0	4-4	13-8
2.	93	10.3	11.9	18.6	68-5	140-6	21.8	40.5	4-5	14-0
3.	97	10.2	11.8	18.4	69-5	142-6	21.6	40.0	4-6	14-2
4.	101	10.1	11.7	18.2	70-5	144-7	21.4	39.5	4-7	14-4
5.	105	10.0	11.5	18.1	72-5	145-7	21.2	39.0	4-7½	14-6
6.	109	9.9	11.4	17.9	73-5	147-9	21.0	38.6	4-8	14-8
7.	113	9.8	11.3	17.7	74-6	149-11	20.9	38.3	4-9	15-0
8.	117	9.7	11.2	17.5	75-6	152-2	20.7	38.0	4-10	15-2
9.	122	9.6	11.1	17.3	76-7	154-5	20.5	37.6	4-10½	15-4
10.	126	9.5	11.0	17.2	77-9	155-7	20.3	37.3	4-11	15-6
11.	131	9.4	10.9	17.0	78-10	157-11	20.1	37.0	5-0	15-8
12.	137	9.3	10.7	16.8	81-2	160-4	19.9	36.5	5-1	16-0
13.	142	9.2	10.6	16.6	82-4	162-10	19.7	36.1	5-2	16-4
14.	147	9.1	10.5	16.5	83-7	164-1	19.5	35.7	5-3	16-8
15.	153	9.0	10.4	16.3	84-10	166-8	19.3	35.4	5-4	17-0
16	159	8.9	10.3	16.1	86-1	169-3	19.2	35.0	5-5	17-2
17	165	8.8	10.2	15.9	87-4	172-0	19.0	34.6	5-6	17-5
18.	172	8.7	10.0	15.7	90	174-9	18.8	34.2	5-7	17-7
19	179	8.6	9.9	15.5	91-4	177-7	18.6	33.8	5-8	18-0
20	186	8.5	9.8	15.4	92-9	179-0	18.4	33.4	5-9	18-3
21.	194	8.4	9.7	15.2	94-2	182-0	18.2	33.0	5-10	18-6
22	202	8.3	9.6	15.0	95-8	185-0	18.0	32.6	6-0	18-9
23	210	8.2	9.5	14.8	97-1	188-1	17.8	32.2	6-1	19-0
24.	219	8.1	9.4	14.6	98-7	191-4	17.6	31.8	6-2	19-4
25.	228	8.0	9.2	14.5	101-9	192-11	17.4	31.4	6-3	19-8
26.	238	7.9	9.1	14.3	103-4	196-3	17.2	31.0	6-5	20-0
27	248	7.8	9.0	14.1	105	199-8	17.0	30.6	6-6	20-4
28.	259	7.7	8.9	13.9	106-8	203-3	16.8	30.2	6-7	21-0
29	271	7.6	8.8	13.7	108-5	206-10	16.6	29.8	6-9	21-4
30.	283	7.5	8.7	13.6	110-2	208-8	16.4	29.4	6-10	21-8
31	295	7.4	8.5	13.4	113-10	212-6	16.2	29.0	7-0	22-0
32.	309	7.3	8.4	13.2	115-9	216-4	16.0	28.6	7-2	22-8
33.	323	7.2	8.3	13.0	117-8	220-5	15.8	28.2	7-3	23-0
34.	338	7.1	8.2	12.8	119-8	224-6	15.6	27.9	7-5	23-4
35.	354	7.0	8.1	12.7	121-8	226-8	15.4	27.5	7-7	24-0
36	371	6.9	8.0	12.5	123-9	231-0	15.2	27.1	7-9	24-4
37	389	6.8	7.8	12.3	128-1	235-6	15.0	26.7	7-11	25-0
38	407	6.7	7.7	12.1	130-4	240-1	14.8	26.3	8-0	25-4
39.	427	6.6	7.6	11.9	132-8	244-11	14.6	25.9	8-2	26-0
40.	449	6.5	7.5	11.7	135	249-10	14.4	25.5	8-5	26-4
41.	471	6.4	7.4	11.6	137-5	252-5	14.2	25.1	8-7	27-0
42.	495	6.3	7.3	11.4	139-11	257-7	14.0	24.7	8-9	27-8
43.	521	6.2	7.2	11.2	142-6	263-0	13.8	24.3	8-11	28-4
44.	548	6.1	7.0	11.0	147-10	268-8	13.6	23.9	9-2	29-0
45.	577	6.0	6.9	10.8	150-8	274-5	13.4	23.5	9-4	29-8
46.	608	5.9	6.8	10.7	153-6	277-5	13.2	23.1	9-7	30-4
47.	642	5.8	6.7	10.5	156-6	283-7	13.0	22.8	9-10	31-0
48.	677	5.7	6.6	10.3	159-7	290-0	12.8	22.4	10-1	31-8
49.	716	5.6	6.5	10.1	162-8	296-7	12.6	22.0	10-4	32-4
50.	757	5.5	6.3	9.9	169-3	303-6	12.4	21.6	10-7	33-4
51.	801	5.4	6.2	9.8	172-9	307-0	12.2	21.2	10-10	34-0
52.	849	5.3	6.1	9.6	176-4	314-4	12.0	20.8	11-1	35-0
53.	900	5.2	6.0	9.4	180	322-0	11.8	20.4	11-5	36-0

Table 87 (continued)

Running Broad Jump	Standing Broad Jump	Running High Jump	8 Pound Shot-put	12 Pound Shot-put	16 Pound Shot-put	Basket Ball Throw for Distance	Baseball Throw	Discus Throw	Pull-ups	Push-ups
7-4			17-0	14-8	13-0	51		41		
7-6	2-5	2-8	17-4	15-0	13-4	52	108			
7-8			17-8	15-4	13-8		110	42		
7-10		2-9	18-0	15-8	14-0	53	113	43		6
8-0	2-6		18-4	16-0	14-4	54	116	44		
8-2		2-10	18-8	16-4	14-8	55	118	45	2	
8-4			19-0	16-8		56	121	46		7
	2-7	2-11	19-4	17-0	15-0	57	124	47		
8-6			20-0	17-4	15-4	58	126	48		
8-8	2-8	3-0	20-4	17-8	15-8	59	128	49		8
8-10			20-8	18-0	16-0	60	131	50		
9-2		3-1	21-4	18-4	16-4	61	133	51		
9-4	2-9		21-8	18-8	16-8	62	136	52	3	9
9-6		3-2	22-4	19-0	17-0	63	140	53		
9-8	2-10		22-8	19-8	17-8	64	143	55		10
9-10		3-3	23-4	20-0	18-0	65	145	56		
10-0	2-11		23-8	20-4	18-4	66	148	57		11
10-2		3-4	24-4	21-0	18-8	67	152	58	4	
10-6	3-0	3-5	25-0	21-4	19-4	68	156	60		12
10-8			25-4	22-0	19-8	69	160	61		
11-0	3-1	3-6	26-0	22-4	20-0	71	164	63	5	13
11-2		3-7	26-8	23-0	20-8	72	168	64		14
11-4	3-2		27-4	23-8	21-0	73	172	66		15
11-8		3-8	28-0	24-0	21-8	74	176	67	6	
12-0	3-3	3-9	28-8	24-8	22-4	76	180	69		16
12-2	3-4	3-10	29-4	25-4	22-8	77	184	71	7	17
12-6			30-0	26-0	23-4	79	188	73		18
12-10	3-5	3-11	31-0	26-8	24-0	80	196	75	8	19
13-2	3-6	4-0	31-8	27-4	24-8	82	200	77		20
13-4		4-1	32-8	28-4	25-4	84	204	79	9	21
13-8	3-7	4-2	33-8	29-0	26-0	85	212	81		23
14-0	3-8	4-3	34-4	29-8	26-8	87	216	83	10	24
14-6		4-4	35-4	30-8	27-4	89	224	86	11	25
14-10	3-9	4-5	36-4	31-4	28-4	91	228	88	12	27
15-2	3-10	4-6	37-8	32-4	29-0	93	236	91	13	29
15-8	3-11	4-7	38-8	33-4	30-0	95	244	93	14	31
16-0	4-0	4-8	39-8	34-4	30-8	97	252	96	15	32
16-6		4-9	41-0	35-4	31-8	99	256	99	17	34
16-10	4-1	4-10	42-0	36-4	32-8	101	264	102	18	37
17-4	4-2	4-11	43-8	37-8	33-8	104	276	105	20	39
17-10	4-3	5-1	45-0	38-8	34-8	106	284	108	21	42
18-4	4-4	5-2	46-4	40-0	36-0	109	292	112	23	45
18-10	4-5	5-3	48-0	41-4	37-0	112	300	115	25	48
19-6	4-6	5-4	49-4	42-8	38-4	114	312	119	27	51
20-0	4-7	5-6	51-0	44-0	39-8	117	320	123	30	55
20-8	4-8	5-8	52-8	45-8	41-0	120	332	127	33	59
21-4	4-10	5-9	54-8	47-0	42-4	123	344	132	36	63
22-0	4-11	5-11	56-8	48-8	43-8	126	356	136	40	68
22-8	5-0	6-1	58-8	50-8	45-4	130	368	142	44	73
23-6	5-1	6-2	60-8	52-4	47-0	133	384	146	48	79
24-4	5-3	6-4	63-0	54-8	49-0	137	396	152	53	85
25-2	5-4	6-6	65-4	56-4	50-8	141	412	158	59	92
26-0	5-6	6-8	68-0	58-8	52-8	145	428	164	65	100

Table 87 (continued)

ATHLETICS QUOTIENT ON BASIS OF UNIVERSAL SCORING TABLES (BOYS)

CLASSIFICATION INDEX: 20 Age (yr.) + 6 Height (in.) + Weight (lb.)

	500 to 524	525 to 549	550 to 574	575 to 599	600 to 624	625 to 649	650 to 674	675 to 699	700 to 724
1.	6.23	6.02							
2.	6.44	6.22							
3.	6.71	6.49	6.23						
4.	6.97	6.76	6.48	6.20					
5.	7.27	7.02	6.74	6.44	6.09				
6.	7.54	7.29	7.00	6.69	6.32				
7.	7.82	7.56	7.25	6.93	6.55	6.16			
8.	8.10	7.83	7.51	7.18	6.78	6.38	6.01		
9.	8.44	8.16	7.83	7.48	7.07	6.65	6.27		
10.	8.72	8.43	8.09	7.73	7.30	6.87	6.47	6.11	
11.	9.07	8.76	8.41	8.04	7.59	7.14	6.73	6.35	
12.	9.48	9.16	8.79	8.40	7.94	7.47	7.04	6.64	6.26
13.	9.83	9.50	9.11	8.71	8.23	7.74	7.29	6.89	6.49
14.	10.17	9.83	9.44	9.02	8.52	8.01	7.55	7.13	6.72
15.	10.59	10.23	9.82	9.39	8.87	8.34	7.86	7.42	7.00
16.	11.00	10.64	10.21	9.75	9.22	8.66	8.17	7.71	7.27
17.	11.42	11.04	10.59	10.12	9.57	8.99	8.47	8.00	7.54
18.	11.90	11.51	11.04	10.55	9.97	9.37	8.83	8.34	7.86
19.	12.39	11.97	11.49	10.98	10.38	9.75	9.19	8.68	8.18
20.	12.87	12.44	11.94	11.41	10.78	10.14	9.55	9.02	8.50
21.	13.43	12.98	12.45	11.90	11.25	10.57	9.96	9.41	8.87
22.	13.98	13.51	12.97	12.39	11.71	11.00	10.37	9.80	9.24
23.	14.53	14.05	13.48	12.88	12.17	11.44	10.79	10.18	9.60
24.	15.16	14.65	14.06	13.44	12.70	11.93	11.25	10.62	10.01
25.	15.88	15.25	14.63	13.99	13.22	12.43	11.71	11.06	10.43
26.	16.47	15.92	15.28	14.60	13.80	12.97	12.22	11.54	10.88
27.	17.16	16.59	15.92	15.21	14.38	13.51	12.74	12.03	11.34
28.		17.32	16.62	15.89	15.01	14.11	13.30	12.56	11.84
29.			17.39	16.63	15.71	14.77	13.92	13.14	12.39
30.				17.36	16.41	15.42	14.54	13.72	12.94
31.					17.10	16.08	15.15	14.31	13.49
32.						16.84	15.87	14.99	14.13
33.						17.60	16.59	15.66	14.77
34.							17.36	16.39	15.45
35.								17.17	16.19
36.									16.96
37.									17.79
38.									
39.									
40.									
41.									
42.									
43.									
44.									
45.									
46.									
47.									
48.									
49.									
50.									
51.									
52.									
53.									

Table 87 (continued)

	725 to 749	750 to 774	775 to 799	800 to 824	825 to 849	850 to 874	875 to 899	900 to 924	925 to 949	950 to 974
1.										
2.										
3.										
4.										
5.										
6.										
7.										
8.										
9.										
10.										
11.										
12.										
13.	6.14									
14.	6.36	6.01								
15.	6.62	6.25								
16.	6.88	6.50	6.09							
17.	7.14	6.74	6.32							
18.	7.44	7.03	6.59	6.14						
19.	7.74	7.32	6.86	6.39						
20.	8.04	7.60	7.13	6.64	6.15					
21.	8.39	7.93	7.43	6.93	6.42					
22.	8.74	8.26	7.74	7.21	6.68	6.16				
23.	9.08	8.58	8.05	7.50	6.95	6.40				
24.	9.47	8.95	8.39	7.82	7.25	6.68	6.12			
25.	9.86	9.32	8.74	8.14	7.54	6.95	6.37			
26.	10.29	9.73	9.12	8.50	7.88	7.26	6.65	6.08		
27.	10.73	10.13	9.50	8.86	8.21	7.56	6.93	6.33		
28.	11.20	10.58	9.92	9.25	8.57	7.90	7.23	6.62	6.09	
29.	11.72	11.07	10.38	9.68	8.97	8.26	7.57	6.92	6.37	
30.	12.24	11.57	10.84	10.11	9.36	8.63	7.91	7.23	6.65	6.10
31.	12.76	12.06	11.30	10.54	9.76	8.99	8.24	7.54	6.93	6.36
32.	13.37	12.63	11.84	11.04	10.23	9.42	8.63	7.89	7.26	6.66
33.	13.97	13.20	12.38	11.54	10.69	9.85	9.02	8.25	7.59	6.96
34.	14.62	13.81	12.95	12.07	11.18	10.30	9.44	8.63	7.94	7.28
35.	15.31	14.47	13.56	12.64	11.71	10.79	9.89	9.04	8.32	7.63
36.	16.05	15.16	14.21	13.25	12.28	11.31	10.36	9.48	8.72	8.00
37.	16.83	15.90	14.90	13.89	12.87	11.86	10.87	9.94	9.14	8.38
38.	17.60	16.63	15.59	14.54	13.47	12.41	11.37	10.40	9.57	8.77
39.		17.45	16.36	15.25	14.13	13.02	11.93	10.91	10.04	9.20
40.			17.20	16.04	14.86	13.69	12.54	11.47	10.55	9.68
41.				16.82	15.59	14.36	13.16	12.03	11.07	10.15
42.				17.68	16.38	15.09	13.83	12.64	11.63	10.67
43.					17.24	15.88	14.55	13.31	12.24	11.23
44.						16.71	15.31	14.00	12.88	11.81
45.						17.59	16.12	14.74	13.56	12.44
46.							16.98	15.53	14.29	13.10
47.							17.93	16.40	15.09	13.84
48.								17.29	15.91	14.59
49.									16.83	15.43
50.									17.79	16.31
51.										17.26
52.										
53.										

PRESENT STATUS

Table 88

ATHLETICS QUOTIENT ON BASIS OF UNIVERSAL SCORING TABLES
(SUPPLEMENT TO TABLE 87)

	Universal Scoring Table Points	220-Yard Run	440-Yard Run	880-Yard Run	Mile Run	60-Yard High Hurdles	60-Yard Low Hurdles	120-Yard High Hurdles	220-Yard Low Hurdles	Pole Vault
1.	90	41.0	1:35	3:41	8:21	16.8	15.0	33.0	50.9	3-4
2.	93	40.7	1:34.2	3:39	8:17	16.6	14.8	32.7	50.3	3-5
3.	97	40.3	1:33.2	3:36.5	8:12	16.4	14.6	32.2	49.7	3-6
4.	101	39.8	1:32.2	3:34	8:07	16.2	14.4	32.0	49.2	3-6
5.	105	39.4	1:31.2	3:32	8:01	16.0	14.2	31.6	48.6	3-7
6.	109	39.0	1:30.2	3:30	7:56	15.8	14.0	31.2	48.0	3-8
7.	113	38.7	1:29.4	3:28	7:52	15.6	13.9	30.8	47.4	3-9
8.	117	38.3	1:28.4	3:26	7:47	15.4	13.7	30.5	46.9	3-10
9.	122	37.9	1:27.3	3:23.5	7:42	15.2	13.6	30.1	46.2	3-11
10.	126	37.5	1:26.8	3:21.5	7:38	15.1	13.5	29.7	45.7	4-0
11.	131	37.1	1:25.8	3:19.5	7:32.5	14.9	13.3	29.3	45.2	4-1
12.	137	36.7	1:24.6	3:17	7:27	14.7	13.1	28.9	44.7	4-2
13.	142	36.3	1:23.8	3:15	7:23	14.5	12.9	28.5	44.0	4-3
14.	147	35.9	1:23	3:13	7:18	14.3	12.8	28.2	43.5	4-4
15.	153	35.5	1:22.2	3:11	7:13.2	14.1	12.6	27.8	43.0	4-6
16.	159	35.1	1:21.2	3:08.7	7:08	13.9	12.5	27.4	42.5	4-7
17.	165	34.7	1:20.3	3:06.7	7:04	13.7	12.3	27.1	41.9	4-8
18.	172	34.3	1:19.6	3:04.7	6:59	13.6	12.1	26.7	41.3	4-9
19.	179	34.0	1:18.5	3:02.3	6:54	13.4	12.0	26.3	40.8	4-11
20.	186	33.6	1:17.7	3:00.3	6:48.7	13.2	11.8	26.0	40.2	5-0
21.	194	33.2	1:16.5	2:58.2	6:44	13.0	11.7	25.6	39.7	5-2
22.	202	32.8	1:15.7	2:56	6:39.6	12.8	11.5	25.2	39.1	5-4
23.	210	32.4	1:14.8	2:54	6:34.8	12.6	11.3	24.9	38.7	5-5
24.	219	32.0	1:13.9	2:51.8	6:29.7	12.5	11.2	24.5	38.1	5-7
25.	228	31.6	1:13	2:49.8	6:25	12.3	11.0	24.2	37.5	5-8
26.	238	31.2	1:12.1	2:47.6	6:20	12.1	10.9	23.8	37.0	5-10
27.	248	30.8	1:11.2	2:45.6	6:14.4	11.9	10.7	23.5	36.4	6-0
28.	259	30.4	1:10.3	2:43.4	6:10.7	11.7	10.6	23.1	35.9	6-2
29.	271	30.0	1:09.3	2:41.5	6:05.8	11.5	10.4	22.7	35.3	6-4
30.	283	29.6	1:08.4	2:39	6:00.8	11.3	10.2	22.4	34.8	6-6
31.	295	29.2	1:07.6	2:37	5:56	11.1	10.1	22.0	34.3	6-8
32.	309	28.8	1:06.6	2:34.7	5:51	11.0	9.9	21.6	33.7	6-11
33.	323	28.4	1:05.6	2:32.7	5:46.7	10.8	9.8	21.3	33.2	7-1
34.	338	28.0	1:04.8	2:30.6	5:41.7	10.7	9.6	20.9	32.6	7-4
35.	354	27.6	1:03.8	2:28.4	5:36.6	10.5	9.4	20.6	32.1	7-6
36.	371	27.2	1:02.9	2:26.3	5:31.7	10.3	9.3	20.2	31.6	7-9
37.	389	26.8	1:01.9	2:24.2	5:26.9	10.1	9.1	19.8	31.1	8-0
38.	407	26.4	1:01.1	2:22	5:22.3	9.9	9.0	19.5	30.6	8-3
39.	427	26.0	1:00.2	2:19.8	5:17.3	9.7	8.8	19.2	30.0	8-6
40.	449	25.6	59.2	2:17.7	5:12.4	9.5	8.7	18.8	29.5	8-9
41.	471	25.2	58.4	2:15.7	5:07.8	9.4	8.5	18.5	29.0	9-1
42.	495	24.8	57.4	2:13.6	5:03.1	9.2	8.4	18.1	28.5	9-5
43.	521	24.4	56.5	2:11.4	4:58	9.0	8.2	17.8	27.9	9-8
44.	548	24.1	55.6	2:09.3	4:53.3	8.8	8.1	17.4	27.4	10-0
45.	577	23.7	54.7	2:07.1	4:48.5	8.7	7.9	17.1	26.9	10-5
46.	608	23.4	53.8	2:05.1	4:43.7	8.5	7.8	16.8	26.4	10-9
47.	642	22.9	52.9	2:02.9	4:38.8	8.3	7.6	16.4	25.9	11-2
48.	677	22.5	52.0	2:00.8	4:34	8.2	7.5	16.1	25.4	11-6
49.	716	22.1	51.0	1:58.7	4:29.2	8.0	7.3	15.7	24.8	12-0
50.	757	21.7	50.2	1:56.5	4:24.3	7.8	7.2	15.4	24.3	12-5
51.	801	21.3	49.2	1:54.8	4:19.6	7.6	7.0	15.1	23.8	12-11
52.	849	20.9	48.3	1:52.4	4:14.7	7.5	6.9	14.7	23.3	13-5
53.	900	20.5	47.4	1:50.4	4:10	7.3	6.7	14.4	22.8	14-0

A more convenient method of computing the athletics quotient[4] than the method just described is presented in Table 89 (p. 203).

The classification index of 819 is in the column headed by 800 to 824 (Tables 87 and 88). In this column the quotient points for the records in each of the events may be found. The sum of the quotient points is 99.01, which number when rounded off gives an athletics quotient of 99, signifying that the performer, in comparison with other performers of his age, height, and weight, is 1 per cent below average in athletic ability.

Table 89

ATHLETICS QUOTIENT: SAMPLE SCORE CARD (BOY)

Age	15.5 (yr.)	20 x 15.5	= 310
Height	65 (in.)	6 x 65	= 390
Weight	119 (lb.)	1 x 119	= 119

McCloy Classification Index = 819*

			Quotient Points**
50-yard dash	7.4	sec.	10.54
100-yard dash	13	sec.	11.54
Standing broad jump	6	ft. 9 in.	9.68
Three standing broad jumps	23	ft.	11.54
Running broad jump	13	ft. 4 in.	10.11
Running high jump	4	ft. 6 in.	12.64
8-pound shot-put	30	ft. 2 in.	8.86
Basketball throw for distance	76	ft.	8.14
Pull-ups (number)	6		7.82
Floor push-ups (number)	16		8.14
		Athletics Quotient	99.01

*Since no valid classification index for girls has been presented, no athletics quotient for girls has been prepared.
**Table 87.

To use Tables 87 and 88 for fewer than ten events, the sum of the quotient points for the number of events used is multiplied by *10* and divided by the *number* of events used. If, for example, only the first six of the events had been used, the sum of the quotient points would have been 66.05. This number multiplied by 10/6 equals 110.08, which when rounded off would give an athletics quotient of 110.

For a decathlon there should be two runs, two broad jumps, one high jump, two throws, pull-ups or push-ups, and any two other events. For a pentathlon there should be one run, one broad jump, one high jump, one throw, and pull-ups or push-ups. For a four-event competition there should be a run, a broad jump, a high jump, and one throw.

If it is desired to use more than ten events, additional events may be selected from *The Measurement of Athletic Power* or from Tables 87 and

[4] McCloy, "A Program of Athletic Activities for Boys," *Journal of Health and Physical Education*, December, 1941.

88. If it is desired to use events not included in the Universal Scoring Tables, directions for the computation of scoring tables for such events may be found in Chapter 7 (see Secs. 116-17).

356. Uses of Universal Scoring Tables

(1) The score for one event may be compared with the score for another event; for example, the points for a record of 8.4 seconds in the 50-yard dash are 194. In the six-second dash, 194 points are given for a distance of 94 feet 2 inches; hence a record of 8.4 seconds in the 50-yard dash is equivalent to a distance of 94 feet 2 inches in the six-second dash.

(2) The sum of the scores for several events is comparable with the sum of the scores for an equal number of other events. The sum of the points, for example, for the 50-yard dash, the standing broad jump, the running high jump, and the basketball throw for distance may be 550; and the sum of the points for the 220-yard dash, the running broad jump, the running high jump, and the twelve-pound shot-put may be 650. The score of 550 may be compared with that of 650. The sum of the points for several events represents the score for all-round competition in track-and-field athletics.

(3) Performers may first be classified into homogeneous groups by means of the classification index, and then subclassified on the basis of total points earned in four or more events.

(4) Performers may be classified for competition on the basis of their athletics quotients, and hence, regardless of age or size, earn scores on equivalent terms. A small boy who is 20 per cent better than the average for his age, height, and weight may surpass in his athletics quotient a larger boy who is only 10 per cent better than boys of his age, height, and size.

(5) Individuals may compete against their best previous abilities by means of the athletics quotient.

357. DETROIT PENTATHLON AND DECATHLON

Standards for the Detroit Pentathlon for girls may be found in Table 3 (p. 41) and for the Detroit Decathlon for boys, in Table 4 (p. 42). Directions for administering events in the pentathlon and in the decathlon that are different from standard directions for track-and-field events follow.

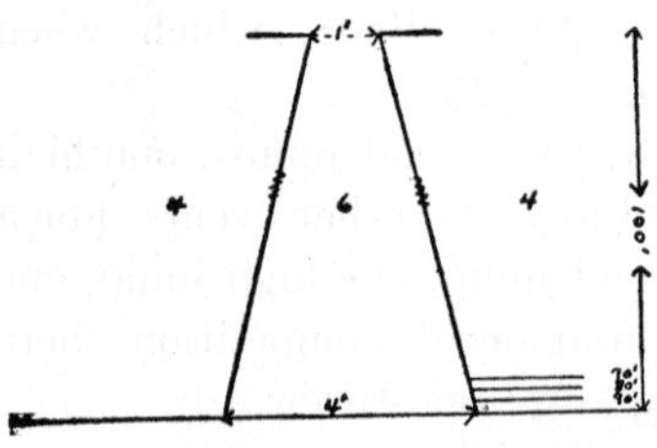

Figure XXII. Baseball Throw (Pentathlon): Field Markings

Decathlon sit-ups. The performer, with the trunk erect and with the feet held down by someone sitting on them, sits on the floor. With the hands behind the head or the neck, the performer lowers the trunk until the head touches the floor, and then returns to the starting position. No credit is given if the shoulders or any part of the back touches the floor.

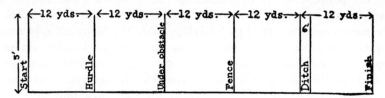

FIGURE XXIII. Obstacle Race (Pentathlon): Field Markings

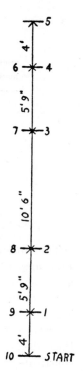

FIGURE XXIV. Shuttle Run: Floor Markings

Pentathlon baseball throw (Fig. XXII, p. 204). A scratch line three inches wide and three feet long is drawn on the ground, and on this scratch line a distance of one foot is marked off. Another line four feet long, which is parallel to and one hundred feet from the scratch line, is also drawn on the ground. The ends of the line that is four feet long are connected to the ends of the interval of one foot that is marked off on the scratch line; thus the lane is one foot wide at the scratch line, and four feet wide at the other end. If the lane is marked off at intervals of ten feet, the process of measuring is expedited.

The throw must be made from behind the scratch line. If any part of the thrower's body touches the ground in front of the line before the throw is measured, the throw does not count, but is considered to be one trial. Two trials are allowed. The measurement is made at right angles from the nearest break in the ground made by the ball to the scratch line extended. If the break is in the center lane, the record is the distance multiplied by 6. If the break is outside the center lane, the distance is multiplied by 4. Any throw under forty feet is not recorded. The throws are recorded as follows: $60 \times 6 = 360$, $60 \times 4 = 240$.

Pentathlon dash and throw. Two parallel lines thirty feet apart are drawn on the ground. Standards are placed at the ends of one line, and a rope is stretched tight between them and seven feet above the line. When the whistle is blown, the performer runs and throws the basketball over the rope, attempts to catch the ball before it touches the ground, and returns to the starting line. When returning to the starting line, the performer does not need to run across the line, but she must touch the line with one foot. She must complete three trips, and at the end of the third trip must cross the finishing line. If the ball is not caught when it is first thrown over the rope, it must be retrieved and thrown again until a fair catch is made. A fair throw and catch is one in which the ball goes over the rope, or touches nothing but the rope, and is caught and held before it touches the ground. It is not permissible for the runner to touch the wall, the rope, or any object during the event. The event should be timed with a stop watch.

Pentathlon obstacle race (Fig. XXIII, p. 205). The following apparatus is required: one fence with the top crossbar (upper edge) two feet six inches from the ground; one two-foot hurdle; one "under obstacle," two feet six inches from the ground. The "under obstacle" is constructed of two-by-four lumber, the stakes being driven at least one foot into the ground, and the top rail of the two-by-four board is nailed down so that it is secure. A "ditch" six feet wide is marked with white lines, and the measurement of the last twelve yards is made from the edge of the ditch nearer the fence. The lanes for the race are five feet wide.

Table 90

SHUTTLE RUN (20 SECONDS): SCORING TABLE (MEN)

Number of Zones	T-score	Number of Zones	T-score
50	105	37	39
49	99	36	35
48	93	35	32
47	87	34	29
46	80	33	26
45	75	32	23
44	70	31	20
43	65	30	17
42	60	29	15
41	55	28	13
40	50	27	10
39	46	26	8
38	42	25	5

The runner must clear the hurdle without knocking off the crossbar. (She may make as many attempts to clear each obstacle as she wishes, and if she is finally successful, any foul is not counted. There should be an assistant to replace the crosspiece on top of the hurdle if it is knocked off.) The runner must climb the fence so that both feet go over the top bar, and clear the entire distance of the ditch without touching either line. Running through the ditch disqualifies the runner. Any infringement of these rules constitutes a foul, and more than one foul disqualifies the runner. The race is timed with a stop watch.

A method for timing a large number of performers running at one time has been presented in Chapter 7 (see Sec. 339).

358. SHUTTLE RUN (Fig. XXIV, p. 205)

The ground or the floor is marked according to the specifications in Figure XXIV. The performer begins from behind the starting line, runs to the other end, touches the floor beyond that line with one foot, and runs back to the starting line. He completes as many trips as possible in twenty seconds. There is assigned to each performer an inspector who notes the zone that his runner has reached at the end of twenty seconds. The score is the number of zones covered in twenty seconds; thus if a performer completes three round trips and reaches the fourth zone on the fourth trip, he receives a score of 34. The shuttle run is not only an excellent track event, but also a fair classifier for general-athletic ability. An r of .77 [5] has been obtained between the shuttle run and the general-athletic ability of a group of junior-high-school girls.

Standards for the shuttle run are available only for adult males (Table 90, p. 206). These standards were developed on army personnel during World War II, and need to be revised for indoor performance at the high-school level.

[5] Marian Niehaus, "A Study of Tests for Dividing Junior High School Girls into Homogeneous Groups for Physical Education" (M.A. Thesis, State University of Iowa, 1935). (The distances proposed above are modified from those given by Niehaus.)

CHAPTER **17**

GENERAL-MOTOR ACHIEVEMENT

359. A BATTERY of tests devised to measure *general*-motor achievement should not include events that involve highly specialized skills. In the development of the general-motor-achievement test, coefficients of correlation were obtained between the scores made in various individual tests and the total scores made in a large battery of achievement tests. Two types of tests were found to have high coefficients of correlation with the large battery of achievement tests: (1) track-and-field events and (2) strength tests.

Further evidence for the validity of track-and-field events for the prediction of general-motor achievement is obtained from a study[1] in which coefficients of correlation were obtained between total points for track-and-field events and ratings of technical skills in soccer, basketball, softball, and volleyball. All the subjects, who had been trained intensively for a number of years in all the events, rated the technical skills of one another, disregarding such psychological elements as quick thinking and courage. The resulting r's of technical skills in basketball, soccer, volleyball, and softball with total points in track-and-field events were, respectively, .92, .84, .88, and .78.

Since r's of about .9 [2] had been obtained between pull-up-strength scores (computed according to the formula in Sec. 273) and total-strength scores, pull-ups were selected as the strength test for the general-motor-achievement battery. The criterion for the battery was, with the omission of the intelligence quotient, the same as that used for general-motor capacity[3] (see Sec. 255).

360. The **McCloy General-motor-achievement Test for boys** is comprised of pull-ups, 50- or 100-yard dash, running or standing broad jump, running high jump, and shot-put or basketball throw for distance or baseball throw for distance. The pull-up-strength score is computed from Table 45 (p. 130), or from Table 49 (p. 132). The points for the track-and-field

---

[1] Published in Chinese by Charles H. McCloy.

[2] Victor C. Dunder, "A Multiple Strength Index of General Motor Ability," *Research Quarterly*, October, 1933.

August H. Rump, "The Relative Contribution of Arm, Back, Abdomen and Leg Strength to the General Athletic Ability of High School Boys" (M.A. Thesis, State University of Iowa, 1931).

[3] McCloy, "The Measurement of General Motor Capacity and General Motor Ability," *Supplement to Research Quarterly*, March, 1934.

208

events are obtained from Tables 87 and 88 (pp. 198-202). The formula is .1022 total points + .3928 pull-up-strength score (Table 91, p. 209, and Table 92, p. 210).

The McCloy General-motor-achievement Test for girls[4] is made up of pull-ups, a dash, a broad jump, and a throw. The pull-ups are performed ac-

Table 91

GENERAL-MOTOR-ACHIEVEMENT TEST: POINTS FOR TOTAL POINTS (BOYS)

TP	0	10	20	30	40	50	60	70	80	90

.1022 Total Points (four events)

TP	0	10	20	30	40	50	60	70	80	90
100	10.22	11.24	12.26	13.29	14.31	15.33	16.35	17.37	18.40	19.42
200	20.44	21.46	22.48	23.51	24.53	25.55	26.57	27.59	28.62	29.64
300	30.66	31.68	32.70	33.73	34.75	35.77	36.79	37.81	38.84	39.86
400	40.88	41.90	42.92	43.95	44.97	45.99	47.01	48.03	49.05	50.08
500	51.10	52.12	53.14	54.17	55.19	56.21	57.23	58.25	59.28	60.30
600	61.32	62.34	63.36	64.39	65.41	66.43	67.45	68.47	69.50	70.52
700	71.54	72.56	73.58	74.61	75.63	76.65	77.67	78.69	79.72	80.74
800	81.76	82.78	83.80	84.83	85.85	86.87	87.89	88.91	89.94	90.96
900	91.98	93.00	94.02	95.05	96.07	97.10	98.11	99.13	100.16	101.18
1000	102.20	103.22	104.24	105.27	106.29	107.31	108.33	109.35	110.38	111.40
1100	112.42	113.44	114.46	115.49	116.51	117.53	118.55	119.57	120.60	121.62
1200	122.64	123.66	124.68	125.71	126.73	127.75	128.77	129.79	130.82	131.84
1300	132.86	133.88	134.90	135.93	136.95	137.97	138.99	140.00	141.04	142.06
1400	143.08	144.10	145.12	146.15	147.17	148.19	149.21	150.23	151.26	152.28
1500	153.30	154.32	155.34	156.37	157.39	158.41	159.43	160.45	161.48	162.50
1600	163.52	164.54	165.60	166.59	167.61	168.63	169.65	170.67	171.70	172.72
1700	173.74	174.76	175.78	176.81	177.83	178.85	179.87	180.89	181.92	182.94
1800	183.96	184.98	186.00	187.03	188.05	189.07	190.09	191.11	192.14	193.16

Interpolation table

1	.1
2	.2
3	.31
4	.41
5	.51
6	.61
7	.71
8	.82
9	.92

cording to the directions given in Chapter 14, and scored by the number of performances. The points for the track-and-field events are obtained from Tables 87 and 88 (pp. 198-202), which are scoring tables for boys. The formula is .42 total points + 9.6 pull-ups (Table 93, p. 211, and Table 94, p. 211).

While the general-motor-capacity score, which is a raw score, indicates what a performer in accordance with his innate capacity *could achieve* in

[4] This test is not so useful as that for boys, for pull-ups are not so valid a measurement of strength for girls as they are for boys.

general-motor development if he had adequate training and experience, the general-motor-achievement score, which is also a raw score, indicates what a performer *has achieved* in *general*-motor development because of his innate capacity, training, and experience.

361. GENERAL-MOTOR-ACHIEVEMENT QUOTIENT

Although the general-motor-achievement score of a performer increases with his training and experience, the rate of increase decreases as the per-

Table 92

GENERAL-MOTOR-ACHIEVEMENT TEST:　POINTS FOR PULL-UP STRENGTH (BOYS)

Pull-up Strength	0	1	2	3	4	5	6	7	8	9
			.3928 Pull-up Strength							
40						17.68	18.07	18.46	18.85	19.25
50	19.64	20.03	20.43	20.82	21.21	21.60	22.00	22.39	22.78	23.18
60	23.57	23.96	24.35	24.75	25.14	25.53	25.92	26.32	26.71	27.10
70	27.50	27.89	28.28	28.67	29.07	29.46	29.85	30.25	30.64	31.03
80	31.42	31.82	32.21	32.60	33.00	33.39	33.78	34.17	34.57	34.96
90	35.35	35.74	36.14	36.53	36.92	37.32	37.71	38.10	38.49	38.89
100	39.28	39.67	40.07	40.46	40.85	41.24	41.64	42.03	42.42	42.82
110	43.21	43.60	43.99	44.39	44.78	45.17	45.56	45.96	46.35	46.74
120	47.14	47.53	47.92	48.31	48.71	49.10	49.49	49.89	50.28	50.67
130	51.06	51.46	51.85	52.24	52.64	53.03	53.42	53.81	54.21	54.60
140	54.99	55.38	55.78	56.17	56.56	56.96	57.35	57.74	58.13	58.53
150	58.92	59.31	59.71	60.10	60.49	60.88	61.28	61.67	62.06	62.46
160	62.85	63.24	63.63	64.03	64.42	64.81	65.20	65.60	65.99	66.38
170	66.78	67.17	67.56	67.95	68.35	68.74	69.13	69.53	69.92	70.31
180	70.70	71.10	71.49	71.88	72.28	72.67	73.06	73.45	73.85	74.24
190	74.63	75.02	75.42	75.81	76.20	76.60	76.99	77.38	77.77	78.17
200	78.56	78.95	79.35	79.74	80.13	80.52	80.92	81.31	81.70	82.10
210	82.49	82.88	83.27	83.67	84.06	84.45	84.84	85.24	85.63	86.02
220	86.42	86.81	87.20	87.59	87.99	88.38	88.77	89.17	89.56	89.95
230	90.34	90.74	91.13	91.52	91.92	92.31	92.70	93.09	93.49	93.88
240	94.27	94.66	95.06	95.45	95.84	96.24	96.63	97.02	97.41	97.81
250	98.20	98.59	98.99	99.38	99.77	100.16	100.56	100.95	101.34	101.74
260	102.13	102.52	102.91	103.31	103.70	104.09	104.48	104.88	105.27	105.66
270	106.06	106.45	106.84	107.23	107.63	108.02	108.41	108.81	109.20	109.59
280	109.98	110.38	110.77	111.16	111.56	111.95	112.34	112.73	113.13	113.52
290	113.91	114.30	114.70	115.09	115.48	115.88	116.27	116.66	117.05	117.45
300	117.84	118.23	118.63	119.02	119.41	119.80	120.20	120.59	120.98	121.38
310	121.77	122.16	122.55	122.95	123.34	123.73	124.12	124.52	124.91	125.30
320	125.70	126.09	126.48	126.87	127.27	127.66	128.05	128.45	128.84	129.23
330	129.62	130.00	130.41	130.80	131.20	131.59	131.98	132.37	132.77	133.16
340	133.55	133.94	134.34	134.73	135.12	135.52	135.91	136.30	136.69	137.09

former approaches his maximum achievement score. Since the maximum achievement score depends upon the capacity of the performer, as well as upon his training and experience, the maximum achievement score can be accurately predicted from the capacity score. Hence "practical maxima" were devised in which standard achievement scores were located two standard deviations of estimate $(2\sigma \sqrt{1 - r^2})$ above average general-motor-achievement scores for each general-motor-capacity score.[5]

The general-motor-achievement quotient may be obtained by dividing the general-motor-achievement score by the "practical maximum" stand-

Table 93

GENERAL-MOTOR-ACHIEVEMENT TEST: POINTS FOR TOTAL POINTS (GIRLS)

TP	0	10	20	30	40	50	60	70	80	90
				.42 Total Points						
0									33.6	37.8
100	42.0	46.2	50.4	54.6	58.8	63.0	67.2	71.4	75.6	79.8
200	84.0	88.2	92.4	96.6	100.8	105.0	109.2	113.4	117.6	121.8
300	126.0	130.2	134.4	138.6	142.8	147.0	151.2	155.4	159.6	163.8
400	168.0	172.2	176.4	180.6	184.8	189.0	193.2	197.4	201.6	205.8
500	210.0	214.2	218.4	222.6	226.8	231.0	235.2	239.4	243.6	247.8
600	252.0	256.2	260.4	264.6	268.8	273.0	277.2	281.4	285.6	289.8
700	294.0	298.2	302.4	306.6	310.8	315.0	319.2	323.4	327.6	331.8
800	336.0	340.2	344.4	348.6	352.8	357.0	361.2	365.4	369.6	373.8
900	378.0	382.2	386.4	390.6	394.8	399.0	403.2	407.4	411.6	415.8
1000	420.0	424.2	428.4	432.6	436.8	441.0	445.2	449.4	453.6	457.8
1100	462.0	466.2	470.4	474.6	478.8	483.0	487.2	491.4	495.6	499.8
1200	504.0	508.2	512.4	516.6	520.8	525.0	529.2	533.4	537.6	541.8

Interpolation table

1	.42
2	.84
3	1.26
4	1.68
5	2.10
6	2.52
7	2.94
8	3.36
9	3.78

Table 94

GENERAL-MOTOR-ACHIEVEMENT TEST: POINTS FOR PULL-UPS (GIRLS)

Pull-ups	0	1	2	3	4	5	6	7	8	9
				9.6 Number of Pull-ups						
30	288.0	297.6	307.2	316.8	326.4	336.0	345.6	355.2	364.8	374.4
20	192.0	201.6	211.2	220.8	230.4	240.0	249.6	259.2	268.8	278.4
10	96.0	105.6	115.2	124.8	134.4	144.0	153.6	163.2	172.8	182.4
0		9.6	19.2	28.8	38.4	48.0	57.6	67.2	76.8	86.4

[5] This standard of two standard deviations above average performance is arbitrary. It is, however, possible of attainment by most performers who train, for the standard is not two standard deviations above the average of all general-motor-achievement scores, but only above the average general-motor-achievement score for each general-motor-capacity score. It is, also, not so high as to be an encouragement to excessive training. Although about two per cent of a random sample surpass the standard, the standard is sufficiently high for most purposes of motivation, and almost all performers can approach or pass the standard after intensive training.

ard and by multiplying the result by 100. Since this quotient represents the percentage relationship of achievement to predicted or standard achievement, *it is not comparable to the usual type of achievement quotient in which a score of 100 represents average achievement*. A general-motor-achievement quotient of 90, for example, indicates an achievement that is 90 per cent of what it should be in accordance with the sex, the innate capacity, the size, and the maturity of the performer.

To facilitate the computation of the general-motor-achievement quotient the formulas for the general-motor-capacity score and the formulas for the general-motor-achievement score have been equated in such a manner that the general-motor-capacity score is, for all performers except girls of elementary-school age, the practical maximum of general-motor achievement. (For the excepted group the general-motor-capacity score minus 90 is the practical maximum.) Hence the general-motor-achievement quotient may be obtained by dividing the general-motor-achievement score by the general-motor-capacity score and by multiplying the result by 100.

362. Since the general-motor-achievement quotient indicates the relationship of a performer's achievement due to his innate capacity, and to his training and experience as well, it is subject to change. Since the motor quotient, on the other hand, indicates the relationship between a performer's innate motor capacity and the *average* innate motor capacity for performers of the same sex, size, and maturity, it should not, theoretically, change. Although the evidence is as yet inconclusive, it indicates that the motor quotient is usually fairly stable for each person.

Since the general-motor-achievement quotient is in terms of innate motor capacity, it is an excellent motivating device. Its usefulness for purposes of grading is discussed in Chapter 31.

363. ADMINISTRATION OF THE GENERAL-MOTOR-CAPACITY AND GENERAL-MOTOR-ACHIEVEMENT TESTS

In one class period height and weight are measured (by a student leader in the upper grades), and the Sargent Jump (usually by the teacher in all the grades) and pull-ups (by a student leader) are administered. In another class period the squat thrust, the Iowa-Brace Test, and the running high jump are administered. In a third class period the dash, the standing broad jump, and the throw are administered. Before the third testing period the lanes for the dash and the circles for the throw are drawn, and the mats are marked for the standing broad jump, and the inspectors for the dash are trained.

In the third testing period the dash is administered first. Then the broad jump is administered to one half of the performers, and the shot-put is administered to the other half. One mat is used for the broad jump. For the throw are used two circles, about fifteen feet farther apart than the

Table 95

GENERAL-MOTOR-CAPACITY AND GENERAL-MOTOR-ACHIEVEMENT TESTS:
SAMPLE SCORE CARD (SENIOR-HIGH-SCHOOL BOY)

			Score	
Age	16 yr.			
Height	65 in.			
Weight	122 lb.			
McCloy Classification Index		832	101.48	(Table 28)
Sargent Jump	57 cm.		67.42	(Table 30)
Squat thrusts (number)	5-3/4		22.84	(Table 32)
Iowa-Brace Test	16		34.07	(Table 35)
McCloy General-motor-capacity Score			225.81	
Norm for general-motor capacity			209.78	(Table 42)
McCloy Motor Quotient $\left(\dfrac{\text{G.M.C.S.}}{\text{Norm for G.M.C.}}\right) \times 100$			107.64	

			Points	
60-yard dash	8.6 secs.		289	(Table 87)
Standing broad jump	6 ft. 8 in.		263	(Table 87)
Running high jump	4 ft. 3 in.		310	(Table 87)
12-pound shot-put	28 ft. 4 in.		285	(Table 87)
Total points		1147	117.22	(Table 91)
Pull-ups (number)	12			
Pull-up-strength Score		210.9	82.88	(Table 92)
McCloy General-motor-achievement Score			200.10	
McCloy General-motor-achievement Quotient $\dfrac{\text{(G.M.A.S.)}}{\text{(G.M.C.S.)}} \times 100$			88.61	

expected distance of the longest throw. The circles are not in a straight
line with each other, but one circle with its zone for throwing is about
fifteen feet at the right of the other circle with its zone for throwing. A
performer throws from the first circle toward the right of the second circle,
and then the second performer throws from the second circle toward the
right of the first circle, etc. A "traffic policeman" is appointed for the
throwing event, and performers are permitted to throw only after they
have been given a signal by the policeman. The broad jumpers are stationed a safe distance away from the throwers.

If the general-motor-achievement test is given alone, pull-ups and the
running high jump are administered in one class period, and the dash, the
broad jump, and the throw are administered in another class period.

A sample score card for the general-motor-capacity and general-motor-
achievement tests is shown in Table 95 (p. 213).

364. CARPENTER GENERAL-MOTOR-ACHIEVEMENT TESTS [6]
(GRADES 1 TO 3)

Boys: 2 standing broad jump (in.) + 2.5 four-pound shot-put (ft.) + .5 weight (lb.); norm = general-motor-capacity score B [7] or general-motor-capacity score J.[7]

Girls: standing broad jump (in.) + 1.5 four-pound shot-put (ft.) + .5 weight (lb.); norm = general-motor-capacity score B [7] or general-motor-capacity score J.[7]

[6] Aileen Carpenter, "The Measurement of General Motor Capacity and General Motor Ability in the First Three Grades," *Research Quarterly,* December, 1942.

[7] Brace-type and Johnson-type tests of motor educability. See Carpenter General-motor-capacity Tests (Secs. 204 and 217).

CHAPTER **18**

MOTOR ABILITY

365. IN THIS CHAPTER are found numerous tests designed to measure *general*-motor ability or *general*-physical efficiency, which tests are excellent for a rapid *preliminary* classification of students into homogeneous groups.

366. OBSTACLE RACES

Many obstacle races used for purposes of physical conditioning, particularly during World War II, are dangerous, and hence are not described in this book.

367. The **Waterbury Obstacle Race,**[1] called a "confidence course," was designed to develop courage and initiative. The performer attempts to surmount the various obstacles without a time limit. The setup is too expensive for most schools, but where trees are numerous, the course might gradually be built.

368. The **Wear Multiple-obstacle Course**[2] (Fig. XXV, p. 216) requires only four chairs, a pair of high-jump standards, a crossbar or a rope, a mat, and a stop watch. An r of $-.777$ was obtained between the first trial on this multiple-obstacle course and instructors' ratings of the athletic ability of the performers. An r of reliability of .949 was obtained between first and second trials.

The performer has a flying start of ten feet. The stop watch is started at the end of the ten feet. The performer executes a forward roll on the mat, and then continues to the chair indicated in the upper left-hand corner of the diagram. He passes the left side of the chair, turns to the right, and continues in this direction for thirty feet. He executes a figure-eight turn around the chairs indicated in the upper right-hand corner of the diagram, which chairs are three feet apart. He continues on the right side of the course, and executes a shuttle run between the two lines, which are thirty feet apart, on the right side of the course. He then continues to the chair indicated in the lower right-hand corner of the course, encircles the chair, and proceeds along the diagonal line to the bar, which is eighteen

[1] *Physical Training,* War Department Field Manual 21-20 (1950), pp. 183-84 and 305-28.

[2] Carlos L. Wear, "The Construction of a Multiple Obstacle Run for Classifying Junior High School Boys into Homogeneous Groups for Physical Education Activities," *Research Quarterly,* May, 1940.

inches from the floor and at right angles to the diagonal line. He jumps over the bar, continues thirty feet along the diagonal line, performs a pirouette, and continues along the diagonal line to the line where the watch is stopped, which is seventy-five feet from the chair indicated in the lower right-hand corner of the diagram, and he is supposed to run ten feet beyond that line.

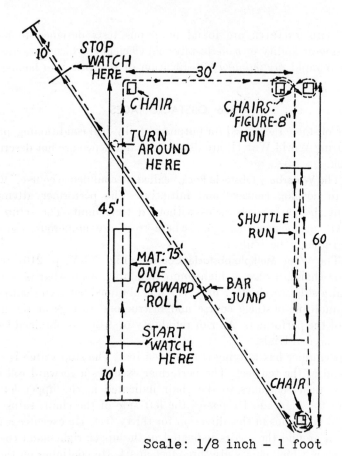

Scale: 1/8 inch — 1 foot

FIGURE XXV. Wear Multiple-obstacle Course: Floor Markings

T-scores computed from Wear's data collected on one hundred junior-high-school boys and extrapolated from two to three seconds in either direction from the lowest and the highest datum may be found in Table 96 (p. 217). The mean of the times was 27.94 seconds, and the standard deviation was 2.84 seconds.

369. For the **Scott Obstacle Course**[3] the only equipment needed is a

---

[3] M. Gladys Scott and Esther French, *Evaluation in Physical Education*, pp. 193–95.

jumping standard and a crossbar. Standards in the form of T-scores[4] are available for high-school girls and for college women.

370. The **University of California Physical-efficiency Test** (Fig. XXVI, pp. 218-19) consists of measurements of agility, tests of swimming, combative activities, and anthropometric measurements. The scoring tables are so arranged that the record for a given point score in one event is equivalent to the record for the same point score in all the other events. The tests of agility and of swimming are scored objectively, but the combative activities are scored subjectively.

Table 96

MOTOR ABILITY--MULTIPLE-OBSTACLE RUN (WEAR):
SCORING TABLE (JUNIOR-HIGH-SCHOOL BOYS)

Time (sec.)	T-score	Time (sec.)	T-score	Time (sec.)	T-score
22	94	28	46	34	27
23	85	29	41	35	24
24	73	30	37	36	22
25	65	31	34	37	20
26	58	32	31	38	19
27	52	33	29		

Since the tests are scaled according to the curve of probability, the superimposition of that curve on the chart indicates the performer's standing relative to that of the total student body of the university.

371. SIGMA DELTA PSI TEST

The following requirements for membership in Sigma Delta Psi[5] indicate all-round athletic ability: (1) 100-yard dash, 11.6 sec.; (2) 120-yard low hurdles, 16.0 sec.; (3) running high jump, 5.0 ft.; (4) running broad jump, 17.0 ft.; and (5) sixteen-pound shot-put (record is according to performer's weight: 30 ft. for 160 lb. or over and proportionately less for weights under 160 lb.) ; (6) rope climb, 20 ft. in 12 sec.; (7) throwing baseball for distance, 250 ft. on the fly; (8) punting a football, 120 ft. on the fly; (9) swimming, 100 yd. in 105 sec.; (10) 1-mile run, 6 min.; (11) tumbling: (a) front handspring, landing on feet, (b) fence vault, with bar at height of chin, (3) handstand, held for 10 sec.; (12) posture, erect; and (13) scholarship, C+. If the candidate has won a letter in a varsity sport, he may substitute the letter for any one of the requirements except the swimming requirement.

[4] *Ibid.*, pp. 200-04.
[5] An athletics fraternity founded at the University of Indiana in 1912. Information concerning the formation of a local chapter may be had by writing to the National Fraternity, Care of the School of Health, Physical Education, and Recreation, Indiana University, Bloomington, Indiana.

TEST	DATE	EVENT	1	2	3	4	5	6	7	8	9	10
		GRADE	E		D		C		B		A	
		PERCENTAGE	7%		24%		38%		24%		7%	
		EFF. POINTS	1	2	3	4	5	6	7	8	9	10
AGILITY	1st	RUN (SEC.)	14⅖	14	13⅗	13⅕	12⅘	12⅖	12	11⅗	11⅕	10⅘
		JUMP (IN.)	146	154	162	170	178	186	194	202	210	218
	2nd	VAULT (IN.)	48	50	52	54	56	58	60	62	64	66
	3rd	SCALE (SEC.)	38	30	23	18	13	10 9 8 7	6⅔	6⅓	5⅔	5⅓
		FALL (IN.)	12	18	24	30	36	42	48	54	60	66
SWIMMING	1st	SPEED (SEC.)	26	24	22	20	18	16	15	14	13	12
		DIVING	⅓	⅔	1	2	3	4	5	6	7	8
	2nd	RESCUE (YDS.)	1	5	9	13	17	21	25	29	33	37
	3rd	STROKES	½	1	2	3	4	5	6	7	8	9
		DISTANCE (YDS.)	20	40	60	100	150	250	350	450	550	750
DEFENSE	1st	WEIGHT CONTROL										
	2nd	BLOCKS AND COUNTERS										
		BLOWS AND HOLDS										
	3rd	INITIATIVE AND SPIRIT										
MEASUREMENTS	1st	STANDING HEIGHT (IN.)	63 64	65	66	67	68	69	70	71	72	73
	2nd	SITTING HEIGHT (IN.)	33		34	35		36	37		38	39
	3rd	WEIGHT (LBS.)	106	114	122	130	138	146	154	162	170	178
		LUNG CAP. (CU. IN.)	175	195	215	235	255	275	295	315	335	355

NAME AGE DATE PREP. COL. CLASS

UNIVERSITY OF CALIFORNIA—DEPARTMENT OF PHYSICAL EDUCATION FOR MEN

RECORD CARD

INTERPRETATION OF CHART

The object of the Physical Efficiency test is to give each man an estimate of his relative physical efficiency. By means of the chart on the opposite side of this card a man may compare his ability in any event with his ability in any other event. For example B plus represents an equal degree of difficulty in all events; thus 12 flat in the dash equals 10.4 inches in the jump or 6½ in the swim, etc.

A man may compare his ability with that of the thousands who have taken the test and upon the statistical analysis of whose performance the chart is based. By adding the percentages to the right of the score recorded one may learn how many men out of every 100 do better than himself in that particular event.

In addition to passing each test with a grade of D, or better, a man is required to make a total of 15 points in each division of the Efficiency Test: Agility, Defense and Swimming. Two points are given for E plus, 4 for D plus, 6 for C plus, etc., therefore it behooves the individual to do his best in each event.

AGILITY.—The 100-yard dash and the broad jump events are conducted as in ordinary track competition, save for the fact that all participants are required to wear tennis shoes to insure comparable results and that the broad jump is measured from the toe of the jumping foot to the nearest heel mark. The hand vault requires that the candidate vault over an obstacle, using one or both hands, no part of the body being allowed to touch the obstacle or pass a vertical plane beneath and parallel to it.

The scaling test requires that the man climb an inch and a half rope to the top of a twelve-foot wall, starting from a hanging position with feet free of the ground, scale the wall and finish by touching the shelf on the opposite side with both feet. The legs and feet must not be used to assist the man in climbing the rope but the toes may be placed against the wall to steady the body and the legs may be used in drawing the body over the top of the wall.

In the falling test the man must run and dive forward, passing head first over an obstacle and alighting on the hands and shoulders in a manner insuring safety to the performer. The take-off must be placed at least three feet in front of the obstacle. Preliminary tests and instruction must be given to discover and prepare individuals not capable of undertaking the event with safety.

SWIMMING.—Scoring on the chart is based upon the following imperial standards. All dives, strokes and rescues must be executed in good form. No credit will be given for indifferent form. The dives, strokes and rescues must be demonstrated in the order listed.

Diving:
- ⅓ Any take off from the side.
- ⅔ Jumping in feet first.
- 1 Standing dive head first, or feet first from high board.
- 2 Preceding plus running straight dive (at least three steps).

3 Swan dive.
4 Front Jack knife dive.
5 Back dive.
6, 7 and 8 Three elective dives.

Strokes:
- ¼ Ability to float at least 30 seconds
- 1 One elective stroke
- 2 Side stroke
- 3 Second elective stroke

4 Elementary back
5 American crawl
6 Third elective stroke

7 Breast stroke
8 Racing back stroke
9 Fourth elective stroke

Rescue: It is required that the candidate bring a helpless companion to shore over the distance mentioned for the various grades. For grade A subject must properly demonstrate the Cross-chest Carry and two elective holds.

DEFENSE.—Grading is based upon the willingness displayed by the candidate, no matter what the test may be, to play the game in a considerate spirit of give and take, and upon the knowledge and skill which he demonstrates (1) in boxing with reference to position, balance and proper use of each hand in hitting or blocking, or (2) in wrestling with reference to weight control and skill in executing holds and counters, or (3) in fencing with reference to skill in thrusting and striking as with a cane for purposes of defense.

UNIVERSITY CREDIT IN PHYSICAL EDUCATION

	Grade		Grade		Grade

Medical Report: | Remarks:

FIGURE XXVI. University of California Physical-efficiency Test: Chart

219

The rules of the National Collegiate Athletic Association are followed for the various events. None of the events may be performed with a favoring wind. The events must be attempted either crosswise of the wind or into the wind.

In the 120-yard low-hurdle race, five standard low hurdles, twenty yards apart, are used for a flight. For the test to be valid, all the hurdles must remain upright after the run.

For the rope climb the candidate starts from a sitting position on the floor, and climbs the rope without the use of the legs. The legs may be used in the descent.

In the handstand the candidate is not compelled to remain absolutely stationary during the test; neither is he allowed to advance or to retreat more than three feet in any direction.

In the test for posture, the candidate is required to meet the B standards of the Harvard Body-mechanics Posture Chart.

372. The **Phillips JCR Test**[6] consists of jumping, pull-ups, and a 100-yard shuttle run. An r of reliability of about .9, and r's of validity from .59 to .90 have been obtained for the test. The jump is the jump-and-reach type (see Sec. 164). The pull-ups are performed with the ordinary (palmsforward) grasp. The run is a 100-yard shuttle run, consisting of ten laps on a ten-yard shuttle run with a forty-degree bankboard at each end for stopping and for starting. A number of runners can be timed at one time by the use of the second and the half-second timing-method (see Sec. 340). Standards for the test may be found in the reference cited.

373. Indiana Motor-fitness Tests. There have been obtained r's of validity of above .80 for the following four Indiana Motor-fitness Tests for highschool and college men:[7]

    (1) (Pull-ups + push-ups) × (jump and reach)

    (2) (Pull-ups + push-ups) × (standing broad jump)

    (3) (Straddle pull-ups (see Sec. 324) + [push-ups × (jump and reach)]

    (4) (Straddle pull-ups + push-ups) × (standing broad jump)

Two sets of norms are presented in the references cited, one set based on the McCloy Classification Index, and the other on the Cozens Classification Index (see Secs. 336-38). Scoring tables for college men based on the equivalents of P-scores with a range of six standard deviations are also available.[8]

[6] Bernath E. Phillips, "The JCR Test," *Research Quarterly,* March, 1947.

[7] Karl W. Bookwalter and Carolyn W. Bookwalter, "A Measure of Motor Fitness for College Men," *Bulletin of the School of Education,* Indiana University, March, 1943.

    Karl W. Bookwalter, "Further Studies of Indiana University Motor Fitness Index," *Bulletin of the School of Education,* Indiana University, September, 1943.

[8] Karl W. Bookwalter, "Test Manual for Indiana Motor Fitness Indices for High School and College Age Men," *Research Quarterly,* December, 1943.

374. The **Indiana Physical-fitness Test for high-school boys and girls**[9] is composed of straddle pull-ups, squat thrusts, push-ups, and the jump and reach. The method of scoring, which consists of multiplying the sum of the scores for the straddle pull-ups, the squat thrusts, and the push-ups by the score for the jump and reach is discussed in the reference cited, and norms based on the McCloy Classification Index are available in the same reference.

375. The **Indiana Physical-fitness Test for elementary-school boys and girls**[10] in the fourth to the eighth grade consists of straddle pull-ups, push-ups, squat thrusts for twenty seconds, and the jump and reach. Norms for this test, which are based on the McCloy Classification Index, are available in the reference cited.

376. For the **Larson Indoor and Outdoor Motor-ability Tests,**[11] r's of .97 and .98 with the total scores of twenty-five events have been obtained. The indoor test consists of the dodging run, the barsnap, pull-ups, push-ups, and the vertical jump; and the outdoor test consists of the baseball throw for distance, pull-ups, the barsnap, and the vertical jump. Scoring tables for college men may be found in the reference cited.

377. For many years several countries in Europe[12] have emphasized an **all-round national-fitness program,** which is intended to promote a continuance of good physical condition over the years. This type of program is, of necessity, limited to individual events and to events that are not dependent upon the co-operation of others except for timing, measuring, and scoring. Usually five categories of events are proposed so that the performer must excel in several specializations.

Six categories of events, which have been adapted from two of the European (German and Swedish) batteries of events, are proposed here. The candidate should choose one event from each of the six groups. After he has met the minimum requirement from each group, and has equaled or exceeded the criterion score for each event, he should be granted a bronze emblem. In many of the European countries, if an individual fulfills these requirements in four different years, he is awarded a silver emblem. If he repeats the requirement for eight different years, he is awarded a gold emblem. In Germany the bronze medal was given to persons between

[9] *Physical Fitness Manual for High School Boys,* Bulletin 136, Indiana State Department of Public Instruction, 1944.
Physical Fitness Manual for High School Girls, Bulletin 137 (Revised), Indiana State Department of Public Instruction, 1944.
[10] C. C. Franklin and N. G. Lehsten, "Indiana Physical Fitness Test for the Elementary Level (Grades 4 to 8)," *Physical Educator,* May, 1948.
[11] Leonard A. Larson, "A Factor Analysis of Motor Ability Variables and Tests, with Tests for College Men," *Research Quarterly,* October, 1941.
[12] H. Meusel, *Körperliche Grundansbildung.*
Johannes Nabholz, "A Suggestion for the National Fitness Program" (mimeographed).

eighteen and thirty-two years of age who passed the six tests within twelve months; the silver medal was awarded (1) to persons between thirty-two and forty years of age who completed the six tests within twelve months and (2) to persons who passed the tests during eight different years; and the gold medal was awarded (1) to persons who already had the silver medal and who passed the tests each year during seven consecutive years and (2) to persons over forty years of age who passed the tests within twelve months.

The following tests and requirements are proposed for men.

Swimming and life saving. Swimming 100 yd. in 1 min. 13 sec.; swimming 300 yd. in 8 min. 20 sec.; Red Cross or YMCA Life-saving Certificate.

Jumping. High jump, 4 ft. 5 in.; running broad jump, 15 ft. 6 in.; straddle vault over long horse 4 ft. high, 5 ft. 6 in. long, without springboard.

Running and skating. Running 100 yd. in 11.4 sec.; running 440 yd. in 1 min. 8.0 sec.; running 1 mi. in 5 min. 45.0 sec.; skating 1 mi. in 4 min. 20.0 sec.

Throwing. Discus throw, 82 ft.; sixteen-pound shot-put, 27 ft.; twelve-pound shot-put, 33 ft.; baseball throw, 250 ft.

Endurance in locomotive events. Distance running 5 mi. in under 40 min.; swimming 880 yd. in under 20 min.; skating 5 mi. in under 24 min.; bicycling 10 mi. in under 36 min.; rowing 7 mi. in under 60 min.; paddling canoe 5 mi. in under 52 min.

Strength and endurance. Weight lifting: sum of the three "Olympic" lifts, namely, the military press, the snatch, and the clean and jerk—$2\frac{1}{2}$ times weight of body. Three of the following events: pull-ups, 15 times; parallel-bar push-ups, 12 times; floor push-ups, 33 times; sit-ups, 70 times in 2 min.; full "knee bends," trunk erect, arms thrusting forward for balance—250 times.

The following tests and requirements are proposed for women.

Swimming and life saving. Swimming 200 yd., no time limit; Red Cross Life-saving Certificate.

Jumping. Standing broad jump, 6 ft.; running broad jump, 11 ft. 8 in.; and running high jump, 3 ft. 7 in.

Running. 100 yd. in 14 sec.; 220 yd. in 32 sec.

Throwing. Baseball throw, 160 ft.; discus throw (women's discus), 64 ft.; eight-pound shot-put, 24 ft.; basketball throw, 52 ft.

Endurance. Walking 8 mi., under 2 hr.; swimming 880 yd., no time limit; paddling canoe 5 mi., under 1 hr.; bicycling 5 mi., under 25 min.

Strength and endurance. Three of the following events: supine pull-ups (see Sec. 324(2)), 25 times; floor push-ups (legs extended), 15 times; full squats, 100 times; and sit-ups (see Sec. 326), 45 times in 2 minutes.

378. The events for which **NSWA Physical-performance Levels for high-**

school girls[13] (Table 77, p. 180) are given include the standing broad jump, the basketball throw for distance, a potato race, modified pull-ups, knee push-ups, sit-ups, the ten-second squat thrust, and the thirty-second squat thrust (see Sec. 334).

The standing broad jump is performed according to standardized directions. In the basketball throw for distance the performer throws from behind a line: only one step forward is permitted. The score is the better record of two trials.

For the potato race, two lines, thirty feet apart, are drawn on the floor. Two small blocks of wood approximately two inches by two inches by four inches are placed on the floor just beyond the second line. The runner stands behind the first line, and on the signal to go, she runs to the second line, picks up a block of wood, runs back to the first line, and places (not throws) the block behind the first line; she then runs back to the second line, picks up the second block of wood, and runs back to, and crosses, the first line. The performance is scored in seconds and tenths of seconds. The score is the better record of two trials. (Time can be saved by having the girls start alternately from behind the first and the second line, this procedure making it unnecessary to move the blocks back to the other line.)

379. The **Scott-French Motor-ability Test**[14] consists of two batteries: (1) four-second dash, basketball throw for distance, standing broad jump, and wall passes with a basketball and (2) obstacle race, standing broad jump, and basketball throw. An R of .91 with teachers' judgments was obtained for the first battery, and an R of .87 for the second battery. Standards in the form of T-scores for these batteries are available.[15] The standards for college women are below those for senior-high-school girls and also below those for college physical-education major students.

380. The **New York Test for girls**,[16] which has been well validated, consists of eight items measuring such fundamental abilities and qualities as running, throwing, catching, jumping, striking, strength, muscular endurance, agility, co-ordination, power, and balance. It is scored on a hundred-point scale.

381. The **Rodgers Motor-ability Test**,[17] which was based on scores in sports-skills tests, on scores in such fundamental racial activities as running, throwing, and jumping, and on subjective ratings of judges, consists of a hurdle race, the standing broad jump, and what is called a "scramble." An r of .73 was obtained between the test and the ratings, and an r of .91 was obtained with a motor-ability criterion. The test

[13] *Journal of Health and Physical Education*, June, 1945.
[14] Scott and French, *op. cit.*
[15] *Ibid.*, pp. 200-07.
[16] *Evaluative Procedures in Physical Activities for Girls and Young Women* (New York State Division of Health and Physical Education).
[17] Elizabeth G. Rodgers, "Evaluation of the Fundamentals of Motor Performance," *Journal of Health and Physical Education*, April, 1947.

appears to be an excellent method of classifying girls in the teaching of motor skills. Achievement scales, together with the description of the test, may be found in the reference cited.

382. The **University of Illinois Screen Tests for Motor Fitness**[18] were designed primarily to select those persons whom it is inadvisable to require to go "all out" in severe tests of motor fitness at the beginning of a college program. The three batteries, which are scored by "pass" or "fail," include measurements of balance, flexibility, agility, strength, power, and endurance. The first battery[19] consists of three tests of balance, three of flexibility, three of agility, three of strength, one of power, and five of endurance. The second battery[20] consists of two tests of balance, two of flexibility, two of strength, two of muscular endurance, two of power, three of agility, and one (the mile run) of circulorespiratory endurance. Because of the fact that in some college situations it may be considered undesirable to use even a fourteen-test battery, a battery of seven items[21] has been presented. This battery provides two substitutions for the mile run: (1) a shuttle run or the dive-and-roll test (which the authors of the battery rightly consider may be dangerous if not practiced for some time in advance) and (2) the breath-holding test (holding the breath for thirty seconds after running in place for two minutes at the rate of three steps a second). Several short batteries of this type are discussed in Chapter 13 of the reference cited.

383. For the development of the **National Recreation Association Physical-achievement Standards** for boys and for girls,[22] large numbers of data were available, but the analysis of these data left very much to be desired. Classification is on the basis of age alone, and there is a great deal of overlapping of standards. In the events for boys the standards are on the "pass or fail" basis, a basis which is not popular with boys. In the events for girls the standards are on a nine-point scale, which, while better than a "pass or fail" basis, is still not adequate.

384. McCLOY HOME TESTS OF PHYSICAL CONDITION (Table 97, p. 225)

The McCloy Home Test for men consists of sit-ups, push-ups, squat jumps, and pull-ups (see Chap. 15). For the pull-ups a bar, which may well be a broom handle, is placed across the backs of two chairs of ordinary height. The broom handle may, if necessary, be held in place by someone other than the performer. The performer grasps the broom handle with a reverse grasp (palms toward the head). Holding the bar against the upper chest just below the top of the sternum, he walks underneath

---

[18] Thomas Kirk Cureton, Jr., and Others, *Physical Fitness Appraisal and Guidance.*
[19] *Ibid.,* p. 401.
[20] *Ibid.,* p. 397.
[21] *Ibid.,* p. 402.
[22] Obtainable from the National Recreation Association, 315 Fourth Avenue, New York City.

the bar until the body is straight. He then flexes the lower legs until the angles behind the knees are each a right angle, and completely extends the forearms. He then pulls himself up until the upper part of the chest touches the bar, and he repeats the movement as many times as possible.

The McCloy Home Test for women consists of sit-ups, knee push-ups, full squats, and chair pull-ups (see Chap. 15).

Table 97

PHYSICAL FITNESS--HOME TESTS (McCLOY):   STANDARDS (MEN AND WOMEN)*

(Numbers not underlined are scores for men)

(Numbers underlined are scores for women)

Standard	Sit-ups		Push-ups	Knee Push-ups		Chair Pull-ups		Squat Jumps	Full Squats
90 superb	112	50	53	60		63	30	127	142
80 superior	82	37	43	43		53	22	98	99
70 excellent	58	28	34	28		45	17	74	69
60 good	42	21	26	20		38	14	54	55
50 fair	32	15	21	15		31	11	42	46
40 poor	25	11	16	10		25	8	31	40
30 very poor	20	8	13	6		19	5	21	32
20 disgraceful	15	4	10	3		14	3	11	25

*Based upon records of 300 men and of 300 women.

MISCELLANEOUS TEST BATTERIES

385. The **Oregon Physical-education Tests** for elementary and secondary schools[23] consist of pull-ups and push-ups for boys and girls, curl-ups, the treadmill, the jump and reach, and a number of "pass-or-fail" Brace-type stunts (see Sec. 201). At least two of these tests are ones not commonly known, and deserve further investigation. Standards are provided with age norms running in groups from eight to eighteen years.

386. Numerous tests for secondary-school and college students of both sexes are available in publications of the **United States Office of Education.**[24] The standards were frequently established more by common agreement of the committees concerned than by extensive testing.

[23] State Department of Public Instruction, Salem, Oregon.
[24] *Physical Fitness through Physical Education for the Victory Corps* and *Handbook on Physical Fitness for Students in Colleges and Universities.*

CHAPTER 19

SPECIAL ABILITIES

387. SOME TESTS frequently designated as tests of special abilities have been presented in Chapter 11 (e.g., tests of balance, Secs. 231-38; tests of sensory rhythm and of timing, Sec. 240; and tests of accuracy, Secs. 226-30). The tests in this chapter are, for the most part, useful primarily for research workers. Those tests that are most likely to be useful for other than research purposes are discussed first.

388. FLEXIBILITY

There should be an adequate warm-up before any test of flexibility is taken.

389. Modification of Cureton Tests of Flexibility.[1] In the scoring of most of the Cureton Tests the sizes of the subjects have not been taken into account. The scoring of this type of test can be easily adjusted to the size of the subject. In the first four of the following five tests (modified from the Cureton battery), the score is in terms of a quotient in which the measurement of flexibility multiplied by 100 is divided by a certain length of the body.

(1) *Forward bending of trunk.* The subject sits on a table. His lower legs, which are extended, are in contact with the table. Keeping his lower legs extended, the subject bends his trunk as far forward as possible. The examiner measures with a tape measure the vertical distance from the suprasternale (the notch at the top of the sternum) to the table. This distance is multiplied by 100, and the product is divided by the trunk length.[2] This measurement of flexibility is more a measurement of the functional length of the hamstrings than it is of ability to bend the trunk forward, although it includes both factors.

(2) *Backward bending of trunk.* The subject lies prone on the table, with his feet held down and with his hips in firm contact with the table. He then raises his trunk as far backward as possible. The examiner measures the vertical distance from the suprasternale to the top of the table. This measurement is multiplied by 100, and the product is divided by the trunk length.

(3) *Upward-and-backward moving of arms.* The subject lies prone on a table,

---

[1] Thomas K. Cureton, Jr., "Objective Tests of Swimming" (M.P.E. Thesis, Springfield College, 1930).

——, "Flexibility as an Aspect of Physical Fitness," *Supplement to Research Quarterly*, May, 1941.

[2] The measurement of trunk length is made with the subject seated on a bench and with the back of the subject against the wall. The vertical distance between the suprasternale and the bench is measured. The subject is instructed not to make any effort to raise his chest high, but to direct the top of his head upward moderately.

with his chin touching the table and with his arms directed forward. He grasps a wand with both hands, and raises his arms as far upward and backward as possible, keeping the forearms extended and the hands in a straight line with the forearms. The examiner measures the vertical distance from the bottom of the wand to the table. This measurement is multiplied by 100, and the product is divided by the length of the arm.[3]

(4) *Sideward-and-backward moving of arms.* A straight crossbar at least eight feet in length is fastened with rubber bands to the front sides of two jumping standards so that it can be moved upward and downward readily. This crossbar, which should be a two-by-two-inch piece of lumber (not a piece of limber bamboo), is placed, at the height of the acromion processes, behind the back. The subject, with his palms forward, raises his arms until they are in a horizontal position and until the fifth fingers (all fingers of each hand held together) touch the crossbar. Keeping the fifth fingers in contact with the crossbar, the subject moves his back as far away (forward) from the crossbar as possible. The examiner measures the distance from the edge of the crossbar (the edge that is the closer to the subject) to the spinous process of the vertebra at that level. This distance is multiplied by 100, and the product is divided by the length of the arm.

(5) *Plantarward-and-dorsalward moving of feet.* The subject sits on a table with the backs of his knees touching the table. Keeping the heel on the table, he plantarflexes the foot as far as possible. On a pad of paper placed in a vertical position at the side of the foot and with a pencil kept in a horizontal position, the examiner traces the outline of the dorsum of the foot from just above the ankle to just beyond the distal end of the uppermost metatarsal bone. The subject then dorsiflexes the foot as far as possible, and the preceding measurement is repeated. In each tracing, a straight line is drawn from the bend at the ankle to the distal end of the metatarsal. The angle of each of these lines with the horizontal is measured with a protractor.

Test 1 has a wide usefulness for high jumping, broad jumping, and hurdling, for tumbling and diving, for various forms of gymnastics, and for the dance. Tests 3 and 4 are particularly applicable to swimming (Test 4 is particularly useful for backstroke and breaststroke swimming) and to gymnastics. Test 5 is useful primarily for swimming and for the dance. Although the tests are of only approximate accuracy, the r's of reliability are about .85 if the subjects are thoroughly warmed up. The tests are practicable in that they can be administered with a minimum of equipment.

390. The **Scott-French Bobbing Tests**[4] and the **Wells-Dillon Sit-and-reach Tests,**[5] which involve the hamstrings, and the muscles and the ligaments of the back, are useful for purposes of motivation, but they result in somewhat crude measurements of flexibility. In neither test is any account taken of the lengths of the extremities; a person with short legs and long arms has, for example, a decided advantage in such tests.

[3] The length of the arm is measured with the arm hanging downward, and the length is the distance from the acromion process to the top of the wand held in the hand.
[4] M. Gladys Scott and Esther French, *Evaluation in Physical Education.*
[5] Katharine F. Wells and Evelyn K. Dillon, "The Sit and Reach—a Test of Back and Leg Flexibility," *Research Quarterly,* March, 1952.

391. In *bobbing*, the performer stands on a bench, with the toes against a board marked off in inches (— above the bench level, and + below the bench level). The subject then "bobs" downward four times, with the lower legs completely extended, and holds the lowest position on the last movement. The lowest point reached by the fingers is recorded.

392. In the *sit-and-reach test*, two stall-bar benches are placed against the wall, with a space of twelve inches between the benches. A scale eleven inches from the floor is fixed between the stall-bar benches so that the feet rest against a crossboard. The + and the — markings are on the board that is parallel to the floor, and the 0 mark is just above the soles of the feet. The subject sits with the feet flat against the crossboard, and "bobs" downward four times, with the arms reaching forward. The subject holds the lowest position on the last movement. The lowest point reached by the fingers is recorded.

DEVICES FOR MEASURING FLEXIBILITY

393. The *goniometer* is an instrument based on the principle of the plumb bob and protractor, except that instead of the use of a string, a small metal bar is suspended from one end. This bar is mounted in the center of a protractor in such a way that when the instrument is fastened to the part of the body to be moved, the degrees of the angle before and after the movement can be read, and the range readily computed.

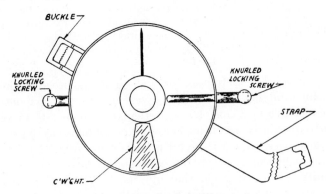

FIGURE XXVII. Leighton Flexometer

394. The *Leighton Flexometer*[6] (Fig. XXVII, p. 228), which is essentially a goniometer, can be fastened with a strap to any part of the body. The instrument consists of two movable parts. There is a movable dial that can, when the initial position is taken, be fixed so that the protractor will not move thereafter during the measurements. The movable hand now points to 0. The individual moves the indicated part of the body through the desired arc of movement. The movement of a screw then im-

[6] Jack R. Leighton, "A Simple Objective and Reliable Measure of Flexibility," *Research Quarterly*, May, 1942. The instrument is obtainable from the C. H. Stoelting Company, 424 North Homan Avenue, Chicago 24.

mobilizes the moving pointer so that the angle indicated by the pointer can be easily read with accuracy. Reliability r's of .889 to more than .98 have been obtained for the instrument. In the reference cited, techniques of measurement for twenty-two movements are described. These twenty-two movements represent thirteen total ranges of movements at various joints. (The total range of movement of the forearm at the elbow joint, for example, is described in terms of both flexion and extension of the forearm.)

395. RESPONSE TIME

The speed of response to a stimulus is associated with the speed of starting in running and in swimming, with the length of time taken by a batter in making up his mind to swing his bat at a pitched baseball, and with the speed with which players in football, basketball, and other athletics may initiate movements in response to those of their opponents.

396. Single-response time. For measuring the length of time required to respond to a single signal, an electrically controlled chronometer, which is connected with make-and-break switches, is used. Some chronometers measure time in hundredths of a second, and others in thousandths of a second. The examiner presses a switch, which starts the chronometer and initiates the stimulus. The stimulus may be a light, such as the flashing of an electric light, or a sound, such as the ringing of a bell or the striking of a gong, or even a slight electric shock. As soon as the subject perceives the stimulus, he presses a key or executes some other predetermined movement that stops the chronometer. If a measurement of single-response time is desired, the subject, usually in a sitting position, has his fingers on a telegraph key. On the indicated signal, he depresses the key, which depression causes the chronometer to stop. The time required for the response is then read on the chronometer. Variations of the type of apparatus for measuring single-response time may involve a more extended movement than that of pressing a key with one finger; for example, lunging a predetermined distance to knock over a target with the hand.

397. Multiple-response time. In the measurement of multiple-response time, a chronometer is also used. Several alternative stimuli are involved, and there is a correct response for each stimulus. Hence the subject, upon perceiving the stimulus, must decide upon the response before executing it. If a telegraph-key type of instrument is used, the stimuli are usually lights. The different telegraph keys should be of equal distance from the subject's hand, which rests on a table. The subject may be instructed to depress a certain key when a certain light signal is given; for example, the left-hand key if the left-hand light signal is flashed; the middle key if the middle light signal is flashed; and the right-hand key if the right-hand light signal is flashed. Or the subject may be instructed to depress the right-hand key if two lights are red, to depress the middle key if one light is red and the other is green, and to depress the left-hand key if two lights are green.

398. In the **Keller Measurement of Response Time**[7] movements of large range and of several choices are involved. There are several targets, each of which is about one foot square. Each target rests on a stand several feet high. The distance that the subject stands from the targets is in proportion to the distance between the ground and the hand when the hand and arm are directed vertically upward. Hence a tall subject with long arms stands farther away from the targets than does a short man with short arms. The subject is instructed to knock over the targets with his hand.

399. **Apparatus for measurement of response time.** A rectangular object of heavy metal is suspended over a frame by two cords running over frictionless pulleys. The other ends of the cords may be fastened to a very light weight, or they may be free. The stimulus is produced by the release of the weight from its position at the top of the frame. The subject stands in front of the apparatus, and is instructed to place his hands against the rectangular weight in order to stop it against the front of the frame. If the weight is not counterbalanced, the length of the time for the response is computed according to the following formula: distance (downward) $= .5gt^2$. The times are in hundredths of a second. The computations for .1 second and for .2 second are, respectively, as follows: distance $= .5 \times 32 \times .1^2 = .16$ foot, and distance $= .5 \times 32 \times .2^2 = .64$ foot. If a counterbalancing weight is used, the slowing effect of that weight should be taken into consideration. The formula for the computation of the speed of falling of the weight on the side facing the subject is

$$d = \frac{.5(m_1 - m_2)}{m_1 + m_2} gt^2,$$

where d = distance that heavier weight falls, m_1 = mass of heavier weight, m_2 = mass of lighter weight, g = gravity = 32.2, and t = time sought.

Note: Nearly frictionless pulleys may be purchased from dealers in physical apparatus.

One of the more recent methods of the use of apparatus for measuring response time is that of Slater-Hammel.[8]

400. **Number of responses.** In the measurement of response time, one or two responses are meaningless, for the subject may be caught in a trough of his attention span, or he may "jump the gun." The recommended number of responses is twenty.[9] The five shortest and the five longest times

[7] Louis F. Keller, "The Relation of 'Quickness of Bodily Movement' to Success in Athletics," *Research Quarterly*, May, 1942.

[8] Arthur T. Slater-Hammel and R. L. Stumpner, "Batting Reaction-Time," *Research Quarterly*, December, 1950.

[9] V. W. Lapp, "An Analysis of Movement on the Basis of Latent Times and Variabilities," *Supplement to Research Quarterly*, October, 1935.

are rejected, and the average of the ten middle times is taken as the average response time.

STATIONARY RUNNING FOR SPEED

401. In the **Carlson Test** of running in place (see Sec. 337) the subject counts the number of contacts of the right foot with the floor. This method of counting is not satisfactory for a period as long as thirty seconds.

402. The **Sills Apparatus**[10] was devised for counting automatically the steps of a subject running in place. The counter[11] is attached to only one piece of the apparatus. The apparatus consists of two pieces, each piece fifteen inches by ten inches. The subject runs, contacting one piece of the apparatus with his right foot, and the other piece of the apparatus with his left foot. The counter is attached to the piece of the apparatus contacted by the left foot. A spring raises the apparatus just enough to break the contact after each step. This type of apparatus has many possibilities for testing speed, skill, and endurance.

403. POTENTIAL VELOCITY

From factorial analyses the following multiple regression equations have been computed for obtaining measurements of *velocity* (as distinct from the association of velocity with force in *power*).

404. Coleman Measurement of Potential Velocity of college men[12] $= 1.65$ four-pound shot-put $+ .282$ Sargent Jump $- .0137$ strength score $- 6.48$ (val., $r = .88$).

405. Stuber Measurement of Potential Velocity of high-school boys[13] $= 2.27$ twelve-pound shot-put $+ .457$ Sargent Jump $- .0216$ strength score $+ 2.68$ (val., $r = .850$).

406. Carpenter Measurement of Potential Velocity of college women[14] $=$ $.580$ standing broad jump $+ .678$ six-pound shot-put $- .0203$ strength score $- 23.22$ (val., $r = .890$).

407. Harris Measurement of Potential Velocity of junior-high-school girls[15] $= .824$ standing broad jump $+ .893$ three-pound shot-put $- .0388$ strength score $- 7.00$ (val., $r = .909$).

[10] Personal communication from Frank D. Sills.

[11] The counter is a small electric device manufactured by Veeder-Root, Inc., Hartford, Connecticut.

[12] James W. Coleman, "The Differential Measurement of the Speed Factor in Large Muscle Activities," *Research Quarterly*, October, 1937. (Modified Formula.)

[13] George M. Stuber, Jr., "The Measurement of Potential Velocity in Post-Pubescent High School Boys" (M.A. Thesis, State University of Iowa, 1940).

[14] Aileen Carpenter, "An Analysis of the Relationships of the Factors of Velocity. Strength, and Dead Weight to Athletic Performance," *Research Quarterly*, March 1941.

[15] Jane E. Harris, "The Differential Measurement of Force and Velocity for Junior High School Girls," *Research Quarterly*, December, 1937.

408. The shots are put from a stand; hence the subject may "follow" the shot over the line after the put. The shot is held in the palm, not up in the fingers. This procedure prevents the subjects who have an over-developed set of palmarflexors from gaining an undue advantage. The shot-put is measured in feet; the Sargent Jump, in centimeters; the standing broad jump, in inches; and the strength score, in pounds. The strength score is computed according to the McCloy method of scoring (see Chap. 14). The velocity score that results is in the form of a T-score, with 50 equaling the mean score of the group, and each ten points either way from the mean being equivalent to one standard deviation. The velocity score is one that indicates the potential contraction-speed of the muscles of one subject as compared with the potential contraction-speed of the muscles of other subjects in the same group. This potential contraction-speed is different from the speed with which the individual can move. As was discussed in Chapter 9, speed or velocity in athletics is a function not solely of the potential contraction-speed of muscles, but of *power*.

409. EYE DOMINANCE

In aiming, as in archery, one eye is, normally, in control. The eye in control may be the eye of which the visual acuity is better than that of the other eye. However, in persons whose visual acuity is the same or about the same in both eyes, one eye is usually dominant in such activities as aiming. The dominant eye may be determined in the following ways.

(1) The subject fixes his eyes on some object eight or ten feet away, and, with both eyes open, "aims" at this object with the forefinger of one hand; that is, he attempts to align the forefinger with the object. He then closes the eyes one at a time. Usually it is found that the finger is in line with one eye, which is the dominant eye, and not with the other eye.

(2) A manoptoscope may be used, which consists of a sighting cone through which the subject looks with both eyes, and attempts to sight some object through the middle of the other (smaller) end of the cone. When the sighting cone is aligned with the object—and the subject can see through the opposite end of the cone with only one eye—the subject closes the eyes one at a time, and the eye that the subject selects for sighting can be readily determined.

Other and more complicated devices than the manoptoscope are available. They are usually available in any psychological laboratory.

410. HANDEDNESS

Numerous tests[16] have been devised to measure handedness. They have, for the most part, been pointed at such usual tasks as picking up articles, putting them down, writing, erasing, pointing with the finger, sharpening

[16] Arthur H. Davison, "The Relationship between Unimanual and Bimanual Handedness," *Journal of Experimental Psychology*, June, 1948.

Wendell Johnson and Darlene Duke, "Revised Iowa Hand Usage Dextrality Quotients of Six-Year-Olds," *Journal of Educational Psychology*, January, 1940.

a pencil, turning the page of a book, cutting with scissors, filling a pen, opening a book, pulling down a window blind, holding a glass of water to drink, using a hammer, emptying an ash tray, pouring something from a bottle into a glass, knocking on a door, turning a key in a lock, combing the hair, eating with a fork, and cutting with a knife. Many of these actions are ones to which an individual has been conditioned at an early age, and many of these actions do not indicate clearly the matter of handedness as related to sports and athletics.

In sports and athletics, right-handedness is not necessarily associated with a socially desirable pattern. A "south-paw" pitcher and a left-handed batter are eagerly sought after on baseball teams. In the game of basketball, a player who can pass, shoot, and dribble with either hand receives social approval. In such a game as handball, the ability to play equally well with the right and the left hand is a skill much sought after. An attempt has been made, therefore, to devise a test of handedness for athletics.

411. TEST OF HANDEDNESS FOR ATHLETICS
(Table 98, p. 234)

The following equipment is needed: one twelve-inch softball, one basketball, one volleyball (for small children, a rubber "playball" about six inches in diameter may be used for both the basketball and the volleyball), a beanbag, a short bat from fifteen to eighteen inches long, and a regulation softball bat (for very young children, a miniature softball bat should be prepared).

(1) The subject stands with his right side toward the examiner. He holds, with both hands, a softball in front of his hips. The examiner, who is six to eight feet away from the subject, requests the subject to toss the ball to him. It should be noted whether the subject tosses the ball with his left hand (i.e., does he swing the ball across in front of his body?) or with his right hand (i.e., does he turn his body and toss the ball, or does he toss the ball with a sideward motion?).

(2) Same as *1*, except that the subject faces the examiner.

(3) Same as *1*, except that the subject stands with his left side toward the examiner. Items *1*, *2*, and *3* are repeated in that order. On the scoring sheet, *R* is encircled if the subject tosses the ball with his right hand; *B*, if he tosses it with both hands; and *L*, if he tosses it with his left hand.

(4) Same as *1*, except that the subject stands in such a position that the examiner is in front of and at the right of the subject (forty-five degrees forward from a transverse axis through the subject's two shoulders).

(5) Same as *4*, except that the examiner is forty-five degrees forward from a position at the left side of the subject. Items *4* and *5* are repeated, and the scoring is the same as for *1*, *2*, and *3*.

(6) Same as *1*, except that a basketball is used instead of a softball. The scoring is the same as that for *1*.

(7) Same as *2*, except that a basketball is used instead of a softball.

(8) Same as *3*, except that a basketball is used instead of a softball.

Items *6*, *7*, and *8* are repeated, and the scoring is the same as that for *1*.

(9) Same as *4*, except that a basketball or a volleyball is used.

(10) Same as *5*, except that a basketball or a volleyball is used.

Items *9* and *10* are repeated, and the scoring is the same as that for *1*.

(11) The position of the subject and of the examiner is the same as in *1*. The subject holds, with both hands, a softball in front of the chest. He is instructed to "put" the softball with either hand to the examiner, who stands eight to ten feet away from the subject.

(12) The position of the subject and of the examiner is the same as in *2*, and the instructions are the same as in *11*.

(13) The position of the subject and of the examiner is the same as in *4*, and the instructions are the same as in *11*.

Table 98

DEXTRALITY TEST: SCORE CARD

1	L B R	17	L		R
	L B R		L		R
2	L B R	18	L		R
	L B R		L		R
3	L B R	19	L		R
	L B R		L		R
4	L B R	20	L		R
	L B R		L		R
5	L B R	21	L		R
	L B R		L		R
6	L B R	22	L		R
	L B R		L		R
7	L B R	23	L (LC) (RC) R		
	L B R				
8	L B R	24	L (LC) (RC) R		
	L B R				
9	L B R	25	(R score_____)		
	L B R		(L score_____)		
10	L B R		L		R
	L B R	26	L		R
11	L R		L		R
	L R	27	L		R
12	L R		L		R
	L R	28	L	B	R
13	L R		L	B	R
	L R	29	L	B	R
14	L R		L	B	R
	L R	30	L		R
15	L R		L		R
	L R	31	L		R
16	L R		L		R
	L R	32	L		R

Athletic Dextrality Quotient = $100 \dfrac{(R + .5B)}{N}$

(14) The position of the subject and of the examiner is the same as in *5*, and the instructions are the same as in *12*.

(15) The position of the subject and of the examiner is the same as in *6*, and the instructions are the same as in *13*.

Items *11, 12, 13, 14*, and *15* are repeated.

(16) An object to be used as a home plate is placed on the floor or on the ground. The subject is given a short bat fifteen to eighteen inches long, and he is instructed to hold it in whichever hand he wishes. He is instructed to take a position relative to the examiner that is customary for a right-handed batter to take relative to a pitcher. The examiner tosses a softball to the subject twelve or fifteen feet away, and instructs him to strike the ball with the bat. The examiner notes with which hand the subject holds the bat. The subject may bat forehanded or backhanded.

(17) Same as *16*, except that the subject stands in the position commonly taken in left-handed batting.

Items *16* and *17* are repeated.

(18) The subject stands facing the examiner. The examiner, a little over an arm's length away from the subject, tosses a beanbag to the subject at a level of about twelve inches above the subject's head. The subject is instructed to catch the beanbag with one hand. The examiner notes with which hand the subject catches the beanbag.

(19) Same as *18*, except that the beanbag is tossed above and to the right of the subject's head.

(20) Same as *18*, except that the beanbag is tossed above and to the left of the subject's head.

(21) Same as *19*, except that the beanbag is tossed about three feet lower than the level of the subject's shoulders and to the right of the subject.

(22) Same as *21*, except that the beanbag is tossed to the left of the subject.

Items *18, 19, 20, 21*, and *22* are repeated, and the preferred hand for each item is recorded.

(23) The subject is given an ordinary softball bat, and is told that the examiner is going to pitch a softball to him. The subject is requested to bat in the way that feels most natural to him. The examiner notes whether it is a left-handed stance or a right-handed stance. The examiner also notes which hand is uppermost on the bat. If the subject bats right-handed with the right hand uppermost, *R* is encircled. If he bats right-handed with the left hand uppermost, *RC* is encircled (*RC* indicates right-handed, cross-handed). Similar records are noted for left-handed batters. This test needs to be given only once. Cross-handed scores are counted as "both" in computing the dextrality quotient.

(24) The examiner requests the subject to throw to him a ball in the way that feels most natural to him. If the subject throws the ball right-handed, *R* is encircled; if left-handed, *L*. If the subject throws the ball right-handed but with the right foot forward, *RC* is encircled; if left-handed, but with the left foot forward, *LC*. If the wrong foot is forward, the score is *B*. This item is administered only once.

(25) The subject stands twenty feet from the wall (ten feet if the subject is under eight years of age). He is instructed to throw a softball with his right hand at a target drawn on the wall. The bull's-eye is one foot in diameter, and there are four concentric circles each six inches wide. (The radii of the concentric circles are 1, 1.5, 2, and 2.5 feet, respectively.) The scoring is as follows: 5 for hitting the bull's-eye; 4 for the circle next to the bull's-eye; and 3, 2, and 1 for the next three circles, respectively. The subject is given ten trials with each hand. If the better score is made with the right hand, *R* is encircled; if with the left hand, *L*.

(26) The examiner, holding a softball bat in his hand, stands in front of the subject. The subject is told that the examiner is going to toss him the bat, and the subject is instructed to catch the bat with one hand. The bat is tossed approximately 1.5 feet to the right of the subject's right shoulder. The examiner notes with which hand the subject catches the bat.

(27) Same as *26*, except that the bat is tossed about 1.5 feet to the left of the subject.

Items *26* and *27* are repeated.

(28) The subject is told that the examiner is going to bounce-pass a volleyball (for a small child, a six-inch playball), and the subject is instructed to *bat* the ball back to the examiner. The ball is bounced to about two feet to the right of the subject. The examiner records whether the subject bats with the right or the left hand, or with both hands.

(29) Same as *28*, except that the ball is bounced to the left of the subject.

Items *28* and *29* are repeated.

(30) The examiner gives the subject a basketball (a volleyball to a child). The examiner stands about eight feet in front of the subject. The subject is instructed to dribble the ball past and to the right of the examiner in such a way that the examiner cannot take the ball away from the subject. The examiner notes whether the subject uses the right or the left hand.

(31) Same as *30*, except that the subject dribbles to the left of the examiner.

Items *30* and *31* are repeated.

(32) The examiner holds a basketball between his two hands with the right hand on the top of the ball and the left hand on the bottom of the ball. He stands at one side of the subject so that the basketball is not between the subject and him. The subject is then requested to strike the ball with a fist and to knock the ball out of the examiner's hands. The examiner records whether the subject uses the right or the left hand. This test is administered only once.

The dextrality quotient is $$\dfrac{100\left(R + \dfrac{B}{2}\right)}{N}.$$

If the thirty-two items are administered with the indicated repetitions, $N = 60$. Example: if a subject uses the right hand 42 times, and both hands 17 times, the dextrality quotient is 84

$$\left\{ \text{i.e., } \dfrac{100\left(42 + \dfrac{17}{2}\right)}{60} \right\}.$$

A score under 50 indicates a preference for the left hand. Norms for this test are not available. It is highly probable that the dextrality quotient is smaller for adult athletes than for younger players and for those who are uninstructed.

412. DEPTH PERCEPTION

It is highly probable that in many athletic sports depth perception is a factor of importance. The ability to field a fly ball, to intercept a hard-driven ground ball in baseball, to intercept and catch a long pass in basketball, to shoot goals, and to execute many other performances would seem to be related to depth perception.

Depth perception has been discussed extensively in textbooks of ophthalmology.[17] A brief review of factors relating to different aspects of depth perception follows.

Extrinsic factors. (1) *Aerial perspective,* with a change of color and with a softening or clouding of contours in distant objects, due to the imperfect transparency of the layers of air between the objects and the eye. This factor would be useful in judging long distances; hence it might be related to judgments of distance in golf. (2) *Distribution of light and of shade* such as the shadows which objects in one plane cast upon those in another, a factor which defines rather clearly the relative positions of each. (3) *Overlapping of contours;* for example, distant hills may appear to be in the same plane until their bases are seen. (4) *Geometrical perspective.* Parallel lines seem to recede, and to converge toward the line of vision; and parallel planes appear to intersect in the plane of the horizon. (5) *Interpretation of size.* As the size of an image diminishes, the distance of the object from the observer increases. (6) *Motion parallax.* As an individual's eyes move, the relationship of objects somewhat in line with each other from the observer's eyes appears to change; for example, as an individual moves the head to the right, objects distant from him seem to move to the right in relation to objects close to him.

Intrinsic factors. (1) *Accommodation of the eye* for various distances through the changing of the curvature of the anterior surface of the lens of the eye. (2) *Convergence,* or the co-ordinated movement of the two eyes toward the fixation of the vision of each eye upon the same near point. (3) *Stereoscopic influence of dissimilar images,* or the presenting of two pictures of the same object seen from slightly dissimilar aspects by each of the two eyes. (4) *Relative size of the retinal image;* this may be related to Extrinsic Factor 5.

Gross binocular visual acuity and gross monocular visual acuity are *prerequisites* to good depth perception.

Little research has been reported concerning the relationship of depth perception to athletic sports, but there is a high probability that Extrinsic Factors 1, 2, 3, and 4 are related to long-distance perspectives in golf and in the fielding of long fly balls. Extrinsic Factors 5 and 6 are probably also important in these same connections. Intrinsic Factors 1, 2, and 3 are important when an object, such as a ball, is closer than twenty feet to the performer.

413. The best-known general test of depth perception is the **Howard-Dohlman Test.**[18] The apparatus for conducting this test may be purchased from any dealer in psychological testing equipment. The original Howard Test [19] consisted of two vertical rods six centimeters apart. The cen-

[17] William S. Duke-Elder, *Text-Book of Ophthalmology I.*

[18] F. W. Weymouth and M. J. Hirsch, "Reliability of Certain Tests for Determining Distance Discrimination," *American Journal of Psychology,* July, 1945.

[19] Harvey J. Howard, "A Test for the Judgment of Distance," *American Journal of Ophthalmology,* September, 1919.

tral portion of these rods was seen through an aperture by the subject from a distance of six meters. The rods were exposed momentarily, and the subject was required to tell whether the right rod was nearer or farther than the left rod. Twenty judgments were made for distance separations of the rods increased by five-millimeter steps, and the linear threshold was taken as the difference in distance from which 75 per cent or more of the correct answers were obtained. Later the movable rod was made controllable by the subject who attempts to place it at the same distance as the standard rod. The average deviation for ten settings is used as the threshold.

Some variations of this test have been made by having three rods, with the middle rod movable. The subject is instructed to tell whether it is closer than the outer two, or whether the rods are at the same distance. Changes are made five millimeters at a time.

414. In one modification[20] of the Howard-Dohlman Apparatus, three rods, with the center rod variable, are moved past the subject at a twenty-foot distance at a standard speed of fifty centimeters a second. A much higher correlation has been obtained between this modification and the ability to land an airplane than has been obtained by the use of the Howard-Dohlman Test without motion. The distance over which the rods move is a total of one meter. The rods move up and down, first in one direction and then in the other. This apparatus, so far as the authors know, cannot be purchased.

The basis for measuring other aspects of depth perception is still lacking. This is a fertile field, however, for experimentation in the field of athletics, and is discussed at some length here in order to stimulate such experimentation.

415. BREATH-HOLDING [21]

The length of time that the breath can be held has for many years been of interest in the measurement of potential endurance. The length of time that the breath can be held has been considered to be a somewhat reliable measurement of the degree of acidosis in the blood.[22] An increase in the amount of carbon dioxide tension in the blood increases, because of the carbonic and the lactic acid, the pH of the blood; hence the respiratory center is stimulated, and the subject is forced to attempt to breathe to relieve the distress.

Various forms of exercise are used in tests of breath-holding: (1) chair stepping at the rate of five steps in fifteen seconds (Schneider Test, Sec.

[20] Personal communication from H. W. Rose to the senior author.

[21] For an excellent recent review of the literature on breath-holding, see: Henry J. Montoye, "Breath-Holding as a Measure of Physical Fitness," *Research Quarterly*, October, 1951.

[22] Yandell Henderson, "The Time the Breath can be Held as an Index for Acidosis," *Journal of the American Medical Association*, July 25, 1914.

486), (2) chair stepping at the rate of thirty steps a minute, (3) chair stepping for five minutes, and (4) stationary running at the rate of 180 steps a minute for two minutes. If stationary running is used, the subject should be instructed to get the feet just off the floor. If a mild form of exercise is used, the second breath after the cessation of the exercise is the one usually held. If a strenuous form of exercise is used, the fourth breath after the cessation of the exercise is the one usually held. The measurement of breath-holding after the performance of a standardized exercise would appear to be preferable to such a measurement without the performance of any exercise. In the latter case it is possible for the subject (by some forced breathing) to double or triple the amount of time of the breath-holding. In the former case, since the subject is usually breathing with a regular rhythm, it is not possible for him to make (by forced breathing) such increases in the time of breath-holding.

In the measurement of breath-holding the subject may simply hold his breath, with an examiner counting the seconds that the breath is held; or he may blow into a U-tube manometer (resistance = 40 mm. Hg.), or a flarimeter (resistance = 20 mm. Hg.). The chief advantage of the use of one of these pieces of equipment is that as soon as the subject stops blowing, the mercury or the water drops, and hence the subject cannot breathe in without being detected.

The coefficients of reliability that have been obtained for measurements of breath-holding are, for the most part, not very high. They become higher, however, as the subject undergoes more and more practice. The difficulty with the test is that it is correlated so highly with the subject's will power. It is not at all uncommon for a subject who can hold his breath only forty-five seconds on the first trial to be able, half an hour later, after having seen others hold their breath longer than forty-five seconds, to hold his breath for as much as a minute and a half. In other words, the test measures will power and determination perhaps more than it measures physiological resistance to acidosis.

416. In the **Flack Test**[23] for aircraft pilots the item of breath-holding is included. A standard resistance of forty millimeters of mercury is used. On the basis of this test, all candidates for pilots who cannot hold the breath forty-five seconds or longer are rejected. The same exercise is used in the Flack Test as in the Schneider Test.

417. In the **Cureton Test**,[24] which is adapted to mass-testing, the subject performs stationary running for two minutes at the rate of three steps a second and then holds his second breath after the cessation of exercise. He holds up one hand as long as he is holding his breath, and lowers his hand at the end of the breath-holding. The examiner counts the seconds aloud,

---

[23] Martin W. Flack, *The Medical Problems of Flying.*
——, "Some Simple Tests of Physical Efficiency," *Lancet,* February 8, 1919.
[24] Cureton and Others, *Physical Fitness Appraisal and Guidance.*

and the subject's partner notes the number of seconds that the breath is held.

418. STATIC EQUILIBRIUM [25]

419. The **ataxiameter** is an instrument for measuring static equilibrium, that is, the relative steadiness of the body in the standing position. A harness with a pointed attachment is fixed on the top of the head, and the pointer with a pencil writes on a tablet fixed in position above the head. This type of apparatus can be improvised in a number of ways. It is essential that the apparatus on the head—which apparatus may be a modification of a football helmet—have a pencil which is rigidly fastened to the helmet. The paper upon which the writing is done must be so fastened that it does not move sideways but yet rests firm enough on the pencil that the movement of the head of the subject is recorded.

Static equilibrium may be measured with the subject's eyes open and with the subject's eyes closed. The subject may, with the eyes open or closed, stand on one foot at a time, or on the toes of one foot. Very little experimentation in athletic skills has been conducted with this type of instrument, which would seem to offer possibilities for the investigation of certain aspects of kinesthesis.

420. PSYCHOLOGICAL TESTS

Researchers in physical education frequently use types of tests that are used primarily by psychologists. Some of these tests are tests of motor skills not often measured by physical educators. Others of these tests are measurements of intelligence, of aptitudes, and of emotional qualities. Selected references in the area of psychological testing that may be useful to physical educators follow:

Apparatus Tests, Army Air Forces Aviation Psychological Program. Research Report 4 (ed. by Arthur W. Melton). Washington: United States Government Printing Office, 1947.

Lee Joseph Cronback, *Essentials of Psychological Testing.* New York: Harper and Brothers, 1949.

Motor Skills Research Exchange (ed. by Robert D. Ammons). Louisville, Kentucky: University of Louisville (Vol. I begun in 1949).

Handbook of Human Engineering Data for Design Engineers, Technical Report SDC 199-1-1 Nav Exos P-643 (ed. by C. P. Seity). Sands Point, Long Island, Port Washington, New York: Special Devices Center, Office of Naval Research.

Robert L. Thorndike, *Personnel Selection: Testing and Measuring Techniques,* New York: J. Wiley, 1949.

G. M. Whipple, *Manual of Mental and Physical Tests.* Baltimore: Warwick and York, 1910.

Robert S. Woodworth, *Experimental Psychology.* New York: Henry Holt, 1938.

[25] Walter R. Miles, "Static Equilibrium as a Useful Test of Motor Efficiency," *Journal of Industrial Hygiene,* February, 1922.

CHAPTER **20**

ACHIEVEMENT IN SPORTS

421. IF ACHIEVEMENT tests in sports are to be practicable, they must, in addition to being valid, be administrable to large groups at one time. If possible, they should be utilizable for developing, as well as for measuring, the desired skill. Since many achievement tests are time consuming in nature, ratings are generally substituted for them. Although ratings by experts may be highly reliable, they are not so satisfactory, either to the pupil or to the teacher, as a well-formulated, specific test.

422. Validation. If a test is designed to measure ability in a sport as a whole, then the criterion should be that ability. If subtests are designed to measure the component skills of the sport, then the subcriteria should be these components. A shortcoming of many achievement tests in sports is that the subtests have been validated against a criterion for ability in the sport as a whole rather than against subcriteria for indicated component skills. The following methods of validating achievement tests are fairly common, and, if skillfully used, generally satisfactory.

(1) The criterion may be experts' ratings of the entire ability. If the ability is analyzed into component skills, each component skill should be rated separately.

(2) The criterion may be the sum of the scores of a number of tests of the skill. For example, a large number of tests of basket-shooting may be given, and each test may be T-scored. The criterion for basket-shooting ability, then, is the sum of the T-scores.

(3) In individual sports the criterion may be the sum of the points won by each player from all the other players in a round-robin tournament; for example, fifty tennis players may play twenty points against each other, each player serving ten times and alternating at each fifth point. In the Karsner Ladder Tournament,[1] which is a modification of the round-robin tournament, players in groups of four play a given number of points. The tournament is so organized that each player of a group plays as a partner with each of the other three players, and each player plays against each other player. There is no saving of time for each player, but four players, rather than only two players, can play on a court

---

[1] Personal communication from Milo G. Karsner.

at one time. In handball, a doubles tournament, with the groups formed at random, has been used as a basis for the criterion.[2]

(4) In a group in which the desired skill is distributed normally,[3] the criterion may be two groups of the players (e.g., varsity players and nonvarsity players) or three groups of the players (e.g., average players, above-average players, and below-average players). A coefficient of biserial or of triserial correlation (see Secs. 669-70) is then computed between each of the tests and the groups of players.

423. Reliability. In the determination of the reliability of a test, the following items should be kept in mind.

(1) A "pass-or-fail" test usually has a lower reliability than tests with graded scoring devices; for example, a test of throwing strikes with a baseball has a lower reliability than does a test of throwing at a concentric-ringed target; and the greater the number of concentric circles, the better the reliability of the test of throwing (see also Sec. 226).

(2) Tests that are entirely unfamiliar have a lower reliability than those that have been practiced; hence the reliability of a test should be determined only after the test has been practiced. This item does not apply to tests designed to measure the ability to learn new skills.

(3) Each of the tests of a battery should have an r of reliability of at least .60. If the r of reliability of each of five tests is .70, the r of reliability of the battery of five tests is approximately .92 (see Sec. 686).

In this chapter a few achievement tests that have not been published elsewhere are described in detail. References are given for a number of achievement tests that appear to be satisfactory.[4]

424. ARCHERY

The achievement scale for the **Hyde Archery Test**[5] is based on 1,502 scores made in twenty-seven colleges. Standards in the form of T-scores are given for the First Columbia Round as a whole. They are given for the Second Columbia Round as a whole, and also for the fifty-yard, the forty-yard, and the thirty-yard range. The forty-yard range was found to be

---

[2] Henry J. Montoye and John Brotzmann, "An Investigation of the Validity of Using the Results of a Doubles Tournament as a Measure of Handball Ability," *Research Quarterly,* May, 1951.

[3] This normality may be partially tested by making distributions of the test scores; if the test scores are distributed normally, the skill is probably distributed normally also.

[4] For an extensive discussion of achievement tests, see: Ruth B. Glassow and Marion R. Broer, *Measuring Achievement in Physical Education.* Most of the tests published before 1938 are described and discussed there.

[5] Edith I. Hyde, "The Measurement of Achievement in Archery," *Journal of Educational Research,* May, 1934.

———, "National Research Study in Archery," *Research Quarterly,* December, 1936.

———. **"An Achievement Scale in Archery,"** *Research Quarterly,* May, 1937.

the best one for testing beginning archers, and the fifty-yard range was found to be the best one for testing advanced archers.

425. BADMINTON

The **Edgren-Robinson Badminton Test**[6] consists of serving, lob strokes, and the smash. No data are available concerning the validity and the reliability of the test.

The **French-Stalter Badminton Test**[7] consists of a shuttle (dodging event) (reliability: $r = .937$), a wrist volley against the wall (reliability: $r = 830$), a short serve (reliability: $r = .511$), and a high-clear serve (reliability: $r = .698$). Validity (college women): $r = .698$ with ratings of four judges.

The **Lockhart-McPherson Badminton Test**[8] consists of volleying against a wall. Reliability (college women): $r = .90$. Validity: $r = .60$ to $.72$ with different criteria.

The **Miller Badminton Test**[9] is based on the high-clear principle. A rubber-nosed shuttlecock is used. The hitting is from behind a ten-foot restraining line, and above a line 7.5 feet high on the wall. There are three thirty-second periods of testing. Reliability (college women): $r = .94$. Validity: $r = .83$.

426. BASEBALL

None of the following baseball tests has been demonstrated to be valid enough to be used for purposes of grading. The difficulties in administering baseball tests are largely those of pitching and of batting balls according to a standard speed and placement. There is a need for the development of an inexpensive standardized pitching or throwing machine. Pitching and throwing tests should not be scored only on strikes or on balls, for that kind of test has a low reliability. While targets of the concentric-ring variety are not "game situations," neither is a hole in a canvas, and the concentric rings increase the reliability of the tests.

The **Rodgers-Heath Baseball Test**[10] is the only one of the baseball tests cited in this section in which an attempt was reported to ascertain the function of the test.

The target described in the **Brophy Baseball Test**[11] is a very useful one.

[6] H. D. Edgren and G. G. Robinson, *Individual Skill Tests in Physical Activities.*
[7] Esther L. French and Evelyn Stalter, "Study of Skill Tests in Badminton for College Women," *Research Quarterly,* October, 1949.
[8] Aileene Lockhart and Frances A. McPherson, "The Development of a Test of Badminton Playing Ability," *Research Quarterly,* December, 1949.
[9] Frances A. Miller, "A Badminton Wall Volley Test," *Research Quarterly,* May, 1951.
[10] Elizabeth G. Rodgers and Marjorie L. Heath, "An Experiment in the Use of Knowledge and Skill Tests in Playground Baseball," *Research Quarterly,* December, 1931.
[11] Kathleen Brophy, "A New Target for Testing Accuracy in Throwing," *Spalding's Athletic Library,* 121R.

The following baseball tests are cited for purposes of reference: Andersen Test,[12] Brace Test,[13] Cozens Test,[14] Edgren-Robinson Test,[15] Hartley Test,[16] Hillas-Knighton Test,[17] Mosbek Test,[18] Palmer Test,[19] Wardlaw Test,[20] and the APEA Test.[21]

427. BASKETBALL TESTS FOR MEN

The **Edgren Basketball Test**[22] was among the first basketball tests in which an attempt was reported to determine the validity of the test. No attempt to determine the reliability of the test was reported.

The **Money Basketball Test**[23] is not a useful measuring device of basketball skill as a whole. Each of the exercises is useful, however, as a drill for specific skills.

In the **Friermood Basketball Test**[24] the pivoting tests are scored, largely, in a subjective manner. The basket-shooting tests have too few trials to be reliable. The battery is useful for purposes of motivation.

The criterion for the **Johnson Basketball Test**[25] was based on a "good" group of players ($N = 50$) and on a "poor" group of players ($N = 130$).[26]

(1) *Johnson Basket-shooting Test.* The player stands, close under the basket, in any desired position. He makes as many baskets as he can in thirty seconds. One point is given for each basket. The median for the 183 players was 9, with a range of 2 to 18. Reliability: $r = .731$. Validity: $r = .713$.

(2) *Johnson Passing Test.* A rectangle sixty inches by forty inches is painted on a canvas. In the center of this rectangle is another rectangle, which is forty inches by twenty-five inches, and inside the second rectangle is a third rectangle, which is twenty inches by ten inches. The canvas is hung on the wall, with the length of the rectangle horizontal and with the bottom of the largest rectangle

---

[12] Leonora Andersen, *An Athletic Program for Elementary Schools.*

[13] David K. Brace, *Measuring Motor Ability.*

[14] Frederick W. Cozens and Others, *Achievement Scales in Physical Education Activities for Secondary School Girls and College Women.*

[15] Edgren and Robinson, *op. cit.*

[16] Grace Hartley, "Motivating the Physical Education Program for High School Girls," *American Physical Education Review,* May, June, and September, 1929.

[17] Marjorie Hillas and Marian Knighton, *An Athletic Program for High School and College Women.*

[18] Ellen Mosbek, "Baseball Skill Tests," *Spalding's Athletic Library,* 121R.

[19] Gladys E. Palmer, *Baseball for Girls and Women.*

[20] Charles D. Wardlaw, *Fundamentals of Baseball.*

[21] "Motor Ability Tests," Report of the Committee of the American Physical Education Association, February, 1929.

[22] Edgren, "An Experiment in the Testing of Ability and Progress in Basketball," *Research Quarterly,* March, 1932.

[23] C. V. Money, "Tests for Evaluating the Abilities of Basketball Players," *Athletic Journal,* November and December, 1933.

[24] H. T. Friermood, "Basketball Progress Tests Adaptable to Class Use," *Journal of Health and Physical Education,* January, 1934.

[25] L. William Johnson, "Objective Basketball Tests for High School Boys" (M.A. Thesis, State University of Iowa, 1934).

[26] The good players were those who "made the squad," and the poor players were those who did not "make the squad."

fourteen inches from the floor. The players stand twenty feet from the canvas. Using either the baseball pass or the hook pass, the player throws ten passes at the canvas. The score is the total points made in the ten throws: three points are given for hitting the innermost rectangle and line, two points for hitting the middle rectangle and line, and one point for hitting the outer rectangle and line. The median for the 183 players was 11, with a range of 2 to 23. Reliability: $r = .796$. Validity: $r = .785$.

(3) *Johnson Dribbling Test* (Fig. XXVIII, p. 245). The starting line is six feet long. The first hurdle is located parallel to and twelve feet from the starting line. The second, third, and fourth hurdles are located, parallel to the first hurdle, eighteen, twenty-four, and thirty feet, respectively, from the starting line. The players start at the right end of the starting line. Dribbling diagonally, the player passes the left end of the first hurdle, the right end of the second hurdle, the left end of the third hurdle, and the right end of the fourth hurdle. He dribbles around the fourth hurdle, and then continues to dribble diagonally past the left end of the third hurdle, the right end of the second hurdle, the left end of the first hurdle, and the right end of the starting line.

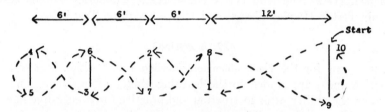

FIGURE XXVIII. Johnson Basketball Dribbling Test 3:
Arrangement of Hurdles

The score is the number of zones passed in thirty seconds, the zones being the areas between the hurdles, and the area between the starting line and the first hurdle. The median for the 183 players was 22, with a range of 10 to 29. Reliability: $r = .780$. Validity: $r = .651$.

The range of the sum of the scores for Tests 1, 2, and 3 was, for the 183 players, 16 to 68. Fifty points are given for a total score of 42, and 1.5 points are added or subtracted for each score above or below 42. These points, although computed differently from T-scores, are almost equivalent to T-scores. Reliability of Tests 1, 2, and 3: $r = .890$. Validity of Tests 1, 2, and 3: $r = .880$.

The following basketball tests are cited for purposes of reference: Bliss Test [27] and Brace Test.[28]

428. BASKETBALL TESTS FOR GIRLS AND WOMEN

The **Young-Moser Basketball Test**[29] consists of the Edgren Basketball Test, a wall-bouncing speed test (30 inches), a free jump, the bounce and shoot,

[27] J. G. Bliss, *Basketball.*

[28] Brace, *Measuring Motor Ability.*

———, "Testing Basket Ball Technique," *American Physical Education Review,* April, 1924.

[29] Genevieve Young and Helen Moser, "A Short Battery of Tests to Measure Playing Ability in Women's Basketball," *Research Quarterly,* May, 1934.

Helen A. Moser, "The Use of Basketball Skill Tests for Girls and Women," *Journal of Health and Physical Education,* March, 1935.

and throwing (from a distance of 10 feet) at a swinging target. Low coefficients of intercorrelation were obtained for these tests; hence the tests must measure various aspects of basketball ability. An r of .859 was obtained between the test and ratings. The test elements are not sufficiently reliable to be used alone as tests of those specific skills, but, as a whole battery, the test is quite satisfactory.

The **Schwartz Basketball Test**[30] was validated largely through experts' opinions, but it is useful, especially for purposes of motivation.

The **Dyer-Schurig-Apgar Basketball Test**[31] consists of throwing at a swinging target, the Edgren Ball-handling Test, the bounce and shoot, and a free-jump-and-reach test. Scoring tables and standards are provided in the publication. Validity: $r = .76$ to $.91$. Reliability: $r = .90$.

The following basketball tests are cited for purposes of reference: Andersen Test,[32] Anderson Test,[33] Brace Test,[34] Cubberley-Cozens Test,[35] Frymir Test,[36] Hartley Test,[37] and Hillas-Knighton Test.[38]

429. BOWLING

The norms for the **Phillips-Summers Bowling Test**,[39] which is a test for college women, are graded to the learning ability of beginners, and are based on the ability after instruction and practice for twenty-five lines of bowling. They present a different concept from the usual one-norm-for-all, and offer encouragement especially to beginners

430. DIVING

The **Bennett Diving Test**[40] consists of fifty items that may be administered in connection with teaching during the course of a semester or a year. Reliability: $r = .95$. Validity: $r = .94$.

[30] Helen Schwartz, "Knowledge and Achievement Tests in Girls' Basketball on the Senior High School Level," *Research Quarterly*, March, 1937.

[31] Joanna T. Dyer and Others, "A Basketball Motor Ability Test for College Women and Secondary School Girls," *Research Quarterly*, October, 1939.

[32] Andersen, *op. cit.*

[33] Lou E. Anderson, *Basketball for Women.*

[34] Brace, "Testing Basket Ball Technique," *American Physical Education Review*, April, 1924.

——, *Measuring Motor Ability.*

[35] Hazel J. Cubberley and Frederick W. Cozens, "The Measurement of Achievement in Basketball," *Spalding's Athletic Library*, 17R.

[36] Alice W. Frymir, *Basketball for Women.*

[37] Hartley, *loc. cit.*

[38] Hillas and Knighton, *op. cit.*

[39] Marjorie Phillips and Dean Summers, "Bowling Norms and Learning Curves for College Women," *Research Quarterly*, December, 1950.

[40] La Verne M. Bennett, "A Test of Diving for Use in Beginning Classes," *Research Quarterly*, March, 1942.

431. FIELDBALL

The **Hillas-Knighton Fieldball Test**[41] was not devised scientifically, but it is useful for purposes of motivation.

432. FIELD HOCKEY

The following tests of field hockey, which consist of tests of dribbling, shooting, scooping, passing, and rolling in, have not been scientifically formulated: Armfield Test,[42] Cozens Test,[43] Cubberley Test,[44] Hartley Test,[45] Hillas-Knighton Test,[46] Maris Test,[47] and the APEA Test.[48]

433. FOOTBALL

The **APEA Football Test**,[49] which was formulated on the basis of opinions, consists of short and long passes, punting, drop-kicking and kicking-off, together with receiving kicks. No data were reported concerning the reliability or the validity of the test.

In the **Cozens Football Test**[50] reasonably satisfactory coefficients of reliability were obtained for the tests of drop-kicking, passing for accuracy, passing for distance, and punting.

The **Borleske Touch-football Test**[51] consists of a forward pass for distance, catching forward passes, punting for distance, fifty-yard dash, carrying the ball after catching pass from center, and zone-pass defense. Validity: $r = .825$ with experts' ratings: $r = .925$ with a large battery, of which these five tests were a part. Validity of Tests 1, 3, and 4: $r = .880$ with the objective criterion.

434. GOLF

The game of golf provides its own test. A number of attempts has, however, been made to measure the elements of the game.

The **Clevett Golf Test**[52] consists of drives with the brassie and the mid-

[41] Hillas and Knighton, *op. cit.*

[42] Helen Armfield, "Some Ideas for a Hockey Practice," *Sportswoman*, October, 1928.

[43] Cozens and Others, *op. cit.*

[44] Cubberley, *Field Hockey Analyzed.*

[45] Hartley, *loc. cit.*

[46] Hillas and Knighton, *op. cit.*

[47] Elizabeth Maris, "Hockey from Fourth Grade through Advanced High School," *Official Field Hockey Guide*, 38R.

[48] "Motor Ability Tests," Report of the Committee of the American Physical Education Association, February, 1929.

[49] *Ibid.*

[50] Cozens, *Achievement Scales in Physical Education Activities for College Men.*

[51] Cozens, "Ninth Annual Report of the Committee on Curriculum Research of the College Physical Education Association. Part III," *Research Quarterly*, May, 1937.

[52] Melvin A. Clevett, "An Experiment in Teaching Methods of Golf," *Research Quarterly*, December, 1931.

iron in a driving cage with a target twenty-one feet from the tee, and of
strokes with the mashie in the gymnasium, with an approach on gymnasium mats. The putting is done on a carpet.

The **Edgren-Robinson Golf Test**[53] is a modification of the Clevett Golf
Test. In the outdoor test, the distance and the direction of the drives may
be measured. Tests for putting and for approaching the green are worked
out on a concentric-target basis.

The **McKee Golf Test**[54] is a test of the full swing with a Number 5 iron
club. Both the regular golf ball and the cotton ball are used. The effect of
back spin on the delay of the ball in falling to the ground is not taken
into account.

Table 99

GOLF--LENGTHS OF DRIVES WITH PLASTIC AND REGULATION BALLS*

Plastic Ball (yd.)	Spalding Dot Golf Ball (yd.)	Plastic Ball (yd.)	Spalding Dot Golf Ball (yd.)
14	98	21	203
15	117	22	212
16	135	23	220
17	152	24	226
18	167	25	231
19	180	26	234
20	192	27	236

*Curves were fitted to the original data.

In the **Neal Golf Test**[55] the distances of drives made with plastic balls
(Pee Bee Gee brand) have been found to be about 10 per cent of the distances of drives made with regulation golf balls. In Table 99 (p. 248) may
be found such distances.

Through the kindness of the Research Laboratories of the A. G. Spalding and Brothers Company, the plastic ball and the Spalding Dot Ball
were tested on the Spalding Driving Machine. A brassie was used.

435. GYMNASTICS (APPARATUS WORK)

The **Edgren-Robinson Apparatus Tests**[56] include tests on the horizontal bar,
the parallel bar, the side horse, and the flying rings. No data were reported
concerning the reliability or the validity of the tests.

[53] Edgren and Robinson, op. cit.
[54] Mary E. McKee, "A Test for the Full-Swinging Shot in Golf," Research Quarterly, March, 1950.
[55] Charlotte F. Neal, "The Value of Variations of Grip in Selected Sports for
Women as Compensating Factors for Sex Differences in Strength" (M.A. Thesis,
State University of Iowa, 1951).
[56] Edgren and Robinson, op. cit.

436. HANDBALL

The **Edgren-Robinson Handball Test**[57] includes a speed test, an accuracy test, a volleying test, a service test, and a back-wall return test.

The **Cornish Handball Test**[58] consists of a thirty-second volley, a front-wall placement test, a back-wall placement test, a power test, and a placement service test. The criterion was the number of "plus points" (points scored in twenty-three games minus points scored by opponents). The pattern for matching the 134 players was not reported.

Validity: $r = .694$ with the criterion; r of the thirty-second volley and the service placement test with the criterion $= .667$. Reliability: not reported.

437. ICE HOCKEY

Brown Ice-hockey Test.[59] Reliability and validity: not reported.

438. RHYTHM

Tests of pure rhythm were discussed in Chapter 11. In the field of the dance no practicable tests have been reported. An R of .611 [60] has been obtained between a "practical" rhythm test and a combination of the Seashore Sensory-rhythm Test and the Seashore Motor-rhythm Test. An R of .511 was obtained between teachers' estimates of dancing ability and a combination of the Brace Test and the Seashore Sensory-rhythm Test. An r of .483, however, was obtained between the teachers' estimates and the Brace Test alone.

The following tests are, largely, laboratory procedures, and they have not been adequately validated: Shambaugh Test,[61] Buck Test,[62] Heinlein Test,[63] McCristal Test,[64] Muzzey Test,[65] and Thompson Test.[66]

[57] *Ibid.*

[58] Clayton Cornish, "A Study of Measurement of Ability in Handball," *Research Quarterly,* May, 1949.

[59] Harriet M. Brown, "The Game of Ice Hockey," *Journal of Health and Physical Education,* January, 1935.

[60] Eloise Lemon and Elizabeth Sherbon, "A Study of the Relationships of Certain Measures of Rhythmic Ability and Motor Ability in Girls and Women," *Supplement to Research Quarterly,* March, 1934.

[61] Mary E. Shambaugh, "The Objective Measurement of Success in the Teaching of Folk Dancing to University Women," *Research Quarterly,* March, 1935.

[62] Nadine Buck, "A Comparison of Two Methods of Testing Response to Auditory Rhythms," *Research Quarterly,* October, 1936.

[63] C. P. Heinlein, "A New Method of Studying the Rhythmic Responses of Children Together with an Evaluation of the Method of Simple Observation," *The Pedagogical Seminary and Journal of Genetic Psychology,* June, 1929.

[64] K. J. McCristal, "Experimental Study of Rhythm in Gymnastic and Tap Dancing," *Research Quarterly,* May, 1933.

[65] Dorothy M. Muzzey, "Group Progress of White and Colored Children in Learning a Rhythm Pattern," *Research Quarterly,* October, 1933.

[66] Betty L. Thompson, *Fundamentals of Rhythm and Dance.*

439. SOCCER TESTS

The **Cozens-Cubberley-Neilson Soccer Test**[67] includes place-kicking for distance, punting, dribbling, the throw-in, and the goal kick. T-score tables are available. Reliability and validity: satisfactory.

The **Heath-Rodgers Soccer Test,**[68] which was devised for fifth- and sixth-grade boys, consists of dribbling, a throw-in, a place kick for goal, and kicking a rolling ball. Reliability: r's between data taken at the beginning and at the end of the season (which r's would be much lower than between data taken a week apart) = .72 and .74. Validity: $r = .60$ and .62 with ratings. Since the r of reliability of the ratings was probably not over .80, the true r is probably about .75.

The following soccer tests have not been as well formulated as the preceding soccer tests: Andersen Test,[69] Brace Test,[70] Hartley Test,[71] Hillas-Knighton Test,[72] and the APEA Test.[73]

440. SPEEDBALL

Two speedball tests are listed for purposes of reference: Colvin Test[74] and Hillas-Knighton Test.[75]

441. SQUASH RACQUETS

Edgren-Robinson Squash-racquets Test[76]

442. SWIMMING AND AQUATICS

Many of the swimming "tests" are simply laboratory procedures. Data have not, for the most part, been presented concerning the reliability and the validity of the tests.

The problem of scale scores for swimming is a complex one. To be able to swim at all is far from the zero point of ability, and to produce a scoring table for the one-hundred-yard swim involves quite different princi-

---

[67] Cozens and Others, *op. cit.*
——— and Hazel J. Cubberley, "Achievement Tests in Soccer and Speedball," *Spalding's Official Soccer and Speedball Guide,* 116R.
[68] Marjorie L. Heath and Elizabeth G. Rodgers, "A Study in the Use of Knowledge and Skill Tests in Soccer," *Research Quarterly,* December, 1932.
[69] Andersen, *op. cit.*
[70] Brace, *Measuring Motor Ability.*
[71] Hartley, *loc. cit.*
[72] Hillas and Knighton, *op. cit.*
Marian Knighton, "Soccer Questions," *Journal of Health and Physical Education,* October, 1930.
[73] "Motor Ability Tests," Report of the Committee of the American Physical Education Association, February, 1929.
[74] Valerie Colvin, "Achievement Tests for Speedball," *Spalding's Official Soccer and Speedball Guide,* 116R.
[75] Hillas and Knighton, *op. cit.*
[76] Edgren and Robinson, *op. cit.*

ples from those used in scoring tables for track-and-field athletics. If it is desired to compute a T-score type of table, the standard group from which the table is to be computed is the first consideration. A random sample would produce a large number of persons that could not swim one hundred yards, if, indeed, they could swim at all. Hence the table computed would depend much on the sample chosen.

The numerous tests and standards for water safety that have been devised by promotional organizations have not been scientifically formulated. They include the *Red Cross Tests*,[77] the *Camp Fire Girls and Girl Scout Tests*,[78] the *American Playground and Recreation Association Swimming Badge Tests*,[79] and the *YMCA Tests*.[80]

Numerous tests to be used for purposes of grading in swimming have been devised. For the most part they have not been scientifically formulated. They include the Anderson Test,[81] the Daviess Test,[82] the Sheffield Test,[83] the Smith Test,[84] the Spindler Test,[85] the Troemel Test,[86] and the Wayman Test.[87]

The following swimming tests are primarily stunts. The outstanding tests in the list are the Cureton Tests, the Broer-Miller Test, and the Parkhurst Test. The Cureton Tests and the Hewitt Tests are the only ones in the list that were devised scientifically. The list includes the Anderson Test,[88] Cureton Tests,[89] Daviess Test,[90] Hartley Test,[91] Hewitt

[77] *Instructor's Manual—Life Saving and Water Safety Courses.*
Instructor's Manual—Swimming and Diving Courses.
Instructor's Guide—Functional Swimming and Water Safety Training Course.
[78] *Camp Fire Girl's Book of Aquatics.*
Camp Fire Girl's Manual.
Girl Scout Handbook.
Scouting for Girls.
[79] "Swimming Badge Tests for Boys and Girls," *American Physical Education Review*, May, 1929.
"Popularizing the Swimming Badge Tests," *Recreation*, July, 1933.
[80] *Y.M.C.A. Swimming and Life Saving Manual.*
[81] Charlotte W. Anderson, "Achievement Records in Swimming," *Journal of Health and Physical Education*, May, 1930.
[82] Grace B. Daviess, *Swimming.*
[83] Lyba and Nita Sheffield, *Swimming Simplified.*
[84] Ann A. Smith, "Aids to Efficient Swimming Instruction for Girls and Women," *Journal of Health and Physical Education*, September, 1931.
[85] Evelyn Spindler, "Do You Grade or Guess?", *Journal of Health and Physical Education*, October, 1931.
[86] Ernestine A. Troemel, "Swimming—On an Efficient Grading Basis," *American Physical Education Review*, June, 1928.
[87] Agnes R. Wayman, *Education Through Physical Education*[2].
[88] Charlotte W. Anderson, *loc. cit.*
[89] Thomas K. Cureton, Jr., *Beginning and Intermediate National Y.M.C.A. Progressive Aquatic Tests.*
———, *How to Teach Swimming and Diving.*
———, *Objective Scales for Rating Swimming Performance and Diagnosing Faults.* (Mimeographed.)
———, *Standards for Testing Beginning Swimming.*
[90] Daviess, *op. cit.*
[91] Hartley, *loc. cit.*

Test,[92] Karpovich Test,[93] Parkhurst Test,[94] and the Reichart-Brauns Test.[95]

In a miscellaneous group of swimming tests should be included the Cureton Test for Swimming Endurance[96] (see Sec. 346), the Wilson Tests for Co-ordination in Swimming,[97] the Cozens-Cubberley-Neilson Speed Scales,[98] and the Edgren-Robinson Tests.[99]

443. TENNIS

The **Dyer Backboard Tennis Test**[100] is one of two tennis tests that have been subjected to rigorous scientific validation. The test, which is very usable for purposes of practice, consists of rallying the ball against a wall for periods of thirty seconds, scoring as many strokes in that time as possible. Reliability: $r = .90$; validity: $r = .85$ to .90 with experts' ratings and with scores in a round-robin tournament. Specific skills are not measured by this test.

The **Broer-Miller Tennis Test**,[101] which is one of two tennis tests that have been formulated scientifically, measures the ability to drive a ball hard and to have it land close to the back line. The subject stands behind the base line, and drives a ball (dropped by the subject) under a rope four feet above the net to a point as near the base line on the opposite side of the net as possible. Using a forehand stroke, the subject drives fourteen balls; and using a backhand stroke, fourteen balls. Balls passing over the rope receive one-half credit. Validity: $r = .85$; reliability: $r = .80$. (This is one of the few instances in which the coefficient of validity is larger than that of reliability. The theoretical limit of the validity is $\sqrt{\text{reliability coefficient}}$, or, in this case, .89 (i.e., $\sqrt{.80}$).

[92] Jack E. Hewitt, "Achievement Scale Scores for High School Swimming," *Research Quarterly*, May, 1949.

———, "Achievement Scale Scores for Wartime Swimming," *Research Quarterly*, December, 1943.

———, "Swimming Achievement Scale Scores for College Men," *Research Quarterly*, December, 1948.

[93] Peter V. Karpovich, "Analysis of the Propelling Force in the Crawl Stroke," *Supplement to Research Quarterly*, May, 1935.

[94] Mary G. Parkhurst, "Achievement Tests in Swimming," *Journal of Health and Physical Education*, May, 1934.

[95] Natalie Reichart and Jeanette Brauns, *The Swimming Work Book*.

[96] Cureton, "A Test for Endurance in Speed Swimming," *Supplement to Research Quarterly*, May, 1935.

[97] Colin T. Wilson, "Coordination Tests in Swimming," *Research Quarterly*, December, 1934.

[98] Cozens and Others, *op. cit.*

[99] Edgren and Robinson, *op. cit.*

[100] Joanna T. Dyer, "The Backboard Test of Tennis Ability," *Supplement to Research Quarterly*, March, 1935.

———, "Revision of the Backboard Test of Tennis Ability," *Research Quarterly*, March, 1938.

[101] Marion R. Broer and Donna M. Miller, "Achievement Tests for Beginning and Intermediate Tennis," *Research Quarterly*, October, 1950.

The **Beall Tennis Test**[102] includes tests of forehand and backhand strokes and of serving. In the formulation of the test a careful analysis of the necessary qualifications of a successful tennis player was made. The test is, however, elementary, and the reliability and the validity of the test were not reported.

In the **Driver Tennis Test,**[103] the subject hits a ball thrown from the other side of the net. The ball must first strike the ground in a circle eight feet in diameter, the center of which is twelve feet from the center of the base line.

In the **Edgren-Robinson Tennis Test**[104] the subject stands in the back corner of the court, and tosses the ball up so that it alights on the other side of the center line of the court. The subject runs to meet the ball, and hits the ball when it bounces.

The following tennis tests consist, for the most part, of forehand or backhand strokes across the net made either from dropping the ball and letting it bounce, or from hitting a ball thrown over the net from the other side; rallying against a wall; and serving either into the service court or into areas marked in the court: Anderson Test,[105] Cozens-Cubberley-Neilson Test,[106] Hartley Test,[107] and Wagner Test.[108]

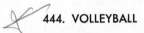

444. VOLLEYBALL

In the **Brady Volleyball Test,**[109] which was scientifically formulated, the subject volleys the ball in a space five feet wide and above a line eleven feet and six inches from the floor. Reliability: $r = .925$; validity: $r = .86$ (men subjects).

The **French-Cooper Volleyball Test,**[110] which was carefully formulated, consists of repeated volleys, a serving test, a set-up-and-pass, and a recovery from the net. Reliability: $r = .94$ and $.96$ (two groups). Validity of the repeated volleys and the serving: $r = .81$; the r was not increased significantly by including the other elements of the test.

[102] Elizabeth Beall, "Essential Qualities in Certain Aspects of Physical Education with Ways of Measuring and Developing the Same," *American Physical Education Review,* June, September, October, November, and December, 1928.

[103] Helen Irene Driver, *Tennis for Teachers.*

[104] Edgren and Robinson, *op. cit.*

[105] Lou E. Anderson, *Tennis for Women.*

[106] Cozens and Others, *op. cit.*

[107] Hartley, *loc. cit.*

[108] Miriam M. Wagner, "An Objective Method of Grading Beginners in Tennis," *Journal of Health and Physical Education,* March, 1935.

[109] George F. Brady, "Preliminary Investigations of Volleyball Playing Ability," *Research Quarterly,* March, 1945.

[110] Esther L. French and Bernice I. Cooper, "Achievement Tests in Volleyball for High School Girls," *Research Quarterly,* May, 1937.

The **Bassett-Glassow-Locke Volleyball Test**[111] has been carefully formulated. Reliability: $r = .83$; validity: $r = .795$.

The **Russell-Lange Volleyball Test**,[112] which consists of volleying and of serving, has been carefully formulated. Reliability: $r = .90$; validity: $r = .67$.

Other volleyball tests include the Cozens-Cubberley-Neilson Test,[113] the Hartley Test,[114] the Hupprich Test,[115] the Laveaga Test,[116] and the Reynolds Test.[117]

445. MISCELLANEOUS TESTS

NATIONAL (RECREATION ASSOCIATION) STANDARDS OF ACHIEVEMENT
FOR BOYS AND FOR GIRLS[118]

These standards have been derived from the records of a very large number of children. For boys, there are tests of track and field, games skills, gymnastics, and aquatics; for girls, there are games skills, self-testing activities, and athletic events. The progression is too slow, the scoring devices are too crude, and the classification (by age) is unsatisfactory.

[111] Gladys Bassett and Others, "Studies in Testing Volleyball Skills," *Research Quarterly,* December, 1937.

[112] Naomi Russell and Elizabeth Lange, "Achievement Tests in Volleyball for Junior High School Girls," *Research Quarterly,* December, 1940.

[113] Cozens and Others, *op. cit.*

[114] Hartley, *loc. cit.*

[115] Florence L. Hupprich, "Volleyball Practice Tests," *Spalding's Athletic Handbook for Women,* 115R.

[116] Robert E. Laveaga, *Volleyball; A Man's Game.*

[117] Herbert J. Reynolds, "Volleyball Tests," *Journal of Health and Physical Education,* March, 1930.

[118] *National Physical Achievement Standards.* National Physical Achievement Standards Committee.

National Physical Achievement Standards for Girls. Prepared by Amy R. Howland.

CHAPTER 21

BODY MECHANICS

446. MANY ATTEMPTS have been made to evaluate objectively and subjectively the carriage of the body and of its parts, and to compare these evaluations with standards that have been prepared for that purpose. These attempted measurements have been concerned, for the most part, with anteroposterior posture and with the mechanics of the feet. No important tests relative to lateral curvature have been presented, probably because the standard involved is noncontroversial: there should be no lateral curvature. Hence any measurement of lateral curvature is concerned only with the kind of curve and with the amount of the deviation. The matter of standards for anteroposterior carriage and for the mechanics of the feet are not so simple as the standard for lateral curvature.

Efforts to establish standards for body mechanics are complicated by many problems. The devisers of most of the existing standards have apparently assumed that there is one best posture applicable to everyone. There is considerable evidence available that this assumption is not in accord with the facts. There are individual differences in skeletal architecture and in build that would seem to make imperative the establishment of standards in accordance with those differences.

447. Distribution of weight. The carriage of a person with a flat abdomen should be different from that of one whose abdomen is covered with a thick layer of fat. The weight distribution of a very slender, linear type of person differs from that of a strictly lateral type.

448. Configuration of bones of spine.[1] The shapes of vertebrae vary from ones that necessitate a hyperstraight vertebral column to ones that necessitate a fairly great degree of curvature in the vertebral column. There is evidence that these different shapes are frequently hereditary.

449. Pelvic architecture.[2] Differences in the shape and in the position of

---

[1] Charles H. McCloy, "X-ray Studies of Innate Differences in Straight and Curved Spines," *Research Quarterly*, May, 1938.

[2] Bernice Boynton, "Individual Differences in the Structure of Pelvis and Lumbar Spine as a Factor in Body Mechanics" (M.A. Thesis, State University of Iowa, 1934).

Ivalclare Sprow-Howland, "A Study of the Position of the Sacrum in the Adult Female Pelvis and Its Relationship to Body Mechanics" (M.A. Thesis, State University of Iowa, 1933).

Veva M. Kummer, "A Study of the Distributions and Relationships of Certain Bony Structures as Related to Static Body Mechanics" (M.A. Thesis, State University of Iowa. 1932).

the pelvis, together with different positions of the sacrum in the pelvis, necessitate individual standards of lumbar posture.

450. Femoral and tibial architecture.[3] Differences in angles between horizontal lines through the center of each acetabulum, and sagittal planes, together with differences in the degrees of torsion of the femurs and the tibias necessitate individual standards of foot placement.

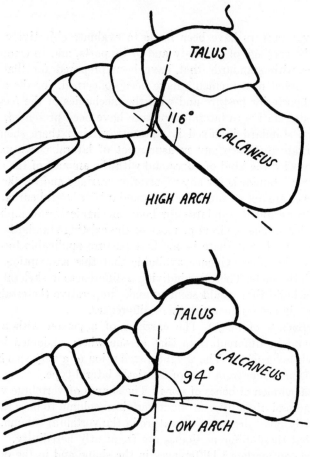

FIGURE XXIX. Foot: Calcaneal Architecture

451. Calcaneal architecture.[4] Differences in the angle between the cuboidal articular surface of the calcaneus and the lower margin of the same bone necessitate differences in the height of the medial longitudinal arch of the foot. An obtuse angle necessitates a high arch, while a right angle necessitates a low arch (Fig. XXIX, p. 256); hence individual standards

[3] Kummer, *loc. cit.*
[4] McCloy, unpublished study.

of foot posture need to be established in accordance with this aspect of calcaneal architecture. Many persons, for example, who have flat feet have feet that do not represent an abnormality for them.

No standards of posture based on the build and the bony architecture of the individual appear to be available. Existing posture measurements concern the arbitrary "standard" type of posture rather than the best-functioning posture for the individual. If it were possible to measure segmental poise and balance accurately, these measurements would probably be excellent relative to posture. At present, photographs obtained by X rays are the best solution for the problem, but only if they are interpreted by trained persons.

SUBJECTIVE ESTIMATES OF POSTURE

452. The **Bancroft Triple Test for Posture**[5] is based upon the so-called "vertical-line test," in which a line is extended from the tragus (the front of the ear) to the forward part of the foot. The standards in the vertical-line test are that the long axis of each of the large segments of the body —neck, trunk, and limbs—should be approximately parallel to the line, and that the tips of the shoulders should be slightly behind the line. In poor posture the long axes of the neck, the trunk, and the limbs form zig-zag lines. The Bancroft Triple Test follows.

Standing test. The subjects stand in single file. Facing the side of the subject, the examiner estimates the anteroposterior posture of each of the subjects. The subjects, who, in the opinion of the examiner, are not adequately erect, are asked to be seated.

Marching test. The subjects who succeeded in the first part of the test march in single file for several minutes, walking at a fairly rapid pace. They are drilled in marching tactics in order that their attention may be distracted. The subjects who, during the marching, revert to faulty postural habits, are asked to be seated.

Calisthenic-exercise test. The subjects who succeeded in the first and the second part of the test are then given calisthenic exercises, especially ones in which the arms are swung forward and upward, and sideward and upward. The subjects who, during the execution of the exercises, revert to faulty postural habits are asked to be seated. Only the subjects who succeed in all three parts of the test are considered to be satisfactory in posture and in carriage.

453. **Iowa Posture Test.**[6] The subjects, who are, preferably, dressed in bathing suits, are divided into groups of ten or twelve, and those in each group sit on chairs arranged in a row and about two feet apart. The names of the subjects are entered in order on a chart, and this order is maintained

[5] Jessie H. Bancroft, *The Posture of School Children.*
[6] Published in mimeographed form by the Women's Department of the Division of Physical Education, State University of Iowa.

Name of Examiner _____ **Class** _____ **Date** _____

Name	Foot Mechanics			Standing	Walking		Sitting		Stooping	Stairs	Total score
	Heel-toe	No pronation	Feet parallel	(optional) Body segments	Body segments	Weight distribution	Natural position	Rising			
	3, 2, 1	3, 2, 1	3, 2, 1	3, 2, 1	3, 2, 1	3, 2, 1	3, 2, 1	3, 2, 1	3, 2, 1	3, 2, 1	

FIGURE XXX. Iowa Posture Test: Score Sheet

throughout the test. For inexperienced subjects, the correct mechanics of each item may or may not be briefly explained before the testing, depending upon whether the examiner wishes to see what the subjects do habitually or what they can do when well motivated. The Iowa Posture Test, together with directions for scoring it, follow.

Foot-mechanics test. Each subject walks in turn about ten steps forward and then back to her chair while the examiner, who stands at the side of the path traversed, checks for heel-toe walking. Then the examiner takes a position in front of the subjects, and each subject walks toward the examiner and then back to her chair while the examiner checks on toeing straight ahead and on the presence or the absence of pronation. The test is scored as follows:[7]

A. *Heel-toe walking*   *Code for scoring*

    1. Heel in contact with ground first   Good   3
    2. Weight transferred through outside of foot to ball   Fair   2
       of foot   Poor (toes down
    3. Toes used in gripping action   first)   1
    4. Spring in walk

B. *Absence of pronation*

    1. No bony bulge in front of and below medial mal-   No pronation   3
       leolus   Some pronation   2
    2. No marked protrusion inward of navicular   Marked
    3. No outward turning of heel cord   pronation   1

C. *Feet parallel*

    1. A very slight angle of toeing out is considered to be
       normal   Feet normal   3
    2. Feet toeing in may be considered to be satisfactory,   Moderate toeing
       although unattractive. (Because of the shape of the   out   2
       foot as seen from behind, it is more accurate to   Marked toeing
       judge *2* from in front than from behind.)   out   1

Standing-position test. Each subject stands with her left side toward the front of her chair. The examiner checks, from the side of each subject, the alignment of the body segments and the weight distribution. The test is scored as follows.

A. *Correct alignment of body segments*   *Code for scoring*

    1. Axis through head, neck, trunk, and legs approxi-   Correct
       mating a straight line   alignment   3
    2. Head and neck erect (may be *slightly* forward)   Slight general de-
    3. Chest high, giving appearance of elevation and of   viation of one
       lift   part   2

---

[7] All the criteria are given in terms of desirable qualities (i.e., no faults are listed). Each lettered item is scored on the basis of the numbered items under it and according to the code at the right. A sample score sheet may be found in Figure XXX (p. 258).

A. *Correct alignment of body segments*   *Code for scoring*

    4. Normal curves in back, a slight roundness of   Marked general
        upper back, slight hollow of lower back   deviation   1
    5. Abdomen flat
    6. Ease and balance throughout
        For later use in conference with student, note, on
        chart, deviations from normal by abbreviations:
        e.g., abdomen, abd; upper back, u.b., etc.

Walking test. The subjects, five or six feet apart, walk around the row
of chairs. The examiner, from a side view of the group, checks for the
alignment of the body segments, the weight distribution, and the amount
of stiffness and of body movement. The test is scored as follows.

A. *Alignment of body segments*   *Code for scoring*

    Check on any changes from standing position   3, 2, 1

B. *Weight distribution*

    Weight should be carried only slightly farther forward   Good weight
    than in standing position   distribution   3
        Some degree of
    Note on chart—weight forward—*F*   deviation from
                —weight backward—*B*   normal   2
        Marked deviation
        from normal   1

Sitting test. The subject sits erect on her chair, and the examiner checks
the posture in this sitting position. Then the subject leans forward about
thirty degrees, and the examiner checks the posture of the subject in this
position. Then the subject rises and walks forward a few steps, and the
examiner checks the carriage in this movement. (The girl's carriage in
sitting down may also be included.) The test is scored as follows.

A. *Sitting position*   *Code for scoring*

    1. Upper trunk well balanced over pelvis
    2. Head erect   Correct position   3
    3. Chest high (not thrust out)   Some degree of
    4. Shoulders well back, but not stiff   deviation   2
    5. Abdomen controlled   Marked deviation   1
    6. Normal upper-back curve
    7. If satisfactory chairs are used, hips should be well
        back, and back of chair used for support

B. *Rising from sitting position*

    1. One foot slightly under chair with other foot a little   Good
        in advance, trunk bent slightly from hips, push-up   performance   3
        from feet   Fair performance   2
    2. Arms relaxed   Poor performance   1
    3. Hips kept well under body
    4. No stiffness

Stooping-to-pick-up-light-object test. Each subject picks up in turn a small object from the floor, and returns it to the floor. (The object may be so placed that the subject has to walk a few steps before she can pick it up.) The test is scored as follows.

	Code for scoring	
1. Feet and hips well under body weight, one foot slightly ahead of other	Good	3
2. Bend at knees, slight bend from hips	Fair	2
3. Relatively straight line of trunk, back controlled (allow slight rounding of back to avoid stiffness)	Poor	1
4. Arms relaxed		
5. Smooth movement, balance maintained throughout		
6. Pick up object slightly ahead of foot		

Ascending-and-descending-stairs test. Each subject ascends and descends eight to ten stairs, and the examiner checks the carriage of the subject. The test is scored as follows.

A. *Ascending*

	Code for scoring	
1. Weight only slightly forward, and bend is from ankles (not hips)	Good	3
2. Straight push-up from ankles and knees, avoiding swing of hips	Fair	2
	Poor	1

B. *Descending*

1. Controlled lowering of weight to foot (not a relaxed drop)	Good	3
	Fair	2
2. Smoothness (avoid bobbing)	Poor	1

454. POSTURE TESTS BASED ON FIXED STANDARDS

455. Four arbitrarily determined standards, which are labeled "excellent," "good," "poor," and "bad," are included in the **Posture Standards of the Children's Bureau.**[8] The essential features of each standard are described in Figure XXXI (p. 262). Separate standards are presented for stocky, thin, and intermediate types of body build. The subject is instructed to stand with his left side toward the examiner, and with as good posture as possible (or to stand as he usually stands). The examiner determines subjectively which picture best represents the subject's standing posture, and the posture is rated *A, B, C,* or *D,*[9] accordingly.

456. The **University of Southern California Posture Standards** (Fig. XXXII, p. 263), which were devised for adult men and women, are used in the same manner as those of the Children's Bureau.

457. The **Brownell Posture Scale** (Fig. XXXIII, p. 264),[10] which is more

[8] Armin Klein and Leah C. Thomas, *Posture Exercises* (Children's Bureau Publication 165).

[9] Plusses and minuses may be used; e.g., *A—, C+*.

[10] Clifford L. Brownell. *A Scale for Measuring the Antero-posterior Posture of Ninth Grade Boys.* (Feet have been added by the present authors to the Brownell Scale.)

refined in form than the two sets of standards just described, includes thirteen standard posture silhouettes, which are scored from 20 at the one extreme to 120 at the other. This scale is used in the same way as the standards of the Children's Bureau; however, finer gradations are possible in the former than in the latter. In the standards of the Children's Bureau the postures are idealized, and hence are applicable to a larger number of persons than are the Brownell standards, in which standards silhouettes of the subjects are used. In the silhouettes of the subjects some individual differences are apparent.

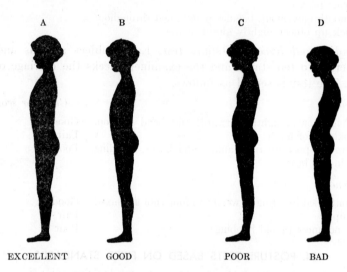

A   B   C   D

EXCELLENT   GOOD   POOR   BAD

FIGURE XXXI. Children's Bureau (U. S. Department of Labor) Posture Standards: Thin-type Girls

458. The **Crook Posture Scale** (Fig. XXXIV, p. 265)[11] for children of preschool ages consists of thirteen silhouettes, which are rated from 0 to 100, the middle silhouette having a scale value of 50.

459. The **Gray Posture Standards** (Fig. XXXV, p. 266)[12] for boys of senior-high-school ages are based on a seven-step scale.

In recent studies conducted at the State University of Iowa, higher coefficients of correlation have been obtained between a criterion of posture and the composite ratings of photographs and silhouettes by experts using scales of the kind described in this section than between a criterion of posture and more specific objective methods of measurements.

[11] Billie L. Crook, "A Scale for Measuring the Antero-posterior Posture of the Preschool Child," *Research Quarterly*, December, 1936.

[12] William S. Gray, Jr., "Standards for the Appraisement of Antero-posterior Posture" (M.A. Thesis, State University of Iowa, 1942).

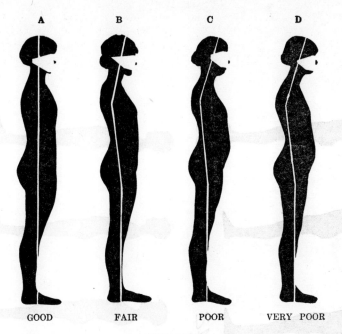

GOOD   FAIR   POOR   VERY POOR

WOMEN

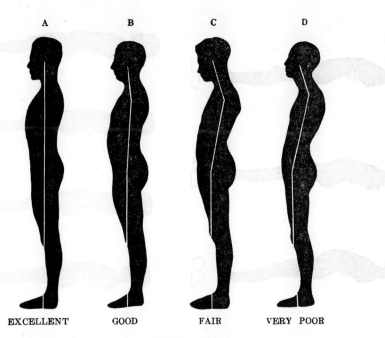

EXCELLENT   GOOD   FAIR   VERY POOR

MEN

FIGURE XXXII. University of Southern California Posture
Standards. Reproduced by permission.

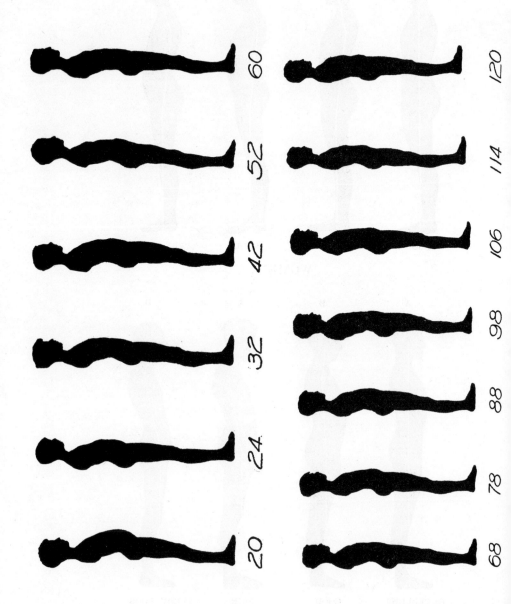

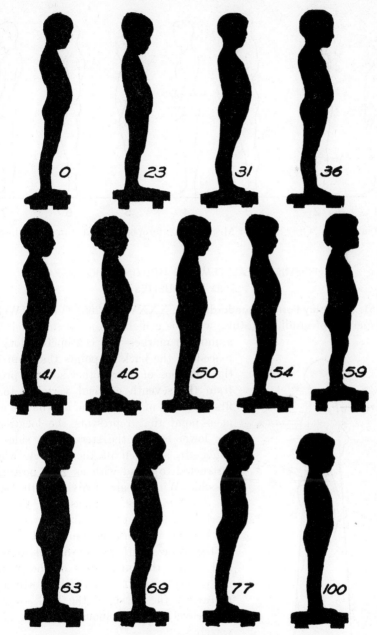

FIGURE XXXIV. Crook Scale for Measuring Anteroposterior Posture of Preschool Children. Reproduced by permission.

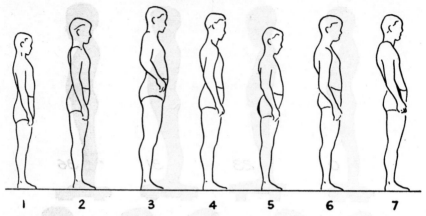

| 1 | 2 | 3 | 4 | 5 | 6 | 7 |

FIGURE XXXV. Gray Scale for Measuring Anteroposterior Posture of High-school Boys

460. POSTURE MEASUREMENTS UTILIZING PHOTOGRAPHS AND SILHOUETTES

461. Wellesley Posture Standards (Fig. XXXVI, p. 266).[13] In the Wellesley method of grading posture, which is a highly objective method, light aluminum markers ten centimeters long are placed on the back at points that represent the locations of every other spinous process from the seventh cervical vertebra to the first segment of the sacrum, and on the chest at a point that represents the location of the lower end of the sternum; a side-view silhouette is taken of the subject, who is instructed to stand with as good posture as possible. With a pair of dividers, the length of these markers is measured; then the markers on the photograph are extended toward the vertebral column until they are of the same length as the actual markers; and finally the inner ends of the markers are connected with a curved line, which line represents the curve of the back over the skin covering the spinous processes of the vertebrae.

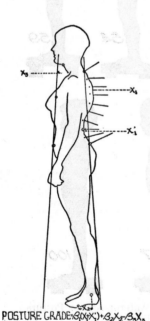

POSTURE GRADE = $\beta_1(X_1X_1') + \beta_2X_2 - \beta_3X_3$

FIGURE XXXVI. Wellesley Posture Measurements

The following landmarks are located on the silhouette: the angle made by the junction of the chin with the neck, the lower end

[13] Charlotte G. MacEwan and Eugene C. Howe, "An Objective Method of Grading Posture," *Research Quarterly*, October, 1932.

of the sternum, the most prominent point of the abdomen, the spinous process of the seventh cervical vertebra, the first segment of the sacrum, and the fibular malleolus. A line, which extends from above the head to below the feet, is drawn through the landmark at the lower end of the sternum and through the landmark at the most prominent part of the abdomen. Another line, which extends to below the feet, is drawn through the landmark of the spinous process of the seventh cervical vertebra and through the landmark of the first sacral segment. A mark is made, at the level of the soles of the feet, half-way between these two lines.

Three celluloid scales (Fig. XXX-VII, p. 267),[14] which have vertical lines drawn on them, are used in the scoring. The first scale is placed over the face and neck, and the distance between the angle of the neck and the anterior line (drawn line) is measured. If the head is forward, the score is positive. The second scale is used for the measurement of the distance between the posterior line (drawn line) and the most prominent part of the curve of the upper back and that of the lower back. The larger the curve, the greater is the score. The third scale is used for the measurement of the horizontal distance from the mid-point, at the level of the soles of the feet, between the anterior and the posterior drawn line to the fibular malleolus. The Wellesley Posture

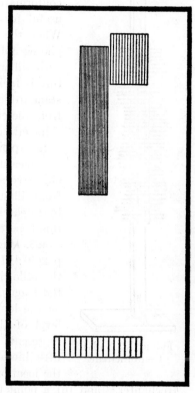

FIGURE XXXVII. Wellesley Posture Scales

Score is the algebraic sum of the four measurements, and is converted into a letter grade as follows: $1 = A+$; 2 to $4 = A$; $5 = A-$; $6 = B+$; 7 to $9 = B$; $10 = B-$; $11 = C+$; 12 to $14 = C$; $15 = C-$; $16 = D+$; 17 to $19 = D$; $20 = D-$; $21 = E+$; 22 to $24 = E$; and $25 = E-$.

If the directions are followed carefully, posture can be scored objectively and rapidly by the Wellesley method. Although, insofar as standards are concerned, there are some difficulties inherent in the method, the results are immediately significant to the pupil and may be compared with future measurements. This method of scoring may be used equally well, and with a great saving of time, with the conformateur (see Sec. 462).

[14] These scales may be purchased from Wellesley College.

462. Springfield Posture Measurements.[15] The *Cureton Conformateur* (Fig. XXXVIII, p. 268) is a device by means of which spinal curves may be measured more rapidly than is possible with the Wellesley aluminum markers. The measurements obtained by the use of the Cureton Con-

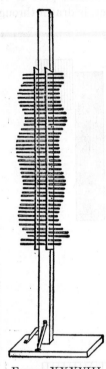

formateur are highly objective, but as yet no standards for their interpretation have been presented. The conformateur, however, gives much promise of being useful for further research in the field of posture. When the conformateur is used in connection with photographs taken from the side of the subject, or with silhouettographs, the interpretation of the picture is facilitated, for the distances indicated by the standard lengths of all of the rods can be measured in from the end of each rod to mark on the picture the silhouette of the surface over the spine itself.

In experiments[16] with the Springfield type of posture measurements there have been presented further objective approaches to the measurement of posture from silhouettes, which approaches should be studied by research workers interested in going further with this type of investigation.

463. Massey Posture Measurements (Fig. XXXIX, p. 269).[17] In the Massey method of measuring posture the following items are marked on the subject: (1) the tragus, (2) the suprasternal notch, (3) a point on the longitudinal midline of the back and at the level of the suprasternal notch, (4) a point that represents the location of the spinous process of the fifth lumbar vertebra, (5) a point that represents the location of the upper anterior part of the greater trochanter,[18] and (6) a point that represents the location of the fibular malleolus. Items 3 and 4 are indicated most conveniently with a conformateur,[19] but they may also be indicated with Wellesley aluminum

Figure XXXVIII.
Conformateur

---

[15] Thomas K. Cureton, Jr., and Others, "Reliability and Objectivity of the Springfield Postural Measurements," *Supplement to Research Quarterly*, May, 1935.

[16] J. Stuart Wickens and Oscar W. Kiphuth, "Body Mechanics Analysis of Yale University Freshmen," *Research Quarterly*, December, 1937.

[17] Wayne W. Massey, "A Critical Study of Objective Methods for Measuring Anterior Posterior Posture with a Simplified Technique," *Research Quarterly*, March, 1943.

[18] The greater trochanter should be marked with the forward point of a small triangular piece of adhesive tape. In view of the fact that the location of the point of the trochanter to be marked is frequently obscured by the tension of the muscles, the subject should be instructed to stand on the opposite leg, thus relaxing the leg on which the marking is to be made.

[19] If the conformateur is used, the length of the rod may be measured. Then, if one point of the dividers is set at the length of the rod and then is placed at the outer end

markers. The subject is then photographed, and on the photograph are marked the center of the knee (7), a point that represents the location of the spinous process of the fourth lumbar vertebra (8), and a point that represents the most prominent part of the abdomen (9). Lines are then drawn between 2 and 3, and between 8 and 9. The mid-point (10) of the line between 2 and 3, and the mid-point (11) of the line between 8 and 9 are marked. Lines are then drawn between 10 and 1, 11 and 10, 5 and 11, 7 and 5, and 6 and 7. Each of the lines is extended upward about two inches.

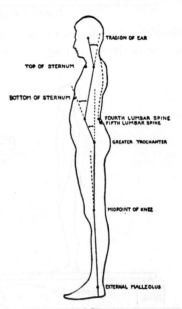

With a protractor is measured the angle of the head and neck with the trunk (I), of the trunk with the hips (II), of the hips with the thighs (III), and of the thighs with the legs (IV). The Massey Posture Score is the sum of the angles, which score may, for men of college ages, be converted into a letter grade as follows: 8° to 22° = A; 23° to 36° = B; 37° to 51° = C; 52° to 65° = D; 66° to 78° = E; and 79° to 93° = F.

Each letter grade represents approximately one sixth of the range between one standard deviation above and below the mean.

FIGURE XXXIX. Massey Posture Measurements

An r of −.97 was obtained between the sums of the angles and ratings of posture made by three experts and further refined by Massey. The ratings were based primarily on segmental balance.

In several other studies in which the Massey technique has been used, the coefficients of correlation between the sums of the angles and judges' ratings have not been nearly so high as those obtained by Massey. The method, however, which is an exceedingly simple one, deserves further study.

464. METHODS OF LOCATING CENTER OF GRAVITY OF HUMAN BODY

The position of the center of gravity of the body relative to the plane that divides the body into a front and a back half may be determined as follows. The subject stands on the middle of a board (Fig. XL, p. 270) that is balanced on the apexes of two triangular blocks, which are

---

of the next rod, the other end of the dividers indicates the location of the spine. Thus, the actual curve of the skin over the spine can be marked despite the muscular mass and the fat.

one meter apart. One block rests on a platform scale,[20] and the other block on a block of the same height as the platform scale. The distance in centimeters that the center of gravity of the body is forward from the edge resting on the block may be determined by the following formula:

$$\frac{\text{(weight of subject on board)} - \text{(weight of board on scale)}}{\text{(total weight of subject)}} \times 100$$

Since the distance of the heel and that of the toe from the mark on the middle of the board may be measured, the center of gravity relative to the position of the foot may be readily found.

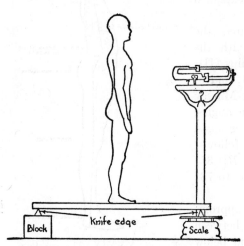

The technique just described may be modified by the use of a scale on either end of the board.[21]

This type of measurement is primarily an indication of the forward or backward tilt of the body. The measurement would appear to add to the information useful in assessing anteroposterior posture, but standards have not been established.

FIGURE XL. Center of Gravity of Human Body: Method of Determining

465. MEASUREMENT OF FOOT MECHANICS

Two items of foot structure that concern the function of the foot can probably be determined with accuracy only by the use of X rays. One item, a frequent and a potent cause of foot discomfort, particularly among adults, concerns the length of the first metatarsal bone. If this bone is considerably shorter than the second and third metatarsal bones, it does not carry its share of the body weight, especially if the rear part of the foot is propped up somewhat by the heel of the shoe. Hence an undue amount of weight is thrown upon the heads of the second and third metatarsal bones, and the result is the kind of pain that has frequently, but erroneously, been declared due to "a fallen metatarsal arch." [22]

[20] If the Toledo type of scale is used, the measurement is greatly expedited.

[21] Thomas K. Cureton, Jr., and J. Stuart Wickens, "The Center of Gravity of the Human Body in the Antero-posterior Plane and Its Relation to Posture, Physical Fitness, and Athletic Ability," *Supplement to Research Quarterly*, May, 1935. Details of procedure and directions for interpreting the results may be found in that publication.

[22] Details concerning this type of deformity and its related structural accompaniments may be found in *The Human Foot; Its Evolution, Physiology and Functional Disorders* by Dudley J. Morton.

The second item of structure that concerns the function of the foot is the height of the longitudinal arch. This arch is largely determined by the angle between the cuboidal articular surface of the calcaneus and the lower border of the calcaneus. In Figure XXIX (p. 256) is shown an outlined drawing of this angle in a very high-arched foot and in a flat foot, both of which feet were entirely normal. This angle and the resultant arch cannot be significantly altered by any amount of foot exercises.

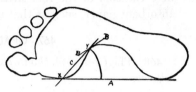

FIGURE XLI. Clarke Footprint Angle

Measurements of the height of the arch alone are not particularly important except for purposes of motivation. In connection with pronation, however, they may be important; hence the following directions for taking and grading footprints are presented.

466. MAKING OF FOOTPRINTS

Footprints may be taken most conveniently with the pedograph.[23] A sheet of paper is inserted under an inked cover, upon which the subject

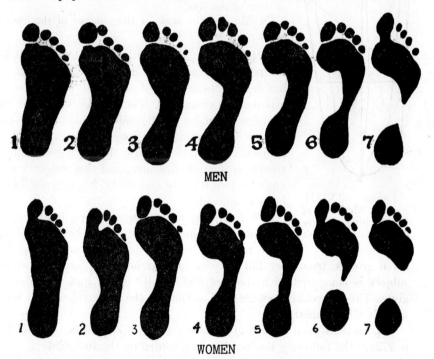

MEN

WOMEN

FIGURE XLII. Footprint Scales

[23] The pedograph may be obtained from the Scholl Manufacturing Company, Inc., 213 West Schiller, Chicago.

steps in order that the footprint may be recorded on the paper. Another method involves the use of a solution of a small bottle of washable ink, sixteen drops of glycerine, and a pint and a half of water. The subject wets the sole of the foot in the solution and then stands on a sheet of absorbent paper, such as that used for mimeographing.

467. GRADING OF FOOTPRINTS

468. The *Clarke method of scoring footprints* (Fig. XLI, p. 271)[24] is as follows.

(1) Draw line *A* to represent the medial border of the foot between the imprint of the head of the first metatarsal bone and the imprint of the calcaneus.

(2) Draw line *B* to represent the slope of the inner segment of the longitudinal arch at its junction with the metatarsal border of the arch.

(3) *X* is located at the point where line *A* first touches the imprint; *Y* is located at the point where line *B* first touches the metatarsal border of the arch.

(4) Draw line *C* between points *X* and *Y*. This line is intended to represent the slope of the metatarsal border of the longitudinal arch. There should be no white space in front of this line.

(5) Measure the angle at the junction of the lines *A* and *C* with a protractor.

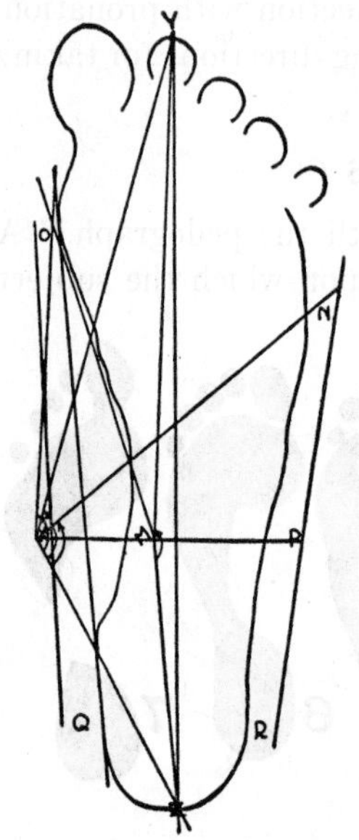

FIGURE XLIII.
Ewing Method of Determining Degree of Pronation of Foot

Although the Clarke method is rather difficult for inexperienced examiners, an *r* of reliability of .97 has been obtained for the method when used by experienced examiners. The Clarke norm for the average angle for adult males is about forty-two degrees. The recommendations have been made that subjects with angles below thirty degrees should receive corrective measures, and that subjects with angles between thirty and thirty-five degrees should be re-examined.

469. *Footprint scales* for assessing footprints of men and of women are given in Figure XLII (p. 271), respectively. These footprints are arranged in seven groups, from very flat to very high arches. The footprint of the subject is compared with the footprints of the scale, and a reading is given. This is probably as useful a method as the more refined but more difficult Clarke method.

470. In the *Ewing method of grading degrees of pronation* (Fig. XLIII, p. 272),[25] the following landmarks are recorded on the footprints:

[24] H. Harrison Clarke, "An Objective Method of Measuring the Height of the Longitudinal Arch in Foot Examinations," *Research Quarterly*, October, 1933.

[25] Neil Ewing, "A Study of the Possibly Significant Functional Angles of the Pronated and Non-pronated Foot" (M.A. Thesis, State University of Iowa, 1937).

Y, the mid-point of the distal end of the second toe
X, the most prominent point of the navicular
Q, the most prominent point on the medial side of the heel
R, the most prominent point on the lateral side of the heel
O, the most prominent point of the head of the first metatarsal
N, the most prominent point of the head of the fifth metatarsal
Z, the mid-point of the heel (*Z* is found in the following manner: Lines *NR* and *OQ* are drawn, and perpendiculars are erected from these lines tangent to the heel. The point of intersection is the mid-point of the heel, or *Z*.)

The following additional lines are drawn:

XY, from the mid-point of the distal end of the second toe to the navicular
XZ, from the mid-point of the heel to the navicular
NX, from the navicular to the most prominent point of the fifth metatarsal

These lines form the following angles:

ZXY, formed by lines drawn from the mid-point of the heel and from the mid-point of the second toe to the navicular
ZXN, formed by lines drawn from the mid-point of the heel and from the most prominent point on the fifth metatarsal to the navicular

The size of angles *ZXY* and *ZXN* is significantly related to pronation of the foot. The multiple regression equation for the prediction of pronation from these angles is 1.19 angle *ZXY* + .60 angle *ZXN* − 180 (Tables 100 and 101, pp. 273-74).

The values derived from the formulas are T-scores, with a score of 50

Table 100

PRONATED AND NONPRONATED FEET (EWING):   ANGLE
FORMED BY LINES FROM MID-POINT OF HEEL TO
NAVICULAR AND TO MID-POINT OF SECOND TOE

X_1 = (size of angle ZXY x 1.1929) - 133.582

Angle in degrees	X_1	Angle in degrees	X_1	Angle in degrees	X_1
112	.02	132	23.88	152	47.74
113	1.21	133	25.07	153	48.93
114	2.41	134	26.27	154	50.12
115	3.60	135	27.46	155	51.32
116	4.79	136	28.65	156	52.51
117	5.99	137	29.85	157	53.70
118	7.18	138	31.04	158	55.40
119	8.37	139	32.23	159	56.09
120	9.57	140	33.92	160	57.28
121	10.76	141	34.61	161	58.47
122	11.95	142	35.81	162	59.67
123	13.14	143	37.00	163	60.86
124	14.34	144	38.20	164	62.05
125	15.53	145	39.39	165	63.25
126	16.72	146	40.58	166	64.44
127	17.92	147	41.77	167	65.63
128	19.11	148	42.97	168	66.83
129	20.30	149	44.16	169	68.02
130	21.50	150	45.35	170	69.21
131	22.69	151	46.55		

representing an average foot with respect to pronation. The Ewing method is used primarily for the assessment of the degree of pronation of the foot —usually a functional deviation only, not a structural deformity.

471. The *Danford Pedorule*[26] is a rectangle of heavy plate glass seven inches wide and nine inches high, with the surface marked with parallel lines .1 inch apart. The directions for measuring the amount of deflection of the tendon of Achilles from the perpendicular are as follows.

Place the pedorule immediately behind the foot to be measured. Mark, with ink, two points: (1) the mid-point of the proximal end of the tendon of Achilles; and (2) the mid-point of the back of the heel. On a normal

Table 101

PRONATED AND NONPRONATED FEET (EWING):
ANGLE FORMED BY LINES FROM MID-POINT OF
HEEL TO NAVICULAR AND TO FIFTH METATARSAL

X_2 = (the size of the angle ZXN x .5993) - 46

Angle in degrees	X_2	Angle in degrees	X_2	Angle in degrees	X_2
80	1.94	97	12.13	114	22.32
81	2.54	98	12.73	115	22.92
82	3.14	99	13.33	116	23.52
83	3.74	100	13.93	117	24.12
84	4.34	101	14.53	118	24.72
85	4.94	102	15.12	119	25.32
86	5.54	103	15.73	120	25.92
87	6.14	104	16.33	121	26.52
88	6.74	105	16.93	122	27.11
89	7.34	106	17.53	123	27.71
90	7.94	107	18.13	124	28.31
91	8.54	108	18.72	125	28.91
92	9.14	109	19.32	126	29.51
93	9.73	110	19.92	127	30.11
94	10.33	111	20.52	128	30.71
95	10.93	112	21.12	129	31.31
96	11.53	113	21.72	130	31.91

foot the center line of the pedorule should bisect the two ink marks. (In the making of the observations one eye should be closed, and the other should be approximately twenty-four inches directly behind the center of the pedorule.) Then take the following readings: (1) from the extreme tip of the fibular malleolus to the center of the tendon, (2) from the tibial malleolus to the center of the tendon, and (3) the distance from the center of the tendon to the center line of the pedorule. (The center line of the pedorule coincides with the center line of the tendon of Achilles if the arch is neither flat nor weak.)

A second method of determining flat-footedness by the pedorule is as follows.

[26] Harold R. Danford, "A Comparative Study of Three Methods of Measuring Flat and Weak Feet," *Supplement to Research Quarterly*, March, 1935.

Place the center line of the pedorule directly behind the center of the tendon at the point where the tendon is bowed medialward the farthest. Count the number of lines from this point to the tips of the malleoli, and subtract the distance between the tendon and the tibial malleolus *from* the distance between the center of the bowed-in tendon and the fibular malleolus. Thus the distance that the tendon of Achilles deviates from the perpendicular is found.

After experimentation with both methods, it has been found that the second method is less confusing than, and just as efficient as, the first method. The score for a "perfect" foot is 0, showing the tendon in its entire length to be equidistant between the malleoli.

An r of reliability of .94 for the use of the pedorule was obtained by Danford. By means of the pedorule is measured primarily inward bend or pronation of the foot, not the same thing measured by the use of the pedograph, for r's obtained between measurements made by the use of the two instruments are only .30. The evidence presented by Danford would indicate that the use of the pedograph is the more valid of the two methods of measurement but that additional information of value is obtained by the use of the pedorule. An r of .70 (corrected for attenuation) has been obtained between measurements made by the use of the pedograph and subjective estimates of foot condition, and an r of .49 between measurements made by the use of the pedorule and subjective estimates of foot condition. An R of .76 (corrected for attenuation) has been obtained between measurements made by both the pedograph and the pedorule, and subjective estimates of foot condition.

472. MEASUREMENT OF LATERAL DEVIATIONS OF THE SPINE

The following method of measuring lateral deviations of the spine is probably as satisfactory as any. The subject is instructed to bend forward slightly. The locations of the spinous processes of all the vertebrae are then marked on the skin with a skin pencil. The subject then bends farther forward, and the observer bends forward so that his line of vision is approximately tangent to the bent spine of the subject, and notes whether or not there is any elevation on either side of the spine. An elevation denotes a rotation of the spine to the side of the elevation.

The subject then stands in front of a plumb line that is so hung that it goes past the middle of the spinous process of the fifth lumbar vertebra. With the subject in this position, the top of the posterior aspect of each ilium is marked. The subject, standing with his back to the camera, is then photographed. The photograph should be taken at a standard distance in order that distances on the photograph may be determined; for example, the photograph might be taken at such a distance that ten centimeters on the photograph would represent twenty inches on the back of the subject. A horizontal line is then drawn on the photograph from the top of each ilium toward the spine to the plumb line in such a way that the drawn line makes a ninety-degree angle with the plumb line. By means of these lines can be determined the amount of deviation of the top of each ilium from the horizontal, and the relative heights of the tops of the ilia. In addition, the lateral deviations of the spine are clearly seen, and can be measured.

In this method of measurement, two things should be kept in mind: (1) By this type of measurement, the amount of rotation of the vertebrae, which amount must be observed while the subject is bending forward, is not taken into account; and (2) even if the two ilia are of the same height, there may be deformities of the sacrum that may cause lateral deviations of the spine. Such deformities can be determined only by means of X rays.

If it is considered desirable to record the amount of apparent rotation, photographs may be taken of the subject in the bent-forward position and at such a distance from the camera as to enable the observer to determine the exact difference between the heights of the structures on either side of the spine.

CHAPTER 22

CHARACTER

473. SINCE THE elements of character do not yield themselves to precise measurement,[1] various types of ratings of character have been proposed. For the purposes of the physical and health educator, character is usually rated in one of two ways: (1) the direct rating of such traits of character as initiative, perseverance, self-confidence, cool-headedness, dependability, and sportsmanship; and (2) the ratings of such frequencies of behavior as "quits when badly roughed," "competes aggressively," "presents alibis for mistakes and deficiencies," and "is punctual at practices." The reliability of the second method, in which the rater indicates the frequency with which he observes semispecific types of behavior, is much higher than that of the first method in which the rater deals with generalities and frequently does not comprehend what he is rating. In the second method the frequencies of undesirable behavior may well be recorded. For example, "controls himself when provoked" is not so easy to rate as "swears freely when provoked" or "makes loud-mouthed comments and criticisms"; and "is co-operatively obedient to accepted authority" is not so readily noted as "he hogs the ball."

The rating of traits has been discredited on the basis that a trait does not correspond to anything real. The use of traits in this discussion would seem to be justified, however, for traits are here used as a sort of magnet by means of which numerous semispecific elements that have a general principle in common are drawn together. The scope of the specific elements embraced by each trait may be significantly reduced if the behavior being rated for its frequency is in terms of physical- and health-education situations. The process of generalization may be illustrated as follows. First, specific behavior frequencies of a positive type may be observed, examples of which are "to dominate others," "the tendency to stand up to opponents heavier than oneself," "the tendency to compete aggressively and to give one's best efforts even though the team is losing," "the willingness to take responsibility and to assume the initiative," "advancing ideas to which the team or group pays attention," and the kind of behavior

---

[1] Hugh Hartshorne and M. A. May in *Studies in Deceit,* and other authors have proposed methods of measuring conduct rather objectively. These methods involve more expenditure of time and of money than would be possible in school situations, even of the most favorable type. Within the limits of the type of measurement developed, the methods may, however, be utilized profitably for purposes of research.

that is frequently spoken of as "egotistical." These types of behavior are far from being specific, but they are all types of behavior in which the person makes things happen rather than waits for them to happen. Second, the types of behavior just listed may be indicated by such traits as decisiveness, initiative, resourcefulness, persistence, self-confidence, self-reliance, dependability, and adaptability. Third, the traits just listed may be indicated by such major groups as qualities of leadership, positive-action qualities, positive attitudes, and qualities of efficiency.

Recent research seems to indicate that all traits of character are formed from a small list of elemental psychological components or *factors*, which are statistically unrelated to each other, but combine to form, with certain specific additions and variations, the traits themselves. To date, fifteen general components or factors have been isolated and identified, and undoubtedly others will be isolated and identified (see Secs. 47-59). It is suggested that eight of these factors or "components of character" be used for purposes of rating. Since the factors frequently involve new concepts, they are difficult to name or to define. The first three factors are *social* (in contrast to antisocial) and more or less passive in nature.

(1) *Group good-citizenship qualities:* for example, fairness, ability to be a good follower, co-operativeness, respect for the rights of others, loyalty, respect for law, self-denial.

(2) *Individual good-citizenship qualities:* for example, trustworthiness, integrity, poise, dependability, thoroughness, conscientiousness, persistence.

(3) *Individual self-sufficiency:* for example, moral courage, coolheadedness, self-sacrifice, modesty, sportsmanship, resourcefulness, self-control.

The next two factors are both active and passive in nature.

(4) *Sociability:* for example, quickness of apprehension, ability to influence others, willingness to work on pleasures.

(5) This factor, as yet unnamed, seems to result in *"individual qualities"* as contrasted with traits that cause individuals to merge with the group. The positive trait is what causes one "to stand out from the crowd." It is the opposite of the quality that causes persons to merge with other gregarious individuals and to lose their individual identities, which quality may, of course, be a desirable one in many cases. The factor may, on the positive side, be illustrated by poise, self-confidence, self-esteem, and popularity and, on the negative side, by more social traits, such as co-operation, readiness to recover from anger, cheerfulness, tact, and respect for the rights of others.

The next three factors are more active than any of the preceding factors.

(6) *Positive-action tendencies:* for example, energy, aggressiveness,

ability to discipline others, adaptiveness, conviction, resourcefulness, and persistence.

(7) *Positive attitudes:* for example, self-confidence, initiative, enthusiasm, and alertness.

(8) *Leadership:* for example, popularity, fairness, enthusiasm, poise, self-control, and ability to discipline others.

The eight general components combine with one another, as well as with certain specific elements, to form what are commonly called "traits." Under these fundamental components are various subgroupings of what might be called "supergeneralizations" of traits. Under the supergeneralizations of traits are the traits themselves. Under each of the traits are specific behaviors, the frequencies of which are to be rated. In physical and health education the teacher in his attempt to rate character should concentrate his attention on the following three items. (1) He should observe each individual carefully and accurately. (The necessity of rating the individual on a number of different aspects of behavior is conducive to such accuracy of observation.) (2) He should individualize much of his instruction and prescribe activity programs according to the needs of

Use the following code: Rate only when you feel fairly sure of your
judgment

Possesses the trait to great excess—should be toned down	A++
Somewhat too much	A+
Entirely satisfactory	A
Good—above average	B
About average	C
Poor—below average	D
Very poor	E
On the opposite extreme	F

	Rating	Group average
1. Group good citizenship		
2. Individual good citizenship		
3. Individual self-sufficiency		
4. Sociability		
5. Individual qualities		
6. Positive action tendencies		
7. Positive attitudes		
8. Leadership		

FIGURE XLIV. Character Factors: Score Card for Rating

	Date of Rating _____
Name of person rated _____	Grade _____ Age _____
In what group _____	School _____
Name of rater _____	

Rater's assurance	Rater's assurance	No opportunity to observe	*Frequency of observation*					SCORE
0 = a mere guess			Never	Seldom	Fairly often	Frequently	Extremely often	
1 = a slight inclination								
2 = a fair assurance								
3 = a positive assurance								
GROUP GOOD CITIZENSHIP								
1. Plays to the gallery			5	4	3	2	1	
2. Hogs the ball, etc.			5	4	3	2	1	
INDIVIDUAL GOOD CITIZENSHIP								
3. Razzes, teases, or bullies opponents			5	4	3	2	1	
4. Acts like a good sport towards opponents			1	2	3	4	5	
5. Takes decisions, wins and loses, in good spirit			1	2	3	4	5	
6. "Crabs" about officiating			5	4	3	2	1	
INDIVIDUAL SELF-SUFFICIENCY								
7. Makes loud-mouthed comments, criticisms, etc.			5	4	3	2	1	
8. Swears freely			5	4	3	2	1	

FIGURE XLV. O'Neel Behavior-rating Scale (Revised)

the individual so that the individual may make as rapid progress as possible in the development of desirable types of behavior and be prevented from developing undesirable types of behavior habits. (3) He should attempt to cause a "transfer of training." (The association of specific actions with fundamental principles is conducive to such a transfer).

	Rater's assurance	No opportunity to observe	Frequency of observation					SCORE
			Never	Seldom	Fairly often	Frequently	Extremely often	
SOCIABILITY								
9. Is chosen by others of group as preferred companion in some activity			1	2	3	4	5	
10. Shows timidity, hurt feelings, oversensitiveness			5	4	3	2	1	
POSITIVE ACTION QUALITIES								
11. Dominates others			1	2	3	4	5	
12. Gives of his best efforts even when the team is losing			1	2	3	4	5	
POSITIVE ATTITUDES								
13. Is cheerful			1	2	3	4	5	
14. Makes fun of others who like games he does not like			5	4	3	2	1	
EFFICIENCY								
15. Works conscientiously to perfect his form in sports			1	2	3	4	5	
16. Thinks ahead of the play			1	2	3	4	5	
LEADERSHIP								
17. Schemes, works underhandedly to get his way			5	4	3	2	1	
18. Advances ideas to which group pays attention			1	2	3	4	5	

FIGURE XLV (continued)

METHODS OF RATING CHARACTER

474. Rating of character factors (Fig. XLIV, p. 279). If a rater is experienced, he may well rate general components directly. Each component is graded from superabundance to utter inadequacy; hence the optimum is represented by neither extreme. At one extreme a person may be so

Name of person rated _____ Grade _____ Age _____
Name of rater _____ Date _____

Rater's Assurance 0 = a mere guess 1 = a slight inclination 2 = fair assurance 3 = positive assurance	Rater's assurance	Frequency of observation						SCORE
		No opportunity to observe	Never	Seldom	Fairly often	Frequently	Extremely often	
GROUP GOOD CITIZENSHIP 1. He is loyal to his group			1	2	3	4	5	
2. He discharges his group responsibilities well			1	2	3	4	5	
3. He is co-operative in his attitude toward the teacher			1	2	3	4	5	
INDIVIDUAL GOOD CITIZENSHIP 4. He makes loud-mouthed criticisms and comments			5	4	3	2	1	
5. He respects the rights of others			1	2	3	4	5	
6. He cheats			5	4	3	2	1	
7. He is truthful			1	2	3	4	5	
INDIVIDUAL SELF-SUFFICIENCY 8. He grumbles over decisions of classmates			5	4	3	2	1	

FIGURE XLVI. Blanchard Classroom-behavior-rating Scale (Revised)

"social" that he sacrifices his family for his friends, so "co-operative" that he becomes the doormat of his acquaintances, so "positive" that he is an arrogant, egotistical nuisance. At the other extreme a person may be so spineless and timid that he responds to every suggestion and never exhibits any initiative. Hence, in the code, A represents the optimum; B, C, D, E, and F indicate diminishing degrees of desirability; and A+ and A++ represent an undesirable superabundance of the quality.

	Rater's assurance	Frequency of observation						SCORE
		No opportunity to observe	Never	Seldom	Fairly often	Frequently	Extremely often	
9. He takes a justified criticism by teacher or classmate without showing anger or pouting			1	2	3	4	5	
SOCIABILITY 10. He is liked by others			1	2	3	4	5	
11. He makes a friendly approach to others in the group			1	2	3	4	5	
12. He is friendly			1	2	3	4	5	
POSITIVE ACTION QUALITIES 13. He quits on tasks requiring perseverance			5	4	3	2	1	
14. He exhibits aggressiveness in his relationships with others			1	2	3	4	5	
15. He shows initiative in assuming responsibility in unfamiliar situations			1	2	3	4	5	
16. He is alert to new opportunities			1	2	3	4	5	

FIGURE XLVI (continued)

475. Revised O'Neel Behavior-rating Scale[2] (Fig. XLV, pp. 280-81). In the original O'Neel Behavior-rating Scale eighteen behavior frequencies, which were found to be the most valid and reliable of fifty carefully studied behavior frequencies, were classified under nine components of

[2] F. W. O'Neel, "A Behavior Frequency Rating Scale for the Measurement of Character and Personality in High School Physical Education Classes for Boys," *Research Quarterly*, May, 1936.

	Rater's assurance	No opportunity to observe	Never	Seldom	Fairly often	Frequently	Extremely often	SCORE
				Frequency of observation				
POSITIVE ATTITUDES								
17. He shows keenness of mind			1	2	3	4	5	
18. He volunteers ideas			1	2	3	4	5	
QUALITIES OF EFFICIENCY								
19. He seems satisfied to "get by" with the tasks assigned			5	4	3	2	1	
20. He is dependable and trustworthy			1	2	3	4	5	
21. He has good study habits			1	2	3	4	5	
LEADERSHIP								
22. He is popular with classmates			1	2	3	4	5	
23. He seeks responsibility in the classroom			1	2	3	4	5	
24. He shows intellectual leadership in the classroom			1	2	3	4	5	

FIGURE XLVI (continued)

character previously suggested by the senior author.[3] In the revised form of the scale these eighteen behavior frequencies are classified under eight objectives similar to the fundamental components outlined earlier in the chapter.

The frequency of each behavior is rated on a five-point scale from "extremely often" to "never," with 5 representing the desirable frequency. The general-trait score is obtained by the division of the sum of the values by the number of the items. In the scoring, due consideration should be given to the number of opportunities that the rater has had for observing the behaviors. The rater's assurance is indicated on a four-point

[3] "Character Building through Physical Education," *Research Quarterly*, October, 1930.

scale, ranging from "a mere guess" to "positive assurance." In the O'Neel study it was found that there was a high degree of agreement in the ratings on the part of raters who indicated fair or positive assurance.

476. Revised Blanchard Classroom-behavior-rating Scale[4] (Fig. XLVI, pp. 282-84). In the original Blanchard Scale the behavior frequencies were classified under the same nine components of character as were those of the O'Neel Scale. The revision of the original scale was similar to that of the original O'Neel Scale. The method of rating in the Blanchard Scale is the same as that in the O'Neel Scale.

RATERS

477. The training of raters has been discussed in Chapter 5. In some cases the teacher may wish to do all the rating himself. In other cases, however, the teacher may wish to have mature students assist in the rating. Raters should not only be trained in the techniques of the rating, but also should be taught the significance of the results. Leaders in school programs should be more than assistant teachers of activities—they should be leaders in school morale, in school traditions, and in the formulation of good habits of conduct. In one study conducted co-operatively with the senior author, a number of student leaders assisting in the ratings effected radical changes in the traditions of school conduct. Apparently the project when approved by the leaders became a project of the students, not simply an objective of the teacher.

Raters should be alert to the need for changing previous ratings, either upon being convinced that they had rated erroneously or that the status of the person rated had changed.

SUGGESTIONS

478. It is suggested that the ratings of character should not be used in the giving of grades. They should be used primarily for making clear to the teacher the person's status relative to conduct, habits, and attitudes; and to guide the teacher in providing laboratory experience in an adequate number and variety of desirable forms of conduct.[5]

479. A method, which is usable in programs of guidance, is presented as an aid in the making of an emotional inventory of a person. Twelve factors of emotions in their relation to adjustment have been isolated (and others will probably be isolated in the future). These factors should be rated according to the code in Figure XLIV (p. 279). In Factor I and in Factors VI through XII a lack of the factor is the desirable condition; hence grades of A, $A+$, and $A++$ should be assigned in cases in which

[4] B. E. Blanchard, Jr., "A Behavior Frequency Rating Scale for the Measurement of Character and Personality in Physical Education Classroom Situations," *Research Quarterly*, May, 1936.

[5] Charles H. McCloy, *Philosophical Bases for Physical Education*, Chap. 13.

Table 102

CHARACTER EDUCATION:　RATING OF FACTORS IN EMOTION (LAYMAN)*

1. Sociability factor A. "Feeling of social inadequacy." The opposite--a feeling of social adequacy--is the desirable condition

   Rating_____

2. Sociability factor B. "Gregariousness," or liking to be with people.

   Rating_____

3. Sociability factor C. "Social Initiative," or tendency toward active participation in a social group, perhaps as a leader.

   Rating_____

4. Sociability factor D. "Social Aggressiveness," or a tendency to dominate the social group.

   Rating_____

5. Self-sufficiency, or independence in planning and in working.

   Rating_____

6. Tendency toward impulsive action. The subject tends to act upon impulse without giving adequate thought to the consequences, and, as a result, frequently "puts his foot in it." The negative--an adequate control over such impulsive action--is the desirable condition.

   Rating_____

7. Changeability of interests. Overchangeability of interests is undesirable; hence the negative is the desirable condition. This does not mean to imply that an individual should not change interests from time to time. It does imply that he should not be "flighty" in his changing of interests.

   Rating_____

8. Feeling of inferiority, or lack of self-confidence The presence of this factor prevents a person, even one with ability, from relying sufficiently upon his own judgments, and causes him to ask constantly the opinions of others upon which to base his decisions; hence the negative is the desirable condition.

   Rating_____

9. Emotionality factor A. A characteristic of persons who tend to be dominated by moods, whose attitudes and general outlook on life are unduly colored by persistent emotional trends; hence the negative is the desirable condition.

   Rating_____

10. Emotionality factor B. Low threshold of emotional stimulation, a characteristic of a person called "thin-skinned." The person is easily upset, and tends to respond excessively in emotion-provoking situations The negative is the desirable condition

    Rating_____

11. Emotionality factor C--tentatively defined as "emotional introversion," or a tendency to repress the emotions within the self rather than express them outwardly Emotional extroversion, the negative of this factor, is the desirable condition.

    Rating_____

12. Inability to face reality, with possibly a consequent withdrawal of attention from the problems of the outside world The negative is the desirable condition.

    Rating_____

*Emma McCloy Layman, "An Item Analysis of the Adjustment Questionnaire " Journal of Psychology, July, 1940

the factor is absent, or present only in a very small degree. In Factors II through V a presence of the factor is the desirable condition; hence a grade of A should be assigned in cases in which the factor is present in a high degree (optimum). As in Figure XLIV, $A++$ indicates a super-abundance of the factor. The twelve factors are presented in Table 102 (p. 286).

It is suggested that the teacher rate each of his students in these factors and that each student rate himself in these factors, and then that the teacher and each student discuss the ratings together. No total score should be computed; rather each rating should be considered in relation to an individual factor.

CHAPTER 23

CARDIOVASCULAR TESTS

480. FOR MANY YEARS physiologists have attempted to analyze cardiovascular responses in order to determine (1) the present status of health, (2) the condition of the heart, (3) general-physical condition, and (4) basal metabolic rate by an indirect measurement. In general, the first three purposes have not been clearly differentiated in the tests that have been proposed; rather, the results have been "shotgun" cardiovascular prescriptions. Few cardiovascular tests measure with accuracy *one specific type* of physiological efficiency. There are several reasons for this lack of accuracy. First, many cardiovascular mechanisms are not thoroughly understood. Second, such significant cardiovascular variables as diastolic pressure and venous pressure have not been generally utilized in the tests that have been proposed. Third, sufficient recognition has not been given to the fact that such individual differences as the size of the heart relative to the size of the body may greatly affect the results of a test. To illustrate: Two persons, A and B, have the same body weight and the same degree of training. The heart of A, however, is 50 per cent larger than that of B. If each of these persons does a standard amount of exercise, executing the same number of foot-pounds of work in the same length of time, the demand for oxygen should be approximately the same for each of the two persons. The heart of B, however, in order to supply the necessary amount of oxygen to the muscles, has to beat approximately 50 per cent more times a minute than does the heart of A. The diastole of the heart of B is, then, shorter than that of A, and there is a smaller amount of time for the heart muscle of B to rest than there is for that of A. These conditions, in turn; introduce other phenomena that make great differences in such cardiovascular functions as blood pressures and pulse rates. The cardiovascular tests that have been presented to date do not take into account individual differences in the size of the heart and of the arteries, and individual differences in neuromuscular qualities, and hence the validity of the tests is low.

The attempt to measure indirectly, by means of cardiovascular tests, physiological conditions that can be better measured directly by other tests (see Chap. 15) does not appear to be an intelligent approach to the problem. For example, the results of many cardiovascular tests that have been devised to measure circulorespiratory endurance do not have an *r* higher than .5 with circulorespiratory endurance measured by such an event as distance running.

481. FACTORS IN CARDIOVASCULAR TESTS [1]

Three factors related to regulation of heart rate

Factor 1 is most readily noted in reclining and in sitting pulse rates, taken one, two, and three minutes after mild exercise consisting of stepping up fifteen times on a bench thirteen inches high.

Factor 2 represents the compensatory mechanism that controls the return of pulse rates to "normal" after strenuous exercise.

Factor 3 seems to represent the mechanism governing the increase in heart rate that occurs immediately upon the beginning of work.

Two factors related to regulation of blood pressure

Factor 4 seems to be a general mechanism for governing minute-volume, for heavy loadings are found in systolic pressures in all positions, in diastolic pressures in the standing position, and in pulse pressures in all positions. (In the study of the senior author cited in footnote 1, this factor was divided into two factors, one factor apparently regulating blood pressure generally and the other factor regulating pulse pressure.)

Factor 5 seems to represent the mechanism controlling the basal motor tonus of the vascular system. It is most highly correlated with sitting and standing diastolic pressures, with a high negative correlation with the standing heart rate minus the reclining rate.

Four factors related to regulation of hydrostatic pressure

Factor 6 seems to be a mechanism governing the general splanchnic accommodation to changes of hydrostatic pressure due to changes of position. It is most highly correlated with standing systolic pressure minus reclining and sitting systolic pressures as well as consistently highly correlated with standing diastolic pressure minus reclining diastolic pressure and with sitting diastolic pressure minus reclining diastolic pressure.

Factor 7 is tentatively identified as a redistribution mechanism of the blood upon a change of position, probably due to general tonus changes of the splanchnic circulation.

Factor 8 seems to represent the redistribution mechanism governing splanchnic relaxation in response to the raising of the hydrostatic pressure during muscular activity. It is most highly correlated with differences in pulse rates and in blood pressures in changes from reclining to sitting and standing positions.

Factor 9 is tentatively identified as the redistribution mechanism corresponding to changes in hydrostatic pressure in response to changes of

[1] Charles H. McCloy, "A Study of Cardiovascular Variables by the Method of Factor Analysis," *Proceedings,* Second Biennial Meeting, Society for Research in Child Development.
Mary A. Murphy, "A Study of the Primary Components of Cardiovascular Tests," *Research Quarterly,* March, 1940.

position. This factor is not unlike Factor 8, but seems to be related to different variables than is Factor 8.

The list of nine factors is an indication of the complex problem of cardiovascular testing. To date, little attempt appears to have been made to devise tests to measure exactly any one of these specific mechanisms; neither has there been any systematic presentation that relates each of these variables to the general purposes, as discussed in Section 480, for which cardiovascular tests have been devised.

482. In factorial analyses, venous pressure has not been included. With the inclusion of venous pressure, the factors listed in Section 481 will undoubtedly need to be re-interpreted. Unless the venous pressure is sufficiently high, the heart cannot fill the arteries as rapidly as is necessary, and hence arterial pressures and heart rates are affected. The glands of internal secretion, especially the adrenal cortex, the adrenal medulla, and the thyroid, have a marked influence on cardiovascular responses, and greatly complicate the problem. The addition of the condition of the myocardium —using the word "condition" both in a medical and in an athletic sense— is of great importance.

483. In general, the following factors accompany good condition: slow pulse, little rise in pulse rate upon arising from a reclining position, normal systolic pressure, rise of systolic pressure upon arising from a reclining position, a fairly high diastolic pressure, a relatively high venous pressure, a relatively small increase in pulse rate after exercise, and a rapid recovery of pulse rate after the cessation of exercise.

In general, the following factors accompany poor condition: a fast pulse, a relatively great change in pulse rate upon arising from a reclining position, a relatively low systolic pressure (too low a pressure is pathological), a drop in systolic pressure upon arising from a reclining position, a fairly low diastolic pressure, a fairly low pulse pressure, a low venous pressure, a great increase in pulse rate after exercise, and a low recovery of pulse rate after the cessation of exercise.

Only those cardiovascular tests that give some evidence of being useful are presented here. Several tests formerly reported are omitted in this edition because of their low validity.

484. TESTS PURPORTING TO MEASURE "PRESENT STATUS OF HEALTH"

By "present status of health" is meant the general cardiovascular functioning of the body from day to day in response to various organic and functional conditions. For example, if suffering from a bad cold, from a prolonged loss of sleep, or from a long bout of worry, the individual feels bad and usually functions considerably below par. This kind of condition also usually follows a somewhat prolonged illness. On the contrary, the individual who has had adequate rest, is not overworked, is getting plenty of sleep, and has been well, usually functions properly. The following tests attempt to measure in quantitative terms and, in one case, in qualitative terms this type of condition.

485. In the **Crampton Blood-ptosis Test,**[2] which is a very simple one, the subject reclines until his pulse rate reaches a constant rate. The observer then records the pulse rate and the systolic blood pressure. The subject is then assisted to stand, and the pulse rate and the systolic blood pressure are again taken. The test is scored from the chart in Table 103 (p. 291).

The efficiency of the Crampton Test is a matter of some dispute. The evidence seems to indicate that the test reflects changes in relative sickness, but that it does not reflect accurately the more positive changes in

Table 103

CARDIOVASCULAR CONDITION:
CRAMPTON METHOD OF RATING (MEN AND WOMEN)

| Heart rate increase | SYSTOLIC BLOOD PRESSURE | | | | | | | | | | |
| | Increase | | | | | Decrease | | | | | |
	+10	+8	+6	+4	+2	0	-2	-4	-6	-8	-10
0 to 4	100	95	90	85	80	75	70	65	60	55	50
5 to 8	95	90	85	80	75	70	65	60	55	50	45
9 to 12	90	85	80	75	70	65	60	55	50	45	40
13 to 16	85	80	75	70	65	60	55	50	45	40	35
17 to 20	80	75	70	65	60	55	50	45	40	35	30
21 to 24	75	70	65	60	55	50	45	40	35	30	25
25 to 28	70	65	60	55	50	45	40	35	30	25	20
29 to 32	65	60	55	50	45	40	35	30	25	20	15
33 to 36	60	55	50	45	40	35	30	25	20	15	10
37 to 40	55	50	45	40	35	30	25	20	15	10	5
41 to 44	50	45	40	35	30	25	20	15	10	5	0

the direction of health, and that it does not adequately reflect differences in athletic condition. The test is probably of more importance to the physician than to the physical and health educator. There seems to be considerable evidence, however, that the test measures rather accurately tendencies toward a profound collapse, which tendencies indicate a danger signal in case a surgical operation is in the offing. The test may be of real importance to the specialist in corrective therapy or reconditioning who may desire to ascertain whether or not a patient who has been critically ill is ready to be subjected to therapeutic bed exercises. Patients exhibiting low scores in the Crampton Test should probably not be considered ready for bed exercises of any degree of severity.

The Crampton Test seems to have its greatest significance if it can be related to an individual's own norm. Individual scores differ considerably;

[2] C. Ward Crampton, "A Test of Condition: Preliminary Report," *Medical News,* September 16, 1905.

hence any deviation upward from the individual's own average score is of significance for good, and any deviation downward from the individual's own average score is of significance for ill. If the individual's own norms are not available, the test is usually useful primarily for indicating relative degrees of illness.

486. In the **Schneider Test**[3] the following data are obtained: (1) reclining pulse rate, (2) reclining systolic pressure, (3) standing pulse rate, (4) standing systolic pressure, (5) pulse rate for fifteen seconds after a standard exercise, and (6) pulse rate for fifteen seconds at one minute, one and one-half minutes, and two minutes immediately after the cessation of exercise. These fifteen-second records are multiplied by 4 to give minute rates.

The subject reclines for five minutes or more before the reclining pulse rate and the reclining systolic pressure are taken, and then stands for a minute or two before the standing pulse rate and the systolic pressure are taken. The standard exercise is as follows. On the command to begin, the subject places one foot on a chair eighteen inches high, and then steps up on it with both feet. He keeps one foot on the chair, and steps down with the other, and continues in this way for a total of five steps in fifteen seconds. On descending the last time, he removes both feet from the chair. He stands at ease during the subsequent pulse-counting.

The Schneider Test is scored from the chart in Table 104 (p. 293). The maximum score is 18, and a score below 9 is supposed to indicate that the person is not in good physical condition. This test has been tried for many purposes. It is probably much better adapted for measuring the present status of health than it is for measuring athletic condition or for any other purpose. While claims have been made that the test measures with a high degree of accuracy circulorespiratory endurance, an examination of the studies presented to support such claims has indicated that there was a high selection of subjects, and that the test was given not with one application, but that the average of a large number of applications of the Schneider Test was used. This procedure in general is impracticable.

The Schneider Test has not shown a high degree of reliability. The senior author obtained an r of .43 between the Schneider Test and a measure of the present status of health. This r should not be taken to indicate the maximum validity of the test: it simply represents the results found in one study. The Schneider Test was used during World War I to determine whether or not fliers were functionally fit to fly, and it seemed to be adequate for that purpose.

It is probable that the exercise in the Schneider Test is too mild, and that, in general, too much importance is placed on systolic pressure, which

---

[3] E. C. Schneider, "A Cardiovascular Rating as a Measure of Physical Fatigue and Efficiency," *Journal of the American Medical Association*, May 29, 1920. The test has been republished by the permission of E. C. Schneider.

Table 104[*]

CARDIOVASCULAR TEST (SCHNEIDER): SCORING TABLE

| PART A | | PART B | | | | |
| RECLINING PULSE RATE | | PULSE RATE INCREASE ON STANDING | | | | |
Rate	Points	0-10 Beats Points	11-18 Beats Points	19-26 Beats Points	27-34 Beats Points	35-42 Beats Points
50- 60	3	3	3	2	1	0
61- 70	3	3	2	1	0	-1
71- 80	2	3	2	0	-1	-2
81- 90	1	2	1	-1	-2	-3
91-100	0	1	0	-2	-3	-3
101-110	-1	0	-1	-3	-3	-3

| PART C | | PART D | | | | |
| STANDING PULSE RATE | | PULSE RATE INCREASE IMMEDIATELY AFTER EXERCISE | | | | |
Rate	Points	0-10 Beats Points	11-20 Beats Points	21-30 Beats Points	31-40 Beats Points	41-50 Beats Points
60- 70	3	3	3	2	1	0
71- 80	3	3	2	1	0	0
81- 90	2	3	2	1	0	-1
91-100	1	2	1	0	-1	-2
101-110	1	1	0	-1	-2	-3
111-120	0	1	-1	-2	-3	-3
121-130	0	0	-2	-3	-3	-3
131-140	-1	0	-3	-3	-3	-3

| PART E | | PART F | |
| RETURN OF PULSE RATE TO STANDING NORMAL AFTER EXERCISE | | SYSTOLIC PRESSURE STANDING COMPARED WITH RECLINING | |
Seconds	Points	Change in mm.	Points
0- 60	3	Rise of 8 or more	3
61- 90	2	Rise of 2-7	2
91-120	1	No rise	1
After 120: 2-10 beats above normal	0	Fall of 2-5	0
After 120: 11-30 beats above normal	-1	Fall of 6 or more	-1

[*]Reproduced by permission of Dr. E. C. Schneider.

seems to be of relatively less value than diastolic pressure in diagnosing present health. No norms are available for children.

487. The **Hindman revision of the Schneider Test**[4] was an attempt to improve the crude method of scoring the Schneider Test. The Hindman method of scoring (Table 105, p. 294) was, however, based on the same assumptions on which the Schneider Test was based.

In addition to the items in Table 105 (p. 294), the last two items in *E* of the Schneider Test are used (see Table 104, p. 293). The Hindman scores seem to give, in certain extreme cases, more consistent results than do the Schneider scores.

Table 105

CARDIOVASCULAR TEST (SCHNEIDER): HINDMAN SCORING TABLES

Table E: Return of Pulse Rate to Standing Normal after Exercise		Table F: Systolic Pressure, Standing, Compared with Reclining	
Seconds	Points		
0- 45	3.00	Rise of 8 or more	3.00
46- 60	2.75	Rise of 7	2.75
61- 75	2.25	Rise of 6	2.50
76- 90	1.75	Rise of 5	2.25
91-105	1.25	Rise of 4	2.00
106-120	.25	Rise of 3	1.75
		Rise of 2	1.50
		Rise of 1	1.25
		No rise	1.00
		Fall of 1	.75
		Fall of 2	.50
		Fall of 3	.25
		Fall of 4	0.00
		Fall of 5	-.50
		Fall of 6	-1.00

488. The **McCloy Cardiovascular Rating of "Present Health"**[5] was based upon a study of diastolic pressures (fourth point), systolic pressures, and pulse rates. In view of the small number of subjects, the study was important more from the standpoint of method used than from the standpoint of the findings, but high coefficients of correlation were obtained with a criterion of "present health." The two formulas derived for the rating of present health are as follows:

Men: 4.46 standing diastolic pressure − standing pulse rate − 3 pulse rate immediately after exercise (validity: $r = .803$)

Women: 3 standing diastolic pressure − 3.4 standing pulse rate − pulse rate immediately after exercise + 160 (validity: $r = .901$)

The exercise used was the Schneider exercise (see Sec. 486).

[4] Darwin A. Hindman, "Nomographs for Interpolating Scores on the Schneider Test," *Research Quarterly*, December, 1930.

[5] McCloy, "A Cardiovascular Rating of 'Present Condition,'" *Arbeitsphysiologie*, March, 1931.

In this study, "good" scores ran as high as 100, with the median at 40. Poor scores ran as low as −260, with the median at −54. Other than from the Keller study,[6] there are no norms for children, and at present the test seems applicable primarily to adults. The test is not intended to measure athletic condition.

489. In the Keller study, which was conducted to determine the usefulness of the McCloy Rating of Present Health as a device for determining when high-school pupils who had been ill might safely resume activity in physical-education classes, the critical ratio between the scores of the same boys, when well and when ill, was 10.74.

Scores above 0 were considered to be "good," and those below 0 to be "poor." In the Keller study on high-school boys, a constant of 40 was added to the formula for men, and the 0 cutting point was then satisfactory.

490. Karpovich Test for ambulatory patients.[7] The judgment of the physician is usually sufficiently accurate to determine whether or not an ordinary medical patient may be assigned to an ambulatory-exercise program in a hospital. In uncomplicated diseases of limited duration it is usually safe to begin exercises on the second day after the cessation of fever. If there is some doubt, however, the physician may wish to check his judgment against the findings of an objective test. For this purpose the Karpovich Test has been shown to be highly valid.

There are two forms of the Karpovich Test. Both forms are based on the response of the heart rate to stepping up on a box twenty inches high at a rate of twenty-four steps a minute. The patient should be rested, and should not have climbed stairs or walked any considerable distance immediately before undergoing the test. The administrator of the test should use a metronome to set the pace. The patient upon the first count places one foot on the box, and steps up until the lower leg is in complete extension. He then similarly places the other foot upon the box on the second count. On the third count he steps off the box with the foot that he moved on the first count, and then on the fourth count he steps off the box with the other foot. The procedure is repeated as directed. For example, if the patient starts with the left foot, the stepping is left, right, left, right. The metronome should be set for ninety-six beats a minute, and a step taken on every beat.

It should be emphasized that it is not necessary to test all patients for whom exercise is to be prescribed. In fact it is probably only the excep-

[6] Arthur T. Keller, Jr., "An Attempt to Determine, through the Use of the McCloy Cardiovascular Test and the Pulse-Ratio Test, the 'Present Health' of Students Recovering from Illness" (M.A. Thesis, State University of Iowa, 1952).

[7] Devised by Peter V. Karpovich while working with the School of Aviation Medicine at Randolph Field, Texas; and adopted by both the Air Force and the Office of the Surgeon General of the Army. The test that is given here is taken from *Physical Reconditioning*, War Department Technical Manual 8-292.

tional patient that needs to be tested. *Cardiovascular tests should be used relative to the prescription of exercise only when the physician is in doubt* concerning whether or not to prescribe a program of exercise. Ordinarily the reactions of the patients to the exercise are sufficient to determine if the patients are ready to progress from an exercise routine of a few repetitions to one that is more strenuous.

Table 106

CARDIOVASCULAR PROGRESSIVE TEST (AIR FORCES):
SCORING TABLE (MEN AND WOMEN)

Duration of Exercise	One-minute Pulse Rate	Classification
Below 2 min.		Orange
	Below 100	Blue
2 min.--2 min. 29 sec.	Above 100	Orange
2 min. 30 sec.--2 min. 59 sec.	Below 130	Blue
	Above 130	Orange
3 min.--3 min. 29 sec.	Below 100	Green
	100-140	Blue
	Above 140	Orange
3 min. 30 sec.--3 min. 59 sec.	Below 110	Green
	110-170	Blue
	Above 170	Orange
4 min.--4 min. 29 sec.	Below 130	Green
	Above 130	Blue
4 min. 30 sec.--4 min. 59 sec.	Below 140	Green
	Above 140	Blue
5 min.	Below 150	Green
	Above 150	Blue

491. The first form of the Karpovich Test may be called a "preliminary test" because "passing" it indicates that the patient is able to undergo the general program of exercises with a few repetitions that are usually prescribed for patients who have very recently been suffering from disease. The other form of the test is more strenuous, and should be administered only to those patients who have passed the preliminary test.

In the Air Force the preliminary test was called the "Orange Test," and subsequent tests were called the "Blue Test" and the "Green Test." This terminology is used here (Table 106, p. 296).

Orange Test. The patient steps up on a box twenty inches high twelve times in thirty seconds. He then sits down, and his pulse is counted for thirty seconds, beginning one minute after the cessation of the exercise. If the pulse rate is less than one hundred beats a minute, the patient is considered to have passed the Orange Test, and to be ready for the least strenuous exercise program prescribed for ambulatory patients.

492. *Progressive Test.* In this test, which is administered a day or two after the Orange Test has been passed, the patient steps up on a box twenty inches high at the rate of twenty-four steps a minute for not more than five minutes. The tester notes the reactions of the patient. If the patient becomes distressed, or if he falters and cannot keep the pace set, the individual administering the test stops the test. If the patient is stopped or if he stops of his own accord (which is the more usual), the time he continued to exercise is noted. The pulse is counted for thirty seconds, beginning one minute after the cessation of the exercise. The patient is then classified according to Table 106 (p. 296).

493. The **Martinet Test**[8] is defective in that it cannot be scored numerically. It has, however, been proved, by European and South American experimenters, to be a valuable test, and is deserving of further study. It is based on three factors: circulatory changes provoked by a change from a reclining to a standing position, circulatory changes brought about as a result of exercise, and the return of blood pressures and pulse rates to normal following a period of exercise.

(1) Systolic and diastolic blood pressures and pulse rates are taken after a five-minute rest in a reclining position. After these records have been obtained, the subject is assisted to stand, and remains standing motionless while the systolic and diastolic pressures and the pulse rates are again taken. In the normal person the expected increases are about as follows: (a) the pulse rate increases less than ten beats a minute; (b) the systolic pressure increases less than twenty millimeters of mercury; and (c) the diastolic blood pressure increases less than ten millimeters of mercury. In a person in poor condition the results are as follows: (d) the pulse rate increases more than ten beats a minute; (e) the systolic pressure has an exaggerated increase for a few seconds and then drops lower; and (f) the diastolic pressure increases twenty or more millimeters of mercury with a corresponding decrease in pulse pressure. In a person in very poor condition there is a simultaneous decrease in both systolic and diastolic pressures, and there is a great decrease in the pulse pressure.

(2) Systolic and diastolic blood pressures and pulse rates are taken in a standing position. These readings may be available from the first part of the test.

The subject then does ten deep (as deep as possible) "knee bends" at the rate of one knee bend every two seconds. (For athletes in excellent

[8] Chailley-Bert, *Education Physique et Contrôle Médical.*

training, twenty deep knee bends are prescribed.) The observer then records the diastolic and the systolic blood pressure and the pulse rate immediately after the subject stops the exercise, and records the same every minute subsequently until the pulse rate has returned to that of the pre-exercise state. Normally the systolic pressure increases not over twenty to thirty millimeters of mercury, and the diastolic pressure increases from zero to twenty millimeters of mercury; sometimes the diastolic pressure even decreases slightly. The pulse rate rises to 100 to 105 beats a minute. The return to the normal condition takes from two to three minutes.

The results of the test are interpreted as follows.

Any increase in the *pulse rate* beyond 105, and any lengthening of the period of recovery beyond three minutes indicate a generally poor condition. The poorness of the condition is in proportion to the height of the pulse rate and to the length of the recovery time. Sometimes the pulse rate returns to normal before the blood pressures have returned to normal.

Any increase in the *diastolic pressure* over twenty millimeters of mercury or any great decrease is a sign of poor condition. Any decrease in the pulse pressure is also held to be a sign of poor condition. Any increase above three minutes in the time for the diastolic pressure to return to normal is also an unfavorable sign.

If the *systolic pressure* increases to thirty millimeters of mercury and does not return to normal within two to five minutes, an unfavorable condition is indicated. The systolic pressure should not rise above twenty millimeters of mercury. It may, however, without indicating an unfavorable condition, descend below normal within two to five minutes after the exercise.

494. The Flarimeter Test[9] attempts to measure medical or longevous, rather than athletic, circulatory fitness. It is a complicated test, and should not be used until the examiner has become thoroughly familiar with the method of its administration. It is, however, an excellent test and one that often detects, especially in older persons, fluctuations in condition as well as poor circulatory functioning. It should be very useful in connection with the evaluation of physical potentialities for purposes of prescribing corrective therapy for middle- and old-age adults.

In addition to a standard set of steps, which may be manufactured locally, a flarimeter is needed.[10] This instrument is also needed for the McCurdy-Larson Test (see Sec. 502).

[9] Formulated by the Medical Department of the Prudential Life Insurance Company of America.
P. V. Wells, *Flarimeter Manual.*
[10] Obtainable from Becton-Dickinson and Company, Rutherford, New Jersey.

CARDIOVASCULAR TESTS OF STATUS OR CONDITION OF HEART

495. Investigations of the **Tuttle Pulse-ratio Test**[11] have shown that the reliability of the test, when the test is used to evaluate general-athletic-condition, is not high enough to justify the use of the test for that purpose. The test is, however, one of the most useful of the cardiovascular tests for detecting pathological hearts. It is administered as follows.

(1) The subject sits at ease in a chair until the pulse has become stabilized. The pulse is then counted for thirty seconds and doubled. This result is recorded as the "normal pulse."

(2) The subject performs the following exercise for one minute. He steps up on a stool, which is thirteen inches high, first with his right foot and then with his left foot. He then steps down, first with his right foot and then with his left foot. This round trip is called one "step." The subject takes fifteen to twenty steps in the minute. (It is usually fifteen steps for girls and women, and twenty steps for boys and men.) The steps may be timed with a metronome. If a metronome is not used, the steps are performed for exactly one minute, and the number of steps performed, even if it is not the number planned, is recorded.

(3) Immediately after the cessation of the exercise, the subject sits down, and the observer counts the pulse for two minutes. (This is best done with a stethoscope.)

(4) The total pulse for two minutes is divided by the normal pulse for one minute, which result is the "first pulse-ratio."

(5) The subject rests until his pulse has returned to normal. Then he again performs steps on the stool, this time taking from thirty-five to forty steps in one minute. The number of steps taken in one minute is recorded.

(6) The subject sits down, and again the pulse is counted for two minutes. This total two-minute pulse is divided by the original one-minute pulse, which result is the "second pulse-ratio."

(7) The number of steps required to obtain a 2.5 ratio is computed as follows:[12]

$$S_1 = \text{steps taken for first pulse-ratio}$$
$$S_2 = \text{steps taken for second pulse-ratio}$$
$$S_0 = \text{steps needed for 2.5 ratio}$$
$$r_1 = \text{pulse-ratio for } S_1$$
$$r_2 = \text{pulse-ratio for } S_2$$

$$S_0 = S_1 + \frac{(S_2 - S_1)(2.5 - r_1)}{r_2 - r_1}$$

[11] W. W. Tuttle, "The Use of the Pulse-Ratio Test for Rating Physical Efficiency," *Research Quarterly*, May, 1931.

[12] Tuttle and his co-workers have found that in the normal heart the relationship between the pulse-ratio and the number of steps is linear, within the range of fifteen to forty steps.

To illustrate:

> Sitting normal pulse = 80
> Two-minute pulse after 15 steps = 174
> First pulse-ratio = 2.175 (i.e., 174 ÷ 80)
> Two-minute pulse after 40 steps = 224
> Second pulse-ratio = 2.80 (i.e., 224 ÷ 80)

$$S_0 = 15 + \frac{(40 - 15)\,(2.5 - 2.175)}{2.80 - 2.175}$$

$$S_0 = 28 \text{ steps}$$

An easier way to determine the number of steps needed for a 2.5 ratio is to use a chart on which steps have been plotted on one axis and pulse-ratios on the other. The point representing the pulse-ratio for S_1 is indicated, and the point representing the pulse-ratio for S_2 is indicated. These points are connected with a straight line, and the number of steps necessary for a 2.5 ratio is read directly from the chart (Fig. XLVII, p. 300).

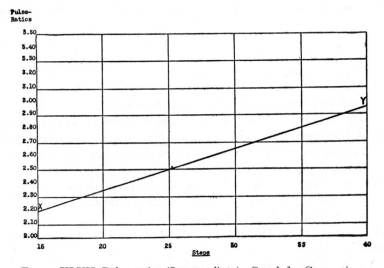

FIGURE XLVII. Pulse-ratios (Intermediate): Graph for Computing

After the individual's pulse has returned to normal and the number of steps necessary to obtain a 2.5 ratio has been computed, the subject performs this computed number of steps in one minute. (This performance is timed with a metronome.) His pulse is taken as before, and the pulse-ratio obtained. If this ratio is more than .07 above or below 2.5, and the same result is found upon subsequent testing, the heart is probably defective, and the individual should be referred to a physician.[13] In several

[13] Henry Sievers, "A Simple Method of Detecting Abnormal Hearts by the Use of the Pulse-Ratio Test," *Research Quarterly*, May, 1935.

different studies, this use of the pulse-ratio test has been found to detect defective hearts that have been missed by somewhat hurried routine school-medical examinations. This test is especially useful in situations in which the school is unable to secure medical examinations. It should be strongly emphasized that under no circumstances should a test of this type be considered to be an adequate substitute for a thorough medical examination of the heart: it is at best a substitute for a lack of a medical examination.

496. The **Barringer Test**[14] of the functional efficiency of the heart is based on the fact that hearts embarrassed by an overdose of exercise show a delayed rise in systolic pressure; that is, after the exercise has been completed, the systolic pressure does not return immediately to near normal, but continues to rise for awhile. The exercise in the Barringer Test consists of the lifting of dumbbells or barbells, with, in general, a maximum weight of twenty-five pounds. For young children dumbbells as light as five pounds are used. The exercise is one of three types. (1) The dumbbells are held at the sides, with the performer in a standing position, and the forearms are flexed alternately until the dumbbells have been raised to a position in front of the shoulders, and then the dumbbells are returned to the starting position. The movements are made at the rate of one second for flexion and one second for extension. (2) The dumbbells are held one in each hand at the sides of the shoulders with the forearms flexed. The arms are alternately thrust upward. This is a sort of seesawing motion, with one dumbbell being pushed upward while the other dumbbell is moving downward. The movements are again at the rate of one complete movement in two seconds. (3) For the most strenuous exercise, either dumbbells or a barbell weighing twenty-five pounds is used, and the weight is lifted from the floor to overhead.

In each of the exercises, the amount of foot-pounds of work is computed. If a performer in the first type of exercise raises the dumbbells two feet, the work done is the weight of the dumbbells multiplied by the number of performances, and by the height (in feet) the bells are raised; for example, if two ten-pound dumbbells are each lifted a distance of two feet ten times, the amount of work done is four hundred foot-pounds (i.e., $2 \times 10 \times 2 \times 10$).

In the lifting of the barbell from the floor, .4 to .5 of the weight of the body is added to the number of foot-pounds of work accomplished by lifting the weight from the floor to overhead. (If the body is slender, .4 is used, and if the body is corpulent, .5 is used. Thus if a corpulent individual weighing two hundred pounds lifts a twenty-five pound barbell seven feet, the number of foot-pounds of work accomplished for each lift is 275 foot-pounds [i.e., $(7 \times 25) + (.5 \times 200)$].

[14] T. B. Barringer, Jr., "Studies of the Heart's Functional Capacity as Estimated by the Circulatory Reaction to Graduated Work," *Archives of Internal Medicine*, May, 1916.

The subject is instructed to lift an amount of weight in accordance with a general estimate of his strength and of the condition of his heart. Immediately upon the cessation of the exercise, the systolic pressure is taken every half minute. If, at the beginning of the period immediately following the exercise, the systolic pressure begins to drop and continues to drop, the exercise is not considered to be too strenuous for the individual's heart. If, however, there is a continued rise in the systolic pressure for from half a minute to a minute followed by a drop, the exercise is considered to be too severe for the heart. By starting with a dosage of exercise that can be readily tolerated, and then increasing the dosage until the delayed rise in systolic pressure is obtained, it has been found that the "average normal" person is able to perform more than a thousand foot-pounds of work without a delayed rise in systolic pressure. The amount varies with the general physical condition of the person. Persons with pathological hearts often show the delayed rise in systolic pressure with as little as two hundred foot-pounds of work accomplished. Smaller amounts of work produce the delayed rise in children than in adults, and in smaller persons than in adults of greater stature.

The Barringer Test, like the Karpovich Step Test (see Sec. 490), is useful primarily in programs of corrective therapy or physical reconditioning, and in classes for adaptive physical education, in which the instructor is working closely with the physician.

TESTS TO DIFFERENTIATE BETWEEN GRADATIONS OF PHYSICAL CONDITION IN THE MIDDLE RANGES

497. The **pulse-ratio test** (see Sec. 495), while lacking a high degree of reliability, has in a number of studies been found to measure, to a fairly accurate degree, physical condition in the mid-range. The following norms of satisfactory condition for the number of steps necessary to produce a 2.5 pulse ratio have been proposed:[15] boys, ages 10-12 years—33

---

[15] Dorothy M. Arnold, "A Study of the Response of the Heart to Different Dosages of Exercise That Are Similar" (M.A. Thesis, State University of Iowa, 1935).

Lois Boulware, "Study of the Physical Efficiency of Freshman Women as Indicated by the Pulse Ratio" (M.A. Thesis, State University of Iowa, 1932).

W. W. Tuttle and Henryetta Frey, "A Study of the Physical Efficiency of College Women as Shown by the Pulse-Ratio Test," *Research Quarterly,* December, 1930.

Elvin R. Handy, "A Further Validation of the Pulse-Ratio Test as a Measure of Physical Efficiency and Endurance" (Ph.D. Dissertation, State University of Iowa, 1937).

Rex M. Millikin, "The Physical Efficiency Rating of Sixth, Seventh, and Eighth Grade Boys as Shown by the Pulse-Ratio Test" (M.A. Thesis, State University of Iowa, 1933).

Raymond W. Nibbe, "The Relationship Existing between the Heart Rate and the Intensity of Exercise" (M.A. Thesis, State University of Iowa, 1931).

Mabel J. Shirley, "The Response of the Normal Prepubescent Heart to Exercise of Graded Intensities" (M.A. Thesis, State University of Iowa, 1934).

W. W. Tuttle, "The Efficiency of High School Boys as Shown by the Pulse-Ratio Test," *Research Quarterly,* October, 1930.

steps; boys, ages 13-18 years—30 steps; adult men—29 steps; and women —25 steps. Standards for younger girls have not been established.

Some athletes and gymnasts in excellent condition have been reported to take as many as forty-two steps a minute to produce a pulse-ratio of 2.5. It is highly probable that a stool thirteen inches in height does not provide strenuous enough exercise to serve as a satisfactory test of physical condition. In view of the fact that better tests for this purpose are offered by the so-called Harvard Step Test (see Sec. 498), the pulse-ratio test will probably be used less and less for the measurement of physical condition.

498. The **Harvard Step Test**[16] is conducted as follows. The subject stands at attention in front of a bench or platform twenty inches high. An ob-

Table 107*

CARDIOVASCULAR TEST--HARVARD STEP TEST: SCORING TABLE (MEN)

Duration of Exercise in Minutes	Score	Sum of Pulse Counts (5 minutes of exercise)	Score	Classification
Less than 2	25	More than 273	55 or below	Poor physical condition
2 - 3	38	233 - 272	56 - 64	Low average physical condition
3 - 3½	48	189 - 232	65 - 79	High average physical condition
3½ - 4	52	168 - 188	80 - 89	Good condition
4 - 4½ 4½ - 5	55 59	167 and under	90 or above	Excellent

*Adapted, with permission, from Lucien Brouha, "The Step Test: A Simple Method of Measuring Physical Fitness for Muscular Work in Young Men." Research Quarterly, March, 1943.

server stands behind the subject. The subject places one foot on the bench, steps up until both feet are fully on the bench, with the legs straightened and the body erect, and immediately steps down again one foot at a time. The pace is counted by one of the observers: *Up*-2-3-4, *up*-2-3-4, as in military marching. The command *up* comes every two seconds. Usually the performer leads off with the same foot each time, but may change the procedure two or three times during the test. The exercise is kept up for five minutes continuously unless the subject stops from exhaustion before the end of that time. In any case, the duration of the exercise in seconds is recorded. The observer must be sure that the subject steps fully

———, "The Use of the Pulse-Ratio Test for Rating Physical Efficiency," *Research Quarterly*, May, 1931.
[16] Lucien Brouha, "The Step Test: A Simple Method of Measuring Physical Fitness for Muscular Work in Young Men," *Research Quarterly*, March, 1943.

up on the platform without assuming any crouching position, and that he keeps pace with the counting. If the subject is unable to keep pace for ten or fifteen seconds, the observer stops him.

As soon as the subject stops of his own accord, or is stopped by the examiner at the end of five minutes, he sits down. The observer notes the duration of the exercise, and records the pulse from 1 to $1\frac{1}{2}$ minutes, from 2 to $2\frac{1}{2}$ minutes, and from 3 to $3\frac{1}{2}$ minutes after the subject has stopped the exercise. The actual number of heart beats during each of these three thirty-second periods is recorded, and the three records are summed. This sum is then multiplied by 2. The score is obtained by multiplying the duration of the exercise in seconds by 100, and by dividing this result by twice the sum of the heart beats. The score may be obtained directly from the duration of the exercise in minutes—up to 5 minutes, or from the sum of the three pulse counts if the duration of the exercise is 5 minutes (Table 107, p. 303).

499. In the **Gallagher-Brouha modification of the Harvard Step Test**[17] the surface area of each boy is computed (see Fig. LIV, p. 370). Each boy whose surface area is less than 1.85 sq. m. is assigned to Group I, which does the steps on a bench or platform eighteen inches high. Each boy whose surface area is 1.85 sq. m. or more is assigned to Group II, which does the test on a bench or platform twenty inches high.

The test is conducted exactly as the Harvard Step Test, except that the time limit is four minutes instead of five. The physical-fitness score, likewise, is obtained by multiplying the duration of the exercise in seconds by 100 and by dividing the result by twice the sum of the pulse counts from 1 to $1\frac{1}{2}$ minutes, from 2 to $2\frac{1}{2}$ minutes, and from 3 to $3\frac{1}{2}$ minutes after the cessation of the exercise. A score of 50 or less indicates very poor condition; 51-60, poor physical condition; 61-70, fair physical condition; 71-80, good physical condition; 81-90, excellent physical condition; and 91 or more, superior physical condition.

500. In the **Clarke adaptation of the Harvard Step Test** for college women,[18] a bench eighteen inches high is used, and the duration of the exercise is four minutes. The test is scored as are the preceding Harvard Step Tests, and physical condition is classified like that for college men. In view of the fact that girls and women in schools of the United States improve little in physical condition after the junior high school, it is highly probable that this test may be validly used for junior- and senior-high-school girls as well as for college girls, and that the same standards are applicable to the three groups.

501. The Harvard Step Tests have been well validated, and measure a sort of general endurance; that is, they do not measure strength, or mus-

[17] J. Roswell Gallagher and Lucien Brouha, "A Simple Method of Testing the Physical Fitness of Boys," *Research Quarterly*, March, 1943.
[18] Harriet L. Clarke, "A Functional Physical Fitness Test for College Women," *Journal of Health and Physical Education*, September, 1943.

cular endurance, or circulorespiratory endurance in any special way. The item measured is what most physical educators mean when they say "he seems to be in pretty good shape." The tests seem to measure a combination of the types of endurance mentioned in Sections 312 to 314. The item measured does not have a high correlation with distance running. However, an *r* of .70 [19] has been obtained by a triserial correlation of the scores of two groups of rowers, varsity squad and beginners, and of an untrained group of men. The type of physical condition measured by the Harvard Step Tests is significantly related to a type of physical condition that might be held to be highly desirable for the average citizen. Such condition is different from that essential to the specialized athlete.

502. The **McCurdy-Larson Test of Physical Condition**[20] was based on data collected on infirmary subjects and varsity swimmers as two contrasting groups. Hence the test probably measures a mixture of endurance and "health," neither to the exclusion of the other. The test consists of (1) sitting diastolic pressure, (2) breath-holding twenty seconds after exercise, (3) difference between normal standing pulse rate and standing pulse rate two minutes after exercise, (4) sitting pulse pressure, and (5) standing pulse pressure. Pulse rates are all taken for fifteen seconds, and multiplied by 4.

The exercise taken is walking over and back on the three-step stairs standardized by Master and Oppenheimer.[21] The number of steps is taken from the reference cited in footnote 21 (see also reference cited in footnote 9), and is based on sex, age, and weight. The subject is seated for the breath-holding test. After fifteen seconds of exercise he takes a deep breath and then (twenty seconds after the exercise) blows as long as possible into the flarimeter (small opening). The test is scored on tables that weigh the tests according to multiple regression loadings.

The test is one of the more satisfactory cardiovascular tests. Detailed directions for giving the test and tables for scoring it may be found in the original reference.

Standards for prepubescent, pubescent, and postpubescent boys ($10\frac{1}{2}$ to 17 years of age) are available.[22]

---

[19] Computed by the senior author from data furnished by the Harvard Fatigue Laboratory.

[20] J. H. McCurdy and L. A. Larson, "Measurements of Organic Efficiency for the Prediction of Physical Condition," *Supplement to Research Quarterly*, May, 1935.

———, "The Measurement of Organic Efficiency for the Prediction of Physical Condition in Convalescent Patients," *Research Quarterly*, December, 1935.

———, "The Reliability and Objectivity of Blood-Pressure Measurements," *Supplement to Research Quarterly*, May, 1935.

[21] Arthur M. Master and Enid T. Oppenheimer, "A Simple Exercise Tolerance Test for Circulatory Efficiency with Standard Tables for Normal Individuals," *American Journal of Medical Science*, February, 1929.

[22] C. Wesley Dane, "A Study of Circulatory-Respiratory Changes as Indicated by the McCurdy-Larson Organic Efficiency Test in Relation to Physiological Age," *Research Quarterly*, May, 1944.

TESTS TO DIFFERENTIATE BETWEEN GRADATIONS OF PHYSICAL CONDITION IN THE UPPER RANGES

503. In the **Taylor Pack Test**[23] a bench eighteen inches high, about fourteen inches wide, and long enough to give stability is used. In order that a number of subjects may be tested at the same time, a long bench is desirable. A crossbar is placed directly over the back edge of the bench, with the upper edge six feet from the floor. This crossbar may be the rung of a stall bar, or a handle fastened to the wall. If shorter people are to be tested, another handle six inches lower may be provided. At the beginning of the test, the subject stands with his left foot on the bench, and grasps the bar or handle with his left hand. He raises himself to a stand on the bench by a combined flexion of the left arm and a thrust of the left leg. He pushes off with the right leg, which touches, at the end of the ascent, the top of the bench. The right arm is not used. The subject must come to an erect standing position on the bench, and must flex the pulling arm.

On the descent the right foot leaves the bench and starts for the floor, while the left arm and the left leg reverse the course taken during the ascent so that the subject comes to the initial position standing on the right foot. The left arm and the left leg maintain a position on the bar and bench between the ascent and the descent cycles. These cycles are carried out to the beat of a metronome at the rate of forty beats a minute. At the end of half a minute the examiner gives the signal to change, at which signal the subject switches to work the right leg and the right arm just as has been described for the left arm and the left leg. Such signals for alternating the working side of the body are given every half minute. If the command to change is given early during the ascent, the change can be made at the top of the ascent without the rhythm being disturbed.

The subject continues the work until he can no longer execute full ascent-descent cycles at the proper rate, that is, until fatigue limits his performance. As the work progresses, there is a gradual increase in general fatigue, and the recovery of each half of the body during its active phase is less complete. The subject is observed to show greater and greater difficulty in continuing the exercise, and his voluntary termination of the work, accompanied by signs of exhaustion, may be accepted as evidence that he cannot continue the exercise.

A preliminary warm-up and practice for one minute are given with the subject "unloaded." Then there is a rest period of fifteen seconds when a weight of ten pounds is placed on the back of the performer. Hence the subject performs the test for the first two minutes with a ten-pound weight

[23] Craig Taylor, "A Maximal Pack Test of Exercise Tolerance," *Research Quarterly,* December, 1944. Because of the fact that the heart rate after exercise is such a minor part of this test, the test should not really be considered a "cardiovascular" test. It is included here primarily because of its resemblance to the Harvard Step Test.

in the pack on his back. Another ten pounds is added each two minutes thereafter for as long as the subject continues the test. The heart rate is counted ten to thirty seconds after the end of the work.

The subject should not stop until there is either great difficulty in maintaining the rate or in coming to a full stand, or until there are signs of great breathlessness and other evidence of distress.

The postexercise heart rate other than indicating that the individual has "gone all out" has not been successfully combined with the exercise part of the test.

Table 108*

CARDIOVASCULAR TEST--TAYLOR PACK TEST: SCORING TABLE (MEN)

Time	Points	Frequency**	Time	Points	Frequency**
10:	100	1	5:	50	22
:30	95	0	:30	45	19
9:	90	5	4:	40	23
:30	85	9	:30	35	17
8:	80	12	3:	30	12
:30	75	8	:30	25	20
7:	70	14	2:	20	4
:30	65	14	:30	15	1
6:	60	18	1:	10	1
:30	55	23	:30	5	1

Height (in.)	Correction Points
76-75	-15
74-73	-10
72-71	- 5
70	0
69-68	5
67-66	10
65-64	15

* Craig Taylor, "A Maximal Pack Test of Exercise Tolerance," Research Quarterly, December, 1944.
**Frequency of occurrence in age 17-25, field study.

A scoring scale for the Taylor Pack Test may be found in Table 108 (p. 307). In the scoring, a correction for the height of the individual is made, for it is more difficult for a short individual to step up on the bench than it is for a tall individual.

Average scores and average heart rates (10 to 30 seconds after the exercise) for different age groups have been reported by Taylor as follows:

Age group (yr.)	17	18-21	22-25	26-29	30-33	34-37	38-46
Mean time (min.-sec.)	6-28	5-30	4-24	3-02	3-19	2-22	1-57
Mean heart rate for twenty seconds	61	61	61	59	59	57	56

It may be noted that the heart rates are for different lengths of time for mounting the bench.

504. Lowsley Criterion of overexercise.[24] Lowsley studied moderate activity such as tennis and baseball conducted from one and one-half to two hours, speed activities such as sprints of 100 yards and 220 yards, distance running such as the mile run, longer distances such as five to nine miles, and exhausting exercises of from ten-to-twenty-five-mile runs. Within thirty seconds after the completion of the exercise Lowsley recorded the pulse rate and the systolic and diastolic blood pressures by means of a recording Erlanger sphygmomanometer.

In all the activities studied, the pulse rates, the systolic pressures, the diastolic pressures, and the pulse pressures rose roughly in proportion to the severity of the exercise. The rise in these rates and in these pressures tended to be influenced greatly by the intensity of the sprint at the end of the run. The most significant finding, however—and the reason that this study is included in this chapter—was that immediately after the activity, the systolic, the diastolic, and the pulse pressures dropped below normal within a few minutes, usually in from five to ten minutes. The performance of the systolic pressure was particularly indicative of the severity of the exercise. Lowsley followed these pressures every few minutes until all the pressures and the pulse rates had returned to normal. In general, in the gentler forms of exercise the pressures and the pulse rates had all returned to normal within one hour. In some of the more severe forms of exercise they returned to normal more slowly than that. In exhausting exercises, sucn as runs of from ten to twenty-five miles, it was frequently as long as four to six hours before the systolic pressure had returned to normal. In many cases the systolic pressure dropped as much as 20 to 25 mm. of mercury below the normal range.

Since Lowsley knew the runners well, he was able, on the basis of his observations, to conclude that if the systolic pressure returned from the subnormal to the normal level within one hour, the exercise was beneficial; that if such a return was delayed as much as two hours, the exercise was relatively exhausting, but not too much so; and that if such a return was delayed more than two hours, the exercise was too severe for the performer.

It is suggested that the Lowsley Criterion might well be applied to the training programs of athletes in order to determine the desirable severity of training activities. If the training activities are so severe as to delay the return of the systolic pressure to normal more than two hours, the dosage should probably be lightened and a greater time taken to condition the athlete to the heavier dosages. This criterion seems to be a very promising one for the study of the effects of athletic-training procedures on the individual.

The study was confined to the upper-secondary-school and college ages.

[24] O. S. Lowsley, "The Effects of Various Forms of Exercise on the Systolic, Diastolic and Pulse Pressures and Pulse Rate," *American Journal of Physiology,* March 1, 1911.

TESTS FOR INDIRECT MEASUREMENT OF BASAL METABOLIC RATE

505. Read Formula for basic metabolic rate[25]

$$BMR = .75 \text{ pulse rate} + .74 \text{ pulse pressure} - 72$$

An r of .804 was obtained between this formula and the basal metabolic rate (600 cases). The scores obtained are in terms of percentages above and below the norm.

506. Read-Barnett Formula for basal metabolic rate[26]

Men: Calories per sq. m. per hr. = .0055 (pulse pressure × pulse rate) + 24

Women: Calories per sq. m. per hr. = .0047 (pulse pressure × pulse rate) + 23

Standards by age groups may be found in Table 109 (p. 309).

Table 109

BASAL METABOLISM: STANDARDS (MALES AND FEMALES 10 TO 70)

Ages (yr.)	Males	Females	Ages (yr.)	Males	Females
10-12	51.5	50	20-30	39.5	37
12-14	50	47.5	30-40	39.5	36.5
14-16	46	43	40-50	38.5	36
16-18	33	30	50-60	37.5	35
18-20	31	38	60-70	36.5	34

Between these formulas and basal metabolic rates r's of over .80 have been obtained. In the use of the Read-Barnett Formulas there seemed to be fewer exceptions in their relationship to the basal metabolic rate as determined by indirect calorimetry than in the use of the Read Formula.

507. Gale Formula for basal metabolic rate[27]

$$BMR = \text{pulse pressure} + \text{pulse rate} - 111$$

The scores obtained are in terms of percentages over and under the normal. This formula is standard for twenty-year-old subjects. One point should be added for each five years over twenty years of age.

[25] J. Marion Read, "Basic Pulse Rate and Pulse Pressure Changes Accompanying Variations in the Metabolic Rate," *Archives of Internal Medicine*, October 15, 1924.

[26] J. Marion Read and Charles W. Barnett, "A New Formula for Prediction of Basal Metabolism from Pulse Rate and Pulse Pressure," *Proceedings* of the Society for Experimental Biology and Medicine, March, 1934.

[27] Annabella M. Gale and G. H. Gale, "Estimation of the Basal Metabolic Rate," *Lancet*, June 13, 1931.

508. The procedure for obtaining the basal metabolic rate must be rigorously standardized. The subject is examined in the morning before eating, and after lying down for at least half an hour in as relaxed a manner as possible. The pulse rates and the pulse pressures are taken several times, and the lowest values are recorded.

In an evaluation of these cardiovascular tests for the prediction of the basal metabolic rate it should be remembered that, in a consideration of correlations with calorimetric readings of basal metabolic rates, the indirect readings are themselves subject to considerable variation. Hence the unreliability of the test may often be as much due to the unreliability of the indirect (oxygen consumption) reading as to that of the cardiovascular reading.

The greatest usefulness of the measurements of basal metabolic rate is to provide a preliminary check in suspicious cases. If a teacher who observes undue nervous activity and other evidences of hyperthyroid activity upon the part of a pupil, or who may think that he sees evidences of myxedema upon the part of a pupil were to suggest immediately that an indirect calorimetric reading be taken, he might quite rightly be blamed by a parent for advising a procedure that might prove to be not only unnecessary, but also expensive. If, however, the teacher checks the probable basal metabolic rate with the formulas suggested in Sections 505 to 507 and after two or three applications of these formulas on different days finds that his suspicions seem to be substantiated, he is well advised to call the condition to the attention of the parent and of the family physician.

OTHER CARDIOVASCULAR TESTS

509. The tests discussed in Sections 485 to 507 seem to be the ones of most interest and of greatest value to physical and health educators. The tests listed in Sections 510 to 513 are tests which are, probably, of greatest interest to physiologists for investigative purposes, and are of little or no interest to the average physical- and health-education teacher.

510. The **Barach Energy Index**,[28] which purports to measure the energy expended by the heart, is

$$\frac{\text{pulse rate (systolic pressure} + \text{diastolic pressure)}}{100}.$$

All records are taken with the subject sitting. The normal range is considered to be from 110 to 160, and the danger limits below 90 and above 200.

[28] J. H. Barach, "The Energy Index," *Journal of the American Medical Association,* February 14, 1914.

511. The **Stone Cardiovascular Score**[29] is

$$\frac{\text{pulse pressure (sitting)}}{\text{diastolic pressure (sitting)}}.$$

Scores over .6 are considered to represent an overload on the heart and scores below .4 to indicate that an actual circulatory embarrassment may have occurred and that the patient may be subject to circulatory failures.

512. The **Tigerstedt Cardiovascular Test** [30] is similar to the Stone Cardiovascular Test except that systolic pressure in the place of diastolic pressure is in the denominator. The formula is

$$\frac{\text{pulse pressure (sitting)}}{\text{systolic pressure (sitting)}}.$$

The normal range is considered to be from .3 to .5, with any value over .5 representing an overload and any value under .3 indicating a potential cardiac failure.

Both the Stone Test and the Tigerstedt Test have certain fallacies for which partial corrections have been made.[31]

513. The **Larson Scale** of cardiovascular variables[32] (available in the publications cited) offers many advantages in making judgments of physical status from cardiovascular variables.

514. NOTES ON USES OF CARDIOVASCULAR TESTS

To administer cardiovascular tests as a routine procedure is a waste of time for both the examiner and the subject. In general these tests should be administered for the following purposes.

(1) In situations in which individuals have been ill, operated on, or otherwise incapacitated, and when corrective therapists or reconditioning specialists are contemplating increasing dosages of exercise, tests in the first category of "present health" may well be administered. One of these tests may also be administered when a pupil has been absent from school for several days and reports back stating that he has had influenza, pneumonia, or some other disease, but bringing no recommendation from his physician.

(2) If such factors as extreme breathlessness on the part of the subject in response to moderate exercise, or cyanosis, indicate to the teacher that

---

[29] W. J. Stone, "The Clinical Significance of High and Low Pulse Pressures with Special Reference to Cardiac Load and Overload," *Journal of the American Medical Association,* October 4, 1913.

[30] J. H. McCurdy and L. A. Larson, *The Physiology of Exercise,* pp. 337-39.

[31] *Ibid.*

[32] Leonard A. Larson, "A Note on Scaling Some Measures of Circulation and Respiration," *Research Quarterly,* December, 1948.

——— and Rachael D. Yocom, *Measurement and Evaluation in Physical, Health, and Recreation Education,* p. 52.

there is a possibility of a heart defect, *and* if it is impracticable to refer the pupil to a physician in the near future, the tests in the second category, namely those of heart function, may well be tried. In the meantime the pupil should be kept from undue activity.

(3) A test for basal metabolic rate may be given if the teacher has reason to believe that a pupil may have either an unduly high or an unduly low basal metabolic rate, but yet hesitates to recommend that, without further evidence, an indirect calorimetric test be administered.

(4) Most of the other tests are useful primarily for research purposes. As was stated early in the chapter, endurance and physical condition of an advanced type may, in general, be better tested by tests given in Chapter 15 than by cardiovascular tests. However, for research purposes both types of tests may frequently be utilized. The cardiovascular tests, however, are probably used less than are direct measurements. In hospitals, however, the tests for physical condition may well be administered to individual patients to determine when more strenuous dosages of exercise should be prescribed, and to determine when a patient has reached a desirable state of physical condition and is ready for discharge to active work—such as return to active duty in the Infantry in the Armed Services, or a return to hard labor in a steel mill after an illness in a hospital. This type of test is often more readily administered to middle-aged and elderly subjects than are the tests of running, and the others of the circulorespiratory- and muscular-endurance type listed in Chapter 15.

CHAPTER **24**

KNOWLEDGE

515. TESTS OF knowledge usable in physical education include those that measure knowledge of such items as the rules of activities, the techniques of performance, the history of sports, and offensive and defensive strategy in sports. They also include those usable for research purposes, that is, in the investigation of the relationship of progress in performance with such items as rules, techniques, and strategy. Tests of knowledge usable in health education are discussed in Chapter 29.

In the construction of a test of knowledge the first step is to provide for an adequate sampling, that is, to prepare the items with which to determine what has been achieved or what can be expected to be achieved in an area. Such a list of items may well be prepared from an outline of the material to be covered by a test. The items include (1) ones that indicate a mastery of the material and (2) ones that indicate the ability to apply the material. Then the various items should be weighed either by the assignment of more points for the more important items or by including more items for the more important part of the content.

516. TYPES OF OBJECTIVE TESTS

Among the requirements for writing good test items is the mastery of verbal communication.[1] Hence since the B.A. degree (and, all too frequently, second and third degrees) no longer guarantees literacy, good test items may soon be of only historical interest. The requirements for writing good test items will not be elaborated here; only a few precautions will be indicated that should be observed in the preparation of items for a test of knowledge. Although the examples presented are the true-false type of item, the precautions are applicable to all types of tests of knowledge.

(1) Avoid ambiguous statements, such as *The most important element in motor learning is insight.* A better item would be *Insight is an important element in motor learning (true).*

(2) Avoid trivial statements, such as *It is important to roll clay courts frequently.* A better item would be *Clay courts to be properly maintained should be rolled daily (true).*

(3) Avoid trick statements, such as *"Chest expansion" is the size of the chest expanded.* A better item would be *The average difference between*

[1] Robert L. Ebel, "Writing the Test Item," in *Educational Measurement* (American Council on Education), p. 187.

313

the circumferences of the chest when the chest is inflated and when it is deflated is six inches in the eighteen-year-old male (false).

(4) Avoid statements that are sometimes true and sometimes false, such as *Low arches cause painful feet*. A better statement would be *In about 50 per cent of the cases low arches are accompanied by painful feet (false)*.

(5) Avoid statements with such words as *never, always, none,* and *all,* such as *Expert professional golfers always have a perfect follow-through*. A better statement would be *The follow-through in a golf drive determines the accuracy of the flight of the ball (false)*.

(6) Avoid statements that are extremely long and involved, such as *"Overlearning pays because there is evidence to show that material 100 per cent overlearned is retained much more than 100 per cent better than material learned to the point where the correct word of a series is antici- pated in 100 per cent of the cases."* [2] A better statement would be *Mate- rial overlearned is retained better than material learned to the point where the correct word of a series is anticipated in 100 per cent of the cases (true)*.

(7) Avoid statements that are based solely on opinion, such as *Luther H. Gulick exerted a more constructive influence on physical education in the United States to date than has any other person*.

(8) Avoid statements that are jabberwocky, such as *Dominance refers to the precedent of movement in homologous structures, that is, the fore- arm (double talk)*.

517. True-false. A statement is marked *true* or *false*. Two or four items can be marked in a minute. Hence a test to which a class period of fifty minutes is to be devoted should include from seventy-five to one hundred items. If fewer than seventy-five to one hundred items are used, the re- sults of several tests should be totaled for a record.

Sample

Directions: Encircle the T before all true statements and the F before all false statements.

T Ⓕ 1. The psoas muscle extends from the greater trochanter of the femur to the ilium.

Ⓣ F 2. The first woman gymnasiarch recorded in the history of ancient Greece was Aurelia Leita.

True-false-doubtful. A statement is marked *true* or *false,* or *doubtful* meaning *alleged, but unproved*.

Sample

Directions: Encircle the T before all true statements, the F before all false state- ments, and the ? before all statements that are alleged but not proved.

[2] Robert M. W. Travers, *How To Make Achievement Tests,* p. 58.

T F (?) 1. There are African Negro tribes that have athletes able to high jump to records greater than the present American record.

True-false—corrected-false. A statement is marked *true* or *false*. If it is correctly marked *false*, one word is changed to make the statement *true*.

Sample

Directions: Encircle the T before all true statements and the F before all false statements. If the statement is false, cross out the word that makes it false, and insert a word that makes it true.

(T) F   1. Claes Julius Enebuske succeeded Posse at the Boston Normal School of Gymnastics.

T (F) 2. The ~~culex~~ *Anopheles* mosquito is the transmitter of the malaria germ.

Correct-incorrect diagram. Diagrams are marked *correct* or *incorrect*.

Sample

Directions: The following diagrams represent the dimensions of certain fields and courts for athletic games. Encircle the + before all correct diagrams and the − before all incorrect diagrams.

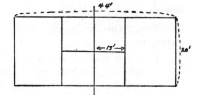

+ − Badminton

True-false—reason. A statement is marked *true* or *false*, with the reason for the marking indicated.

Sample

Directions: Encircle the T before all true statements and the F before all false statements. In the space below each statement state in one sentence the reason for the marking.

T (F) 1. The validity of the posture standards of the Children's Bureau has been established.
This statement is false because posture standards should depend upon individual differences in skeletal build.

(T) F   2. Movements made by a high jumper after he has left the ground do not add to the height of his center of gravity.
This statement is true because action and reaction are equal and opposite.

518. **Multiple-choice.** Choices are given for making a statement correct. If five choices are given, there is one chance in five of the student's selecting the correct choice by guessing, and hence this form of test is usually considered to be superior to the true-false type in which there is one chance in two of the student's marking the statement correctly by guessing. It does not follow, however, that test scores on a true-false test are 2.5 times as erroneous as test scores on multiple-choice items. "In fact, if chance responses are given to the same number of true-false and four-choice items, the error variance due to chance response is only one-third

larger in the case of the true-false items than in the case of four-choice items." [3] A test to which a class period of fifty minutes is devoted should include fifty to seventy-five multiple-choice statements.

Sample

Directions: On the line at the left, write the letter of the correct choice for each statement.

_a_ 1. A muscle that can flex the upper leg at the hip joint is the (a) iliopsoas, (b) biceps femoris, (c) flexor hallucis longus, (d) pyriformis, (e) adductor magnus.

_c_ 2. A muscle that cannot dorsiflex the foot at the ankle joint is the (a) peroneus tertius, (b) tibialis anterior, (c) peroneus brevis, (d) extensor digitorum longus, (e) extensor hallucis longus.

A variation of the multiple-choice type is the selection, from a group of five items, the item of best choice.

Sample

Directions: On the line at the left, write the letter of the *best* choice for each statement.

_c_ 1. A new football coach assumes responsibility for directing the program of football of a high school that held the conference championship last year and that lost only three letter men. In selecting his system of play, the coach should: (a) adopt last season's system, (b) discuss the various systems he knows with the principal and then make his decision, (c) investi-

Organisms \ Diseases	Tuberculosis	Syphilis	Hookworm	Diphtheria	Amoebic dysentery	Typhoid fever	Pneumonia
Uncinaria Americana							
A bacillus that stains evenly							
A bacillus that stains in segments							
Spirochaeta pallida							
Fasciola hepatica							
A gram-positive coccus							
A gram-negative coccus							
Amoeba coli							
Amoeba histolytica							

[3] Ebel, *loc. cit.*, p. 206.

gate the type of material he has and decide upon a system himself, (d) investigate the type of material he has and discuss the various systems with the boys and abide by their decision.

Tabular. Items arranged in tabular form (see p. 316) are checked.

Sample

Directions: Under the name of each disease given at the top, check the row corresponding to the organism related to that disease.

Matching. The items in one or more columns are marked to indicate their relationship to items in another column.

Sample

Directions: Write the number belonging to the approximately correct date in the first column and the number corresponding to the correct name in the second column.

Dates	Names		Dates	Names
1	1	Introduction of a physical education program at the Philanthropinum in Dessau	1. 1774	1. Basedow
			2. 1799	2. Beck
			3. 1804	3. Bukh
5	2	Establishment of physical education at the Round Hill school in the United States	4. 1810	4. de Coubertin
			5. 1823	5. Gulick
			6. 1887	6. Hitchcock
6	5	Opening of a department of physical education in the YMCA Training School at Springfield, Massachusetts	7. 1896	7. Jahn
			8. 1902	8. Ling
			9. 1906	9. McCurdy
			10. 1924	10. Nachtegall
2	10	Appointment by King of Denmark as professor of physical education		
7	4	Revival of the modern Olympic games		

The items in the second column are arranged chronologically and those in the third column are arranged alphabetically to facilitate the finding of the correct items. (There should be more items than blanks.)

519. Completion. Blanks in a statement are filled in to produce an accurate statement. The completion form requires the student to recall information rather than merely to recognize information. Incorrect answers in completion tests may be used as incorrect choices in multiple-choice tests.

Sample

Directions: Complete each statement by writing the correct answer in the blank.
1. The control of sugar metabolism is the function of the glands called the *Islands of Langerhans.*
2. In the college low-hurdle race the number of yards from the start to the finish is ____*220*____ .

520. SCORING OBJECTIVE EXAMINATIONS

Objective examinations may be scored by (1) totaling the correct responses or (2) subtracting the number of incorrect responses from the number of correct responses by the following formula that corrects for guessing:

$$\text{Score} = \text{number of correct items} - \frac{\text{number of incorrect items}}{\text{number of choices} - 1}$$

Hence if, in a multiple-choice test of fifty statements with five choices for each statement, a student made forty correct choices, five incorrect choices, and did not indicate any choices for five statements, the score would be $38.75 \left(\text{i.e., } 40 - \dfrac{5}{5-1} \right)$. In a true-false test of fifty items the score would be $35 \left(\text{i.e., } 40 - \dfrac{5}{2-1} \right)$.

If most of the students answer all the questions, their relative standings are about the same for both methods of scoring.

Methods for analyzing the difficulty of test items may be found in Appendix B.

521. A list of tests of knowledge alphabetically arranged according to activities and subject matter follows.

522. ARCHERY

Snell, Catherine. "Physical Education Knowledge Tests," *Research Quarterly*, VI (October, 1935).

523. BADMINTON

Phillips, Marjorie. "Standardization of a Badminton Knowledge Test for College Women," *Research Quarterly*, XVII (March, 1946).

Scott, M. Gladys. Achievement Examinations in Badminton," *Research Quarterly*, XII (May, 1941).

524. BASEBALL

Rodgers, Elizabeth, and Marjorie L. Heath. "An Experiment in the Use of Knowledge and Skill Tests in Playground Baseball," *Research Quarterly*, II (December, 1931).

Snell, Catherine. "Physical Education Knowledge Tests," *Research Quarterly*, VII (May, 1936).

525. BASKETBALL

Bliss, J. G. *Basketball*. Philadelphia: Lea and Febiger, 1929.

Schwartz, Helen. "Knowledge and Achievement Tests in Girls' Basketball on the Senior High School Level," *Research Quarterly*, VIII (March, 1937).

Snell, Catherine. "Physical Education Knowledge Tests," *Research Quarterly*, VII (March, 1936).

526. BASKETBALL OFFICIATING

Rubin, Robert. "A Rating Scale for Basketball Officials," *Journal of Health and Physical Education*, VII (January, 1936).

Schleman, Helen B. "A Written-Practical Basketball Officiating Test," *Journal of Health and Physical Education*, III (March, 1932).

Scott, M. Gladys. "Written Test for Basketball Officials," *Journal of Health and Physical Education*, VIII (January, 1937).

Women's National Officials' Rating Committee. "Officials' Written Tests in Basketball. . . ." (Mimeographed).

527. DANCE

Murray, Josephine Ketcik. "An Appreciation Test in Dance." Master's Thesis; Los Angeles, University of California, 1943.

Shambaugh, Mary Effie. "The Objective Measurement of Success in the Teaching of Folk Dancing to University Women," *Research Quarterly*, VI (March, 1935).

Thompson, Betty Lynd. *Fundamentals of Rhythm and Dance.* New York: A. S. Barnes and Company, 1933.

528. FUNDAMENTALS

Snell, Catherine. "Physical Education Knowledge Tests," *Research Quarterly*, VI (October, 1935).

529. GOLF

Murphy, Mary Agnes. "Criteria for Judging a Golf Knowledge Test," *Research Quarterly*, IV (December, 1933).

———. "Grading Student Achievement in Golf Knowledge," *Research Quarterly*, V (March, 1934).

Snell, Catherine. "Physical Education Knowledge Tests." *Research Quarterly*, VII (May, 1936).

530. GYMNASTICS

Zwarg, Leopold F. "Judging and Evaluation of Competitive Apparatus or Gymnastic Exercises," *Journal of Health and Physical Education*, VI (January, 1935).

531. HANDBALL

Phillips, Bernath E. *Fundamental Handball.* New York: A. S. Barnes and Company, 1937.

532. HOCKEY

Brown, Harriet M. "The Game of Ice Hockey," *Journal of Health and Physical Education*, VI (January, 1935).

Deitz, Dorothea, and Beryl Frech. "Hockey Knowledge Tests for Girls," *Journal of Health and Physical Education*, XI (June, 1940).

Grisier, Gertrude J. "The Construction of an Objective Test of Knowledge and Interpretation of the Rules of Field Hockey for Women," *Supplement to Research Quarterly*, V (March, 1934).

Schmithals, Margaret, and Esther French. "Achievement Tests in Field Hockey for College Women," *Research Quarterly*, XI (October, 1940).

Snell, Catherine. "Physical Education Knowledge Tests," *Research Quarterly*, VI (October, 1935).

533. HOCKEY OFFICIATING

French, Esther. "Knowledge for Field Hockey Officials." United States Field Hockey Association, 1939, 1940, 1941.

534. HORSEBACK RIDING

Snell, Catherine. "Physical Education Knowledge Tests," *Research Quarterly*, VII (May, 1936).

535. PHYSICAL FITNESS

Stradtman, Alan D., and T. K. Cureton. "A Physical Fitness Knowledge Test for Secondary School Boys and Girls," *Research Quarterly*, XXI (March, 1950).

536. PROFESSIONAL COURSES

French, Esther. "The Construction of Knowledge Tests in Selected Professional Courses in Physical Education," *Research Quarterly*, XIV (December, 1943).

537. SOCCER

Heath, Marjorie L., and Elizabeth G. Rodgers. "A Study in the Use of Knowledge and Skill Tests in Soccer," *Research Quarterly*, III (December, 1932).

Knighton, Marian. "Soccer Questions," *Journal of Health and Physical Education*, I (October, 1930).

Snell, Catherine. "Physical Education Knowledge Tests," *Research Quarterly*, VII (March, 1936).

538. SOFTBALL

Women's National Officials' Rating Committee. "Officials' Written Tests in Softball. . . ." (Mimeographed).

539. SWIMMING

Scott, M. Gladys. "Achievement Examinations for Elementary and Intermediate Swimming Classes," *Research Quarterly*, XI (May, 1940).

540. TEAM-GAME ACTIVITIES

Rodgers, Elizabeth G. "The Standardization and Use of Objective Type Information Tests in Team Game Activities," *Research Quarterly*, X (March, 1939).

541. TENNIS

Hewitt, Jack E. "Comprehensive Tennis Knowledge Test," *Research Quarterly*, VIII (October, 1937).

Scott, M. Gladys. "Achievement Examinations for Elementary and Intermediate Tennis Classes," *Research Quarterly*, XII (March, 1941).

Snell, Catherine. "Physical Education Knowledge Tests," *Research Quarterly*, VII (May, 1936).

Wagner, Miriam M. "An Objective Method of Grading Beginners in Tennis," *Journal of Health and Physical Education*, VI (March, 1935).

Women's National Officials' Rating Committee. "Officials' Written Tests in Tennis. . . ." (Mimeographed).

542. VOLLEYBALL

Snell, Catherine. "Physical Education Knowledge Tests," *Research Quarterly*, VII (March, 1936).

Women's National Officials' Rating Committee. "Officials' Written Tests in Volleyball. . . ." (Mimeographed).

543. EPILOGUE

Although the discussion in this chapter has been limited to the objective type of examination, the importance of the essay type of examination should not be minimized. Otherwise illiteracy, which has been associated with making an X, may well come to be associated with making a mark with a special kind of pencil on a special kind of paper.

CHAPTER 25

POTENTIALITY FOR DIFFERENT SPORTS

544. IN THIS CHAPTER are presented tests (1) for the determination of potentiality for sports, generally, and (2) for the determination of potentiality for specific sports. All the tests for potentiality for specific sports are for boys and men. With the exception of the tests for football and for wrestling, the same tests may be used for girls and for women, but the resulting scores will have to be modified as the result of experimentation.

GENERAL

545. The **McCloy General-motor-capacity Test** (see Chap. 12) is a useful test for the determination of potentiality for sports, generally, and especially for the determination of potentiality for sports that require a high degree of speed and of co-ordination.

546. Other factors being equal, a strong person can become a better athlete than can a weak person. Hence the **Intercollegiate, Rogers, and McCloy Strength Tests** are useful for the determination of immediate potentiality for such sports as football, wrestling, weight-throwing, and gymnastics.

Also, other factors being equal, a person whose muscles relevant to a specific activity are well developed can become more proficient in that activity than can a person in whom those muscles are less well developed; hence the usefulness of tests for measuring the strength of specific muscles. For example, a right-handed shot-putter needs to have the following right muscles especially well developed: anterior deltoid, coracobrachialis, pectoralis major, subscapularis, and serratus anterior. It should be remembered that most men and women are much less strong than they could be were they to seek systematically to build up their strength by appropriate methods of training. Hence strength at the time of testing should be considered in relationship to possible strength under favorable training conditions. (See also the formula for predicting potential strength, Sec. 289.)

The McCloy General-motor-capacity Test and the Intercollegiate, the Rogers, or the McCloy Strength Test should, in addition to the specific tests listed, be used with each of the sports discussed in this chapter.

547. The **speed of response time,** which is exceedingly important in many combative and competitive activities, may be tested by the usual psychological laboratory-methods (see Secs. 395-99).

548. BASEBALL

549. Throwing a baseball for distance. The ability to throw a ball fast is one of the skills required of a baseball player. This ability may be measured by the distance that a ball can be thrown, for the distance varies with the square of the velocity.[1]

550. The formula for the determination of baseball ability by the **Everett Baseball Test**[2] follows.

T-score = 1.16 Sargent Jump (cm.) + .021 baseball throw (ft.) − .27 McCloy Blocks Test (sec.) − 9.47.

An R of .616 was obtained between this test and ratings of the baseball ability of baseball players of a large university. If ratings of high-school players were used, this R would probably be about .8.

551. McCloy Pendulum Test for batting ability. A swinging pendulum is suspended from a frame with a target or a dial made of seven circular pieces of brass each insulated from the other (Fig. XLVIII, p. 323). This dial is connected to a piece of hollow pipe through which pass copper, insulated wires. These wires are connected with small electric bulbs, which are mounted on a panel and attached to a frame below the pendulum. The length of the pendulum can be varied from approximately three feet to almost five feet. The bull's-eye of the target or the dial is one inch in diameter, and each of the six rings is one-half inch wide. A transformer makes possible the use of an alternating current. Connected in circuit is an aluminum stylus, which, when contact is made with any of the rings of the dial, lights the appropriate light. This pendulum can be swung through any desired arc; thus the speed with which it passes the lowest point of the arc can be varied.

For the McCloy Pendulum Test for batting ability a pendulum $3\frac{1}{3}$ feet in length is used, and the stylus is set with liquid cement into the bat through a hole $\frac{3}{4}$ inch in diameter made six inches from the far end. The directions used for the test are as follows. The performer holds the bat in a manner similar to that used in hitting a baseball except that the hands are slightly separated in order that adequate contact between the stylus and the dial may be made. The score is the average number of points made in ten trials: nine points for the bull's-eye, seven points for the first ring

---

[1] Range $= \dfrac{V^2 \sin 2\theta}{g}$. The optimum angle between the ground and the flight of the ball is approximately 45 degrees. Since the sine of an angle of 90 degrees (i.e., 2θ) is 1, V equals, approximately, $\sqrt{Rg}$. For example, if a subject throws a ball 300 feet, the approximate V is 98 feet per second (i.e., $\sqrt{300 \times 32}$). Since the air resistance is not accounted for in this formula, the actual initial velocity is somewhat higher, but the computed velocities are relative to each other.

[2] Peter W. Everett, "The Prediction of Baseball Ability," *Research Quarterly*, March, 1952.

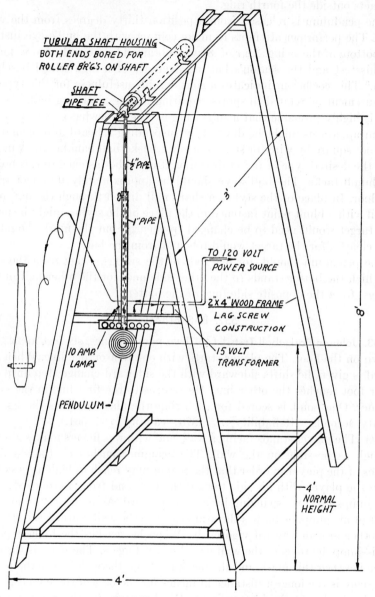

TUBULAR SHAFT HOUSING
BOTH ENDS BORED FOR
ROLLER BR'G'S. ON SHAFT

SHAFT
PIPE TEE

½" PIPE

1" PIPE

3'

TO 120 VOLT
POWER SOURCE

2"X 4" WOOD FRAME
LAG SCREW
CONSTRUCTION

8'

10 AMP.
LAMPS

15 VOLT
TRANSFORMER

PENDULUM

4'
NORMAL
HEIGHT

4'

FIGURE XLVIII. Pendulum Test for Batting Ability

outside the bull's-eye, five points for the next ring, and no points for contacts outside the fourth ring.

The pendulum is released from a position thirty degrees from the vertical. The performer attempts to make contact with the bull's-eye just at the bottom of the swing. An r of .81 was obtained between the scores made on this test and the season's batting averages of a high-school baseball team.[3] This coefficient indicates a considerable usefulness for this type of measurement as related to sports requiring hitting a moving ball.

It is highly probable that a substitute for the somewhat expensive pendulum apparatus might be devised by suspending a board approximately one foot square by wires or strings below a basketball bankboard. A paper with the desired type of target drawn on it could be fastened to this board by thumb tacks. The bull's-eye should be approximately four feet from the floor. In place of the stylus, a sharp nail driven through the bat, or a pencil with a blunt point fastened in the place of the stylus, might be used. The target would need to be changed frequently, but the mark should be seen clearly, for the target would rebound from the bat.

The pendulum should, for one half of the swings, swing *from* the side on which the batter stands *to* the other side and, for the other half of the swings, *from* the opposite side *toward* the batter.

552. BASKETBALL

553. Johnson Basketball Tests.[4] (A) Two parallel lines, six feet apart, are drawn on the floor. The player starts with one foot on one line. When the signal is given, he shifts sideward with the sideward change step until the other foot touches the other line. He returns to the first line in the same manner. One point is scored for each time the player crosses the lane in twenty seconds. (Reliability, $r = .870$; validity, $r = .561$.)

(B) The player stands facing a wall, and with wet fingers makes a mark as high as possible on the wall. The examiner pushes on the shoulder blades of the player in order that the player may reach as high as possible. Then the player with his side toward the wall and from a crouched position jumps upward, swinging both arms upward. As he nears the highest point of his jump, he pushes the arm nearer to the wall upward and thrusts the other arm downward vigorously. When he reaches the highest point of his jump, he touches the wall with his wet fingers. The score is the distance between this mark and the mark made on the wall before the jump. The score is the longest distance in inches for the best of three trials. This test should be practiced according to the directions for the Sargent Jump (see Sec. 159). (Reliability, $r = .916$; validity, $r = .537$.)

[3] Frank H. Bates, "The Relationship of Hand and Eye Coordinations to Accuracy in Baseball Batting" (M.A. Thesis, State University of Iowa, 1948).
[4] L. William Johnson, "Objective Basketball Tests for High School Boys" (M.A. Thesis, State University of Iowa, 1934).

(C) The player runs through the zigzag course indicated in Figure IX (p. 79) for thirty seconds. He follows the path indicated by the arrow, circles around the end hurdle, and returns along the same path. The score is the number of zones passed in thirty seconds. (Reliability, $r = .841$; validity, $r = .675$.)

(D) The Iowa-Brace Test. (Reliability, $r = .792$; validity, $r = .642$.)

If the battery of four tests is used, the formula is A (in points) $+ B$ (in.) $+ 6\ C$ (number of zones) $+ 4\ D$ (in points). Fifty points are given for a score of 213 (the median), and $\frac{1}{2}$ point is added to 50 for each score above 213 and $\frac{1}{2}$ point is subtracted from 50 for each score below 213. (Reliability, $r = .927$; validity, $r = .842$.)

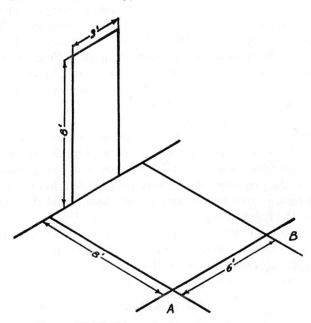

FIGURE XLIX. Edgren Ball-handling Test: Floor Markings

The Johnson Test is an excellent one for determining potentiality for basketball. If the subjects have participated rather extensively in basketball, the Johnson Test may be supplemented by the following test.

554. McCloy Revision of Edgren Basketball Test.[5] A line twelve feet long is drawn eight feet from and parallel to the wall (7 feet for girls). Two lines six feet apart (5½ feet for girls) are drawn at right angles to this line. Two other lines three feet apart and eight feet high are drawn vertically on the wall so that the zone enclosed by them is midway between the two lines at right angles to the wall. The two lines at right angles to

[5] H. D. Edgren, "An Experiment in the Testing of Ability and Progress in Basketball," *Research Quarterly*, March, 1932.

the wall should cross the eight-foot line and project two feet beyond this line. The letters A and B should be marked on the floor as shown in Fig. XLIX (p. 325).

The subject, with the ball in the hands, stands in area A facing the wall. On the sound of the whistle, he throws the ball against the wall at any height to the right of the three-foot zone. He catches the ball on the rebound somewhere in area B, and then throws the ball against the wall at any height to the left of the three-foot zone, and catches the ball in area A. The subject continues, alternating throws to the left and to the right. If the ball is dropped or rebounds wide, the subject recovers it, dribbles it back to area A or to area B, and continues throwing. The test is continued for thirty seconds. One scorer counts the number of times the ball hits the wall on the correct side of the zone lines. A second scorer counts the number of times the ball is thrown from any area other than that designated by the letters A or B. A timer indicates the time. The total score is the number of points counted by the first scorer minus the number of faults indicated by the second scorer. (Validity, r = .77. Reliability not computed.)

Since a knowledge of how to perform this test makes a considerable difference in the score, the examiner should demonstrate the best techniques for the test and give each person an opportunity to practice. In passing the ball with the right hand from area A to the opposite side of the wall zone, the performer should have his right foot in area A. His left foot should have started toward area B, but should not have touched the floor beyond the line limiting the A area.

The second best method is to use an underhand two-handed pass or a chest-push pass with the same footwork as that just described.

Standards for this test are not available, but the records of individuals being tested may be T-scored.

555. FOOTBALL

556. Brechler Test for backs and ends[6]

T-score = .126 McCloy Classification Index + .564 parallel-bar dips (no.) + 2.633 ten-second squat thrust (no.) + 1.164 Iowa-Brace Test (raw score) − 104.4.

An R of .770 was obtained between this formula and coaches' ratings of football ability.

557. Cormack Tests for linemen[7]

(1) T-score = .274 McCloy General-motor-capacity Score + .086 McCloy Dipping-strength Score (on parallel bars) − 44.4.

---

[6] Paul W. Brechler, "A Test to Determine Potential Ability in Football (Backs and Ends)" (M.A. Thesis, State University of Iowa, 1940).

[7] Herbert P. Cormack, "A Test to Determine Potential Ability in Football (Linemen)" (M.A. Thesis, State University of Iowa, 1940).

An R of .718 was obtained between this formula and coaches' ratings of linemen's ability.

(2) T-score = .062 McCloy Classification Index − 11.7 forty-yard dash (sec.) + 1.304 twelve-pound shot-put from a stand (ft.) + .034 McCloy Dipping-strength Score (on parallel bars) + 13.58.

An R of .831 was obtained between this formula and coaches' ratings of linemen's ability.

558. Hatley Test for backs and ends[8]

Score = .069 McCloy General-motor-capacity Score − 4.704 Cozens Dodging Run[9] (sec.) + .0761 twelve-pound shot-put (ft.) + standing broad jump (in.) + weight (lb.) − 75.41.

The mean score was 13.48, and the range was 7 to 28. An R of .8277 was obtained between this formula and the sum of the ratings (on a seven-point scale) of four judges. An r of .6785 was obtained between the McCloy General-motor-capacity Score and the sum of the ratings of the four judges.

559. Hatley Test for linemen[10]

Score = .1038 McCloy General-motor-capacity Score − 3.7262 Cozens Dodging Run (sec.) + .3372 twelve-pound shot-put (ft.) − 64.58. The mean was 12.04. An r of .6785 was obtained between this formula and the ratings of four judges.

560. GYMNASTICS

561. The **Wettstone Gymnastics Test**[11] consists of the following items:

(1) *Thigh girth.* The subject stands with the feet about one foot apart and with each foot supporting an equal amount of the weight of the body. The measurement, which is taken with a tape just touching the skin, is the circumference of the thigh just below the gluteal fold and parallel to the floor. The measurement is recorded in centimeters. (2) *Height* (see Secs. 591-92). The measurement is recorded in centimeters. (3) *Squat thrusts for ten seconds* (see Sec. 172). This item is scored in whole movements and in quarters of movements. (4) *Pull-ups.* This item is scored by the number of performances executed. (5) *Dipping* (on parallel bars) (see Sec. 294). This item is scored by the number of performances executed. (6) *Leg lifts.* The performer hangs with the ordinary

[8] Fred J. Hatley, "A Battery of Functional Tests for the Prediction of Football Potentiality" (M.A. Thesis, State University of Iowa, 1942).

[9] The Cozens Dodging Run is the same as the dodging run in the Johnson Basketball Tests, except that the distance from the starting line to the first hurdle is fifteen feet instead of nine feet. The time is taken from the start until the performer has run beyond the finish line. Each performer is timed individually with a stop watch.

[10] Hatley, *loc. cit.*

[11] Eugene Wettstone, "Tests for Predicting Potential Ability in Gymnastics and Tumbling," *Research Quarterly,* December, 1938.

grasp from a horizontal bar. Keeping the lower legs extended, he flexes the thighs until the thighs and lower legs are parallel to the floor. This item is scored by the number of times that the thighs are so flexed.

The regression equation that follows is a conversion of the Wettstone regression equation into the form of a T-score.

$$\frac{-2.048 \ (100 \times \text{thigh girth})}{\text{height}} + 1.15 \ (4 \times \text{squat-thrust score}) + 1.804$$

(pull-ups + dips + leg lifts) + 75.94

An r of .7893 was obtained between this formula and ratings of gymnastics ability of a State University of Iowa gymnastics team with a small range of abilities. If the range of abilities had been greater, the coefficient of multiple correlation would undoubtedly have been higher than it was.

The T-score for the best gymnast was 62; for the average gymnast, 59; and for the poorest gymnast, 32. Hence a T-score of 50 represents excellence in gymnastics ability.

562. TRACK-AND-FIELD ATHLETICS

General

563. *McCloy General-motor-capacity Test.* Performers who do not have high motor quotients almost never become proficient track-and-field athletes.

564. *The Sargent Jump and the McCloy Classification Index* may be combined according to the following formulas for the prediction of track-and-field ability:

10 Sargent Jump (cm.) + McCloy Classification Index *or*
25 Sargent Jump (in.) + McCloy Classification Index

Table 110

TRACK-AND-FIELD POTENTIALITY: PREDICTION TABLES
(BOYS 12 TO 18 AND OVER)

Per-centiles	12 yrs.	13 yrs.	14 yrs.	15 yrs.	16 yrs.	17 yrs.	18 yrs. and over
10th	909	956	1055	1112	1192	1249	1260
20th	947	1000	1103	1169	1243	1298	1308
30th	976	1035	1140	1208	1281	1334	1350
40th	1002	1065	1173	1241	1314	1367	1376
50th	1020	1093	1203	1273	1346	1397	1405
60th	1044	1127	1234	1299	1372	1422	1428
70th	1070	1151	1266	1332	1405	1454	1460
80th	1099	1186	1303	1372	1443	1490	1496
90th	1137	1236	1351	1428	1494	1539	1544
95th	1170	1275	1399	1472	1537	1580	1584
97th	1192	1302	1422	1501	1566	1603	1612
98th	1204	1323	1444	1519	1589	1625	1628
99th	1231	1354	1477	1553	1618	1658	1660

In Table 110 (p. 328) under the column headed by the age of the boy, the number should be located that corresponds with the total points computed by one of the above formulas. Then in the left-hand column opposite this number may be read the percentile, which predicts the boy's track-and-field potentiality. Performers at the fiftieth percentile are about average, while those at the ninetieth or the ninety-fifth percentile are probably varsity track-and-field material.

R's of about .70 have been obtained between the formulas given in this section and total points in four track-and-field events.

565. R's averaging .85 have been obtained between the following specific track-and-field events and the items suggested for their measurements. Such coefficients have been obtained only after the specific events have been adequately practiced.

High hurdles and high jump. Items important for performance in these events are a high general-motor-capacity score, height, and arm strength.

Low hurdles. The McCloy General-motor-capacity Test or the combination of the McCloy Classification Index with the Sargent Jump may be used for the determination of potentiality in low hurdling.

Pole vault. The McCloy General-motor-capacity Score, the short form of the McCloy Athletic-strength Score (see Sec. 282), and tumbling ability may be used for the determination of potentiality in pole vaulting.

Javelin throw. Throwing a sixteen-inch softball for distance may be used for the determination of potentiality in throwing the javelin.

Shot-put and discus throw. The McCloy General-motor-capacity Score and the short form of the McCloy Athletic-strength Score may be used for the determination of potentiality for these weight events.

566. WRESTLING

567. The **Sievers Wrestling Test**[12] is made up of the following items.

McCloy *Athletic-strength Quotient* (see Sec. 284).

Front-and-back leaning-rest. Two parallel lines ten inches apart and four feet long are drawn on the floor. With the hands on the floor between these lines, the performer starts from a front leaning-rest position. He turns to the right to a back leaning-rest position (1 point), returns to the starting position (1 point), turns to the left to a back leaning-rest position (1 point), and returns to the starting position (1 point), and repeats these movements as many times as possible in ten seconds. One point is deducted for each time that the performer places any part of his hands outside the parallel lines.

Sustained grip. A Smedley Hand Dynamometer with two pointers[13] is used for this test. One pointer of the dynamometer is set at two thirds of

[12] Harry L. Sievers, "The Measurement of Potential Wrestling Ability" (M.A. Thesis, State University of Iowa, 1934).

[13] Obtainable from C. H. Stoelting Company, 424 North Homan Avenue, Chicago 24.

the grip strength recorded for the athletic-strength score. This grip strength is that of the right hand of a right-handed performer and that of the left hand of a left-handed performer. At the signal "Go" the performer raises the variable pointer on the dynamometer to the pointer that has been set at two thirds of the grip strength. The examiner starts a stop watch with the signal "Go," and every five seconds states the position of the movable pointer. If the movable pointer drops, even momentarily, more than two kilograms (4.4 lb.), the test is stopped; or if the performer permits the variable pointer to fall any distance below the fixed pointer and to remain there for three or four seconds, the test is terminated.

This test is probably a fairly valid measure of competitive spirit.

The regression equation for predicting wrestling ability follows: T-score = .2282 McCloy Athletic-strength Quotient + .8853 front-and-back leaning-rest + .143 sustained grip + 2.31.

A T-score of 50 represents better-than-average wrestling ability for a high-school or a college wrestling team, and T-scores of 70 to 80 represent exceptionally good wrestling ability. An R of .972 was obtained between this formula and coaches' ratings of wrestling ability.

In the use of the tests listed in this chapter it must be remembered that the item of strength can, by means of progressive-resistance exercises, be developed 70 to 80 per cent in three or four months in the average person. Hence if the sport is one that requires strength, a performer with a high motor quotient can usually develop the necessary amount of strength. If the sport is one that requires speed, a performer with a low motor quotient seldom can become proficient in it.

568. For tests of "athletics educability," see Sections 243 to 247.

PART **V**

Health

CHAPTER **26**

INTRODUCTION

569. IN EDUCATIONAL agencies, programs of health are usually divided into three areas: examination, service, and instruction. Sometimes the examination is a part of the service. The examination and the service should be under the supervision of a physician, who may, in turn, utilize the assistance of the nurse and of the teacher. Instruction is usually under the direction of educators, and frequently under the direction of physical educators.

Measurement in the field of health is usually confined to the following areas: (1) the medical examination (see Chap. 27), (2) anthropometric measurements of physical and nutritional status (see Chap. 28), (3) tests for use in the health service (see Chaps. 21 and 23), (4) tests of health knowledge (see Chap. 29), and (5) ratings or records of health practices and habits (see Chap. 29).

570. SELECTION OF TESTS

The criteria for the selection of tests in the field of health are the same as those for the selection of tests in any area of education (see Chap. 3). The objectives of the tests in the five areas listed above are discussed in the chapters indicated in parentheses. Because of the various ways in which departments of health education are organized, it is not feasible at the present time to propose a standardized program of measurement in the field of health.

CHAPTER 27

MEDICAL EXAMINATIONS[1]

571. The medical examination, perhaps the most important measurement in the health-education program, must, of necessity, be performed by a competent physician, who should consider the examination to be not only an effort to detect disease but also a part of the program of education. Among the functions of the medical examination may be included the following: (1) to detect indications of conditions that may impair the health of the person or hinder his development, and to prescribe appropriate remedial measures; (2) to check the progress or the retrogression of the physical status of each person year by year in order both to serve the person himself and to indicate one aspect of the educational efficiency of the institution; (3) to detect defects that may lead to severe physical disorders and to prescribe appropriate remedial measures to avert the disorders; (4) to detect and to eliminate and/or to correct such handicaps as defective vision, adenoids, focal infections, and defective hearing in order that the general-educational efficiency of the institution may be raised; (5) to serve as a partial basis for the admission of students to institutions with limited enrollments; and (6) to detect by daily inspection, if at all practicable, in the elementary and the secondary schools, indications of infectious disease.

The type of blank used for recording the results of a medical examination depends in part upon the preferences of the physician and in part upon the time that can be given to the examination. If the examinations are cursory, lasting about five minutes for a person, the examiner cannot, of course, consider so many items as he could if the examination lasted from twenty to thirty minutes for each person. The scoring blank presented in this chapter (Fig. L, pp. 334-35) is not intended to be a model but rather to be suggestive of a device whereby medical examinations may be scored somewhat objectively.

The purpose of scoring the medical examination is not only to increase the efficiency of the examination from the standpoint of the examiner but also to increase its motivating power from the standpoint of the person examined. If the results of a medical examination are expressed in general

---

[1] This chapter originally was prepared by Dr. S. M. Woo and the senior author in collaboration with a group of college physicians who studied several suggested drafts and made numerous suggestions. Minor revisions were made after two years of further study by the department of medicine of a university.

terms to the person examined and to the parents of the person examined, the experience of school physicians has been that little is done to correct the defects indicated.[2] If the results of a medical examination are expressed in somewhat objective terms and then scored, the person examined, the parents of the person examined, and the nonmedical administrative officers (the school nurse, the teacher of physical education, the chairman of the health committee) are motivated in a definite way to undertake remedial measures. If each physician uses his own code in recording the results of an examination, the results are meaningful to him but probably not to anyone else attempting to use the results, and the results obtained by one physician cannot, for the purpose of comparative statistical studies, be combined with the results obtained by another physician.

The first part of the scoring blank presented in this chapter concerns a personal medical history. The purpose of the history is to provide the examiner with a background for arriving at proper conclusions as to interpretations of other phases of the examination; that is, many of the diseases indicated in the history have common sequelae. Each item should be carefully explained by a physician or by a qualified layman. In the upper grades this part of the blank may then be filled in by the pupils under the direction of the teacher. In the lower grades it probably has to be filled out by a parent, who should, if possible, be present at the time of examination.

The items in the scoring blank presented in this chapter were selected on the basis of a statistical study of seven hundred very complete histories of college students. In the analysis of these histories many items were found which should, theoretically, be productive of much useful information but which did not give any pertinent information whatsoever. The items that were retained for the blank in this chapter met the following criteria: (1) reliable information about the item can be provided by the person being examined or by his parents; and (2) the information relative to the item can be of service to the physician in the diagnosis and/or in further aid to the person being examined. Items that were significant statistically only were not included in the blank.

572. If a code is used for the scoring of the medical examination, the results can be expressed with a fair degree of uniformity. It is strongly emphasized, however, that such uniformity will be attained only if the physician is sufficiently interested to study the scoring method carefully and to attempt to utilize it consistently. In studies of the code for scoring suggested in this chapter, the reliability of the scoring has been as high as the reliability of the procedures of the examination. The scoring device is such that the physician who has neither the time nor the inclination to go

---

[2] *Physical Defects, The Pathway to Correction* (American Child Health Association).

Code:

o   No defect found
oo   Defect corrected
?   Questionable
1   Slight defect
2   Moderate defect
3   Severe defect
x   Refer to follow-
       up agent
NW   Not examined

Name _Smith, John_ Date of birth _8/22/22_ No. _114_

Date of last successful vaccination _4 years ago_

How many times a week do you defecate? _Daily_

Does any member of your household or any close relative have tuberculosis? _No_

Underline any of the following diseases which you have had, Underline twice if severe:

1. Chronic cough. 2. Spitting of blood. 3. Afternoon fever. 4. Chronic headache. 5. Insomnia. 6. Malaria. 7. Frequent or painful urination. 8. Typhoid fever. 9. Tonsilitis. 10. Rheumatic fever. 11. Pains in bones and joints. 12. Ear disease.

Date of examination	11/30/1938								Health Score	Disease Score
Age of student	16 Yrs. 3 Mo.				Yrs.	Mo.				
	1	2	3	Score	1	2	3	Score	100	0
Height	165 cms.									
Weight	57 Kgms.								90	10
Normal weight	59 Kgms.								80	20
1. Weight index Overweight (3) Underweight (6)	0								1938 70	30
									60	40
Chest girth Inspiration Expiration Mean	77 71 74								50	50
									40	60
Lung capacity	206									
Normal lung capacity	225								30	70
2. Lung capacity index (4)	91		4						20	80
3. Muscular development (3)	1		3						10	90
4. Posture (5)	2		10							
5. Feet (3)	0								0	100
6. Clubbed Fingers										

FIGURE L. Health Examination: Sample Score Card

	1	2	3	Score	1	2	3	Score
7. Vision (2) R L	20/20 20/20							
8. Hearing (1) R L	20/20 20/20							
9. Otitis media (4)	0							
10. Scalp (1)	0							
11. Eyes Conjunctivitis (2) Trachoma (3)	0							
12. Nose Chronic inflammation (1) Obstruction (3)	1			1				
13. Teeth C—Caries (1) P—Pyorrhoea (3) A—Abscess (2)	8765432112345678 8765432112345678			2	8765432112345678 8765432112345678			
14. Tonsils Enlarged (2) Infected (3)	0							
15. Adenoids (3)	0							
16. Lymph glands Enlarged (1) Suppurating (4)	1			1				
17. Lungs (10)	0							
18. Heart Functional (3) Organic (10)	0							
19. Hernia (3)	0							
20. Genitalia (1)	0							
21. Skin (1)	0							
22. Color mucous membranes (3)	2			6				
23. Feces ( )	MM							

Total Score: 27
Health Score: 73
Miscellaneous:

FIGURE L (Continued)

335

into the matter in great detail may still use the code with fair accuracy. This statement should in no wise be interpreted to mean that the physician who wishes to record his findings in great detail should not do so.

The suggested code is as follows: no evidence of any defect = 0; corrected defect (e.g., adequately removed tonsils, vision corrected by refraction) = 00; suspicious findings, but no conclusive evidence of a present defect = ?; item not examined = W; minor defect (e.g., slight pit cavities in the teeth, 20/30 vision, slightly enlarged but not infected tonsils) = 1; minor defect requiring further examination and treatment = 1X; defect of moderate severity = 2; defect of moderate severity requiring further examination and treatment = 2X; defect of great severity = 3; defect of great severity requiring further examination and treatment = 3X. If the examiner is not sure as to whether a defect should be scored 1 or 2, the defect may be scored 1.5; whether a defect should be scored 2 or 3, 2.5.

The method of scoring is a simple one and is not presented to be an adequate basis for details of treatment. However, recommendations for details of treatment are not generally, according to the statements of numerous school physicians, based on what can be recorded in the short time given to such examinations in the schools. The important thing in a school examination is *that the defects be found and referred to the proper medical authorities.* The physician treating the condition subsequently, even though he be the same person who conducts the original examination, makes an unhurried and a detailed examination before he prescribes treatment. For example, if a physician finds numerous râles in the lungs, he marks the condition 2X or 3X, and does not at the time of the examination need to spend further time upon a detailed analysis, which is left to the physician to whom the case is referred. If a physician finds tonsils enlarged about halfway from their normal condition to the midline, he marks the condition 2X, indicating that the throat should be examined in detail later by a competent specialist.

573. After each of the defects listed in the scoring blank is a number in parentheses for indicating the approximate importance of the defect. These weightings were based on a consensus of a large number of practitioners of internal medicine. A defect of the lungs, for example, has a weighting of 10. If the lungs are marked with a 2, then the score for the condition is 20 (i.e., 2 × 10). Infected tonsils have a weighting of 3. If this item is marked with a 3, the score is 9 (i.e., 3 × 3). Some items may appear to have too low weightings. Such defects, however, are generally accompanied by other defects, with the result that the total score is high; for example, pulmonary tuberculosis, which has a weighting of 10, is usually accompanied by such defects as poor posture, poor muscular development, underweight, and enlarged glands. Some items, such as pyorrhea, are given high weightings because they are not usually accompanied by other defects or because they are difficult to cure. Other items, such as adenoids, are given low weightings because they are easily remedied.

574. The health score is 100 minus the disease score. A health score of 60 is considered to be a "failing score." It has been found that persons are more likely to undergo remedial measures if they are told that their health is a certain percentage, for example 62 per cent, of what it should be, than if they are just told what defects they have. This finding is especially in evidence if the persons are encouraged to have the corrections made and to have their health re-scored, for no deduction is made from the health score for defects that have been corrected.

The results of the examination may be expressed graphically by the use of horizontal lines under the code numbers indicating the severity of the defects. These lines should be extended to the right to the column headed by the number corresponding to the code number assigned to the defect; hence the severity of the defect is represented by the length of the line. In the scoring blank in this chapter the horizontal lines are in heavy black, but it is suggested that red lines would be more effective than the black lines.

575. EXAMINATION

In the examination blank the items beginning with "age of student" and ending with "hearing" may be checked by a competent layman. Directions for scoring the items follow.

(1) **Weight index,** (2) **Breathing-capacity index.** Directions for taking the anthropometric measurements involved and for computing the designated indices may be found in Chapter 28. If the "present health" of persons of high-school age or older is to be assessed, the McCurdy-Larson Test (see Sec. 502) or the McCloy Test (see Sec. 488) may be used. The items should be scored according to the standards given with those tests. If a defect of the heart is suspected, the pulse-ratio test (see Sec. 495) may be used to detect evidence of noncompensated hearts, although the physician's examination is the most important procedure.

(3) **Muscular development.** Excellent or very good $= 0$; good or better than average $= \frac{1}{2}$; average $= 1$; poor $= 2$; very poor $= 3$. Muscular development can be scored more validly on the basis of the strength quotient than on the basis of inspection. The scoring may be as follows: strength quotient over $100 = 0$; 95 to $99 = \frac{1}{2}$; 85 to $94 = 1$; 75 to $84 = 2$; below $75 = 3$.

(4) **Posture.** The standards for scoring posture may be any of those suggested in Chapter 21. If the examiner is not accustomed to scoring posture objectively, he can perhaps use to the best advantage the four diagrams illustrating A to D posture (see Secs. 455-59).

(5) **Feet.** The presence and the severity of the following conditions

should be indicated: (1) deformed feet, (2) pronated feet, (3) fallen longitudinal arches, (4) metatarsal pain, and (5) epidermophytosis or "athlete's foot." (The fifth item is a skin disease but is included here because it may be conveniently included in the foot examination.)

(6) **Clubbed fingers** (Fig. LI, p. 338). The defect of clubbed fingers is often closely associated with an organic heart lesion, although it is not a certain sign of heart disease. A person with clubbed fingers should be examined by a physician. This item is marked positively or negatively, followed by an X, but no deduction from the health score is made for it.

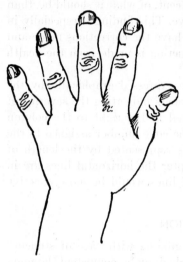

(7) **Vision.** In the Snellen type of chart, which is commonly used, there are several rows of letters which the person being examined tries to read with each eye from a distance of twenty feet. A person is considered to have "passed" a row if he reads it with not more than a 20-per-cent error. The vision is recorded as a fraction: the numerator is the distance of the person being examined from the chart, and the denominator is the distance at which the last line that can

FIGURE LI. Clubbed Fingers

be read with not more than a 20-per-cent error should be clear to one with normal vision. Thus, if the person being examined is twenty feet from the chart and can read only the row that should be visible forty feet from the chart, his vision is recorded as 20/40. Each eye should be tested, and the results for each eye recorded.

In a study conducted by the United States Public Health Service,[3] it was found that, in the testing of eyes by means of the Snellen Chart only, myopia (nearsightedness) was readily detected, but hyperopia (farsightedness) and slight astigmatism were frequently missed. It was further found that if the eye muscles of accommodation were relaxed by means of a cycloplegic, there was practically a normal distribution of visual acuity in terms of percentage of acuity. It is therefore recommended that hyperopia be checked in the following manner.

Two lenses, one of +.75 diopter and the other of −.75 diopter, are used. After the vision has been tested by the Snellen Chart, the convex or plus lens is placed in front of the eye. If the vision is improved with the glass or if it is made no worse, then no further testing of that eye is necessary: the subject is farsighted. If the vision is neither improved

[3] Grover A. Kempt and Others, "A Special Study of the Vision of School Children," *Public Health Reports*, July 6 1928.

nor made worse, the score is 1. If the vision is improved, the score is 2. If the vision is blurred, the minus lens is used. If then the vision is improved, the person being examined is at least not farsighted, and if the vision is less than 20/20 he is probably either near-sighted or astigmatic, or both. The scores for vision checked by this test are as follows: normal vision = 0; normal vision with, but not without, glasses = 00; 20/30 vision = 1; 20/40 vision = 2; under 20/40 vision = 3.

A very convenient method for the measurement of visual acuity is afforded by an instrument called the Keystone Telebinocular,[4] which is a form of stereopticon. The slides used enable the examiner to determine rapidly the following items about vision, and with little chance of cheating upon the part of the subject: the usable vision of each of the eyes at the far point, the usable vision at the near point, color perception, simultaneous perception with the two eyes, vertical imbalance, lateral imbalance, fusion at the near point and the far point, and a rough estimate of stereopsis or depth perception. The instrument may be used for the testing of vision of small children or of illiterates since the test is not dependent on the ability to read. At the far point, usable vision that is due to normal eyes cannot be differentiated by the instrument from that due to hyperopia.

The Keystone Telebinocular Test, like the other tests of vision listed in this chapter, is a screening test: persons failing the test or seeming to be subnormal in vision should be referred to an oculist.

(8) **Hearing** (a) *Whispering test.* A rough test, which may be used when no more accurate method is available, may be set up by having the examiner first determine how loudly he must whisper to be just heard at a distance of twenty feet by a person with normal hearing. The test must be conducted in a room that is absolutely quiet. The subject is directed to close his eyes, and to close his far ear with his finger while the examiner whispers questions or directions. If the subject does not respond, the examiner moves closer and repeats the questions or directions until the subject does hear them. The distance at which the subject responds to the whispering is used as the numerator of a fraction, and the "normal" distance of twenty feet used as the denominator. Each ear is tested separately.

Since a whisper usually has a decidedly higher pitch than does a vocal utterance, and since some persons have normal hearing for low pitches, but not for high pitches, a person who cannot hear a high-pitched whisper may hear a lower-pitched vocal utterance fairly satisfactorily. (There is little pitch difference between whispers of men and women.) Similarly, there may be a difference between the acuity of hearing a low-pitched male voice and that of hearing a high-pitched soprano female voice. Hence in case of doubt concerning the results of tests of vocal utterances,

[4] Manufactured by the Keystone View Company, Meadville, Pennsylvania.

the tests may be made at greater distances than the whispering tests were made.

(b) *Group voice test.* The subjects are seated in a quarter circle and about twenty feet from the tester. Each subject sits with (for example) his left ear toward the tester, and closes the right ear with a finger. The tester, with a piece of thin gauze in front of his mouth to eliminate the possibility of lip reading by the subjects, reads two-place numbers (e.g., 24, 85, 97) in a moderately low-speaking voice that should be heard at a distance of perhaps sixty feet. As he reads the numbers, the subjects all attempt to write them down. The tester lowers his voice progressively, and continues to say the numbers until he has lowered his voice to a faint utterance. The tester, just before each lowering of his voice, should say in a loud voice: "Now write the number 40 and encircle it," (35, 30, etc.) so that there will be a code for identifying the distance at which the various subjects can no longer hear well enough to record the test numbers accurately. The last test numbers recorded accurately (provided that the preceding numbers were correct) determine the lowest degree of loudness that is heard by the subject. Since the majority of a school population has normal hearing, the point at which the small minority begins to have trouble hearing distinctly may be taken as the lower limit of normal hearing. Those who show hearing losses may be tested individually later, using the method for individuals described in *a*, or using one of the more accurate methods described in *c* to *e*.

(c) *Watch-ticking test.* The examiner determines at what distance a person with normal hearing can hear the ticking of a given watch. The subject keeps his eyes closed and reports when he can hear the ticking, and when he can no longer hear it. The examiner varies the distances (i.e., sometimes increases them and sometimes decreases them) to eliminate the influence of imagination upon the part of the subject. The distance at which the subject can hear the ticking is used as the numerator, and the distance at which a person with normal hearing can hear the ticking is used as the denominator. The ticking of a watch is a high-pitched sound and the same precautions should be observed that were mentioned in connection with the whispering test.

(d) *Tuning-fork test.* Directions for testing hearing with a tuning fork are the same as those for testing hearing by the ticking of a watch. If deafness is found, the tuning fork is again struck, and the handle touched to the mastoid bone behind the ear. If with the deaf ear the subject hears the sound as well as, or better than, with the normal ear (the latter condition is often the case), the defect is usually in the middle ear and can generally be helped. If the subject cannot hear the sound so well with the deaf ear as with the normal ear, the defect is probably in the internal ear, and treatment may be difficult.

The tests for hearing described in *a* to *d* are scored as follows: normal hearing at a standard distance = 0; hearing at one half of the standard distance = 1; hearing at one fourth of the standard distance = 2; hearing at one eighth of the standard distance = 3. The teacher should investigate seating positions in the room for any pupils with ratings of 2 or more.

(e) *Audiometer.*[5] The phonograph audiometer, which is frequently used to detect auditory acuity, is equipped with headphones (as many as forty persons may be tested at one time). The audiometer calls out numbers which are recorded on paper by the subjects. As the sounds become fainter and fainter, the subject whose hearing is defective begins to miss numbers and either fails to record them, or records them incorrectly. The lack of auditory acuity at the different pitch ranges cannot be differentiated by this instrument.

There are several types of elaborate audiometers for testing persons one at a time. These not only test the auditory acuity in each ear, but test auditory acuity over a fairly large range of pitches. For example, it is rather common to find in older adults that the auditory acuity for high-pitched sounds is decidedly less than that for the lower-pitched sounds. Some persons hear over a larger range of pitches than do other persons. The audiometer may also be adapted to mass testing and is much to be preferred to the phonograph type, for the test covers both a larger frequency and a larger intensity range than does the phonograph type. The loss of hearing is in terms of *decibels.*

The numerical scoring may be as follows: loss in decibels of 0 to 5 at 1000 cycles per second [6] = 0; 6 to 15 = 1, 16 to 25 = 2; 26 and over = 3.

(9) **Otitis media.** *Intermittent flow* from one ear only = 1; intermittent flow from both ears = 2. *Excessive wax* = X. Any other ear disorders are scored according to severity and noted separately under "Other Findings."

(10) **Scalp.**[7] *Ringworm:* fewer than three isolated patches = 2; more than three isolated patches = 3. *Pediculosis:* if the nits are hard to find = 1; nits moderate in extent = 2; nits very plentiful = 3. If any other defect of the scalp is found, it may be written in either here or under "Other Findings."

(11) **Eyes.** All nonspecific acute inflammations of the conjunctiva and chronic infections presenting only slight redness = 1; chronic infections of moderate and severe degree = 2 or 3; trachoma = 3.

(12) **Nose.** *Chronic rhinitis:* moderate catarrh = 1; severe catarrh = 2;

---

[5] Information concerning audiometers may be obtained from the Maico Company Incorporated, 21 North Third Street, Minneapolis 1, Minnesota, from the Sonotone Corporation, Elmsford, New York, or from the Audiometer Sales Corporation, Minneapolis, Minnesota.

[6] It may be considered to be better to average the loss at 500, 1000, and 2000 cycles, which frequencies cover the range most essential for understanding speech.

[7] Since many persons object strenuously to anyone's examining the hair for nits or other abnormalities, much of the examination of the scalp should be conducted inconspicuously during the examination of the ears.

ozena = 3. *Obstruction:* unilateral and only partial = 1; unilateral and total, or bilateral and partial = 2; bilateral and total = 3. *Polyps and defective septum* = 1, 2, or 3.

(13) **Teeth.** *Caries:* small pit cavities not through the enamel, or dirty green or brown stain = 1; cavities large enough to permit a probe the size of the point of a pencil to be moved around in them = 2; badly broken-down tooth or only a stump or broken root left = 3. *Pyorrhea:* slight evidence of pus around the gums = 1; slight evidence of pus around the gums and slight receding of the gums = 2; teeth loose in their sockets = 3. *Abscess:* gumboil without other symptoms = 1; gumboil with a slightly swollen cheek = 2; gumboil with a badly swollen cheek or other involvement = 3. An abscess should always be scored if there is a history of recent pain in an unrepaired tooth.

(14) **Tonsils.** *Enlarged:* slight enlargement, but not interfering with the breathing = 1; enlargement halfway to median line = 2; enlargement nearly to, to, or past the median line = 3. *Infected:* chronically infected with pus pockets in the crypts = 2; broken down or caseous = 3.

(15) **Adenoids.** Impossible to ascertain the cause of an apparent obstruction = 2; some adenoid tissue, but not obstructing the breathing and not giving any facial change = 1.

(16) **Lymph glands, cervical.** *Enlarged:* as large as a shelled peanut = 1; as large as a chestnut = 2; as large as a walnut = 3. *Suppurating* = 3. Large and softened glands not discharging outwardly = 3.

(17) **Lungs.** The lung lesion most commonly found is active tuberculosis. The scoring should be understood to mean probable active tuberculosis only until a sputum test or X ray has given a positive result, but it should be scored as if it were positive, for the treatment should be undertaken if the signs and symptoms be present, regardless of whether or not the bacilli are found.

If only signs (as dullness or râles, etc.) are found, with or without morning cough, but no symptoms, as chronic cough, hemoptysis, fever, night sweats, loss of weight and strength, etc. = 1; if signs, with or without morning cough, with any other symptoms = 2; if signs with or without morning cough with hemoptysis, fever over 100, weight index under 92 per cent, or any other combinations of symptoms = 3.

(18) **Heart.** *Functional* (if there is doubt, heart defects should be scored as organic rather than functional): slight arhythmia, tachycardia, etc., unknown to the examined = 1; moderate arhythmia, tachycardia, etc., giving symptoms on exertion (usually known to the examined) = 2; severe arhythmia, tachycardia, etc. causing distress on exertion = 3. *Organic:* slight and perfectly compensated, causing no symptoms on exertion = 1; compensation with hypertrophy, with shortness of breath upon slight exertion = 2; signs of decompensation with ordinary activities = 3.

(19) **Hernia.** Orifice larger than usual, without other finding = 1; moderate or severe = 2 or 3; omentum or intestine protruding = 3.

(20) **Genitalia.** Phimosis, hydrocele, etc., scored according to the amount of interference with function or the amount of nervous irritation produced: slight = 1; moderate = 2; severe = 3; conditions requiring surgery = 2 or 3; venereal diseases scored under "Other Findings."

(21) **Skin.** Beginning processes, strictly localized = 1; processes of moderate severity on more than one part, or well spread = 2; widespread infections or infections with secondary infections = 3.

(22) **Color of mucous membranes.** Since the color of the skin is influenced by such items as the room temperature, nervousness, and recency of exercise, it is difficult to score accurately. Furthermore, persons with thick mucous membranes appear to have paler lips than those with thin mucous membranes. This item should be checked by the teachers. Color of lips and inner eyelids: slightly pale = 1; moderately pale = 2; very pale = 3. The hemoglobin test should be used for suspicious cases: 10 per cent below the normal of the locality = 1; 20 per cent below normal = 2; 30 per cent below normal = 3. Altitude and perhaps other factors affect this test, the hemoglobin being lower at sea level than at heights above sea level. If the local standard is not used, the use of the Tallqvist Scale, with 80 per cent taken as normal, is recommended. Chlorosis should be scored under this heading of color.

576. OTHER FINDINGS

The scoring for the most commonly found diseases not included in the examination blank follow. The numbers in parentheses are the weightings for the diseases similar to those indicated in parentheses on the examination blank.

Arrested tuberculosis (5). No symptoms for one year, normal weight, signs in one small area only (e.g., dullness in one apex) = 1; no symptoms for one year—extensive, but not active, signs = 2; no symptoms for less than one year—weakness = 3.

Pott's disease and other forms of bone tuberculosis; active (10); arrested (6). Moderately severe = 1; very severe = 2; extremely severe = 3.

Pleurisy (4). If pleurisy is found, a careful search for pulmonary tuberculosis should be made. Slight lesion, with no general symptoms (e.g., fever) = 1; extensive lesion, considerable pain, no fever or other symptoms = 2; constitutional symptoms (e.g., daily fever, loss of weight), no lung signs of tuberculosis = 3.

Chronic bronchitis; local (3); over all of lungs (6). Not inconvenient to subject, no symptoms other than cough = 1; distressing to subject, no loss of weight, no other symptoms than cough = 2; loss of weight and other symptoms of constitutional disturbances = 3.

Chronic laryngitis (2). No signs other than slight redness, no symptoms other than slight huskiness of voice = 1; larynx red and somewhat swollen, voice very much affected = 2; nontuberculous ulcers, which may result in scarring and in permanent voice deterioration = 3. Tuberculous ulcers should be scored like tuberculosis of the lungs.

Chronic indigestion (3). Occasional and easily controlled = 1; continuous, not particularly distressing = 2; severe, causing patient to go to bed = 3.

Chronic appendicitis (4). Occasional flare-ups = 1; frequent flare-ups, no fever = 2; severe flare-ups, fever and other signs = 3.

Chronic constipation (3). One movement every other day = 1; one movement every three days = 2; one movement not oftener than every four days = 3.

Ascites (5). Slight swelling in one part of body = 1; moderate swelling in one or more parts of body = 2; excessive swelling in one or more parts of body = 3.

Benign goiter (1). Slightly noticeable on careful inspection = 1; slightly noticeable at first glance = 2; large = 3.

Hyperthyroidism (4).[8] Slight tremors or other nervous symptoms, no exophthalmos = 1; marked nervous systems, fast heart = 2; severe symptoms and signs = 3.

Hypothyroidism (4).[8] Discoverable only by functional tests = 1; easily diagnosed but not severe symptoms of *beginning* cretinism or myxedema = 2; marked or severe = 3.

Bone defects (2). Only the bone defects not listed elsewhere should be included here. Slight defect = 1; defect slightly hindering the use of a part of the body = 2; defect markedly hindering the use of a part of the body = 3.

Abdominal findings other than such diseases as appendicitis are not included in the list, for they are seldom diagnosed in a routine examination. If abdominal difficulties are suspected, the examinee should undergo special examination. Acute and temporary findings, such as measles and rhinitis (acute), are not deducted from the score.

---

[8] *Hyper- and hypothyroidism.* If the basal metabolic rate is one of the aiding criteria in connection with a diagnosis of hyperthyroidism or hypothyroidism, a cardiovascular test of basal metabolic rate may be useful (see Chap. 23, Secs. 505-08).

CHAPTER 28

ANTHROPOMETRY

577. THE RELATIONSHIP of anthropometric measurements to the appraisement of physical status was discussed in Chapter 26.

Anthropometric measurements consist of objective measurements of structures and of functions of the body. The measurement of structures includes such items as weight, total height, and the width, the depth, and the circumference of the chest. The measurement of function includes such items as pulse rate, arterial and venous blood pressures, muscular strength, basal metabolic rate estimated from cardiovascular variables, posture, and breathing capacity.

The anthropometric examination is a supplement to, and not a substitute for, the medical examination. It may, however, and frequently does, indicate incipient physical disorders that are not sufficiently advanced to be detected as specific pathologies by the physician. The anthropometric examination can be administered by trained persons who are not physicians, and it can aid the health administrator in outlining appropriate medical follow-ups.

In this chapter the contributions of anthropometry to physical and health education are discussed in relation to body build and to physical growth.

578. BODY BUILD

Early standards for weight were, in most cases, based upon averages of measurements taken on persons of all types of body build, with race, sex, age, and perhaps nationality held constant. The same standards, however, cannot be validly used for both the slender and the stocky type of body build: a race horse and a dray horse may be of the same height and of the same length, but they do not weigh the same amount or have the same amount of strength.

Anthropometrists and physicians have, from an early time, suggested categories of body build, with a very tall and slender person representing one extreme of body build, and with a somewhat shorter but very stocky person representing the other extreme of build. In this system a category of normality in body build was usually placed between the two extremes of body build, and in a few cases variations were proposed within these categories. Later, the question arose concerning whether there were several

345

distinct body builds, or simply a distribution of body builds extending between the two most different body builds.

579. In accordance with the assumption that body builds vary, according to the curve of probability, from one extreme to the other, various anthropometric indices have been devised to assess body build. The best of these indices are the following:

$$\frac{1000 \sqrt[3]{\text{weight (kg.)}}}{\text{height (cm.)}} \quad and \quad \frac{10^6 \times \text{weight (kg.)}}{\text{height}^3 \text{ (cm.)}}$$

Although these indices indicate stockiness (or a lack of stockiness), they are not valid methods for assessing qualitative as well as quantitative variations in body build.

580. In a factorial analysis[1] of body builds the following four factors were isolated and identified: fatty growth, cross-sectional growth, "general growth" (most distinct in tall, slender body builds), and a growth termed "Factor IV" (most distinct in persons strongly developed in the part of the body above the waist, including the upper limbs, and especially in persons with wide shoulders).

581. Body builds have, on a subjective basis, been classified into an endomorphic (predominantly soft, round, fat), a mesomorphic (rugged and muscular), and an ectomorphic (tall, slender, delicate) type.[2] In this classification and in the four factors of body build, the stocky body build has been subclassified into a muscular type and a round, fat type. In view of the present widespread acceptance of the terms "endomorphy," "mesomorphy," and "ectomorphy," this terminology has been adopted in this book, and in the interest of harmony with that terminology[3] Factor IV is termed "omomorphy."

The endomorphic, the mesomorphic, and the ectomorphic body build can be readily explained in terms of the four factors of growth. Endomorphy is based on a high development of the fat factor, on a very moderate development of the cross-section factor and of the general-growth factor, and on a negligible development of Factor IV. Mesomorphy is based on a high development of the cross-section factor, on a moderate development, especially in middle and old age, of the fat factor, and frequently, on a considerable development of Factor IV, with a negligible development of the factor of general growth. Ectomorphy is based on a high development of the general-growth factor, on almost no development

---

[1] Charles H. McCloy, "An Analysis for Multiple Factors of Physical Growth at Different Age Levels," *Child Development*, December, 1940.

[2] W. H. Sheldon and Others, *The Varieties of Human Physique.*

[3] The terminology for the first three types seems to be an unfortunate one, for the assumption is that the three different types of body build are exemplifications of a predominance of growth in each of the three major germ layers of the embryo. This assumption seems to numerous writers, physicians, and anthropologists to be without justification.

of the fat factor, on very little development of the cross-section factor, and on very little development of Factor IV.

582. The theory has been advanced that body build does not change throughout life.[4] This theory appears, on the basis of the following evidence, to be untenable. In a study[5] on the body build of boys and girls from six to eighteen years of age, marked changes in body build were frequently found within three-year periods. In highly endomorphic persons who have followed rigid diets and engaged in programs of heavy-resistance exercise, very striking changes in apparent body build have occurred.[6] It seems likely that major changes in body build do not occur often. Some slight changes do occur, possibly because of changes in the amounts of different internal secretions. This is a subject needing much further research.

583. Generalizations concerning the likes and the dislikes of persons of various body builds are untrustworthy. In YMCA's, teachers of physical education who have had experience with persons who have been motivated to come to the gymnasium classes have found persons of almost every body build responding favorably to well-taught programs of physical activity. Although persons with different body builds may vary in their responses to specific types of motivation and in the extent to which they can develop physically, exceptions occur so frequently that one should not, by preconceived ideas concerning various body builds, be discouraged from attempting to serve persons of certain body builds.

584. In studies of the relationship of strength to body build,[7] mesomorphs have been found to be strongest for their body weight, endomorphs weakest, and ectomorphs intermediate in strength. These findings should not indicate that persons of all types of body build should not attempt to develop an adequate amount of strength for carrying out their daily tasks, nor that persons who are overweight should not reduce their caloric intakes. The findings may indicate that persons of certain body builds develop strength, for example, with more difficulty than do persons of other body builds, and that persons of various body builds cannot develop the same amounts of strength for their body weights. Somatotypy, the study of body builds, has come to be almost a religion in many places in this country. Caution is here advanced that it is better, educationally, to aim at an optimum development for every person rather than to attempt to impose, in accordance with as yet unproved findings relative to body builds, arbitrary limits upon such development.

585. The characteristics of endomorphs, ectomorphs, and mesomorphs

[4] Sheldon and Others, op. cit.

[5] Eleanor Metheny, "The Variability of the Percentage Index of Build as Applied to the Prediction of Normal Weight," Human Biology, December, 1939.

[6] Personal communication from Frank D. Sills.

[7] Carl E. Willgoose and Millard L. Rogers, "Relationship of Somatotype to Physical Fitness," Journal of Educational Research, May, 1949.

TABLE 111

BODY BUILD: CHARACTERISTICS OF ENDOMORPHS, MESOMORPHS, AND ECTOMORPHS

Items preceded by an asterisk must be evaluated, wholly or in part, by means other than the inspection of photographs. Where an item is characterized as "large," "small," or "medium," reference is to the average-sized person of that height.

Item Rated	Endomorph	Mesomorph	Ectomorph
GENERAL CHARACTERISTICS			
Shape and texture of body	Smoothness and roundness	Squareness and unevenness	Linearity and flatness; transverse diameters longer than anteroposterior diameters
Longest transverse diameter below waist	Above iliac crests	At bitrochanteric level	At bitrochanteric level
Prominence of abdomen	Extreme	Almost lacking	Almost lacking
Volume of thorax and of abdomen	Volume of abdomen larger than volume of thorax	Volume of thorax larger than volume of abdomen	Under average; flatness of thorax and of abdomen
General impression	Stocky, globular, "inflated"	Stocky, rugged, muscular	Linear, delicate
Surface area relative to volume	Below average	Average	Above average
*Manifestation of energy	Anabolic	Catabolic	Neutral
*Toleration for extreme heat and for extreme cold	Good	Good	Poor (Caucasian ectomorphs frequently unable to live in tropics)
BONES			
*Development of bones	Small	Large and heavy	Small and delicate
*Prominence of projections	Lacking	Above average	Below average
CONNECTIVE TISSUE			
*Amount	Below average	Above average	Very much below average
JOINTS			
*Size	Smaller than average	Larger than average	Very much smaller than average
MUSCULATURE			
Relief	Lacking, or very much below average	Prominent; very much above average	Lacking, or very much below average
SKIN			
*Texture	Like that of apple	Like that of orange	Like that of skin of onion

348

Table 111 (Continued)

Body Build: Characteristics of Endomorphs, Mesomorphs, and Ectomorphs

Item Rated	Endomorph	Mesomorph	Ectomorph
*Wrinkling of skin	If fat, unwrinkled; if panniculus is lost, skin wrinkles in soft folds	Skin thin and tightly bound to subcutaneous tissue; hence any wrinkling is of heavy, course folds	Fine wrinkling, even in youth, of exposed surfaces
*Elasticity of skin and of subcutaneous tissues	Loosely bound, except in the Negro	Firmly elastic; springs back quickly when pinched	Loosely bound; returns slowly when pinched

HEAD

Item Rated	Endomorph	Mesomorph	Ectomorph
Shape	Globular	Cubical	Pear-shaped (point down)
Size	Larger than average	Average	Smaller than average, but appears large relative to neck
*Baldness (if present)	Circular, with a highly polished surface	When it appears, comes first on front of head	No special characteristic
*Hair	More manageable than average	No definite trend	Less manageable than average
Ears	Flat; equally developed as to lobes and pinnae	More heavily developed than average	Pinnae project laterally; pinnae better developed than lobes; lobes attached to sides of head
Supraorbital ridges	Less prominent than average	More prominent than average	Inconspicuous

FACE

Item Rated	Endomorph	Mesomorph	Ectomorph
Shape	Round	Pentagonal	Elliptical
*Consistency of skin	Soft, bland	Hard, tight	Infantile
Muscular development	Below average	Above average	Below average
Cheekbones	Not discernible	More massive and more prominent than average	More delicate and less prominent than average
Nose	Does not protrude in lateral view	Strong	Bridge narrow, often sharp like a slender prow
Mouth	Smaller than average	Average	Average
Lips	More protruding (like sucking lips) than average	More developed muscularly than average	Thinner and more delicate than average

349

TABLE 111 (Continued)

BODY BUILD: CHARACTERISTICS OF ENDOMORPHS, MESOMORPHS, AND ECTOMORPHS

Item Rated	Endomorph	Mesomorph	Ectomorph
*Palate	Parabolic in shape; wider and lower than average	Parabolic in shape; wider and lower than average	U-shaped; narrower and higher than average
Jaws	Not strong	Square; more massive than average	Higher and narrower than average
Chin	Not strong	More massive than average	Pointed; less developed than average
NECK			
Transverse diameter relative to anteroposterior diameter	Index about equal to 1	Index above 1	Index about equal to 1
Length	Shorter than average	Longer than average	Longer and more slender than average
Angle of neck with chin	Obtuse	Right angle	Right angle
Muscular development, especially of trapezii	Inconspicuous, much below average	Much above average	Below average
Carriage of head and neck	Erect	Moderately erect	More forward than average
TRUNK—GENERAL			
Transverse diameter relative to anteroposterior diameter	Index almost equal to 1	Index much over 1	Index over 1
Vertebral column (lateral view)	Straighter than average	Thoracic spine straighter than average; lumbar spine more curved than average	Thoracic spine more curved than average
Length relative to length of limbs	Index is larger than average	Index is larger than average	Index is smaller than average
Muscular development	Under average	Above average	Under average
*Sacrum (X ray)	Top slants very moderately forward and downward; is set well forward in pelvis	Top slants forward and downward more than average	Top slants forward and downward more than average
THORAX			
Width of base relative to width of upper part	Index larger than average	Index smaller than average	Index smaller than average
*Costovertebral and costosternal angles	Larger than average	Average	Smaller than average

TABLE 111 (Continued)

BODY BUILD: CHARACTERISTICS OF ENDOMORPHS, MESOMORPHS, AND ECTOMORPHS

Item Rated	Endomorph	Mesomorph	Ectomorph
Thoracic cage	Shorter than average; round	Broader than average	Flatter than average
Volume of abdomen relative to volume of thorax	Index larger than average	Index smaller than average	Index smaller than average
*Ribs	Small and covered with fat	More massive than average	More delicate than average
ABDOMEN			
Volume of abdomen relative to volume of thorax	Index larger than average	Index smaller than average	Index about equal to 1
Waist	Waist line higher than average and less prominent than average	Waist line lower than average and small relative to thorax	Lower than average and slender
Muscular development (front view)	Poor	Above average	Under average
MALE GENITALIA			
Development	Under average; hypoplastic relative to average	Above average	Above average; more linear than average
*Scrotum	Smaller than average	Thicker and firmer than average	Longer and looser than average
Penis	Shorter and smaller than average; may be almost completely hidden in pubic hair	Longer than average	Longer than average
*Corona	Smaller than average	Better developed than average	Better developed than average
*Testes	Small	Normal	Normal
SHOULDERS			
Development of deltoids and of trapezii	Almost lacking	Above average	Under average
Height	Above average (square)	Appears below average because of sloping contours due to muscular development of neck	(Square)
Width	Average	Appears above average because of muscular development	Under average

TABLE 111 (Continued)

BODY BUILD: CHARACTERISTICS OF ENDOMORPHS, MESOMORPHS, AND ECTOMORPHS

Item Rated	Endomorph	Mesomorph	Ectomorph
Carriage	Normal	Normal	More forward than average; scapulae more winged than average; arms more forward than average
UPPER ARM			
Shape	Rounder and with more hamming than average	Without hamming	More slender than average
Length relative to length of forearm	Index above 1	Index about equal to 1	Index under 1
Anteroposterior diameter relative to lateral diameter	Index equal to about 1	Index above 1	Index equal to about 1; both small
FOREARM			
Anteroposterior diameter relative to lateral diameter	Index equal to about 1	Index under 1	Index under 1
Massiveness relative to massiveness of upper arm	Less well developed than upper arm	Index equal to about 1	Better developed than upper arm
HANDS			
Size relative to size of body	Index smaller than average	Index larger than average	Index larger than average
Wrists	Tapering	Heavier and more massive than average	Flatter and more slender than average
Fingers	Tapering	Heavier and more massive than average; spatulate	More delicate than average
UPPER LEG			
Size relative to size of lower leg	Index above average	Index about equal to average	Index below average
Contour of thigh	Feminine contour on outer side	Masculine ruggedness	Slender, masculine
Shape	Fat and hamming	Muscular	Slender, not muscular
Dimpling in lateral aspects	Absent	Present	Absent
Muscular development	Almost lacking	Above average	Below average
PELVIS			
*Prominence	Not prominent; covered with fat	More sturdy than average	More delicate than average

TABLE 111 (Continued)

BODY BUILD: CHARACTERISTICS OF ENDOMORPHS, MESOMORPHS, AND ECTOMORPHS

Item Rated	Endomorph	Mesomorph	Ectomorph
LOWER LEGS			
Transverse diameter relative to anteroposterior diameter	Index about equal to 1	Index greater than 1	Index less than 1
Muscular development	Below average	Much above average	Below average
Length relative to length of upper legs	Average to long	Short	Long
FEET			
Size relative to size of body	Smaller than average	Larger than average	Smaller than average
Toes	Tapering	Rugged	Slender

may be found in Table 111 (pp. 348-53).[8] Omomorphy, which usually accompanies mesomorphy and ectomorphy but seldom accompanies endomorphy, is characterized by a strongly developed chest, by strongly developed arms, and especially by broad shoulders accompanied by a smaller development of the lower half of the body.

586. A procedure for somatotyping is herewith described.[9]

The subject stands erect on a revolving pedestal. The arms are straight, and the palms, which face the thighs, are about six inches out from the thighs. The feet are turned slightly outward, and the heels are two to three inches apart. A photograph of the front view is taken. Then the pedestal is rotated, and a photograph of the side view is taken. The pedestal is rotated again, and a photograph of the back view is taken. Ordinarily, artificial lights are used, and, frequently, the photographs are taken with a modified camera, which by a sliding of the film-holder across in front of the lens, permits three exposures to be taken on one film.

The photographs are then assessed according to the criteria in Table 111 (pp. 348-53). Each of the three body builds is indicated numerically on a scale from 1 to 7, 1 indicating a minimum of the component, 7 indicating a maximum, and 4 being the mid-point. A three-figure number is then used to designate the somatotype, with the first number indicating the endomorphic component, the second number the mesomorphic component, and the third number the ectomorphic component. A somatotype of 1-4-7, for example, indicates a body build that has a negligible amount of endomorphy, an average amount of mesomorphy, and a very high

[8] Partially based on *The Varieties of Human Physique*.
[9] For more detailed directions see *The Varieties of Human Physique*, Chap. 4. Sheldon and Others, *Atlas of Men*.

amount of ectomorphy. If it is desired to add omomorphy—and this addition is not usually necessary—a number in parentheses may be added to the three numbers.

The procedure presented here for somatotyping is, first, to assess, for the body as a whole, the amounts of endomorphy, mesomorphy, and ectomorphy in terms of little of the component (A), an average amount of the component (B), and a large amount of the component (C); and second, after the photographs have been re-examined, to assign numerical values to the letter ratings. ($A = 1$ and 2; $B = 3$, 4, and 5; and $C = 6$ and 7). If doubt exists whether, for example, a rating of 4 or 5 should be assigned, an average (i.e., 4.5) of the ratings may be used. Then the same procedure is repeated on the following five regions of the body: (1) head and neck, (2) thorax, (3) abdomen, (4) arms and hands, and (5) legs and feet. The numbers assigned to a somatotype are the averages of the numerical values assigned to each component. The Sheldon procedure here is to drop any decimals below .3, to consider .4 to .6 as .5, and to represent .7 to .9 by the next whole number; for example, 1.8 is considered to be 2; 3.1 is considered to be 3; and 2.4 and 2.6 are considered to be 2.5.

587. In the prescription of exercise, differences in body build need not be considered, for the same type of exercise may be validly prescribed for a weak endomorph, a weak mesomorph, and a weak ectomorph. In advice concerning personal hygiene, however, there is considerable evidence to the effect that body build [10] should be considered. For example, endomorphs—and to a slightly less extent mesomorphs—seem to have a larger amount of digestive organs per unit of body volume than do ectomorphs. Endomorphs (and mesomorphs), therefore, have comparatively more area from which to absorb food than do ectomorphs, and hence endomorphs (and mesomorphs) tend to put on more weight than do ectomorphs, and to be much better nourished than ectomorphs, who tend toward malnourishment. As a result of chronic overnourishment, endomorphs and mesomorphs, especially in sedentary life, tend to place a greater burden upon the kidneys and the circulatory system and to suffer more from diseases of these organs than do ectomorphs, while ectomorphs tend to suffer more from diseases of the lungs and the digestive organs and from other types of diseases associated with poor nutrition than do endomorphs

---

[10] R. Bennett Bean, "The Two European Types," *American Journal of Anatomy*, March, 1923.

John Bryant, "The Carnivorous and Herbivorous Types in Man: The Possibility and Utility of Their Recognition. I. Introduction and Outline," *Boston Medical and Surgical Journal*, March 4, 1915.

Charles B. Davenport, "Body-Build and Its Inheritance," *Carnegie Institute of Washington Publications*, 329 (Paper 35 of the Department of Eugenics), 1923.

George Draper and Others, *Human Constitution in Clinical Medicine.*

Maria Montessori, *Pedagogical Anthropology.*

Charles R. Stockard, "Human Types and Growth Reactions," *American Journal of Anatomy*, January, 1923.

and mesomorphs. These assertions are upheld by such life-insurance statistics as those in Table 112 (p. 355). The studies of Draper and Others[11] indicate that the problem is considerably more complex than it has been made to appear here.

In advising endomorphs, the teacher of physical and health education should emphasize the necessity of low-caloric diets. The adviser should impress upon endomorphs the fact that they will probably always have to watch their diets if they are not to become excessively fat. As mesomorphs become older they usually tend to put on fat, and hence, relative to diet, should be advised like the endomorphs. Both endomorphs and mesomorphs should be warned that if they let themselves become excessively

Table 112

BODY BUILD: RELATIONSHIP TO DISEASE

| | PHYSIQUE | | |
Cause of Death	Thin	Medium	Stout
	%	%	%
Tuberculosis	25.7	13.1	4.1
Apoplexy	4.9	9.2	12.3
Circulatory disturbances	9.4	14.8	22.7
Pneumonia	11.7	10.3	7.7
Malignant tumors	6.4	8.3	7.1
Infectious disorders	5.4	4.6	4.1
Brain disorders	10.6	9.8	6.6
Suicide	4.7	5.1	4.1
Various other diseases	21.2	24.8	31.3
Total	100.0	100.0	100.0

fat, they will probably be more susceptible to high blood pressure, to apoplexy, to circulatory disturbances of heart and blood vessels generally, to kidney troubles, and will probably die earlier than if they control their body weights. In advising ectomorphs, the adviser should emphasize the desirability of high-caloric diets and of considerable rest and relaxation.

The regimens for the various body builds are not so simple as presented here, for persons are not completely endomorphic, mesomorphic, or ectomorphic. The regimens may, however, serve as guides.

588. SOMATIC ANDROGYNY [12]

The types of body build discussed in Section 586 may be assessed for masculinity and femininity by the use of Table 113 (pp. 356-60) and of

[11] *Human Constitution in Clinical Medicine.*

[12] Nancy Bayley and Leona M. Bayer, "The Assessment of Somatic Androgyny," *American Journal of Physical Anthropology,* December, 1946.

George Draper, "The Mosaic of Androgyny," *New England Medical Journal,* September 11, 1941.

——and Others, *Human Constitution in Clinical Medicine,* Chap. 6.

Carl C. Seltzer and Lucien Brouha, "The 'Masculine' Component and Physical Fitness," *American Journal of Physical Anthropology,* March, 1943.

Table 113

BODY BUILD: SOMATIC ANDROGYNY[*]

Exponent	Strongly Masculine 5	Weakly Masculine 4	Intermediate 3	Weakly Feminine 2	Strongly Feminine 1
Muscularity					
Definition	Exaggerated	Fair (veins and tendons perhaps prominent)	Negligible to nonexistent (with or without fat)	Negligible	Nonexistent
Texture	Very firm 15	Not very firm 12	Not firm 9	Very soft 6	Very flabby 3
Shoulders					
Width	Very wide	Fairly wide	Average	Narrow	Very narrow
Contour	Massive	Not well developed muscularly	Poorly developed muscularly; bony or fat	Slight (may be fat)	Very slight (may be fat)
Biacromial width x 100 Bicristal width	149 and over 5	139 to 148 4	129 to 138 3	119 to 128 2	118 and under 1

Table 113 (continued)

Exponent	5	4	3	2	1
Interspace between legs	Large above and below knees — 5	Small above and below knees — 4	Intermediate — 3	Nonexistent above knees, very small below knees — 2	Nonexistent above and at knees, some between ankles — 1
Calves					
Bulges	Very prominent, more convex on the inner than on the outer side — 10	Prominent, more convex on the inner than on the outer side — 8	Small, equally convex on the inner and the outer side, or not noticeable — 6	Small, more convex on the outer than on inner side — 4	Much more convex on the outer than on the inner side — 2
Muscularity	Very well developed — 10	Well developed — 8	Moderately or little developed — 6	Little developed — 4	Very little developed — 2
Abdominal protuberance					
Size	Not noticeable — 5	Very slight — 4	Moderate — 3	Marked — 2	Very marked — 1
Location	If existent, very high — 5	High — 4	Intermediate — 3	Low — 2	Very low — 1

Table 113 (continued)

Exponent	5	4	3	2	1
Neck					
Size	Large	Moderate	Fair	Small (with or without fat)	Very small (with or without fat)
Musculature	Well developed — 20	Fairly well developed — 16	Not well developed — 12	Negligible to nonexistent — 8	Negligible to nonexistent — 4
Chest					
Size	Very large — 15	Larger than average — 12	Intermediate — 9	Small — 6	Very small — 3
Breast					
Fat (male)	Nonexistent or evenly distributed — 10	Distributed slightly in pattern of female mammary gland — 8	Distributed somewhat in pattern of female mammary gland — 6	Distributed very much in pattern of female mammary gland — 4	Excessive fat over breast area — 2
Size (female)	Rudimentary — 10	Very small — 8	Small — 6	Average — 4	Large — 3 Very large — 2

Table 113 (continued)

Exponent	5	4	3	2	1
Waistline relative to hip flare					
Height	Very low	Low	Intermediate	High	Very high
Indentation	Very slight	Slight	Intermediate	Marked	Very marked
	10	8	6	4	2
Buttocks					
Contour	Very flat	Flat	Intermediate	Rounded and full	Rounded and broad
Fat	Negligible or nonexistent	Some on posterior surfaces	Some on posterior and lateral surfaces	Much on posterior and lateral surfaces	Very much on posterior and lateral surfaces
	15	12	9	6	3
Thighs					
Shape	Cylindrical	Very cylindrical	Intermediate	Funnel-shaped	Very funnel-shaped
Texture	Muscular	Somewhat rugged with, perhaps, some fat	Intermediate	Soft	Very soft
	15	12	9	6	3

Table 113 (continued)

Exponent	5	4	3	2	1
Body hair	Heavy, especially over thighs and chest	Considerable	Sparse	Almost absent	Absent
	10	8	6	4	2
Pubic hair	Heavily distributed over almost all lower abdomen	Distributed in a triangular pattern above the pubic hair triangle	Sparsely distributed in a line on the center of the lower part of the abdomen	Distributed primarily in lower triangle; a few hairs are found immediately above the lower triangle	Distributed on lower triangle only; upper line horizontal
	10	8	6	4	2
Total points	150 and over	117 to 149	84 to 116	49 to 83	48 and under

*Compiled, in part, from: Nancy Bayley and Leona M. Bayer, "The Assessment of Somatic Androgyny," American Journal of Physical Anthropology, December, 1946, and in part from Carl C. Seltzer and Lucien Brouha, "The 'Masculine' Component and Physical Fitness," American Journal of Physical Anthropology, March, 1943.

Figure LII (p. 362). In the table numerical values are indicated for each criterion.

Masculinity and femininity of body build do not appear to be modified by exercise. A high degree of physical fitness appears not to be associated with males whose body builds have weak masculine components.[13] Excellence of women in track-and-field athletics appears to be associated with females whose body builds have strong masculine components.

In one study[14] in which an attempt was made to measure femininity objectively by means of bodily measurements, an R of .674 was obtained with biserial correlations of measurements of the two sexes. Further studies in somatic androgyny both on the basis of inspection and by the use of anthropometric measurements need to be conducted on both males and females.

589. ASSESSMENT OF PHYSICAL STATUS

For many years students of applied anthropometry have attempted to formulate methods of using anthropometric measurements for the assessment of physical status. The earliest studies concerned the prediction of normal weight and the use of deviations from normal weight to indicate deviations from normal health. In those studies, normal weight was predicted from sex, age, and height; that is, each normal weight was the average weight of a large number of supposedly normal persons of the same sex, age, and height. In this type of norm—the best known of which is the **Wood-Baldwin Age-height-weight Tables** (Tables 123 and 124, pp. 376-83)—no allowance is made for differences in body build; thus the norms for extreme ectomorphs and for extreme endomorphs are the same. Among the earliest weight standards based on differences in body build were **weight standards based on height and chest girth**.[15] These standards are for Chinese men and women of college ages and above. Similar standards are available for North American adults.[16]

The **Franzen Standards**, which were based on a large number of measurements, including measurements of, but not corrections for, fat, were devised for three ages of childhood.[17] In connection with this study, practicable methods of measuring fat and subcutaneous tissues were developed to a high degree of accuracy.

[13] Seltzer and Brouha, *loc. cit.*

[14] Aileen Carpenter, "Strength, Power, and 'Femininity' as Factors Influencing the Athletic Performance of College Women," *Research Quarterly*, May, 1938.

[15] McCloy, "A Combination of Weight, Height, and Chest Girth," *Chinese Journal of Physical Education and Hygiene*, 1926. (In Chinese).

———, "Weight Standards for the Individual," *American Physical Education Review*, September, 1926.

[16] McCloy, "Individual Weight Standards for Adults," *Journal of Physical Education*, January, 1929.

[17] Raymond Franzen, *Physical Measures of Growth and Nutrition* (School Health Research Monograph 2).

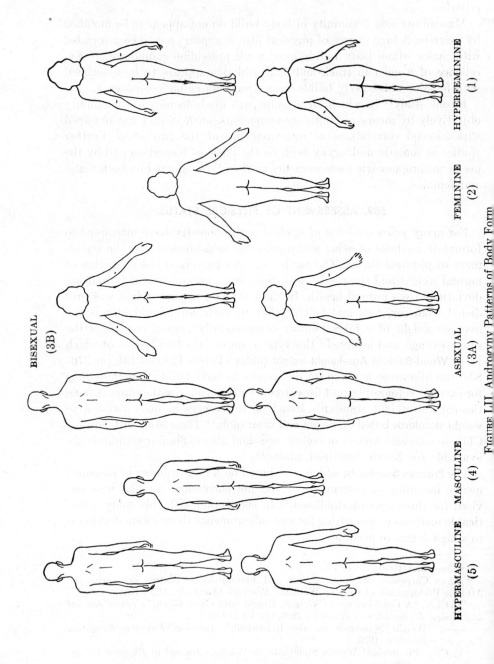

FIGURE LII. Androgyny Patterns of Body Form

In the **Wetzel Grid** [18] normal weight is in terms of the rate of growth. Although the grid is useful for the untrained teacher, it makes no allowance for changes in body build [19] and for marked changes in rate of growth in height and in weight, which changes are likely to occur particularly at the time of puberty; for example, children who are of the same height at eight years of age may differ as much as 15.5 cm. (6 in.) in height at the age of seventeen years. [20]

In the **Pryor Width-weight Tables** [21] the standards for normal weight are based on height and on the width of the hips, with no allowances made for fat. Although height and hip width are much less highly correlated with weight than are height and measurements of the chest, the Pryor standards were a real advance over the age-height-weight standards.

In the **Cureton method** [22] of predicting normal weight from anthropometric measurements, girths are measured with a tape pulled tight around a limb in which the muscles have been made firm. Hence a subjective element is introduced into the measurement, thus decreasing the reliability and the validity of the measurement.

590. McCloy method for the prediction of normal weight. The following method for the prediction of normal weight was, for the most part, developed at the Iowa Child Welfare Research Station.

591. The measurements [23] that have been found to be the most satisfactory for predicting normal weight are height, chest girth, hip width, and knee width. Chest girth and hip width need to be corrected for deficiencies or excesses of fat. This correction is based upon measurements of skin and subcutaneous tissue taken with fat calipers. The measurement is referred to hereafter as a fat measurement.

(1) *Weight.* The subject, nude, if feasible, stands in the center of the platform of the scales. If he has on some garment, the weight of this garment is subtracted from the weight shown on the scales.

(2) *Standing height.* A stadiometer may be used for the measurement of height, or a meter stick or a strip of adhesive tape marked in centimeters may be fastened to a wall. The lower end of the meter stick or of the tape is one meter from the floor. The subject stands as erect as possible, with heels together, and with heels, backs of hips, upper part of back, and back of head against the wall, [24] and with the arms hanging naturally at the sides. The measurer places a square instrument, such as a wooden chalk box, on top of the subject's head, keeping the instrument

---

[18] Norman C. Wetzel, "Physical Fitness in Terms of Physique, Development and Basal Metabolism," *Journal of the American Medical Association*, March 22, 1941.

[19] Metheny, *loc. cit.*

[20] Howard V. Meredith, "Stature of Massachusetts Children of North European and Italian Ancestry," *American Journal of Physical Anthropology*, January-March, 1939.

[21] Helen B. Pryor, *As the Child Grows.*

[22] Thomas K. Cureton, Jr., and Others, *Physical Fitness Appraisal and Guide.*

[23] McCloy, *Appraising Physical Status: The Selection of Measurements*, pp. 43-65.

[24] If, because of corpulent hips and/or an excessively curved thoracic spine, a subject cannot so stand, care should be taken that the long axis of the trunk is vertical.

parallel to the floor, and presses firmly enough upon the top of the head to press down the hair, and then reads the height on the scale.

(3) *Hip width.* Although flat metal calipers are excellent for this measurement, they are expensive; wooden calipers if used carefully are entirely satisfactory. The examiner marks with a skin pencil the crests of the ilia of the subject. Standing in front of the subject, he places, at as nearly right angles as possible, the calipers on the outermost points of the crests of the ilia. Usually, in the measurement of the male, the arms of the caliper are directed backward and downward. Frequently, in the measurement of the female, they are directed upward and

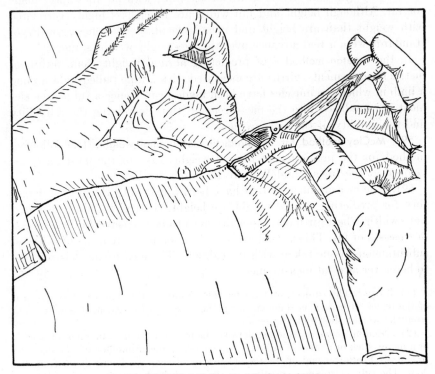

FIGURE LIII. Fat Calipers: Method of Using

backward. The examiner exerts on the calipers a maximum pressure not painful to the subject. The pressure should not be exerted on the parts of the blades near the long rods, for in such a case the blades may spring, and hence a spuriously small measurement would result.

(4) *Chest girth.* The measurer, standing behind the subject, places the midpoint of the tape at the level of the xiphoid cartilage (about one-half inch below the lower end of the sternum), and so adjusts the tape that the plane of the tape is at right angles to the long axis of the trunk; that is, the examiner looks at the trunk from the side and imagines an axis that would be about halfway between the front and the back of the chest. It should be noted that the tape is not at a right angle to either the front or the back of the chest but to this long axis. The

tape is not pulled tight, but is merely in contact with the skin.[25] The measurement is read at the end of quiet inspiration and at the end of quiet expiration, and the mid-point between the two readings is taken as the girth of the chest. In the case of adult females with drooping breasts, the subject may be instructed to raise the breasts with the hands. In view of the fact that numerous individuals, particularly men and boys, like to appear to have large chests, they frequently overexpand the chest when being measured. This overexpansion can usually be avoided by asking the subject a question, and recording the measurements when he relaxes to answer the question.

(5) *Knee width*. The subject places the left foot on a stool in order to bend the lower leg to about a right angle and to relax the muscles of the leg. The measurer places the blades of the calipers over the epicondyles[26] of the upper leg in such a way that the blades bisect the angle behind the knee. He exerts a maximum pressure not painful to the subject.

(6) *Measurements of fat*. These measurements are taken with fat calipers (Fig. LIII, p. 364), two types of which may be found. In the earlier type of fat caliper, no longer available, the calibration began at 6 mm.[27] In the type of calipers now available[28] the calibration begins at 0 and goes to 47 mm.

The fat measurements are difficult to standardize without considerable practice. The measurer grasps a double layer of skin in the thumb and the forefinger of the left hand, with the thumb and the forefinger pointing toward each other (Fig. LIII, p. 364). He should get a complete double layer of skin and fat (but no muscle), but not so much skin and fat as to cause too great an amount of tension beyond the finger tips. He holds the fold of skin and fat somewhat loosely, and applies the calipers in such a way that the calipers are about two millimeters above the ends of the thumb and fingers. He releases the spring of the calipers, holds the calipers down against the fold of skin to prevent the skin from slipping away, and records the measurement. In grasping the skin, the measurer should avoid pulling the skin away from the subject; rather he should press slightly against the subject with the tips of the fingers.

The fat measurements described in this section are usually taken on the left side of the body. If there are scars or deformities of the skin on the left side of the body, the measurements should be taken on the right side of the body.

The fat measurements offer few difficulties in the case of children. In the case of older adults, two difficulties are sometimes found. (1) In the case of persons who are rapidly becoming fatter, the skin may be tight and the fat difficult to pick up. (2) In the case of persons who have become thinner, the skin may be loose and baggy, covering a mass of very soft movable fat. If the same measurement is taken several times in succession, it becomes smaller each succeeding time; that is, the fat is squeezed out from under the place measured. In such cases the best procedure is to pick up the skin and the fold of fat carefully, avoiding too much pressure with the fingers, adjust the calipers without allowing too much

[25] This regulation concerning the method of applying the tape applies to anthropometric measurements generally, but particularly to the standards described in this chapter. In all cases the system of measurement should be used upon which the standards for that measurement are based.

[26] That is, at the widest part of the lower end of the femur just above the articulation of the knee.

[27] This calibration was due to the fact that these calipers were adapted from calipers originally made for measuring the inside of a pipe. Standards for these calipers are different from those for the calipers now available.

[28] Obtainable from C. H. Stoelting Company, 424 North Homan Avenue, Chicago 24.

Table 114

CHEST GIRTH CORRECTION: NORMS
(MALES AND FEMALES, 9 TO 29 AND UP)*

| | NORM | | | |
Age (yr.)	Male	Female	Deviation	Correction
29 & up	29	37	1	.1
28	29	36	2	.3
27	29	36	3	.5
26	29	36	4	.6
25	28	35	5	.8
24	27	34	6	.9
23	27	32	7	1.1
22	26	32	8	1.3
21	24	32	9	1.4
20	23	32	10	1.6
19	22	32	11	1.7
18	22	31	12	1.9
17	21	29	13	2.0
16	19	27	14	2.2
15	17	25	15	2.4
14	17	23	16	2.5
13	16	22	17	2.7
12	15	21	18	2.8
11	15	20	19	3.0
10	15	19	20	3.1
9	15	18	21	3.3
8	14	18	22	3.5
7	14	16	23	3.6
6	14	15	24	3.8
5	14	15	25	3.9
4	13	15	26	4.1
3	16	16	27	4.2
			28	4.4
			29	4.6
			30	4.7

*The fat calipers that are now procurable start at 0. If the older fat calipers, which started at 6 mm. are used, 12 should be added to each of the norms.

Table 115

FAT MEASUREMENTS: ABDOMEN AND CHEST FRONT:
EQUIVALENTS (MALES AND FEMALES)*

| Abdomen | CHEST FRONT | | Abdomen | CHEST FRONT | |
	Males	Females		Males	Females
5	5	5	20	16	14
6	6	5	21	17	15
7	6	6	22	17	15
8	7	6	23	18	16
9	8	7	24	19	17
10	9	8	25	20	17
11	9	8	26	20	18
12	10	9	27	21	18
13	11	10	28	22	19
14	12	10	29	23	20
15	12	11	30	23	20
16	13	11	31	24	21
17	14	12	32	25	22
18	15	13	33	25	22
19	15	13	34	26	23

*The fat calipers that are now procurable start at 0. If the older fat calipers, which started at 6 mm. are used, 6 should be added to each of the norms.

Table 116

HIP-WIDTH CORRECTION: NORMS
(MALES AND FEMALES, 3 TO 18 AND UP)

Age (yr.)	NORM Male	NORM Female	Deviation	Correction
18 & up	12	20	1	.1
17	11	20	2	.2
16	11	19	3	.2
15	11	19	4	.3
14	11	17	5	.4
13	11	17	6	.5
12	11	16	7	.6
11	11	16	8	.7
10	11	15	9	.8
9	10	15	10	.9
8	10	14	11	1.0
7	9	12	12	1.1
6	9	11	13	1.1
5	9	11	14	1.2
4	9	11	15	1.3
3	9	11	16	1.4
			17	1.5
			18	1.6
			19	1.7
			20	1.8
			21	1.9
			22	1.9
			23	2.0
			24	2.1
			25	2.2
			26	2.3
			27	2.4

Table 117

FAT MEASUREMENTS (SUM): AVERAGE AND MINIMUM AMOUNTS
(MALES AND FEMALES, 4 TO 18 AND UP)

Age (yr.)	MALES Mean	MALES Minimum	MALES Difference	FEMALES Mean	FEMALES Minimum	FEMALES Difference
4	30	15	15	34	19	15
5	29	15	14	34	19	15
6	28	16	12	34	19	15
7	29	16	13	36	20	16
8	31	16	15	41	20	21
9	32	16	16	43	20	23
10	34	17	17	45	20	25
11	34	18	16	46	20	26
12	34	18	16	50	22	28
13	36	18	18	52	25	27
14	37	18	19	55	25	30
15	38	20	18	58	27	31
16	38	21	17	59	30	29
17	39	22	17	61	32	29
18 & up	44	23	21	70	33	37

367

pressure from the spring, and make an estimate of the thickness of the layer of fat. This procedure is more accurate than not to reduce the pressure of the springs on such loose skins.

In young adult subjects, R's of .9253 for males and .9586 for females have been obtained between four measurements of fat and the sum of fourteen measurements of fat taken on fifteen parts of the body. Since the four fat measurements correlated almost perfectly with the criterion, they were not weighted in the formula for the prediction of weight.

Fat measurement on front of chest. The measurer applies, approximately halfway between the sagittal planes passing through the sternum and tangent to the side of the chest, the calipers to the skin at the level of the xiphoid cartilage.

Fat measurement on back of chest. The measurer applies, at the level of the horizontal plane passing through the xiphoid cartilage, the calipers over the most prominent part of the muscles of the back. The blades of the caliper are approximately vertical. If the natural line of the fold of the skin departs slightly from the vertical, this fold should be followed.

Fat measurement over hip (supra-ilium measurement). The measurer applies the calipers about one inch above the crest of the left ilium in a line vertically downward from the left armpit. The blades of the calipers are usually vertical, but may depart somewhat from this line if the natural fold of the skin seems to demand it.

Fat measurement on abdomen. The measurer applies the calipers on the front of the abdomen in a line between the nipple and the umbilicus just over the border of the rib cartilages. The blades of the caliper are parallel to the line from the nipple to the umbilicus.

592. *Correction of chest girth and hip width for fat.* If a person with a chest circumference of 80 cm. accumulates a layer of fat averaging 2 cm. in thickness, he increases his chest circumference by 12.6 cm. (i.e., $\pi \times 4$ cm.). The fat measurements on the front and the back of the chest are double thicknesses. Hence the sum of these double measurements represents twice the average variation in the diameter of the chest. Therefore, the formula for the correction of the chest girth for fat is as follows: π (sum of fat measurements on the front and the back of the chest − average sum of fat measurements for each age) $\div$ 2. If this correction is positive, it is subtracted from the chest girth; if it is negative, it is added to the chest girth. Norms for the correction of chest girth may be found in Table 114 (p. 366).

If it is difficult to pick up a fold of skin on the front of the chest, the fat measurement on the abdomen may be substituted for that on the front of the chest. Since the fat measurement on the abdomen usually runs larger than that on the front of the chest, the former measurement must be equated to the latter measurement according to the values given in Table 115 (p. 366).

Norms for the correction of hip width may be found in Table 116 (p. 367).

593. *Computation of normal fat.* Norms for the sum of the four fat measurements may be found in Table 117 (p. 367). The formula for the determination of the percentage of over- or under-fat follows:

$$100 \times \frac{\text{(four fat measurements} - \text{norm)}}{\text{(difference between norm and minimum)}}$$

An example of the computation of the percentage of over- and under-fat may be found in Table 118 (p. 369).

Weights of from 4 per cent underweight to 8 per cent overweight are considered to be within the range of normal variation in persons under thirty-five years of age. After this age, overweight should be held to not over 4 per cent. Since there is considerable variation in fatness, the suggestion is here made that the zone of normality be from −33 per cent to +66 per cent.[29]

Table 118

FAT MEASUREMENTS: SAMPLE WORKSHEET FOR
COMPUTATION OF OVER AND UNDER FAT

Measurement		Norm	Minimum	Norm minus minimum
		First girl (age 18)		
Chest front	11			
Chest back	13			
Abdomen	12			
Supra-ilium	16			
Sum	52	70 (Table 117)	33 (Table 117)	37

$$100 \left(\frac{\text{measurement} - \text{minimum}}{\text{norm} - \text{minimum}}\right) = 100 \frac{(52-33)}{(70-33)} = 51\% = 49\% \text{ under fat}$$

Measurement		Norm	Minimum	Norm minus minimum
		Second girl (age 18)		
Chest front	16			
Chest back	22			
Abdomen	24			
Supra-ilium	25			
Sum	87	70	33	37

$$100 \left(\frac{\text{measurement} - \text{minimum}}{\text{norm} - \text{minimum}}\right) = 100 \frac{(87-33)}{(70-33)} = 146\% = 46\% \text{ over fat}$$

594. An estimate of the total amount of fat may be obtained by estimating the fat from the average of the four measurements taken in terms of millimeters of fat above or below normal, then expressing this result in centimeters, and then multiplying this result by the surface area of the body (Fig. LIV, p. 370). For example, if the height of the first girl in Table 118 (p. 369) is 155 cm. and her weight is 52 kg., her surface area is, according to the chart, approximately 1.49 sq. m., or 14,900 sq. cm. Her average deficiency in fat is 2.25 mm. [i.e. (52-70) ÷ 8]; the four fat

---

[29] This applies to caliper measurements of fat, *not* to over- or underweight!

measurements, it must be remembered, represent eight layers of skin and fat or, in this illustration, a deficiency of .225 cm. When multiplied by 14,900 sq. cm. (the surface area), this gives 3,352 cc. of fat. Since each 1,000 cc. may be assumed to weigh approximately 2 lb., this girl is approximately 6.7 lb. underweight *because of lack of fat.*

If the second girl is 160 cm. tall and weighs 60 kg., her surface area is approximately 1.66 sq. m., or 16,600 sq. cm. The average excess of fat is .201 cm., or 3,337 cc., and hence the girl is, approximately, 6.7 lb. over-weight *because of fat.*

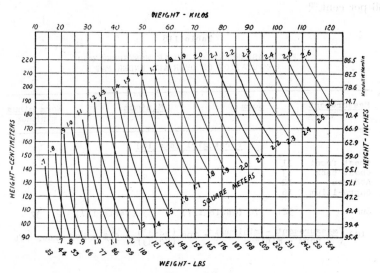

FIGURE LIV. Surface Area of Man in Square Meters: Chart for Determining from Height and Weight according to Area (sq. m.) = 394.56 W.575 × H.275 (After Scammon)

It is recognized that all parts of the body do not have the same amount of fat. There is little excess fat on the soles of the feet and on the palms of the hands. The wrists and the ankles do not get as fat as does the trunk. On the other hand, there are fat pads on the backs of the upper arms, between the shoulders, on the hips, and on the thighs, which fat pads more than make up for the smaller amounts of fat elsewhere. Hence this rough rule of calculating the amount of excess or deficient fat is a fairly useful one. It frequently comes as quite a shock to some middle-aged women to find that every quarter inch of excess fat that they put on, on the average, makes them carry approximately twenty pounds of excess fat—almost three gallons!

It is very probable that errors of some magnitude may occur in the correction of the chest girth and the hip width of the corpulent. It is equally probable, however, that the errors in the correction of hip width in the

Table 119

WEIGHT (W): PREDICTION EQUATIONS BASED ON HEIGHT (H),
HIP WIDTH (HP), CHEST CIRCUMFERENCE (C),
AND KNEE WIDTH (K) (MALES AND FEMALES 4 TO 18)

Age (yr.)	Males
4	W = .1315 H + .3082 Hp* + .2339 C* + 1.7623 K - 26.7253 R = .9124 N = 69
5	W = .1128 H + .1961 Hp + .3951 C + 1.6586 K - 30.2065 R = .9100 N = 146
6	W = .1912 H + .3785 Hp + .5907 C + .7245 K - 46.4538 R = .9224 N = 149
7	W = .1293 H + .6199 Hp + .4890 C + 1.3739 K - 42.9970 R = .9042 N = 135
8	W = .1607 H + .4028 Hp + .6789 C + 2.1453 K - 60.2709 R = .9247 N = 115
9	W = .1906 H + .5886 Hp + .5477 C + 1.9372 K - 58.4834 R = .9237 N = 137
10	W = .2183 H + .2743 Hp + .7577 C + 2.1438 K - 70.5147 R = .9180 N = 138
11	W = .2297 H + .1934 Hp + .5615 C + 3.1072 K - 66.1434 R = .9011 N = 132
12	W = .2230 H + .2457 Hp + .5204 C + 5.7727 K - 69.7569 R = .8960 N = 129
13	W = .2476 H + .0812 Hp + .8151 C + 4.2135 K - 93.4790 R = .9682 N = 131
14	W = .2712 H + .7361 Hp + .7935 C + 3.1487 K - 101.9942 R = .9573 N = 141
15	W = .3008 H + .9060 Hp + .6489 C + 4.3726 K - 111.8544 R = .9500 N = 126
16	W = .2808 H + .6960 Hp + .7840 C + 5.0191 K - 119.3305 R = .9196 N = 107
17	W = .2897 H + .7082 Hp + .7270 C + 5.0149 K - 115.2652 R = .9233 N = 78
18	W = .2359 H + 1.1402 Hp + .9641 C + 2.4796 K - 112.7968 R = .8946 N = 266

Age (yr.)	Females
4	W = .1298 H + .3304 Hp* + .4819 C* + .7320 K - 32.0832 R = .9636 N = 70
5	W = .1502 H + .3327 Hp + .4730 C + 1.1673 K - 36.9006 R = .9442 N = 151
6	W = .1053 H + .2633 Hp + .5137 C + 1.6253 K - 35.3942 R = .8972 N = 110
7	W = .1945 H + .3750 Hp + .6070 C + 1.2585 K - 50.9433 R = .9340 N = 100
8	W = .1798 H + .1687 Hp + .5505 C + 2.1443 K - 48.2626 R = .9077 N = 102
9	W = .1391 H + .3127 Hp + .7506 C + 1.9510 K - 56.6639 R = .9481 N = 114
10	W = .0966 H + .7730 Hp + .7034 C + 2.4933 K - 61.8757 R = .9315 N = 124
11	W = .1593 H + .8849 Hp + .5217 C + 2.3366 K - 60.2732 R = .9385 N = 132
12	W = .1234 H + 1.0364 Hp + .6959 C + 3.3690 K - 78.0477 R = .9289 N = 151
13	W = .1337 H + 1.4422 Hp + .4933 C + 4.3232 K - 83.9531 R = .9279 N = 164
14	W = .2170 H + .8422 Hp + .6187 C + 3.7842 K - 84.4909 R = .9041 N = 146
15	W = .1546 H + .7290 Hp + .5870 C + 4.7586 K - 77.6805 R = .8480 N = 136
16	W = .1347 H + 1.0977 Hp + .5353 C + 4.8507 K - 82.2678 R = .8749 N = 113
17	W = .1233 H + 1.0291 Hp + .4985 C + 3.7574 K - 64.6120 R = .8729 N = 97
18	W = .3165 H + .6508 Hp + .8041 C + 3.6080 K - 105.23 R = .9275 N = 214

*Chest circumference and hip width corrected for fat.

undernourished are negligible, and it is the normal weight of this group that it is most important to predict with the greatest accuracy.

595. *Computation of normal weight.* Multiple regression equations for the prediction of normal weight may be found in Table 119 (p. 371).[30] An example of the computation of the normal weight of a sixteen-year-old girl may be found in Table 120 (p. 372).

Table 120

WEIGHT: SAMPLE WORKSHEET FOR COMPUTATION OF NORMAL WEIGHT

Sixteen-year-old Girl

Height 163.9   Chest circumference 75.8   Hip width 22.8

Correction of Chest Girth

Fat chest front	=	6
Fat chest back	=	8
Total	=	14
Norm (Table 114)	=	27
Deviation	= -	13	(i.e., 27 - 14)
Correction (Table 114)	=	2
Corrected chest girth	=	77.8	(i.e., 75.8 + 2)

Correction of Hip Width

Fat supra-ilium	=	11	
Norm (Table 116)	=	19	
Deviation	= -	8	(i.e., 19 - 11)
Correction (Table 116)	=	.7	
Corrected hip width	=	23.5	(i.e., 22.8 + .7)

Prediction of Normal Weight
Table 119

$(.1347 \times 163.9) + (1.0977 \times 23.5) + (.5353 \times 77.8) + (4.8507 \times 8.4) - 82.2678 = 47.9977$ kg. $= 105.59$ lb. (i.e., 47.9977×2.2), or Table 76 in *Appraising Physical Status: Methods and Norms.*

Height	=	163.9
Corrected hip width	=	23.5
Value in table 2.16 + interpolation .45	=	2.61
Corrected chest girth	=	77.8
Knee width	=	8.4
Value in table 44.96 + interpolation .428	=	45.39
Normal weight in kg.	=	48.00
Normal weight in lb.	=	105.60

596. ABNORMALITIES OF BODY BUILD AND THEIR EFFECT ON THE PREDICTION OF NORMAL WEIGHT

If all individuals were consistent in body build, the R's of normal weights with the formulas for the prediction of normal weight would be almost 1.00. Such consistency is not the case, however, and allowances for deviations from "biological consistency" must be made. "Biological consistency" may be defined and illustrated as follows. There are wide vari-

---

[30] McCloy, *Appraising Physical Status: Methods and Norms,* pp. 38-39.

ations in body build—from the very slender linear type to the very stocky lateral type. In the average person of each body build, the various parts of the body are in harmony with that build. Such a harmony is here called "biological consistency." In some persons, one or more parts of the body may be out of harmony with the rest of the body. A person may have a long stocky trunk, but instead of relatively short thick limbs that usually go with that kind of trunk, he may have thin limbs, both in external dimensions and in size and in coarseness of bones. The normal weight of such a person differs somewhat from that obtained from the previously presented formula of normal weight for a person of his age. Even though the width of the knee is included in the regression equation

Table 121

CHEST INDICES: AVERAGES (MALES AND FEMALES 6 MONTHS TO 20 YEARS)

Age	Males	Females	Age	Males	Females
\multicolumn{6}{c}{$100 \dfrac{\text{Chest Depth}}{\text{Chest Width}}$}					
6 months	82	83	11	72	72
1 year	79	79	12	72	72
2	76	76	13	71	72
3	74	74	14	71	72
4	74	73	15	71	72
5	74	72	16	71	71
6	74	72	17	71	71
7	73	72	18	71	71
8	73	72	19	72	71
9	73	72	20	72	71
10	73	72			

for normal weight, this measurement does not compensate for such a deviation in body build. The body build of such an individual is "biologically inconsistent," and some allowance should be made for it.

597. Abnormal shapes of chest. The weight may be affected by differences in the shape of the chest. The shape of the chest is usually indicated by the chest index, $100 \times \dfrac{\text{chest depth}}{\text{chest width}}$, for which, averages for each age and sex are given in Table 121 (p. 373). If the chest indices differ markedly from the average proportions, these differences produce some effect on weight. The reason for these differences may be presented in the following analogy. The perimeter (chest girth) of each of the following figures is 78.54 cm.: (1) a circle with a diameter of 25 cm., (2) two semicircles with a diameter of 20 cm. separated by a rectangle 20 cm. by 7.854 cm., (3) two semicircles with a diameter of 15 cm. separated by a rectangle of 15 cm. by 15.708 cm. The areas, however, are approximately 481, 471, and 412 sq. cm., respectively. These perimeters and areas correspond to "chest indices" of 100, 71.8, and 48.9. In other words, chests with the same perimeter may vary in cross section if the shape of the chests varies. Corrections for this variance were devised by correlating the chest index against the amount of under- and overweight, and by deriving the following correction equation from the regression equation:

$$Y = .2 \text{ (chest index)} + .867$$

Y is a value by which the percentage of over- or underweight is *divided* to give the corrected normal weight. In practice, differences in the shape of the chest have very little influence on the weight predicted, but in extreme cases this correction may need to be used.

598. Masculinity and femininity of body build. A high degree of femininity of body build in a male and a high degree of masculinity of body build in a female affect the prediction of normal weight. The formulas for the prediction of weight for females, especially in the postpubescent ages, predict normal weights that are about 8 per cent heavier than those predicted by the formulas for males for the same skeletal dimensions. Since the cause for this difference has not as yet been investigated experimentally, statements are made here upon the basis of observations. Such observations concern (1) females whose predicted weights are much higher than the actual weights but which underweight cannot be accounted for by deficiencies in fat and in limb girths, and (2) males whose predicted weights are much lower than the actual weights but which overweight cannot be accounted for by excess fat or by excessive limb girths. In the case of these females, two outstanding differences from the average have been noted. (1) The chest is larger than the average for the build. Since the average regression weighting for chest girth is smaller in females than in males, this larger chest gives a somewhat smaller predicted weight. (2) The fat on the hips and thighs is markedly less than average for females, approaching the fat distribution in males. This female, then, weighs less for the same skeletal measurements than does a female of average fat distribution. In the males the opposite is true. Males that are heavier than the measurements seem to warrant tend to have smaller chests and a feminine fat distribution.

At the present no objective method for allowing for differences in normal weight on the basis of body build is available. It is suggested, however, on the basis of some empirical evidence, that if the predicted weight is not in accord with the measurements of fat and with the limb girths, the measurer rate the subject for masculinity and femininity of body build (Table 113, pp. 356-60) to see whether the subject deviates from the normal body build for his or her sex, and if there is such deviation, to compute normal weight from the formulas for both sexes, and to interpolate to the degree that seems to be correct for the individual.

599. Abnormal size for age. The normal weight of a child who is exceedingly tall or exceedingly short for his age is not accurately predicted by the formula for the prediction of weight for his age. Such abnormalities fall into two categories.

(1) *Discrepancy between maturational and chronological age.* If a person is exceedingly tall or exceedingly short for his age and if he has no glandular abnormalities, his normal weight can be most practicably approximated by the use of the formula for the age in which his height falls within two standard deviations of the average height for the age (Table 122, p. 375). To illustrate: A twelve-year-old boy is 108 cm. tall (an actual case). The prediction of his normal weight from the formula for the age of twelve years is unreliable, for this formula was not computed

Table 122*

HEIGHT: AVERAGES AND NORMAL RANGES (MALES AND FEMALES 2 TO 18)

Age (yr.)	MALES			FEMALES		
	-2 SD	Mean	+2 SD	-2 SD	Mean	+2 SD
2	85.9	92.3	98.8	85.5	91.5	97.5
3	89.5	96.8	104.1	91.4	98.9	106.5
4	99.9	106.8	114.5	98.1	105.7	113.2
5	104.6	113.0	121.3	104.3	112.4	120.5
6	108.9	118.9	128.9	108.3	118.0	127.6
7	114.8	125.0	135.2	113.3	123.8	134.4
8	120.0	130.9	141.9	118.5	129.6	140.8
9	125.2	136.3	147.5	123.5	135.1	146.7
10	129.0	141.1	153.2	128.4	140.6	152.9
11	132.9	145.5	158.1	133.2	147.0	160.8
12	135.8	150.6	165.3	139.4	153.1	166.8
13	139.3	156.4	173.4	145.6	157.7	169.8
14	145.0	162.3	179.5	149.5	160.1	170.7
15	152.3	167.4	182.6	150.9	161.2	171.2
16	158.8	171.6	184.4	150.0	161.4	172.7
17	161.3	173.8	186.3	149.2	161.4	173.6
18	162.5	175.0	187.5	149.3	161.4	173.6

*From C. H. McCloy, Appraising Physical Status: Methods and Norms, p. 45.

from data that included such a height. A height of 108 cm. falls within two standard deviations of the mean of the heights for the age of six years. Hence the weight of the person should be predicted from the formula for the age of six years. It is emphasized, however, that this method yields only an approximation of normal weight. The only scientifically valid method is to determine anatomical or maturational age by means of X rays of the bones of the hand and of the wrist,[31] and then to use the formula for the maturational age. A child may, for example, be twelve years old chronologically and six years old anatomically.

(2) *Glandular abnormalities.* No weight standards are available for

[31] Standards may be found in the *Atlas of Skeletal Maturation* by Thomas W. Todd.

Table 123

WEIGHT-HEIGHT-AGE STANDARDS (NUDE) FOR AMERICAN-BORN
BOYS OF SCHOOL AGE (BALDWIN-WOOD)

Height Cm.	Age, Years						
	6	7	8	9 Weight Kg.	10	11	12
97	15.0*						
98	15.1*						
99	15.3*						
100	15.5*						
101	15.7*						
102	15.9*						
103	16.1*						
104	16.6						
105	16.8	16.8*					
106	17.0	17.0*					
107	17.2	17.2*	17.2*				
108	17.5	17.6*	17.4*				
109	17.8	17.9*	17.7*				
110	18.3	18.4*	18.2*				
111	18.9	18.9*	18.8*				
112	19.4	19.4	19.4*				
113	19.7	19.7	19.7*				
114	20.0	20.0	20.0*				
115	20.4	20.4	20.4*	20.3*			
116	20.7	20.8	20.7	20.6*			
117	21.1	21.2	21.1	21.2*			
118	21.5	21.5	21.4	21.4*			
119	21.9	21.9	21.8	21.7*			
120	22.3	22.4	22.2	22.2*	22.2*		
121	22.5	22.8	22.7	22.7*	22.7*		
122	22.9	23.2	23.1	23.2	23.2*		
123	23.4	23.5	23.6	23.6	23.5*		
124	23.9	23.8	24.1	24.0	23.8*		
125	24.3	24.3	24.5	24.4	24.2	24.4*	
126	24.6*	24.9	24.9	24.9	24.8	24.9*	
127	25.0*	25.3	25.3	25.3	25.4	25.4*	25.4*
128		25.9	25.7	25.7	25.9	25.9*	25.9*
129		26.4	26.5	26.2	26.4	26.4*	26.4*
130		26.9	27.0	26.7	26.8	27.0	26.9*
131		27.2	27.4	27.3	27.3	27.5	27.3*
132		27.5	27.9	27.8	27.8	28.0	27.7
133		28.0*	28.4	28.4	28.3	28.5	28.3
134		28.5*	28.9	28.9	28.8	28.9	29.0
135			29.4	29.4	29.3	29.4	29.6
136			30.0	29.9	29.7	29.8	30.3
137			30.6	30.4	30.2	30.2	30.9
138			30.9*	30.8	30.9	30.8	31.3
139			31.2*	31.1	31.5	31.5	31.9
140			31.6*	31.6	32.2	32.2	32.4
141			32.1*	32.3	32.9	32.8	32.9
142			32.6*	33.1	33.7	33.5	33.4
143				33.6*	34.1	34.2	34.1
144				34.1*	34.4	35.0	34.7
145				34.6*	34.9	35.7	35.4
146				35.3*	35.7	36.2	36.2
147				36.0*	36.5	36.7	36.9
148					37.0	37.2	37.6
149					37.5	37.8	38.2

Table 123 (continued)

			Age, Years				Height Cm.
13	14	15	16	17	18	19	
			Weight Kg.				
							97
							98
							99
							100
							101
							102
							103
							104
							105
							106
							107
							108
							109
							110
							111
							112
							113
							114
							115
							116
							117
							118
							119
							120
							121
							122
							123
							124
							125
							126
							127
							128
							129
							130
							131
							132
28.5*							133
29.3*							134
29.9*							135
30.3*							136
30.7*							137
31.2	31.7*						138
31.8	32.0*						139
32.4	32.5*						140
33.2	33.1*						141
34.0	33.7*						142
34.7	34.5	35.3*					143
35.2	35.5	35.8*					144
35.8	36.3	36.3*					145
36.5	36.9	37.0*					146
37.1	37.4	37.7*					147
37.8	38.0	38.2					148
38.4	38.6	38.7					149

Table 123 (continued)

Height Cm.	6	7	8	9	10	11	12
				Weight Kg.	Age, Years		
150					38.1	38.5	39.0
151					38.7*	39.2	39.5
152					39.4*	39.9	40.0
153						40.5	40.6
154						41.0	41.4
155						41.5	42.1
156						42.3*	42.9
157						43.2*	43.8
158						44.0*	44.6
159						44.9*	45.4
160						45.8*	46.2
161							47.4
162							48.7
163							49.4
164							49.6*
165							49.7*
166							
167							
168							
169							
170							
171							
172							
173							
174							
175							
176							
177							
178							
179							
180							
181							
182							
183							
184							
185							
186							
187							
188							

Table 123 (continued)

			Age, Years				
13	14	15	16	17	18	19	Height Cm.
			Weight Kg.				
39.1	39.3	39.3	39.2				150
39.7	40.0	40.3	40.3				151
40.3	40.7	41.3	41.5				152
41.1	41.6	42.1	42.6				153
41.9	42.5	42.8	43.7				154
42.7	43.4	43.5	44.8	46.3*			155
43.4	44.0	44.2	45.5	47.2*			156
44.1	44.7	44.9	46.3	48.1			157
44.9	45.5	45.8	47.3	49.2	51.3*		158
45.8	46.4	46.9	48.6	50.3	52.6*		159
46.7	47.4	48.0	49.8	51.5	53.9	55.4*	160
47.3	48.1	48.8	50.2	52.0	54.4	55.9*	161
48.0	48.8	49.6	50.6	52.5	54.9	56.4*	162
48.8	49.6	50.5	51.2	53.2	55.5	57.0*	163
49.9	50.5	51.4	52.1	54.1	56.3	57.7*	164
50.9	51.4	52.3	53.1	55.1	57.1	58.3	165
51.4	52.1	53.2	54.1	56.1	57.9	59.3	166
51.8	52.9	54.0	55.1	57.0	58.7	60.3	167
52.3	53.7	54.8	56.1	57.8	59.4	61.0	168
53.1*	54.7	55.7	57.1	58.5	60.0	61.4	169
53.9*	55.6	56.5	58.1	59.1	60.5	61.7	170
	56.7	57.3	58.8	59.9	61.2	62.5	171
	57.8	58.0	58.5	60.9	62.0	63.4	172
	58.7	58.7	60.2	61.8	62.8	64.2	173
	59.2	59.6	61.1	62.7	63.8	65.1	174
	59.7	60.4	61.9	63.5	64.7	65.9	175
	60.5	61.2	62.5	64.0	65.3	66.5	176
	61.4	62.0	62.9	64.3	65.7	67.2	177
	62.4	62.8	63.4	64.7	66.1	67.8	178
	63.3*	63.9	64.5	65.4	66.6	68.4	179
	64.2*	65.1	65.7	66.1	67.1	68.8	180
		65.8	66.4	66.7	67.7	69.6	181
		66.3	67.0	67.3	68.3	70.4	182
		66.9	67.6	68.0	69.0	71.2	183
		67.5*	68.6	69.1	70.1	71.8	184
		68.2*	69.5	70.3	71.3	72.5	185
		68.8*	70.3	71.3	72.2	73.2	186
		69.3*	71.0	72.3	73.1	73.8	187
		69.8*	71.7	73.3	73.9	74.4	188

*The starred figures represent values based upon theoretical computations, rather than on exact averages.
Age is taken at the nearest birthday; for example, a boy is considered 6 years old between 5 years, 6 months and 6 years, 5 months, and 29 days. Height is taken at the nearest centimeter, weight at the nearest tenth of a kilogram.
These tables have been translated and extended from the Baldwin-Wood tables in the English system of measurement by B. T. Baldwin, Ph.D.
Issued by the Iowa Child Welfare Research Station, State University of Iowa, Iowa City, Iowa, September, 1924.

Table 124

WEIGHT-HEIGHT-AGE STANDARDS (NUDE) FOR AMERICAN-BORN
GIRLS OF SCHOOL AGE (BALDWIN-WOOD)

Height Cm.	Age, Years						
	6	7	8	9 Weight Kg.	10	11	12
97							
98							
99							
100	15.3						
101	15.7						
102	16.0	16.0*					
103	16.1	16.1*					
104	16.3	16.3*					
105	16.6	16.6*					
106	16.8	16.8*					
107	17.1	17.1					
108	17.6	17.5					
109	18.0	17.8					
110	18.2	18.1	18.2*				
111	18.4	18.5	18.4*				
112	18.6	18.8	18.6*				
113	19.2	19.3	19.1*				
114	19.7	19.8	19.7*				
115	20.2	20.1	20.2				
116	20.6	20.3	20.8				
117	21.0	20.5	21.3	21.2*	21.2*		
118	21.4	21.1	21.5	21.5*	21.5*		
119	21.8	21.8	21.8	21.9*	21.9*		
120	22.3	22.3	22.2	22.3*	22.3*		
121	22.7	22.7	22.7	22.7*	22.9*		
122	23.1	23.1	23.1	23.2	23.4	23.4*	
123	23.3	23.4	23.5	23.6	23.8	23.7*	
124	23.4	23.7	23.8	24.2	24.1	24.0*	
125	23.7	24.1	24.3	24.7	24.6	24.7*	
126	24.2*	24.4	24.8	25.2	25.3	25.8*	
127	24.7*	24.8	25.4	25.8	26.0	26.9	27.3*
128		25.2	25.8	26.2	26.4	27.2	27.1*
129		25.7	26.2	26.6	26.7	27.5	26.9
130		26.3*	26.7	27.0	27.1	27.9	27.3
131		27.1*	27.4	27.5	27.7	28.2	28.4
132		27.8*	28.1	28.0	28.2	28.6	29.5
133		28.4*	28.5	28.6	28.8	29.1	29.9
134		28.9*	29.1	29.2	29.5	29.6	30.3
135			29.6	29.8	30.1	30.1	30.7
136			30.0	30.4	30.5	30.7	31.0
137			30.4	31.0	31.0	31.3	31.4
138			30.9*	31.6	31.6	31.9	32.0
139			31.4*	32.3	32.3	32.5	32.6
140				32.9	32.9	33.1	33.2
141				33.3	33.6	33.7	34.0
142				33.6	34.4	34.3	34.8
143				34.2*	35.1	35.0	35.5
144				34.9*	35.9	35.6	36.0
145					36.6	36.4	36.6
146					36.8	37.3	37.3
147					37.1	38.2	37.9
148					37.6	38.9	38.6
149					38.2	39.5	39.2

Table 124 (continued)

13	14	15	16	17	18	Age, Years Weight Kg.	Height Cm.
							97
							98
							99
							100
							101
							102
							103
							104
							105
							106
							107
							108
							109
							110
							111
							112
							113
							114
							115
							116
							117
							118
							119
							120
							121
							122
							123
							124
							125
							126
							127
							128
							129
							130
							131
							132
							133
							134
31.5*							135
31.9*							136
32.2*							137
32.8*							138
33.4*							139
34.1	34.8*						140
34.9	35.6*						141
35.8	36.5*						142
36.3	37.4*						143
36.7	38.4*						144
37.2	39.3	41.1*					145
38.0	40.3	42.0*					146
38.8	41.4	42.8*					147
39.5	42.0	43.5*	45.1*				148
40.3	42.5	44.0*	45.5*				149

Table 124 (continued)

Height Cm.	6	7	8	9	10	11	12
				Age, Years			
				Weight Kg.			
150					38.8	40.2	39.9
151					39.5*	41.0	40.8
152					40.2*	41.8	41.7
153						42.6	42.7
154						43.4	43.8
155						44.2	44.8
156						44.1*	45.5
157						44.0*	46.2
158							47.0
159							47.9
160							48.9
161							49.6*
162							50.3*
163							51.0*
164							51.7*
165							52.4*
166							
167							
168							
169							
170							
171							
172							
173							
174							
175							
176							
177							
178							
179							
180							

Table 124 (continued)

13	14	15	16	17	18	Height Cm.
			Weight Kg.			
41.1	43.0	44.6	45.9*	46.4*		150
41.9	43.8	45.5	46.8*	47.3*		151
42.7	44.6	46.4	47.7*	48.1		152
43.5	45.4	47.1	48.6	48.9	49.9*	153
44.2	46.2	47.6	49.4	49.7	50.7*	154
45.0	47.0	48.1	50.2	50.4	51.4	155
45.7	47.5	48.9	50.7	51.1	51.7	156
46.5	48.1	49.8	51.1	51.8	52.0	157
47.4	48.7	50.5	51.4	52.2	52.4	158
48.3	49.2	51.0	51.7	52.5	52.7	159
49.2	49.8	51.5	51.9	52.8	53.1	160
49.9	50.7	52.1	52.6	53.3	53.6	161
50.6	51.5	52.7	53.2	53.7	54.0	162
51.4	52.3	53.3	53.8	54.2	54.6	163
52.2	53.2	53.7	54.3	54.8	55.3	164
53.1	54.0	54.2	54.8	55.4	55.9	165
54.0	54.5	54.6	55.7	56.1	56.6	166
54.9	54.9	55.0	56.6	56.9	57.4	167
55.6*	55.5	55.7	57.4	57.6	58.2	168
56.2*	56.6	56.9	58.2	58.2	59.2	169
56.8*	57.6	58.0	58.9	58.9	60.1	170
57.3*	58.2	58.8	59.5	59.7	60.7	171
57.8*	58.7	59.5	60.0	60.7	61.1	172
	59.1	60.1	60.5	61.4	61.6	173
	59.6*	60.5*	60.9*	61.8*	62.3*	174
	60.0*	60.8*	61.2*	62.1*	62.9*	175
	60.2*	61.0*	61.6*	62.5*	63.4*	176
	60.4*	61.2*	62.0*	62.8*	63.7*	177
	60.6*	61.5*	62.4*	63.2*	64.0*	178
	60.9*	61.8*	62.7*	63.5*	64.2*	179
	61.3*	62.2*	63.0*	63.9*	64.4*	180

*The starred figures represent values based upon theoretical computations, rather than on exact averages.

Age is taken at the nearest birthday; for example, a girl is considered 6 years old between 5 years, 6 months and 6 years, 5 months, and 29 days. Height is taken at the nearest centimeter, weight at the nearest tenth of a kilogram.

These tables have been translated and extended from the Baldwin-Wood tables in the English system of measurement by B. T. Baldwin, Ph.D.

Issued by the Iowa Child Welfare Research Station, State University of Iowa, Iowa City, Iowa, September, 1924.

children with such conditions as gigantism, adiposogenital dystrophy (Froehlich's syndrome), and cretinism due to abnormal functionings of the pituitary and the thyroid gland.

600. Pubescence. The average age for the onset of pubescence is, approximately, fourteen and one-half years in boys and thirteen and one-half years in girls. Hence the weight norms for fourteen-year-old boys and for thirteen-year-old girls are based on samplings that are approximately half prepubescent and half postpubescent. The norms for thirteen-year-old boys and for twelve-year-old girls are, predominantly, based on prepubescent children, and those for fifteen-year-old boys and for thirteen-year-old girls are, predominantly, based on postpubescent children. Until different standards become available for prepubescent and postpubescent boys of twelve to sixteen years of age and for prepubescent and postpubescent girls of eleven to fifteen years of age, the following method is recommended for the prediction of normal weight for these groups. If, for example, a twelve-year-old boy is postpubescent, his weight should be predicted from the formula for the age of fourteen years; and if a fifteen-year-old girl is prepubescent, her weight should be predicted from the formula for the age of twelve years.

The most accurate method would be to use the formula for the maturational age determined by X rays of the hand and the wrist.

601. SHORT-CUT PROCEDURE FOR THE PREDICTION OF NORMAL WEIGHT

Since changes in body build do not occur frequently in shorter than two-year periods before and after the ages of twelve and sixteen years, it is recommended that normal weight and the percentage of this normal weight of the average weight according to sex, age, and height (Tables 123 and 124, pp. 376-83) be computed for the ages of two, four, six, eight, ten, twelve, thirteen, fourteen, fifteen, sixteen, and eighteen years. For example, an eight-year-old girl is 124 cm. tall, and the index of her body build is 1.04 (proportion of normal weight). Three months later the girl is 127 cm. tall. The average weight for an eight-year-old girl of this height is 25.8 kg. (Table 124, pp. 380-83). The normal weight of this girl (clothed) then is 26.8 kg. (i.e., 25.8 × 1.04). The next year the girl is 131 cm. tall. The average weight for a nine-year-old girl of this height is 27.5 kg. The normal weight of this girl then is 28.6 kg. (i.e. 27.5 × 1.04).

602. BREATHING CAPACITY [32]

By breathing capacity is meant the measured amount of air that an individual can breathe out by forced exhalation following as full an in-

---

[32] A history of the uses of the measurement of breathing capacity may be found in *Vital Capacity of the Lungs* by J. A. Myers, which is a handbook for clinicians and others interested in the examinations of the heart and the lungs in both health and disease.

halation as it is possible for him to take. This has also been called in the literature "lung capacity" and "vital capacity." The first term, lung capacity, is a misnomer, for this measurement does not determine the capacity of the lungs, for after the complete exhalation there is still the residual air that cannot be exhaled. The term "vital capacity" is meaningless and misleading, and is based upon questionable assumptions.

Breathing capacity has long been used as one measurement of physical status, usually in the form of an index expressed as a percentage of the norm for the individual. The best variables upon which to base norms for breathing capacity are probably yet to be determined.[33] At present, norms based on sex, age, height, and normal weight seem to be as satisfactory as any.

It is common to find that correlations of different variables with breathing capacity are reduced between the ages of fourteen and seventeen years, the period of adolescence. Findings on motor performance, height, and weight show that, with other variables held constant, these three variables have a high correlation with physiological age or state of pubescence.[34] This renders it desirable that separate norms for breathing capacity be prepared for the different stages of pubescence.

There seems to be some relationship between body build and breathing capacity, although as yet this has not been statistically determined. The more slender, not too heavily muscled, individual of the linear (ectomorphic) type seems to have a greater breathing capacity for his height and weight than do the more stocky, lateral types (endomorphic and mesomorphic types). The cause of this phenomenon and the reasons for exceptions to it do not appear to be known.

603. Directions for measuring breathing capacity. The temperature of the water in the spirometer should be approximately room temperature. The subject is instructed to take as deep a breath as possible and to exhale it as completely as possible through the tube into the spirometer. Mouthpieces of relatively large size (at least ⅜ inch in inside diameter) should be used. Care should be taken that the blow is a continuous one, and that the individual does not expel air through the nose while exhaling through the mouth into the spirometer. It is wise to have several individuals lined up waiting to take the test in order to conserve time in giving instruction. The individuals watch the person being tested and gain insight into the procedure. Each subject should be given at least three trials, but may be given further trials as long as his record continues to improve. This is one test in which strict standardization of technique is undesirable, particularly as to instructions, for it may be as much an intelligence test for some people as it is a measure of the breathing capacity; hence it is important to take every precaution to insure that the subject understand what he is trying to do and that he exert a maximum effort.

[33] McCloy, *Appraising Physical Status: The Selection of Measurements*, Chap. 7.
[34] McCloy. *Appraising Physical Status: Methods and Norms*, pp. 93-96.

Table 125

BREATHING CAPACITY: NORMS (BOYS 12 TO 18)*

Nude Weight lb. (kg.)	Age (yr.)	\#56 (143)	57 (145)	58 (148)	59 (150)	60 (153)	61 (155)	62 (158)	63 (160)	64 (163)	65 (165)	66 (168)	67 (170)	68 (173)	69 (176)	70 (178)	71 (181)
							Estimated Breathing Capacity (cu. in.)									
65 (29.5)	12	116															
	13	122															
	14	128															
	15	134															
	16	140															
71 (32.2)	12	121	125	128	132	136	140										
	13	127	130	134	138	142	146										
	14	133	136	140	144	148	152										
	15	139	142	146	150	154	158										
	16	145	148	152	156	160	164										
	17	151	154	158	162	166	170										
77 (35)	12	125	129	133	137	141	145	149	154								
	13	131	135	139	143	147	151	155	160								
	14	137	141	145	149	153	157	161	166								
	15	143	147	151	155	159	163	167	172								
	16	149	153	157	161	165	169	173	178								
	17	155	159	163	167	171	175	179	184								
	18								190								
83 (37.7)	12	130	134	138	141	145	150	154	158	163							
	13	136	140	143	147	151	157	160	164	169							
	14	142	146	149	153	157	162	166	170	175							
	15	148	152	155	159	163	168	172	176	181							
	16	154	158	161	165	169	173	178	182	187							
	17	160	164	167	171	175	179	184	188	193							
	18								194	199							

Table 125 (continued)

Nude Weight, lb. (kg.)	Age (yr.)	Height, in. (cm.)															
		56 (143)	57 (145)	58 (148)	59 (150)	60 (153)	61 (155)	62 (158)	63 (160)	64 (163)	65 (165)	66 (168)	67 (170)	68 (173)	69 (176)	70 (178)	71 (181)
		Estimated Breathing Capacity (cu. in.)															
89 (40.4)	12	135	138	142	146	150	154	159	163	168	172	177	182				
	13	141	144	148	152	156	160	165	169	174	178	183	188				
	14	147	150	154	158	162	166	171	175	180	184	189	194				
	15	153	156	160	164	168	172	176	181	186	190	195	200				
	16	159	162	166	170	174	178	182	187	191	196	201	206				
	17	164	168	172	176	180	184	188	193	197	202	207	212				
	18							194	199	203	208	213	218				
95 (43.1)	12	139	143	147	151	155	159	163	168	172	177	182	187	192			
	13	145	149	153	157	161	165	169	174	178	183	188	193	198			
	14	151	155	159	163	167	171	175	180	184	189	194	199	204			
	15	157	161	165	169	173	177	181	186	190	195	200	205	210			
	16	163	167	171	175	179	183	187	191	196	201	206	211	216			
	17	169	173	177	181	185	189	193	197	202	207	212	217	222			
	18								203	208	213	218	223	228			
101 (45.9)	12			148	151	155	159	163	168	172	177	182	187	192	197		
	13			154	157	161	165	169	174	178	183	188	193	198	203		
	14			159	163	167	171	175	180	184	189	194	199	204	209		
	15			165	169	173	177	181	186	190	195	200	205	210	215		
	16			171	175	179	183	187	192	196	201	206	211	216	221		
	17			177	181	185	189	193	198	202	207	212	217	222	227		
	18									208	213	218	223	228	233		
107 (48.5)	12			156	160	164	168	172	177	181	186	191	196	201			
	13			162	166	170	174	178	183	187	192	197	202	207	213	218	224
	14			168	172	176	180	184	189	193	198	203	208	213	219	224	230
	15			174	178	182	186	190	195	199	204	209	214	219	225	230	236
	16			180	184	188	192	196	201	205	210	215	220	225	231	236	242
	17			186	190	194	198	202	207	211	216	221	226	231	237	242	248
	18			192	196	200	204	208	213	217	222	227	232	237	242	248	254

Table 125 (continued)

Estimated Breathing Capacity (cu. in.)

Nude Weight lb. (Kg.)	Age (yr.)	59 (150)	60 (153)	61 (155)	62 (158)	63 (160)	64 (163)	65 (165)	66 (168)	67 (170)	68 (173)	69 (176)	70 (178)	71 (181)	72 (183)	73 (186)	74 (188)	75 (191)
113 (51.1)	12	164	169	173	177	181	186	191	196	201	206							
	13	170	174	179	183	187	192	197	202	207	212	217	223	229				
	14	176	180	185	189	193	198	203	208	213	218	223	229	234	240	246		
	15	182	186	191	195	199	204	209	214	219	224	229	235	240	246	252	258	265
	16	188	192	197	201	205	210	215	220	225	230	235	241	246	252	258	264	271
	17	194	198	202	207	211	216	221	226	231	236	241	247	252	258	264	270	277
	18	200	204	208	213	217	222	227	231	237	242	247	253	258	264	270	276	283
119 (54)	12	173	177	182	186	191	195	200	205	211	216							
	13	179	183	188	192	197	201	206	211	217	222	227	233	239				
	14	185	189	194	198	203	207	212	217	223	228	234	239	245	251	257		
	15	191	195	199	204	209	213	218	223	228	234	240	245	251	257	263	269	275
	16	197	201	205	210	215	219	224	229	235	240	246	251	257	263	269	275	281
	17	203	207	211	216	221	225	230	235	241	246	252	257	263	269	275	281	287
	18	209	213	217	222	227	231	236	242	247	252	257	263	269	275	281	287	293
126.5 (57.4)	12	179	183	187	192	196	201	206	211	216								
	13	185	189	193	198	202	207	212	217	222	228	233	239	245				
	14	191	195	199	204	208	213	218	223	228	234	239	245	251	257	263		
	15	197	201	205	210	214	219	224	229	234	240	245	251	257	263	269	275	281
	16	203	207	211	216	220	225	230	235	240	246	251	257	263	269	275	281	287
	17	209	213	217	222	226	231	236	241	247	252	257	263	269	275	281	287	293
	18	215	219	223	228	232	237	244	247	254	259	264	270	275	281	287	293	
135.5 (61.5)	12			194	199	203	208	213	218	223								
	13			200	205	209	214	219	224	229	235	240	246					
	14			206	211	215	220	225	230	235	241	247	252	258	264			
	15			212	217	221	226	231	236	241	247	253	258	264	270	276	282	
	16			218	223	227	232	237	243	248	253	258	264	270	275	282	288	
	17			224	229	233	238	243	248	254	259	264	270	276	281	288	294	
	18			230	234	238	244	249	254	259	265	270	276	281	287	293	300	

Table 125 (continued)

Estimated Breathing Capacity (cu. in.)

Nude Weight, lb. (kg.)	Age (yr.)	59 (150)	60 (153)	61 (155)	62 (158)	63 (160)	64 (163)	65 (165)	66 (168)	67 (170)	68 (173)	69 (176)	70 (178)	71 (181)	72 (183)	73 (186)	74 (188)	75 (191)
144.5 (65.5)	12				201	206	210	215	220	225	230							
	13				207	212	216	221	226	231	236	242	247	253				
	14				213	218	222	227	232	237	242	247	253	259	265	271		
	15				219	224	228	233	238	243	248	253	259	265	270	276	283	289
	16				225	229	234	239	244	249	254	259	265	271	276	282	289	295
	17				231	235	240	245	250	255	260	265	271	277	282	288	295	301
	18				237	241	246	251	256	261	266	271	277	282	288	294	301	307
153.5 (69.6)	12				213	217	222	227	232	237								
	13				219	223	228	233	238	243	248	254	260	265				
	14				224	229	234	239	244	249	254	260	266	271	277			
	15				230	235	240	245	250	255	260	266	272	277	283	290	296	
	16				236	241	246	251	256	261	266	272	277	283	289	296	302	
	17				242	247	252	257	262	267	272	278	283	289	295	301	308	
	18				248	253	258	263	268	273	278	284	289	295	301	307	314	
162.5 (73.8)	12				219	224	229	234	239	244								
	13				225	230	235	240	245	250	255	261	267					
	14				231	236	241	246	251	256	261	267	272	278				
	15				237	242	247	252	257	262	267	273	278	284	290	296	303	
	16				243	248	253	258	263	268	273	279	284	290	296	302	309	
	17				249	254	259	264	269	274	279	285	290	296	302	308	315	
	18				255	260	265	269	275	280	285	291	296	302	308	314	321	
173 (78.5)	14							254	259	264	269	275	281	286	292	299		
	15							260	265	270	275	281	286	292	298	305	311	
	16							266	271	276	281	287	292	298	304	310	317	
	17							**272**	**277**	**282**	**287**	**293**	**298**	**304**	**310**	**316**	**323**	
	18							**278**	**283**	**288**	**293**	**299**	**304**	**310**	**316**	**322**	**329**	

Table 125 (continued)

Nude Weight, lb. (kg.)	Age (yr.)	59 (150)	60 (153)	61 (155)	62 (158)	63 (160)	64 (163)	65 (165)	66 (168)	67 (170)	68 (173)	69 (176)	70 (178)	71 (181)	72 (183)	73 (186)	74 (188)	75 (191)
												Height, in. (cm.)						
185 (84)	15							269	274	279	285	290	296	302	308	314	320	
	16							275	280	285	290	296	302	308	314	320	326	
	17							281	286	291	296	302	308	313	319	326	332	
	18							287	292	297	302	308	314	319	325	332	338	
197 (89.5)	15									288	294	299	305	311	317	323	329	
	16									294	300	305	311	317	323	329	335	
	17										300	306	311	317	323	329	335	341
	18										306	312	317	323	329	335	341	347
209 (95)	15													314	320	326	332	339
	16													320	326	332	338	344
	17													326	332	338	344	350
	18													332	338	344	350	356

Equation: B.C. (cu. in.) = .000381 height^3 (in.) + .767587 weight (lb.) + 5.953352 age (yr.) - 71.959

*Helen Garside Kelly, A Study of Individual Differences in Breathing Capacity in Relation to Some Physical Characteristics.

Table 126

BREATHING CAPACITY: NORMS (GIRLS 12 TO 18)*

Estimated Breathing Capacity (cu. in.)

Nude Weight, lb. (kg.)	Age (yr.)	Height, in. (cm.) 50 (127)	51 (130)	52 (132)	53 (135)	54 (137)	55 (140)	56 (142)	57 (145)	58 (147)	59 (150)	60 (153)	61 (155)	62 (158)	63 (160)	64 (163)	65 (165)	66 (168)
47 (21.4)	12	89																
	13	82																
53 (24.1)	12		94	98	101	104	107	111										
	13		89	93	97	101	105	109										
	14							107										
59 (26.8)	12		97	100	103	106	110	113	116									
	13		91	95	99	103	107	112	116									
	14							109	114									
65 (29.5)	12			102	105	109	112	115	118	122	125	128	131	135				
	13			98	102	106	110	114	118	122	126	130	134	138				
	14							111	116	121	126	131	136	141				
	15									129	132	138	142	147				
	16									133	137	135	138	141				
	17									127	132	141	145	149				
	18											137	141	146				
71 (32.2)	12							117	121	124	127	130	134	137				
	13							116	120	124	129	133	137	141				
	14							113	118	123	128	133	138	143				
	15								127	131	135	140	144	149				
	16									135	139	138	141	144				
	17									130	135	143	147	151				
	18											139	144	149				

Table 126 (continued)

Nude Weight lb. (Kg.)	Age (yr.)	Height, in. (cm.)																
		52 (132)	53 (135)	54 (137)	55 (140)	56 (142)	57 (145)	58 (147)	59 (150)	60 (153)	61 (155)	62 (158)	63 (160)	64 (163)	65 (165)	66 (168)	67 (170)	68 (173)
		Estimated Breathing Capacity (cu. in.)																
77 (35)	12	107	110	113	116	120	123	126	129	133	136	139	142	146				
	13	102	106	110	115	119	123	127	131	135	139	143	147	151				
	14	95	100	105	110	115	120	125	130	135	140	145	150	155				
	15																	
	16																	
	17																	
	18																	
83 (37.7)	12	109	112	115	119	122	125	128	132	135	138	141	145	148	151			
	13	105	109	113	117	121	125	129	133	137	141	146	150	154	158			
	14	98	103	107	112	117	122	127	132	137	142	147	152	157	162			
	15						130	135	139	144	148	153	157	161	166			
	16						136	139	142	146	147	150	153	156	159			
	17							135	140	145	149	157	161	165	168			
	18													163				
89 (40.4)	12	111	115	118	121	124	127	131	134	137	140	144	147	150	153			
	13	107	111	115	119	123	127	131	136	140	144	148	152	156	160			
	14	100	105	110	114	119	124	129	134	139	144	153	154	159	164			
	15						132	137	141	146	150	154	159	163	168			
	16						139	142	145	148	150	153	156	159	162			
	17							138	143	147	152	159	163	167	170			
	18									147	152	157	161	166				
95 (43.1)	12		120	120	123	127	130	133	136	139	143	146	149	152	156	159	171	
	13		117	117	122	126	130	134	138	142	146	150	154	158	162	167	176	
	14		112	112	117	122	126	131	136	141	146	151	156	161	166	171	178	
	15						134	139	143	148	152	156	161	165	170	174	171	
	16						142	145	148	154	154	156	166	162	174	178	182	
	17							146	150	150	158	162	164	170	173	178	182	
	18							141	145		155	159		168				

Table 126 (continued)

Estimated Breathing Capacity (cu. in.)

Nude Weight, lb. (Kg.)	Age (yr.)	54 (137)	55 (140)	56 (142)	57 (145)	58 (147)	59 (150)	60 (153)	61 (155)	62 (158)	63 (160)	64 (163)	65 (165)	66 (168)	67 (170)	68 (173)	69 (176)	70 (178)
101 (45.9)	12		126	129	132	135	138	142	145	148	151	155	158	161				
	13		124	128	132	136	140	144	148	153	157	161	165	169	173			
	14		119	124	129	133	138	143	148	153	158	163	168	173	178	180		
	15				136	141	145	149	154	158	162	165	172	176	180			
	16				145	148	151	154	157	160	165	173	168	171	174	185		
	17					149	153	157	161	165	169	173	177	181	185			
	18					143	148	153	157	162	167	171	176	180	185			
107 (48.5)	12				134	138	141	144	147	150	154	157	160	163				
	13				134	139	141	144	147	150	154	157	167	171	175	180		
	14				131	136	141	145	150	155	160	165	170	175	180	185		
	15				138	143	147	151	156	158	166	169	174	177	182	187		
	16				148	151	154	157	160	163	166	168	174	177	177	180		
	17				147	154	155	162	166	170	171	175	179	183	187	191		
	18				141	146	151	155	160	165	169	174	178	183	188	192		
113 (51.1)	12				137	140	143	146	150	153	156	159	162	166				
	13				137	141	145	148	153	157	161	165	170	174	178	182		
	14				133	138	143	148	153	157	162	167	174	177	182	187	192	197
	15				140	145	149	153	158	162	167	171	175	180	184	189	193	198
	16				152	154	157	160	163	167	169	172	174	177	180	183	186	189
	17				150	154	158	163	166	170	174	178	182	186	190	194	198	202
	18				144	149	153	158	163	167	172	177	181	186	190	195	200	204
119 (54)	12				139	142	145	149	152	155	158	162	165	168				
	13				139	143	147	151	156	160	164	168	172	176	180	184		
	14				135	140	145	150	155	160	169	169	174	179	184	189	194	199
	15				142	146	151	155	160	164	169	173	177	182	186	191	195	199
	16				155	158	160	163	166	169	172	175	178	180	183	186	189	192
	17				153	157	161	163	169	173	175	181	185	189	193	197	201	205
	18				147	151	156	161	165	170	175	179	184	188	193	198	202	207

Table 126 (continued)

Estimated Breathing Capacity (cu. in.)

Nude Weight, lb. (Kg.)	Age (yr.)	54 (137)	55 (140)	56 (142)	57 (145)	58 (147)	59 (150)	60 (153)	61 (155)	62 (158)	63 (160)	64 (163)	65 (165)	66 (168)	67 (170)	68 (173)	69 (176)	70 (178)
126.5 (57.4)	12						148	151	155	158	161	164	168	171				
	13						150	154	157	163	167	171	175	179	183			
	14						147	152	158	162	167	172	177	182	187	187	197	202
	15						153	158	162	167	171	175	180	184	189	192	197	202
	16						164	167	170	173	176	179	182	184	187	193	193	196
	17						164	168	172	176	180	184	188	192	196	190	204	208
	18						159	164	169	173	178	183	187	192	196	201	206	210
135.5 (61.5)	12							155	158	161	164	168	171	174				
	13							158	162	166	170	174	178	182	187	191		
	14							155	160	165	170	175	180	185	190	195	200	205
	15							161	165	169	174	178	183	187	192	196	200	205
	16							172	175	178	181	183	186	189	192	196	198	200
	17							172	176	180	184	188	192	196	200	204	208	212
	18							168	173	177	182	187	191	196	204	205	210	214
144.5 (65.5)	12								161	165	168	171	174	178				
	13								165	170	174	178	182	186	190	194		
	14								163	168	173	178	182	183	193	198	203	208
	15								168	172	177	181	186	190	194	199	203	208
	16								180	182	185	188	191	194	197	200	202	205
	17								180	184	188	192	196	200	204	208	212	216
	18								177	181	186	191	195	200	204	209	214	218
153.5 (69.6)	12										171	175	178	181				
	13										177	181	185	189	194	198		
	14										176	184	186	191	196	201	206	211
	15										180	184	189	193	197	202	206	211
	16										190	193	196	199	201	204	207	210
	17										192	196	200	204	208	212	216	220
	18										190	195	199	204	208	213	218	222

Table 126 (continued)

Nude Weight, lb. (Kg.)	Age (yr.)	Height, in. (cm.)																
		54 (137)	55 (140)	56 (142)	57 (145)	58 (147)	59 (150)	60 (153)	61 (155)	62 (158)	63 (160)	64 (163)	65 (165)	66 (168)	67 (170)	68 (173)	69 (176)	70 (178)
		Estimated Breathing Capacity (cu. in.)																
162.5 (73.8)	12												181	189	197	205		214
	13												189	193	201	209	214	214
	14												190	194	200	204	215	215
	15												191	196	206	209	212	224
	16												200	203	212	216	222	226
	17												204	208	212	217	220	222
	18												203	208	212	217	221	226
173.0 (78.5)	13												205	209	213	217	225	226
	14												208	213	213	221	217	222
	15												208	214	214	217	220	229
	16												221	221	220	229	229	231
	17												222	222				
	18												218	217	220	229	231	

Equations:

12 years B.C. = 3.240 height + .378 weight - 90.840
13 years B.C. = 4.092 height + .391 weight - 140.636
14 years B.C. = 4.945 height + .348 weight - 188.467
15 years B.C. = 4.418 height + .323 weight - 148.209
16 years B.C. = 2.852 height + .525 weight - 70.281
17 years B.C. = 4.015 height + .445 weight - 129.292
18 years B.C. = 4.635 height + .445 weight - 170.416

*From Helen Garside Kelly, A Study of Individual Differences in Breathing Capacity in Relation to Some Physical Characteristics.

604. Kelly Standards of breathing capacity.[35] Norms for breathing capacity for the ages of twelve to eighteen years[36] may be found in Tables 125 and 126 (pp. 386-95). (Satisfactory norms for ages under twelve years are not available.) These norms were computed from height and weight in English units, and give breathing capacity in cubic inches. The volumes given in the tables are for room temperature of the water.

605. Breathing capacity should be interpreted in the form of a percentage deviation above or below the norm. A variation of 16 per cent in a *volume*, such as breathing capacity or weight, is of approximately the same significance as a variation of 5 per cent in a linear dimension. This difference may be explained by the fact that a volume varies in three dimensions, and hence the total varies as the cube of a linear dimension. To reduce this volumetric variation to a linear equivalent, the cube roots of the deviations are used. For example, a falling-off from 300 to 270 cubic inches is a drop of 10 per cent in volumetric units $\left(\text{i.e., } \frac{270}{300} = .90 \right)$. If the cube roots are compared $\left(\sqrt[3]{\frac{270}{300}} = .965 \right)$, there is a falling-off of only 3.5 per cent in linear units.

The influence of disease on breathing capacity has been elaborately discussed by Myers.[37] There are two types of pathological factors influencing breathing capacity. The first consists of conditions that cause a reduction in the breathing capacity but which have no marked significance. So far as children are concerned, these may be illustrated by such conditions as old pleural adhesions, certain deformities of the thorax, premature ossification of the costal cartilages, lack of will power, and malingering. The second type consists of pathological entities that have definite clinical significance, such as cardiac disease, hyperthyroidism, asthma, emphysema, bronchitis, pleurisy, pneumothorax, pulmonary abscess, bronchiectasis, pneumonia, and pulmonary tuberculosis.

Not all the diseases falling under these classifications produce a decided reduction in breathing capacity. The most of them, however, do produce such a reduction, and not infrequently this reduced breathing capacity may be the first significant symptom found, particularly in the more chronic conditions.

If there is an excess or supernormal breathing capacity at the beginning

[35] Helen G. Kelly, *A Study of Individual Differences in Breathing Capacity in Relation to Some Physical Characteristics.*

[36] The standards for the age of eighteen years are also applicable up to about thirty-five years. After the age of thirty-five years there is a progressive falling-off in breathing capacity until at seventy-five years of age it is only 62 per cent of normal. According to B. D. Bowen and D. L. Platt (*Archives of Internal Medicine*, April, 1923, p. 579) this decrease in breathing capacity with age is as follows: 35 yr., 100%; 40 yr., 98%; 45 yr., 95%; 50 yr., 93%; 55 yr., 86%; 60 yr., 80%; 65 yr., 74%; 70 yr., 69%; 75 yr., 62%.

[37] *Op. cit.*

of the pathological process, the reduction may not be noticeable at the time of the examination. This makes it advisable to have comparable records kept in schools from year to year in order that any reduction from the individual's normal may be seen. The *change* in the breathing capacity varies with the clinical course of the disease, improving with an amelioration of the disease process and dropping off when the disease is aggravated. Since allowance must be made for the normal growth of the child in comparing present readings of breathing capacity with past readings, it is advisable that the quotients be compared rather than the original readings.

It has usually been suggested that a variation of 15 per cent under the normal for a given height and weight is almost certain to be medically suspicious and calls for a careful medical examination. With the development of better norms which take into account individual variations in build, it should be possible to reduce this to 10 per cent. At the present time it is the feeling on the part of many clinicians of experience that any child whose breathing capacity is 10 per cent below normal should be watched.

The Kelly Standards are for white subjects. A number of studies has been made which indicate that for the Negro race the normal lung capacity averages almost exactly 80 per cent of the lung capacity of the white race. Hence if these tables are used with Negroes, the values indicated should be multiplied by .8. This proportion seems to apply even to persons of only one-eighth Negro ancestry.

606. In conclusion, in the light of present knowledge, it would seem that breathing capacity should be measured as a routine under conditions that insure accuracy of measurement and that norms for the individual should be determined as accurately as possible from sex, age, height, and weight. All children whose breathing capacity is as much as 10 per cent below this standard should be referred for examination by a physician and put upon a regimen of hygiene and exercise calculated to bring the individual up to normal. This is especially true if the quotient of 100 times lung capacity, divided by the norm, represents a falling-off over a period of several months. In such a case the indications for a medical examination are multiplied.

607. GENERAL CONSIDERATIONS

After measurers have become experienced—and no measurer should consider himself qualified to measure accurately until he has measured enough subjects to raise the reliability of his measurements to .9 or above —the average person can, doing all the measurements recommended in this chapter, measure about twelve to fifteen subjects in an hour. If the examiner utilizes trained student help to take such measurements as height, weight, and breathing capacity, and if he uses recorders and hence does not have to take the time to put down the findings himself, he can readily raise this number to approximately twenty to twenty-five an hour. If he uses the method advocated in Section 601, on the alternate years, this measurement output may be raised to as much as thirty subjects an hour. Hence the examination is not unduly time consuming. More time is taken for the computation of the standards. If adequate tables are prepared for these, even the computation is something that can be held to within a reasonable limit.

At the present time there is a very limited amount of knowledge as to what real use the physical educator can make of estimates of body build and of the degree of masculinity and femininity. These, however, are pieces of information that can well be made available to the teacher of physical or health education. Further research can be conducted concerning the meaningfulness of these concepts, and the accumulating experience of the individual teacher will, undoubtedly, make them more and more meaningful. At the present time, however, physical educators should be cautious in claims made for the significance of findings of body build.

The findings on normal weight, on breathing capacity, and on fat are of special interest to adult groups in such organizations as YMCA's and YWCA's, and in hospitals, but the findings relative to over- and under-weight, and changes in breathing capacity of the lungs, may very well be of extreme interest at the school level.

CHAPTER **29**

HEALTH KNOWLEDGE

608. HEALTH-KNOWLEDGE tests may be used to determine the amount of the pupils' health knowledge at the beginning and/or at the end of a unit of instruction. A list of health-knowledge tests, alphabetically arranged according to the authors or the editors of the tests, or, if the authors or the editors are not indicated, according to the titles of the tests, follows.

Boyer, P. A. *Survey Test in Health Education*. Philadelphia: Division of Educational Research, Philadelphia Public Schools, 1940.

Brewer, J. W., and H. E. Schrammel. *Brewer-Schrammel Health Knowledge and Attitude*. Emporia, Kansas: Bureau of Educational Measurements, Kansas State Teachers College, 1935.

Brody, Leon. *Home Safety Test for High School Students and Adults: National Safety Education Tests*. New York: Center for Safety Education, New York University, 1940.

Brownell, Clifford L., and Others. *H. E. T.: Knowledge and Application*. Rockville Center, New York: Acorn Publishing Company, 1946-47.

Burt, C., and Others. *Twelfth Year Health Test; Manchester Semester-End Achievement Tests*. North Manchester, Indiana: Bureau of Tests and Measurements, Manchester College, 1936.

Byrd, Oliver E. *Byrd Health Attitude Scale*. Stanford University, California: Stanford University Press, 1940.

Cottle, William E., and Fredrika Moore. *Health Awareness*. Boston: Department of Public Health, State House, 1936.

Crow, Lester D., and L. C. Ryan. *Health and Safety Education Test*. Rockville Center, New York: Acorn Publishing Company, 1947.

Denenholz, Sylvia O. "Knowledge Test of Syphilis and Gonorrhea," *Research Quarterly*, XI (March, 1940).

Doscher, Nathan. "Two First-Aid Examinations for College Students and Adult Groups," *Research Quarterly*, XIV (May, 1943).

Forsythe, Warren E., and Mabel E. Rugen. "A Health Knowledge Test," *Research Quarterly*, VI (May, 1935).

Franzen, Raymond. *Health Education Tests*, Second Health Research Monograph, No. 1. New York: American Child Health Association, 1929.

————, and Others. *Health Awareness Test*. New York: Bureau of Publications, Teachers College, Columbia University, 1937.

Fuller, A. C. "Tests in Health and Hygiene," *Instructor*, XLVII (October, 1938).

Gallien, Shelby, and Hilda Schwehn. *Health and Safety Education Test: State High School Tests for Indiana*. Lafayette, Indiana: State High School Testing Service, Purdue University, 1945-46.

Gates, Arthur I., and Ruth Strang. *Gates-Strang Health Knowledge Tests*. New York: Bureau of Publications, Teachers College, Columbia University, 1936.

――――. *Gates-Strang Health Knowledge Test.* New York: Bureau of Publications, Teachers College, Columbia University, 1940.

General First-Aid Test for Senior-High-School Students: Nationai Safety Education Tests. New York: Center for Safety Education, New York University, 1940.

General Safety Education Test for Junior-High-School Pupils: National Safety Education Tests. New York: Center for Safety Education, New York University, 1940.

Gold, Leah. "A New Test in Health Knowledge," *Research Quarterly,* XVI (March, 1945).

Health Inventories, Co-operative Study in General Education. Chicago: American Council on Education.

"Health Tests for Elementary School Children," *Grade Teacher,* LXIV (May 1947), LXV (December, February, March, and May, 1948) *Instructor,* L (September, 1941), LI (May, 1942).

Hemphill, Fay. "Information Tests in Health and Physical Education for High School Boys," *Research Quarterly,* III (December, 1932).

Johns, Ned B. *Health Practice Inventory.* Stanford University, California: Stanford University Press, 1943.

Kilander, H. F. "Health Knowledge of High School and College Students," *Research Quarterly,* VIII (October, 1937).

――――. *Kilander Health Knowledge Test* (revised). 25 North Nelson Street, Arlington, Virginia: the Author, 1948.

――――. *Kilander Nutrition Information Test.* 25 North Nelson Street, Arlington, Virginia: the Author, 1942-46.

Lorenz, Alfred L. *National Bicycle Tests.* New York: Center for Safety Education, New York University, 1940.

Manuel, H. T. *Auto and Highway Safety Test.* Austin, Texas: Steck Company, 1938.

Murphy, Mary Agnes. "Gain in Health Knowledge of Two Groups of Women Students Classified in Physical Education," *Research Quarterly,* VIII (December, 1937).

Neher, Gerwin. *Health Inventory for High School Students.* Los Angeles: Test Bureau, Board of Education, 1944.

Orleans, Jacob, and Glen A. Sealy. *Public School Achievement Tests: Health.* Bloomington, Illinois: Public School Publishing Company, 1928.

Painter, R., and W. Stone. *Health Knowledge Test.* Chelsea, Massachusetts: Room 208, City Hall, 1935.

Pryor, H. C. *Pryor Health Test.* Pittsburg, Kansas: Kansas State Teachers College, 1930.

Rooks, Roland. "The College Freshmen's Knowledge of and Interest in Personal Hygiene," *Supplement to Research Quarterly,* VI (October, 1935).

Rosell, R., and Others. *Health Education and Hygiene: Every Pupil Test.* Columbus, Ohio: State Department of Education, 1937-38.

Rosenthal, W. F. *Health Education and Hygiene: Every Pupil Test.* Columbus: Department of Education, State of Ohio, 1935.

Rugen, Mabel E. *The Measurement of Understanding in Health Education,* Forty-fifth Yearbook. Chicago: The University of Chicago Press, 1946.

Sefton, Alice A. "Knowledge Test on Source Material in Physical Education, Including Aspects of Health Education and Recreation," *Research Quarterly,* VII (May, 1936).

Shaw, John H., and Maurice T. Troyer. *Health Education Test: Knowledge and Application*. Rockville Center, New York: Acorn Publishing Company, 1946 and 1948.

————, and Clifford L. Brownell. *Health Education Test: Knowledge and Application*. *National Achievement Tests*. Rockville Center, New York: Acorn Publishing Company, 1947.

Shupe, E. *Health Knowledge and Attitude: Every Pupil Scholarship Test*. Emporia, Kansas: Bureau of Educational Measurements, Kansas State Teachers College, 1936.

Snell, Catherine. "Physical Education Knowledge Tests," *Research Quarterly*, VI (October, 1935).

Southworth, W. H., and Others. "A Study of the Health Practices, Knowledge, Attitudes, and Interests of Senior High School Pupils," *Research Quarterly*, XV (May, 1944).

Speer, Robert K., and Samuel Smith. *Health Test*. Rockville Center, New York: Acorn Publishing Company, 1937.

————. *National Achievement Tests*. Rockville Center, New York: Acorn Publishing Company, 1938.

Stack, H. J. *Home Safety Test*. 1 Park Avenue, New York: National Bureau of Casualty and Surety Underwriters, 1935.

————. *National Safe Drivers Tests*. 1 Park Avenue, New York: National Bureau of Casualty and Surety Underwriters, 1933.

Swope, Ammon. *Judgment Test on Safe Driving Practices*. Bloomington, Illinois: McKnight and McKnight, 1939.

Test of Health Awareness. 44 West Tenth Street, New York: distributed by M. Derryberry, 1927.

Trusler, V. T., and Others. *Trusler-Arnett Health Knowledge Test*. Emporia, Kansas: Bureau of Educational Measurements, Kansas State Teachers College, 1940.

Turner, C. E. *Test Questions and Teaching Aids for Use with Personal and Community Health*. St. Louis: C. V. Mosby Company, 1949.

————, and N. C. Turner. *Objective Tests for Cleanliness and Health*. 69 Massachusetts Avenue, Cambridge, Massachusetts: the Authors, 1934.

Wilson, J. J., and A. L. Long. *Final Test in Fifth-Grade Hygiene: Comprehensive Tests for Fifth-Grade Pupils in Texas*. Oklahoma City: Harlow Publishing Company, 1933.

609. In some instances the published health-knowledge tests may, in their present form, be used profitably for certain classes. In a number of cases, however, the published health-knowledge tests need to have some items deleted and some items added in order to be usable for given classes. In most cases, probably, the published health-knowledge tests are valuable primarily for their suggestions to the teacher who would do well to construct his own tests. If the teacher constructs his own health-knowledge tests—and the directions for the construction of knowledge tests given in Chapter 24 are applicable here—he can make sure that the test items are based on the content covered in his own teaching.

610. In addition to instruction in principles, in connection with which health-knowledge tests are useful, the course in hygiene is concerned with the development of health habits, in connection with which checklists of health habits are useful. An excellent example of such a checklist may be found in *Health Education* (National Education Association, 1941). Items for inclusion in such a checklist for preschool to adult ages may be found in *Health Behavior* by Thomas D. Wood and Marion O. Lerrigo (Public School Publishing Company, Bloomington, Illinois, 1927).

A list of health habits may be checked by two-category responses indicating whether a certain health practice is or is not followed. It may also be checked by more than two-category responses; for example, the response may be as follows: 4 = practically always; 3 = usually; 2 = about half the time; 1 = seldom; 0 = never. If the two-category response is used, the score is the number of affirmative checks. If the five-category response is used, the score is the total value of the checked 4's, 3's, 2's, and 1's. The scores should be used to help the pupils discover and evaluate their own weaknesses and thereby to encourage them to improve their health habits. The scores should not be used for purposes of grading, and the score of one person should not be made known to another person by the teacher.

PART **VI**
Practical
Considerations

CHAPTER **30**

CLASSIFICATION

611. VALID METHODS of classifying pupils for participation in a program of physical education are based on such factors as size, maturity, strength, speed, ability to learn physical skills, and motor achievement. If the teacher is responsible for not more than one hundred pupils, he usually can, during the first two or three weeks of the program, make such classifications on the basis of ratings with a high degree of validity. If he is responsible for more than one hundred pupils, he may not become well enough acquainted with the pupils even during the course of a year to make such valid classifications on the basis of ratings. In the latter situation objective methods of classification need to be used. This chapter concerns such objective methods.

All classifications should be considered to be tentative, and to be subject to change in accordance with individual differences. They may be general or specific. By "general" is meant classification for participation in the entire program of physical education. By "specific" is meant classification for participation in certain sports, such as intramural football, basketball, and track-and-field athletics.

612. GENERAL CLASSIFICATION

Standards for general classification may be divided into three types: absolute standards, relative standards, and a combination of absolute and relative standards.

613. Absolute standard. Classification according to an absolute standard is classification on a scale running from zero achievement to "perfect" achievement. In this type of classification, achievement is not scored in relation to such factors as age, size, and previous experience. The following scores may be used as absolute standards for purposes of classification: the general-motor-capacity score, the Sargent Jump, the weighted- or the unweighted-strength score, the pull-up-strength score, the power score, the physical-efficiency score, total points in track-and-field athletics, and the classification index.

614. Relative standard. Classification according to a relative standard is classification according to the pupil's variation from established norms. In this type of classification, achievement is scored in relation to such factors as age, size, and maturity. The following scores may be used as relative standards for purposes of classification: the strength quotient, the motor quotient, the Brace Score, the Iowa-Brace Score, and the Johnson Score. The Johnson Test, the Brace Test, and the Iowa-Brace Test have been included under relative standards because their correlation with size is small. The strength quotient and the motor quotient seldom correlate more than .3 with subjective classifications.

A relative standard is ordinarily useful only within categories of absolute standards. For example, two sophomores in a high-school football league may have the same strength quotients. One boy, however, may be twelve years old and weigh ninety pounds, while the other may be fifteen years old and weigh one hundred and fifty pounds. Although their strength quotients may be equal, the boys would not be equated for playing football.

615. Combination of absolute and relative standards. Scores in the following events may be considered to be a combination of absolute and relative standards for purposes of classification: an obstacle race (see Chap. 18) and the motor quotient (see Chap. 12).

616. Choice of methods. In general, the tests discussed above under the heading of relative standards are recommended for purposes of classification only after the group has first been classified by an absolute standard or by a combination of an absolute and a mixed standard. For example, after a group of boys has been classified by the classification index, they may be subclassified by the strength quotient, the motor quotient, or some other relative standard.

The method used for purposes of classification may be chosen solely on the basis of its accuracy for purposes of classification, or it may be chosen on the basis of the amount of useful information that it provides in addition to that of an accurate classification. It is chosen, of necessity, on the basis of the time and the equipment available. For example, the classification index classifies boys well, is exceedingly convenient to administer, requires no apparatus not present in every gymnasium, but it gives the least amount of information useful for purposes other than classification. The general-motor-capacity test classifies well, but takes more time to administer than does the classification index; it does not require expensive equipment, and it supplies the teacher with a large amount of information useful for purposes other than classification; and it can be interpreted in terms of its individual tests as well as in terms of the motor quotient. The strength test classifies well, but requires considerable time and effort to administer, and requires very expensive apparatus; but when interpreted in terms of the strength quotient as well as in terms of the strength score (weighted or unweighted), it gives information useful for purposes other than classification.

In the tabulations that follow, tests of classification are ranked according to three criteria: (1) accuracy in classification, (2) convenience in administration, and (3) provision of information in addition to that of classification. Of the tests listed, the strength test is the only one that involves expensive equipment. The number within the parentheses after each test in the first tabulation is an average coefficient of correlation of the test with subjective ratings of classification by experienced teachers.

617. Classification Tests Ranked according to Accuracy

For Boys

1. McCloy General-motor-capacity Score (.88)
2. Total points (.86)
3. Stansbury Power Score (.85)
4. McCloy or Cozens Classification Index (.81)
5. McCloy Strength Score (.80)
6. McCloy Pull-up-strength Score (.78)
7. Wear Obstacle Race (.77)
8. Sargent Jump (.76)
9. Brace Test (.74)

For Girls

1. Wear Obstacle Race (.87)
2. McCloy General-motor-capacity Score (.81)
3. McCloy Shuttle Race (see Sec. 358) (.77)
4. Sargent Jump (.73)
5. Brace Test (.71)
6. Iowa-Brace Test (.68)
7. Johnson Test (.68)
8. Anderson-McCloy Power Score (.63)

618. Classification Tests Ranked according to Convenience of Administration

For Boys

1. McCloy or Cozens Classification Index
2. McCloy Pull-up-strength Score
3. Sargent Jump
4. Wear Obstacle Race
5. Stansbury Power Score
6. Brace Test
7. Total points
8. McCloy Strength Score
9. McCloy General-motor-capacity Score

For Girls

1. McCloy Shuttle Race
2. Wear Obstacle Race
3. Sargent Jump
4. Anderson-McCloy Power Score
5. Iowa-Brace Test
6. Brace Test
7. Johnson Test
8. McCloy General-motor-capacity Score

619. Classification Tests Ranked according to Provision of Information in Addition to That of Classification

For Boys

1. McCloy General-motor-capacity Score
2. McCloy Strength Score
3. Total points
4. McCloy Pull-up-strength Score
5. Stansbury Power Score
6. Sargent Jump
7. Brace, Iowa-Brace, or Hill Test
8. Johnson Test
9. McCloy or Cozens Classification Index

For Girls

1. McCloy General-motor-capacity Score
2. McCloy Strength Score
3. Anderson-McCloy Power Score
4. Sargent Jump
5. Brace or Iowa-Brace Test
6. Johnson Test
7. Wear Obstacle Race or McCloy Shuttle Race

620. The accuracy of the classification of boys may be increased by the use of two tests. The number within the parentheses after each test in the following tabulation is the coefficient of correlation of a combination of the two tests with other objective methods of classification. Only slightly higher coefficients of correlation have been obtained by the use of more than two tests.

Combinations of Tests Ranked according to Accuracy in Classification

McCloy General-motor-capacity Score and McCloy Strength Score	(.90)
McCloy Classification Index and total points	(.88)
Total points and McCloy General-motor-capacity Score	(.88)
McCloy Classification Index and Shuttle Run	(.87)
McCloy Classification Index and shot-put (ft.)	(.87)
McCloy Shuttle Run and shot-put (ft.)	(.87)
Total points and Brace, Iowa-Brace, or Hill Test	(.86)
McCloy General-motor-capacity Score and McCloy Pull-up-strength Score	(.86)
McCloy Classification Index and ten-second squat thrust	(.85)

SPECIFIC CLASSIFICATION

621. For track-and-field athletics. The following formula is excellent for classification, especially for running, jumping, and vaulting events:

$$10 \text{ Sargent Jump (cm.)} + \text{McCloy Classification Index}$$

The following formula is excellent for classification for the shot-put and the discus throw:

$$10 \text{ Sargent Jump (cm.)} + \text{McCloy Classification Index} + \text{McCloy Strength Score}$$

622. For sports. A combination of the Cozens Zigzag Run and the Iowa-Brace Test (see Sec. 427) is a useful device for classification in basketball. An *r* of .76 has been obtained between this battery and subjective estimates of basketball ability. It is probable that this coefficient would be increased if the classification index were included in the battery.

An r of .847 [1] has been obtained between the general-motor-capacity score and sports skills of boys. This coefficient was not increased significantly by the addition of other events to the general-motor-capacity battery. The general-motor-capacity score has been found to be as valid for the classification of girls [2] as for that of boys.

623. No standards for use with the various classification devices have been suggested because such standards are dependent upon the number of pupils in the program. The best practice is to test the first year, make a distribution of the scores from the best to the poorest, determine the number of groups to be formed, and divide the distribution to obtain that number of groups.

624. Any classification is subject to change because of such factors as the energy, the interest, the past experience, and the special aptitudes of the pupils. It is well, however, to make, at the beginning of the program, as accurate classifications as possible, and then, whenever necessary, to change such classifications. For girls, after the age of about fourteen years has been reached, changes in classification are needed primarily because of developing skills. For boys, however, sudden changes in classification are needed because of spurts of growth, which are frequently accompanied by great increases in strength.

[1] Joy W. Kistler, "The Establishment of Bases for Classification of Junior and Senior High School Boys into Homogeneous Groups for Physical Education," *Research Quarterly,* December, 1937.

[2] Theresa Anderson and C. H. McCloy, "The Measurement of Sports Ability in High School Girls," *Research Quarterly,* March, 1947.

CHAPTER 31

GRADING

625. GRADES MAY be assigned for performances in specific activities: for example, A in basketball, C in apparatus work, D in swimming, and B in tumbling. These grades, which may or may not be weighted, may be averaged for the assignment of a general grade: for example, if A, C, D, and B are not weighted, the average grade may be $C+$; if A is weighted by 3 and B by 2, the average grade may be B. Although the grading system should not become unduly complicated, the more grades that can be given in specific activities, the more useful the grades are in motivating pupils to attempt to improve each of their performances.

626. Grades may be assigned on an absolute or a relative basis: an absolute grade, as the term is used here, is assigned solely on the basis of achievement, while a relative grade is assigned on the basis of achievement in reference to potentiality. Both absolute and relative grades are useful, both from the point of view of the teacher and from that of the pupil. Whether absolute or relative grades should be assigned is a problem that could be discussed at great length without the attainment of definite conclusions. It is here recommended that in all classes in physical education except professional-training courses, absolute grades be kept in the records but that grades relative to the potentialities of the pupils be assigned to the pupils. For an oversimplified example, a boy who because of his size and his speed of muscular contraction cannot run one hundred yards in less than fourteen seconds should, according to the proposal, receive an A if he does run one hundred yards in fourteen seconds. On the other hand, a boy who has the potentiality for running one hundred yards in eleven seconds but who runs the distance in fourteen seconds should, according to the proposal, receive a D or a lower grade. Methods for the assignment of relative grades in general-motor achievement, in strength, in sports and in self-testing activities follow.

627. General-motor achievement. The McCloy General-motor-achievement Quotient (see Chap. 17), which represents the achievement of a performer in relation to his potentiality, may be used numerically, or such letter grades as A for quotients of 90 to 100, B for quotients of 80 to 90, and C for quotients of 70 to 80 may be assigned.

628. Strength. The McCloy Strength Quotient (see Chap. 14), which represents the strength of a performer in relation to his sex, age, and weight, may be assigned such letter grades as A for quotients of 115 and over, B for quotients of 105 to 114, C for quotients of 95 to 104, D for quotients of 85 to 94, and F for quotients below 85.

629. Sports.[1] A sports quotient, which represents the sports achievement of a performer in relation to that of all the other performers in his grade in school *and* in relation to the performer's own motor quotient, may be determined as follows. A performer may be rated on a seven-point scale in relation to all the other performers in his grade in school, and such numerical values may be assigned to the ratings as 120 for varsity caliber, 110 for superior, 100 for good (better than average), 90 for fair (above average), 80 for poor (below average), 70 for very poor, and 60 for terrible(!). Grades of 70 and below are probably "failing" grades. Intermediate scores may be used; for example, if the rater is undecided concerning whether a performer should be rated fair or poor, he may assign a numerical grade of 85 to the rating. The sports quotient, then, is obtained by the division of the numerical value of the rating by the motor quotient, and such letter grades may be assigned as $A+$ for a sports quotient of more than 105, A for sports quotients of 96 to 105, B for sports quotients of 88 to 95, C for sports quotients of 76 to 85, D for sports quotients of 66 to 75, and F for sports quotients of 65 and under. If, for example, a performer when compared with other performers of his age and size is rated as average in basketball, *average* being assigned a numerical rating of 80, and if the performer has a motor quotient of 88, his sports quotient is 91 $\left(\text{i.e., } \dfrac{80 \times 100}{88} \right)$, to which quotient is assigned a letter grade of B.

For an *improvement* of each ten points in sports quotients below 80, 5 should be added to the final numerical grade; for example, if a sports quotient were improved from 60 to 70, the final numerical grade should be 75, to which a letter grade of D is assigned. For an improvement of each five points in sports quotients of 80 and above, 5 points should be added to the final numerical grade; for example, if a sports quotient were improved from 85 to 90, the final numerical grade should be 95, to which a letter grade of B is assigned.

630. Self-testing-activities quotients.[2] The three major prerequisites to success in self-testing activities are muscular strength, motor educability, and courage. Although no criteria for capacity in self-testing activities have been validated, a combination of the strength quotient and either the Johnson Test or one of the Brace-type Tests might prove to be an adequate criterion.

Absolute grades may be based on the number of stunts mastered in a

[1] For the relationship of the ratings of sports to the motor quotient, see "The Measurement of Sports Ability in High School Girls" by Anderson and McCloy, *Research Quarterly*, March, 1947.

[2] McCloy, "The Organization and Teaching of Apparatus Work and Tumbling," *Journal of Physical Education*, January to April, 1937.

given amount of time, with the stunts weighted for difficulty. Stunts performed successfully by a small percentage of the performers trying to execute the stunts are rated higher in difficulty than are stunts performed successfully by a large percentage of the performers trying to execute the stunts. A convenient method for indicating the difficulty of stunts is by the use of the T-score (see Sec. 121).

A self-testing-activities quotient might, then, be determined by the division of the absolute grade by the criteria suggested in Section 629, and letter grades assigned to the numerical values.

If relative grades are used, it is possible, under optimum conditions, for all grades to be *A*'s. Although the absolute grades of achievement would undoubtedly be according to the curve of probability, the division of these absolute grades by the expectancy for each performer might result in every performer's receiving an *A*. This result, in the opinion of the authors, would not represent a defect in the system of grading, but would, on the other hand, indicate excellence in teaching and maximum co-operation in learning.

For comments on the grading of character and attitudes, see Section 478.

CHAPTER 32

ORGANIZATION OF PROGRAM
OF MEASUREMENT

631. IT IS RECOMMENDED that the testing program be so organized that certain tests be given once every three years,[1] and that other tests be, for the most part, given once or twice each year.

632. TESTS TO BE ADMINISTERED EVERY THREE YEARS

The tests discussed in this section may well be administered at the beginning of the fourth, the seventh, and the tenth grade, and at the time of the entrance to college; or at the end of the third, the sixth, the ninth, and the twelfth grade. If the tests are administered at the end of the various grades, the scores should be transmitted to the teachers concerned in the immediately following grades.

Sargent Jump. The Sargent Jump, which is, primarily, a test of the performer's power relative to his size, is especially significant in the prediction of athletic ability and in the measurement of potential velocity.

Test of motor educability. The Brace Test, the Iowa-Brace Test, or the Johnson Test should be administered once every three years. The Johnson Test is recommended for a school system in which stunts are used extensively in the general program. Each of the tests measures rather accurately the ease with which an individual learns new motor skills.

It is recommended that the general-motor-capacity score (the Sargent Jump, the Iowa-Brace Test, the ten-second squat thrust, and the McCloy Classification Index for boys) and the motor quotient be computed once every three years. The motor quotient changes very little during a three-year period unless the strength quotient increases markedly during the same period. The motor quotient, together with the T-scores of the Sargent Jump, the Iowa-Brace Test, and the ten-second squat thrust provide an excellent profile of the innate motor capacity of the pupil.

633. TESTS TO BE ADMINISTERED ONCE A YEAR OR MORE FREQUENTLY

Tests of strength. The strength test is the most important battery of tests, for strength in an amount relative to weight and to maturity is one of the most important qualities to be developed by a program of physical

[1] More frequently to pupils who develop exceptionally during the three-year period.

education. For reasons discussed in Chapter 14 the McCloy Strength Test appears to be preferable to the Rogers Strength Test. Either test, however, is satisfactory. If the back-and-leg dynamometer is not available, the short form of the strength test may be used. The short form, however, is much less satisfactory for girls than for boys.

The combination of the strength quotient with the Sargent Jump and the classification index is excellent for the prediction of athletic ability.

Classification index. The classification index, which is a measure of size and maturity, should be computed for boys at the beginning of each semester. With girls, age alone up to thirteen and one-half years is as useful as the classification index.

Measurements of body mechanics. Although measurements in the field of body mechanics do not have a high degree of validity, they may have a value for the purpose of motivation. Some measurement of posture, footprints, and the measurement of pronation by means of a pedorule or by the Ewing method may well be included in the program.

Tests in track-and-field athletics. Three or four track-and-field events should be administered twice a year. Scored on the Universal Scoring Tables or on other standard tables, track-and-field events, together with a strength test, are the best means available for the measurement of general-motor achievement. The general-motor-achievement score should be equated against the general-motor-capacity score to obtain the general-motor-achievement quotient, which is a measure of the performer's ability in relation to his motor capacity. The general-motor-achievement quotient may also be used, for boys, with the classification index or, for girls, with age to obtain the athletics quotient, which is a measure of a performer's achievement relative to the achievement of other performers of the same size and maturity.

Tests of sports skills. If satisfactory objective tests are available, they should be administered at the beginning and at the end of the period in which the sport is presented; if not, the sport skills should be rated.

Knowledge tests. Written tests of knowledge of rules and of techniques, and of health information should be used only in schools in which there is an adequate amount of time for the program of physical and health education. They may be corrected by the pupils and used as a basis for discussion.

Character ratings. The use of scales for the rating of character is important in that it causes the teacher to observe the pupils in an effort to discover their strengths and their weaknesses. Character ratings should be made several times a year, and recorded in the roll book.

Cardiovascular tests. If the school has an adequate medical service, the teacher of physical education probably has little use for cardiovascular tests. If, however, medical supervision is either lacking or inadequate, cardiovascular tests should be used, not as a matter of routine, but as indicated in specific instances. For example, the step test may be used by the teacher when in doubt as to the dosage of exercise to be given to any individual. The pulse-ratio test may also be used by a teacher who wishes to check on the probable condition of a pupil's heart.

Among the tests of "present condition," the Schneider Test, the Mc-Curdy-Larson Test, and the McCloy Test seem to be the most useful in determining the general present-health condition of the individual, a condition which may fluctuate markedly from day to day. Their primary usefulness in the schools is for checking upon the condition of pupils who have been out of school with illness to determine when they are ready for full participation in either the general physical-education program or the competitive athletics program.

The flarimeter test should be used only on a few pupils in the restricted-exercise group, but might be used annually or oftener for that group.

634. CHOICE OF TESTS

If adequate time and equipment are provided for the program of physical education, and if a leaders' group is well organized, it should be practicable to administer all the tests listed in the preceding sections. If the suggested program needs to be reduced, the elimination should begin at the end of the following tests, which are presented in their order of importance: (1) general-motor-capacity test, (2) strength tests (for boys, the classification index is combined with this test), (3) character ratings, (4) Sargent Jump and tests of motor educability, (5) sports-achievement tests and ratings, (6) measurements of body mechanics, (7) knowledge tests, and (8) cardiovascular tests.

The best educational results from a program of physical and health education come only when the needs of the individual are understood and provisions are made for their fulfillment. This involves a knowledge of (1) innate capacities, (2) present achievement, both absolute and relative to innate capacities, (3) the reasons for specific disabilities or shortcomings, (4) devices for adequate classifications, and (5) standards adapted to individual capacities for purposes of motivation and for use in grading and in promotion. To ascertain accurately and economically these facts concerning the individual, there is a need for using the valid measuring devices that exist and for developing valid measuring devices for qualities not as yet capable of valid measurement.

Possession of the requisite information concerning the individual does not in itself insure that the teacher will develop a superior program. It does imply that he can formulate as superior a program as his training, ability, and industry will permit.

CHAPTER 33

ADMINISTRATION OF PROGRAM
OF MEASUREMENT

635. BEFORE THE administration of any tests, the necessary equipment should be arranged in appropriate places, the heights of equipment should be adjusted, necessary markings on the floor or on the ground should be made, and scoring blanks and/or rating scales should be prepared. An adequate number of recorders should be instructed in the directions for scoring, and an adequate number of assistants (usually student leaders) should be thoroughly trained in the administration of the events.

636. The instructions for the subjects, which should be as clear and as precise as possible, should include a statement of the purpose of the test. Verbal instructions should, if at all possible, be accompanied by demonstrations.[1]

637. If an event can be scored rapidly, it should be scored at the time of the performance and the result announced at that time to the performer. If this procedure is not feasible, the results should be announced to the performers at the earliest-possible time.

638. If tests in a number of track-and-field events are being conducted in the same class period, different squads may start different events at the same time. In this way, for example, the high jump may be run off with only a small fraction of the class at one time, thus expediting the conduct of the event. Time is usually saved by handling the groups in military formation, moving to command, but without the necessity for strict military discipline.

639. Specific instructions concerning the administration of various tests have been presented in connection with the description of the tests, including the necessary amount of preliminary practice. In this chapter is presented general information concerning equipment, timing of events, and measuring of heights and distances.

640. EQUIPMENT

Shots and balls used for testing purposes should be of standard weights. The weight of the indoor baseball, especially, should be checked, for it varies more than that of the outdoor baseball.

---

[1] Examples of well-prepared instructions for testing may be found in *Measuring Motor Ability* by David K. Brace, and in *Group Examination Alpha* (May 20, 1918) of the Division of Psychology, of the Medical Department of the U.S. Army.

414

Dynamometers should be tested when they are purchased; if found to be inaccurate, they should be returned to the factory. They should also be checked at the beginning of every period of strength testing (see Sec. 299, footnote 25).

Spirometers. Dry spirometers, with the exception of the flarimeter, are not recommended for use because of their inaccuracy. Flarimeters are not recommended for use with children because children usually are not able to keep the water line of the indicator at the proper level. If wet spirometers are used, the water should not fluctuate more than one or two degrees from 26 degrees Centigrade or 79 degrees Fahrenheit.

Sphygmomanometers, stethoscopes, and metronomes. The level of the mercury in the mercury sphygmomanometer should be checked daily. The aneroid sphygmomanometer should be checked against a mercury sphygmomanometer periodically. Although any standard stethoscope is satisfactory, the flat, Bowles type, which conducts sounds very well, is somewhat more convenient to use than some of the other types. A metronome with a bell that rings at the end of each fourth beat is the recommended type, and may be purchased at any of the better psychological instrument houses.

Scales. Platform scales, which are usually accurate, should be tested when they are purchased, and should then be balanced every day. Spring scales should be tested before each period of testing: a common method for this testing is to put a weight of exactly one hundred pounds on the scales. Another method is to weigh any person on the spring scales, and then to weigh that person on platform scales of known accuracy.

641. TIMING OF EVENTS

Events may be timed by the use of stop watches. This method is a slow one unless many stop watches and an equal number of expert timers are available. Short-distance running events may also be timed in terms of the number of zones run if the necessary markings are prepared (see Sec. 117); longer events may be timed in seconds (and if desired, in half seconds) by counting the seconds aloud (see Sec. 340).

642. MEASUREMENT OF HEIGHT OR OF DISTANCE

Running broad jump. Several sets of three markers each should be available. The three jumps of each performer should be indicated by markers of one kind. After several performers have jumped three times, the best jump for each performer should be measured. The starting line should be on smooth ground, the measurement being taken from the outline of the toe on the ground.

Standing broad jump. If the standing broad jump is conducted indoors, lines, one inch apart, should be painted on the mat from three feet in front of the take-off to eleven feet. The lines indicating every inch should be painted one color, and the lines indicating every twelfth inch should be painted another color and the feet numbered. At the completion of each jump the judge marks the distance on the edge of the mat with chalk, or records at once the distance jumped.

It is usually thought desirable to permit the toes to project over the edge of the board marking the starting line to prevent slipping.

Throwing events. In events like putting a shot or throwing a baseball for distance, arcs may be drawn at convenient intervals, with the center of the throwing circle as the center of the arcs. In the shot-put, the arcs may be one foot apart, beginning at a distance that can be exceeded by the poorest performer and continuing beyond the distance that the best performer is expected to attain. In events like the discus throw or the basketball throw, the marks may be from five to ten feet apart.

In throwing events it is convenient to have two sets of arcs opposite each other, and an adequate distance apart. Thus, a shot put from the first circle may be returned by another competitor in the second circle.

In the javelin throw the markings, which are similar to those of a football field, are parallel lines five or ten feet apart. The javelin is thrown from behind one end line by one performer, and returned from behind the other end line by another performer.

High jumps. The performers may be divided into squads according to one of several heights at which they wish to begin, or the performers may be divided into squads according to their own heights.

If enough standards are available, five heights may be selected arbitrarily. The performer attempts to jump over the lowest bar. If he clears the bar, he tries to jump over the next highest bar. He continues to attempt to jump over each bar, taking up to three trials over each. The highest jump made, regardless of whether or not bars of preceding heights were missed or cleared, is taken as the record. Although this method is not particularly satisfactory, it is sometimes used as a rough screening device.

The performer may attempt to jump over a bar of a given height. If he succeeds, the bar is moved up one inch, and this procedure may be continued as long as the performer wishes to attempt to clear the bar (even though he may have failed to clear the bar at a lower height). Either the best height cleared is recorded, or a height one inch lower than the height attempted when the bar is touched or removed in such a way as to make it certain that the next height below would have been cleared is recorded. If only one trial or two trials are given for each height, the latter method is somewhat fairer to the performer than is the former method.

If a bar is used, it should be put on with the same side up each time. If sticks or ropes are used, the degree of sag should be standardized. Measurements should be made from the top of the middle of the bar (stick or rope) to the mat, or the floor, or the ground.

APPENDIX A

STATISTICAL METHODS

643. IN THIS APPENDIX an attempt has been made to present, and to give examples of, statistical devices commonly used in analyses of data in the field of physical and health education. It has been assumed that the reader would have read Chapter 4 of this textbook and that he would have had at least an introductory course in the use of measurements in education. Hence the explanations have been reduced to a minimum, and the formulas have been presented primarily for the convenience of the reader who might want to refer to them in connection with materials presented in this textbook. Although an attempt has been made to provide a guide to the utilization of statistical techniques, it must be kept in mind that a brief treatise on statistical techniques cannot be a substitute for the detailed information presented in books[1] completely devoted to statistical techniques, which information, together with experience in the use of statistics in a particular area, is prerequisite to sound analyses of data in that area.

SAMPLES AND POPULATIONS

644. A **population** is a defined group, and a **sample** is a part of that group. If, for example, a study were conducted to determine the average height of all the male students attending the universities of the Western Intercollegiate Conference (the "Big Ten"), the entire number of these male students would represent the population. If, in order to determine the best estimate of the average height of this population, the heights of fifty male students who had been selected at random[2] from each of the ten univer-

---

[1] The following references are especially useful to researchers in the area of physical and health education:

Herbert Arkin and Raymond R. Colton, *An Outline of Statistical Methods*[4].
———, *Tables for Statisticians.*
Ronald A. Fisher, *Statistical Methods for Research Workers*[11].
Henry E. Garrett, *Statistics in Psychology and Education*[4].
Karl J. Holzinger, *Statistical Methods for Students in Education.*
Darrell Huff, *How to Lie with Statistics.*
Truman L. Kelley, *Statistical Method.*
Everett F. Lindquist, *A First Course in Statistics.*
———, *Statistical Analysis in Educational Research.*

[2] If, in a university with seventy-five hundred male students and with the names of these students arranged alphabetically, students 1, 151, 301, 451, etc. were selected, the selection would usually be considered to have been made *at random.* Tables of random numbers may be found in: Arkin and Colton, *Tables for Statisticians;* Ronald A. Fisher and Frank Yates, *Statistical Tables for Biological, Agricultural and Medical Research;* M. G. Kendall and B. B. Smith, *Tables of Random Sampling Numbers;* and Lindquist, *Statistical Analysis in Educational Research.*

sities were averaged, these five hundred male students would represent a sample.

METHODS OF STATISTICAL ANALYSIS

645. A sample of fewer than fifty subjects is seldom justifiable in the area of physical and health education. Although there are formulas for the analyses of data of fewer than fifty subjects, small numbers of subjects are still small numbers of subjects, and hence, regardless of the method of selection of the subjects or of the method of the analysis of the data, small samples are frequently unrepresentative of the populations from which they were drawn.

646. The data of a random sample, as well as the data of a population, are usually distributed according to the normal probability curve (see Sec. 72). To illustrate the normal probability curve, it is suggested that each student flip four coins, and that the number of heads resulting from the trials of all the students be tabulated. It is further suggested that the teacher keep a cumulative record of such trials for a number of years. The following data represent such a collection.

Number of heads in one flipping	4	3	2	1	0
Number of heads in 1954 flippings	132	498	726	477	121
Percentage of heads of total number of flippings	6.755	25.486	37.155	24.411	6.192
Theoretical percentage (on basis of normal probability curve) of heads of total number of flippings	6.25	25.00	37.50	25.00	6.25
Difference between percentages	.505	.486	−.345	−.589	−.058

647. The classification of data into a **frequency distribution** involves (1) the determination of the range (see Sec. 68) of the data, (2) the determination of the size of the class interval (see Sec. 69), and (3) the tabulation of the data.

The **range** of the weights in Table 127 (p. 419) is 85 (i.e., 180-95).

The number of **class intervals** (CI) should be small enough for the distribution of the data to be meaningful, and large enough for distinctions among the data to be retained. It is recommended that the number of CI's be not less than twelve[3] nor more than twenty. It is further recommended that the size of the CI be 1, 2, 3, 5, 10, or a multiple of 5 or of 10. If the range is divided by the desired number of CI's, the quotient represents the size of the CI. If the range of the data for the weights is divided

[3] If the data are of such nature that the range is less than 12, a correspondingly smaller number of CI's may be used; for example, the range of data for pull-ups may be 8, in which case there would be eight CI's.

Table 127*

RAW SCORES

Subject	Weight (lb.)	Strength Score (lb.)		
	Group I	Group I	Group II i	Group II f
1	139	1231	1358	1584
2	135	1259	1194	1277
3	133	1277	1384	1379
4	147	1447	943	1254
5	173	1538	1469	1781
6	123	1215	1185	1216
7	131	1126	1088	1000
8	142	1270	1284	1566
9	125	1199	1351	1722
10	138	1136	1522	1439
11	132	1317	1405	1210
12	137	1287	1422	1402
13	147	1211	1180	1221
14	123	1223	1301	1614
15	115	1110	1377	1612
16	180	1431	1442	1521
17	124	1099	1269	1316
18	132	1137	1447	1733
19	143	1387	1367	1529
20	137	1297	1563	1599
21	159	1250	1336	1458
22	150	1330	1257	1512
23	95	743	1388	1412
24	124	1300	1242	1511
25	130	1318	1289	1392
26	114	1390	1639	1802
27	127	1185	1590	1612
28	159	1506	1484	1692
29	130	1498	1717	1940
30	129	986	1708	1951
31	149	1232	1178	1233
32	178	1378	1145	1402
33	105	1141	1472	1528
34	135	1112	1493	1490
35	104	954	1587	1782
36	142	1370	1471	1697
37	145	1308	1880	1999
38	160	1729	1293	1467
39	143	1635	1053	1042
40	161	1533	1287	1416
41	171	1660	1758	1836
42	115	1264	1350	1514
43	137	1454	1261	1389
44	133	1517	1898	2102
45	163	1611	1058	1167
46	171	1581	1346	1483
47	137	1531	1714	1814
48	147	1525	1486	1724
49	156	1486	1509	1711
50	139	1287	1240	1394

*The weights and the strength scores of Group I are the data for
subjects 71 to 120 in a series of data for 406 subjects in secondary schools collected by Louis E. Hutto, and analyzed by him
in the Measurement of the Velocity Factor and of Athletic Power
in High School Boys. The initial (i) strength scores of Group II
are the data for subjects 121 to 170 in the same series of data.
The final (f) strength scores of Group II are fictitious data.

by 17, the quotient is 5 (i.e., $85 \div 17$); hence *5* is the recommended size of the *CI* for the weights. For the other data in Table 127 (p. 419) the recommended size of the *CI* is *60*.

In the selection of the lower and the upper limit of a *CI* it is recommended that a whole number be used for the **mid-point** (*Mp*) of the *CI*, and that a *Mp* be selected that is divisible by the size of the *CI*. In the data for the weights the *Mp*'s of the *CI*'s are multiples of 5. The lower limit and the upper limit of the lowest *CI* are 92.5 and 97.4, respectively. In the data for the strength scores, the *Mp*'s are multiples of 60. The lower limits and the upper limits of the lowest *CI*'s of Group I,

Table 128[*]

FREQUENCY DISTRIBUTION

Frequency Distribution				Supplementary Computations			
CI	Mp	Tabulation	f	d	fd		fd²
177.5 - 182.4	180	//	2	9	18		162
172.5 - 177.4	175	/	1	8	8		64
167.5 - 172.4	170	//	2	7	14		98
162.5 - 167.4	165	/	1	6	6		36
157.5 - 162.4	160	///	4	5	20		100
152.5 - 157.4	155	/	1	4	4		16
147.5 - 152.4	150	//	2	3	6		18
142.5 - 147.4	145	卌 /	6	2	12		24
137.5 - 142.4	140	卌	5	1	5	+ 93	5
132.5 - 137.4	135	卌 ///	8	0	0		0
127.5 - 132.4	130	卌 /	6	-1	- 6		6
122.5 - 127.4	125	卌 /	6	-2	-12		24
117.5 - 122.4	120		0	-3	0		0
112.5 - 117.4	115	///	3	-4	-12		48
107.5 - 112.4	110		0	-5	0		0
102.5 - 107.4	105	//	2	-6	-12		72
97.5 - 102.4	100		0	-7	0		0
92.5 - 97.4	95	/	1	-8	- 8	- 50	64
			N = 50		Σfd = 43		Σfd² = 737

[*]The raw scores are the weights in Table 127.

Group II *i*, and Group II *f* are 690 and 749, 930 and 989, 990 and 1049, respectively.

The data for the weights are tabulated in the fourth column, and the frequencies (*f*) are indicated in the fifth column of Table 128 (p. 420), which columns, together with the *CI*'s, represent a frequency distribution for the weights.

MEASURES OF CENTRAL TENDENCY

648. The **arithmetic mean** (*Mn*) is the most commonly used measure of central tendency. It is advantageous in that it can be used in further statistical computations. It is disadvantageous in that its value can be distorted by data of either extremely low or extremely high values.

The Mn (see Sec. 71) of the weights is 139.2800 (i.e., 6964 ÷ 50).[4]

The Mn is that value above which and below which the sums of (Σ) the deviations (d) of the scores from the Mn are equal, and it may be computed with sufficient accuracy from a frequency distribution. If this method of computation is used, an **assumed mean** (AMn) is selected. The Mp of any CI may be selected as an AMn. It is recommended, however, that a CI with a large frequency and near the center of the distribution be selected. In the distribution of the weights in Table 128 (p. 420), 135 has been selected as the AMn. The numbers in the d column represent the numbers of the CI's above and below the CI of which 135 is the Mp. The numbers in the fd column are the results of the f column multiplied by the d column. The difference between the AMn and the Mn may be computed by the following formula for the correction (c) of the AMn:

$$c = \frac{\Sigma fd}{N} \times CI$$

The Mn computed from grouped data is the result of the c added algebraically to the AMn. The Mn of the weights computed in this manner is 139.3000 $\left[\text{i.e., } 135 + \left(\frac{43}{50} \times 5\right)\right]$, which is the value used hereafter in this appendix.

649. The **Median** (Mdn) (see Sec. 71) is advantageous in that it is easily computed and is not distorted in value by data of extremely high or extremely low values. It is disadvantageous in that it cannot be manipulated algebraically.

In an odd number of data arranged in value from the lowest to the highest datum, the Mdn is the middle datum. In an even number of data similarly arranged, the Mdn is the average of the two data nearest the middle of the data. The Mdn of the weights is 137.0000 $\left(\text{i.e., } \frac{137 + 137}{2}\right)$.

The weights arranged in order from the highest to the lowest weight follow: 180, 178, 173, 171, 171, 163, 161, 160, 159, 159, 156, 150, 149, 147, 147, 147, 145, 143, 143, 142, 142, 139, 139, 138, 137, 137, 137, 137, 135, 135, 133, 133, 132, 132, 131, 130, 130, 129, 127, 125, 124, 124, 123, 123, 115, 115, 114, 105, 104, 95.

The Mdn may be computed with sufficient accuracy from a frequency distribution. In this method of computation it is assumed that the data in

---

[4] Unless otherwise indicated, all the computations in this chapter have been carried to five places and rounded off to four places. This procedure is recommended in the area of physical and health education in such computational procedures as factorial analyses, partial correlations of high order and multiple correlations. The numbers themselves are not significant to such a large number of decimals, but rounding off can introduce systematic errors that can cumulate and hence cause unnecessary divergences from the correct figures. If only the mean or the standard deviation or the coefficient of a zero-order correlation is computed, two decimal places (i.e., computations carried out to three places and rounded off to two places) are sufficient.

each CI are distributed uniformly in that CI. The Mdn of the weights computed from a frequency distribution is 136.8750, which is the value used hereafter in this appendix.

(1) The half sum, which is 25, is $N \div 2$ (i.e., $50 \div 2$).

(2) The subtotal, which is 18, is the number of f's counted from the bottom of the distribution as far upward as possible without exceeding the half sum (i.e., $1 + 0 + 2 + 0 + 3 + 0 + 6 + 6$).

(3) The difference between the half sum and the subtotal, which is 7 (i.e., $25 - 18$), is divided by the frequency in the first CI that is above the CI used to obtain the subtotal and that has a frequency of more than 0. The result is $\frac{7}{8}$ $\left(\text{i.e., } \frac{25 - 18}{8}\right)$. The c is this result multiplied by the size of the CI, which product is 4.3750 $\left(\text{i.e., } \frac{7}{8} \times 5\right)$. The Mdn is the result of the c added to the lower limit[5] of the CI above the one that was taken for the subtotal (i.e., $132.5 + 4.375$).

650. The **mode** (Mo) is that measure that occurs most frequently in a series of data. It is advantageous in that it is not affected by extremely high or extremely low values. It is disadvantageous in that it is an accurate measure of central tendency only if a large number of data is present. The Mo of the unclassified weights is 137.

The Mo may also be determined from a frequency distribution. It is the Mp of the CI that has the largest f. The Mo of the weights arranged in a frequency distribution is 135.

The Mo may be determined more accurately by the following formula than by the preceding two methods:

$$Mo = Mn - 3(Mn - Mdn)$$

Computed by this formula, the Mo of the weights is 132.0250 [i.e., $139.3 - 3(139.3 - 136.875)$].

651. The **harmonic mean** is a useful measure in problems dealing with velocities and times. If three performers, for example, run the 100-yard dash in 10, 12, and 20 seconds, respectively, the average velocity is 7.7778 yards per second $\left(\text{i.e., } \dfrac{\dfrac{100}{10} + \dfrac{100}{12} + \dfrac{100}{20}}{3}\right)$. The harmonic mean is 12.8571 seconds (i.e., $100 \div 7.7778$), which is the time corresponding to the average velocity for these three performers for the 100-yard dash.

---

[5] If the half sum falls immediately below a CI with a f of 0, the Mp of the CI with a f of 0 is taken as the Mdn. If the half sum includes all the cases through a certain CI, and the CI immediately above has a f of 1 or more, the upper limit of the CI in which the half sum falls, or the lower limit of the CI above, is taken as the Mdn.

652. In a bilaterally symmetrical distribution, the Mn, the Mdn, and the Mo coincide. If these values do not coincide, the distribution is said to be **skewed.** If the low data are spread out gradually and the high data are massed together, the distribution is said to be skewed negatively (to the left). If the high data are spread out gradually and the low data are massed together, the distribution is said to be skewed positively (to the right). The skewness may be computed by

$$Sk = \frac{3(Mn - Mdn)}{SD \text{ (see Sec. 653)}}.$$

Computed by this formula, the Sk of the weights is .3889

$$\left[\text{i.e., } \frac{3(139.3 - 136.875)}{18.7085} \right].$$

If the distribution is bilaterally symmetrical, $Sk = 0$.

MEASURES OF VARIABILITY

653. The **standard deviation** (SD or σ) is advantageous in that the deviation of every score from the Mn is taken into consideration, and it is useful in numerous further statistical computations. It may be computed by (Table 129, p. 424)

$$SD = \sqrt{\frac{\Sigma d^2}{N}}.$$

In this formula, d represents the deviation of each datum from the Mn. Computed by this formula, the SD of the weights is 18.6720 (i.e., $\sqrt{17432.10 \div 50}$).

The SD may also be computed by (Table 130, p. 424)

$$SD = \sqrt{\frac{\Sigma \text{ score}^2}{N} - Mn^2}.$$

Computed by this formula, the SD of the weights is 18.5221

$$\left(\text{i.e., } \sqrt{\frac{987,378}{50} - 139.3^2} \right).$$

The SD may also be computed with sufficient accuracy from a frequency distribution by (Table 128, p. 420)

$$SD = \sqrt{\frac{\Sigma fd^2}{N} - \left(\frac{\Sigma fd}{N}\right)^2} \times CI.$$

Computed by this formula, the SD of the weights is 18.7085

$$\left(\text{i.e., } \sqrt{\frac{737}{50} - \left(\frac{43}{50}\right)^2} \times 5 \right),$$

which is the value used hereafter in this appendix.

Table 129

STANDARD DEVIATION BY $\sqrt{\dfrac{\Sigma d^2}{N}}$: WORKSHEET

$$Mn = 139.3$$

Weight	d	d^2	Weight	d	d^2
139	.3*	.09	114	25.3	640.09
135	4.3	18.49	127	12.3	151.29
133	6.3	39.69	159	19.7	388.09
147	7.7**	59.29	130	9.3	86.49
173	33.7	1135.69	129	10.3	106.09
123	16.3	265.69	149	9.7	94.09
131	8.3	68.89	178	38.7	1497.69
142	2.7	7.29	105	34.3	1176.49
125	14.3	204.49	135	4.3	18.49
138	1.3	1.69	104	35.3	1246.09
132	7.3	53.29	142	2.7	7.29
137	2.3	5.29	145	5.7	32.49
147	7.7	59.29	160	20.7	428.49
123	16.3	265.69	143	3.7	13.69
115	24.3	590.49	161	21.7	470.89
180	40.7	1656.49	171	31.7	1004.89
124	15.3	234.09	115	24.3	590.49
132	7.3	53.29	137	2.3	5.29
143	3.7	13.69	133	6.3	39.69
137	2.3	5.29	163	23.7	561.69
159	19.7	388.09	171	31.7	1004.89
150	10.7	114.49	137	2.3	5.29
95	44.3	1962.49	147	7.7	59.29
124	15.3	234.09	156	16.7	278.89
130	9.3	86.49	139	.3	.09
				$\Sigma d^2 =$	17432.10

*i.e., 139.3 - 139
**i.e., 147 - 139.3

Table 130

STANDARD DEVIATION BY $\sqrt{\dfrac{\Sigma \, score^2}{N} - Mn^2}$: WORKSHEET

Weight	Weight^2	Weight	Weight^2
139	19321	114	12996
135	18225	127	16129
133	17689	159	25281
147	21609	130	16900
173	29929	129	16641
123	15129	149	22201
131	17161	178	31684
142	20164	105	11025
125	15625	135	18225
138	19044	104	10816
132	17424	142	20164
137	18769	145	21025
147	21609	160	25600
123	15129	143	20449
115	13225	161	25921
180	32400	171	29241
124	15376	115	13225
132	17424	137	18769
143	20449	133	17689
137	18769	163	26569
159	25281	171	29241
150	22500	137	18769
95	9025	147	21609
124	15376	156	24336
130	16900	139	19321
		$\Sigma score^2 =$	987378

424

If N = less than 50, the SD may be computed by (Table 131, p. 425)

$$SD = \sqrt{\frac{\Sigma d^2}{N-1}}.$$

If the sample is comprised of the fifth, the tenth, the fifteenth . . . the fiftieth strength score (Table 127, p. 419) of Group I, the SD of the sample of

ten cases is, computed by the preceding formula, 231.9420 $\left(\text{i.e., } \sqrt{\frac{484174}{10-1}}\right)$.

The limits within which, according to the SD (see Sec. 72, Table 132, p. 426, and Fig. LV, p. 428), various percentages of the fifty weights lie are given in Table 133 (p. 427).

Table 131

STANDARD DEVIATION OF SMALL SAMPLE: WORKSHEET

Strength Score	$\underline{d}$	$\underline{d}^2$
	Mn = 1277	
1538	261*	68121
1136	141	19881
1110	167**	27889
1297	20	400
1318	41	1681
986	291	84681
954	323	104329
1533	256	65536
1611	334	111556
1287	10	100
$\Sigma = \overline{12770}$		$\Sigma = \overline{484174}$

*i.e., 1538 - 1277.
**i.e., 1277 - 1110.

654. The **probable error** (PE) is .6745 times the SD. Hence the PE of the weights is 12.6189 (i.e., .6745 × 18.7085).

In a normal distribution the PE may be interpreted as follows (Fig. LVI, p. 428) : 50 per cent of the data lie between one PE above and one PE below the Mn; 16.13 per cent of the data lie in the second PE above the Mn, and 16.13 per cent of the data lie in the second PE below the Mn; 6.72 per cent of the data lie in the third PE above the Mn, and 6.72 per cent of the data lie in the third PE below the Mn; 1.8 per cent of the data lie in the fourth PE above the Mn, and 1.8 per cent of the data lie in the fourth PE below the Mn; and .35 per cent of the data lie above the fourth PE above the Mn, and .35 per cent of the data lie below the fourth PE below the Mn.

655. The **quartile deviation** (Q) is a deviation on either side of the Mdn that may be used to determine the range of the middle 50 per cent of the data. The first quartile (Q_1) represents the upper limit of the range in which the lowest 25 per cent of the data lie. The third quartile (Q_3)

Table 132

NORMAL PROBABILITY CURVE: FRACTIONAL PARTS OF TOTAL AREA
(TAKEN AS 10,000)

$\frac{x}{\sigma}$	.00	.01	.02	.03	.04	.05	.06	.07	.08	.09
0.0	0000	0040	0080	0120	0160	0199	0239	0279	0319	0359
0.1	0398	0438	0478	0517	0557	0596	0636	0675	0714	0753
0.2	0793	0832	0871	0910	0948	0987	1026	1064	1103	1141
0.3	1179	1217	1255	1293	1331	1368	1406	1443	1480	1517
0.4	1554	1591	1628	1664	1700	1736	1772	1808	1844	1879
0.5	1915	1950	1985	2019	2054	2088	2123	2157	2190	2224
0.6	2257	2291	2324	2357	2389	2422	2454	2486	2517	2549
0.7	2580	2611	2642	2673	2704	2734	2764	2794	2823	2852
0.8	2881	2910	2939	2967	2995	3023	3051	3078	3106	3133
0.9	3159	3186	3212	3238	3264	3290	3315	3340	3365	3389
1.0	3413	3438	3461	3485	3508	3531	3554	3577	3599	3621
1.1	3643	3665	3686	3708	3729	3749	3770	3790	3810	3830
1.2	3849	3869	3888	3907	3925	3944	3962	3980	3997	4015
1.3	4032	4049	4066	4082	4099	4115	4131	4147	4162	4177
1.4	4192	4207	4222	4236	4251	4265	4279	4292	4306	4319
1.5	4332	4345	4357	4370	4383	4394	4406	4418	4429	4441
1.6	4452	4463	4474	4484	4495	4505	4515	4525	4535	4545
1.7	4554	4564	4573	4582	4591	4599	4608	4616	4625	4633
1.8	4641	4649	4656	4664	4671	4678	4686	4693	4699	4706
1.9	4713	4719	4726	4732	4738	4744	4750	4756	4761	4767
2.0	4772	4778	4783	4788	4793	4798	4803	4808	4812	4817
2.1	4821	4826	4830	4834	4838	4842	4846	4850	4854	4857
2.2	4861	4864	4868	4871	4875	4878	4881	4884	4887	4890
2.3	4893	4896	4898	4901	4904	4906	4909	4911	4913	4916
2.4	4918	4920	4922	4925	4927	4929	4931	4932	4934	4936
2.5	4938	4940	4941	4943	4945	4946	4948	4949	4951	4952
2.6	4953	4955	4956	4957	4959	4960	4961	4962	4963	4964
2.7	4965	4966	4967	4968	4969	4970	4971	4972	4973	4974
2.8	4974	4975	4976	4977	4977	4978	4979	4979	4980	4981
2.9	4981	4982	4982	4983	4984	4984	4985	4985	4986	4986
3.0	4986.5	4986.9	4987.4	4987.8	4988.2	4988.6	4988.9	4989.3	4989.7	4990.0
3.1	4990.3	4990.6	4991.0	4991.3	4991.6	4991.8	4992.1	4992.4	4992.6	4992.9
3.2	4993.129									
3.3	4995.166									
3.4	4996.631									
3.5	4997.674									
3.6	4998.409									
3.7	4998.922									
3.8	4999.277									
3.9	4999.519									
4.0	4999.683									
4.5	4999.966									
5.0	4999.997									

EXAMPLE:

		%	%
Mn + 1 SD	= 34.13	(	
			(68.26
Mn − 1 SD	= 34.13	(	
Mn + 2 SD	= 47.72	(	
∴ 13.59% (i.e., 47.72 − 34 13) is within SD 2 above mean			(95.44
Mn − 2 SD	= 47 72	(	
Mn + 3 SD	= 49.865	(	
∴ 2.145% (i.e., 49.865 − 47 72) is within SD 3 above mean			(99.73
Mn − 3 SD	= 49.865	(	

Mn ∓ 1.96 SD = 95.00 (i.e., 47.5 x 2)
Mn ∓ 2.58 SD = 99.02 (i.e , 49.51 x 2)

represents the lower limit of the range in which the highest 25 per cent of the data lie. The value of Q_1 and that of Q_3 may be computed as follows from a frequency distribution (Table 128, p. 420). The Q_1 of the weights is

$$127.9167 \left(\text{i.e., } N \div 4 = 50 \div 4 = 12.5; \text{subtotal} = 12; c = \frac{12.5 - 12}{6} \times 5; \right.$$

$$\left. Q_1 = 127.5 + .4167 \right). \text{ The } Q_3 \text{ of the weights is } 148.75 \left(\text{i.e., } \tfrac{3}{4}N = 37.5; \right.$$

$$\text{subtotal} = 37; c = \frac{37.5 - 37.0}{2} \times 5 \left. \right). \text{ The } Q \text{ may be computed by}$$

$$Q = \frac{Q_3 - Q_1}{2}.$$

Table 133

STANDARD DEVIATION: EXAMPLE OF ITS USE

Subjects		Range of Weights
Percentage	Number*	
68.26	34.13	120.5915 [i.e., 139.3 (Mn) - 18.7085 (SD)] - 158.0085 (i.e., 139.3 + 18.7085)
13.59	6.795	120.5915 - 101.8830 [i.e., 139.3 - (2 x 18.7085)]
13.59	6.795	158.0085 - 176.7170 [i.e., 139.3 + (2 x 18.7085)]
2.145	1.0725	101.8830 - 83.1745 [i.e., 139.3 - (3 x 18.7085)]
2.145	1.0725	176.7170 - 195.4255 [i.e., 139.3 + (3 x 18.7085)]
.135	.0675	below 83.1745
.135	.0675	above 195.4255
100.00	50.0000	

*Statistically, such numbers as 34.13 subjects, etc. are meaningful.

Computed by this formula, the Q of the weights is 10.4167

$$\left(\text{i.e., } \frac{148.75 - 127.9167}{2} \right).$$

Hence the middle 50 per cent of the weights lie between 126.4583 [i.e., $136.875(Mdn) - 10.4167$] and 147.2917 (i.e., $136.875 + 10.4167$).

RELIABILITY OF STATISTICAL ANALYSES

656. The measures of central tendency and of variability that were presented in Sections 645 to 655 are values based on the records of selected boys in secondary schools in Iowa, and hence are *statistics*, that is, measures calculated from samples. Similar measures based on the records of all the boys in all the secondary schools in Iowa, which records would be difficult, if not impossible, to obtain, are called **parameters**. The relationship of statistics of central tendency and of variability to the best estimates of the corresponding parameters can be determined by the standard errors, the probable errors, and the critical ratios (t values if $N =$ less than 50) of the statistics involved.

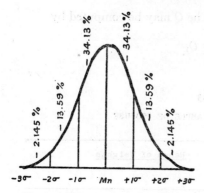

FIGURE LV. Area under Normal Probability Curve (SD or σ) (In a normal distribution 99.73 per cent of the data fall within three SD's from the Mn.)

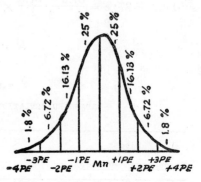

FIGURE LVI. Area under Normal Probability Curve (PE) (In a normal distribution 99.3 per cent of the data fall within four PE's from the Mn. The SD and the PE have the following interrelationships: PE = .6745 SD; SD = 1.4826 PE.

657. If $N = 50$ or more, the **standard error of the mean** may be computed by

$$SE_{Mn} = \frac{SD}{\sqrt{N}}.$$

Computed by this formula, the SE of the Mn of the weights is 2.6458 (i.e., $18.7085 \div \sqrt{50}$). This value may, in a normal distribution, be used as follows to determine the best estimate of the upper and the lower limits of various intervals in which the Mn of the weights of the entire population from which Group I was drawn may be expected to lie. The Mn of the weights of 95 per cent of that population may be expected to be no larger than 144.4858 [i.e., 139.3 [6] + (1.96 [7] × 2.6458)] and no smaller than 134.1142 [i.e., 139.3 − (1.96 × 2.6458)]; and the Mn of the weights of 99 per cent of that population may be expected to be no larger than 146.1262 [i.e., 139.3 + (2.58 × 2.6458)] and no smaller than 132.4738 [i.e., 139.3 − (2.58 × 2.6458)].

658. The method of determining best estimates of parameters may, in

[6] Mn of sample.
[7] Table 132 (p. 426).

terms of the fifty weights, be explained as follows. If the Mn of the weights of each of one hundred samples of fifty subjects drawn at random from the same population from which Group I was drawn, was obtained, the one hundred Mns would tend to be normally distributed. The Mn of the one hundred Mns is the best estimate of the Mn of the weights of the entire population, and the SE of the Mn of the sample of fifty cases is the best estimate of the SE of the Mn of the one hundred Mns.

If $N = $ less than 50, the SE of the Mn may be computed by

$$SE_{Mn} = \frac{SD \text{ (Table 131)}}{\sqrt{N}}.$$

Computed by this formula, the SE of the Mn of the ten strength scores (Table 131, p. 425) is 73.3460 (i.e., $231.9420 \div \sqrt{10}$). This value may be interpreted like the SE of the Mn of the fifty weights except that Table 135 is used instead of Table 132. Hence the Mn of the strength scores of 95 per cent of the entire population from which Group I was drawn may be expected to be no larger than 1442.7620 [i.e., $1277 + (2.26$ [8] $\times 73.3460)$] and no smaller than 1111.2380 [i.e., $1277 - (2.26 \times 73.3460)$]; and the Mn of the strength scores of 99 per cent of that population may be expected to be no larger than 1515.3745 [i.e., $1277 + (3.25 \times 73.3460)$] and no smaller than 1038.6255 [i.e., $1277 - (3.25 \times 73.3460)$].

659. If $N = 50$ or more, the **SE of the difference between two Mns** of the same test given to different groups, or of uncorrelated tests[9] given to the same group, may be computed by

$$SE_{\text{Dif}_{Mns}} = \sqrt{SE^2_{Mn_1} + SE^2_{Mn_2}}.$$

Computed by this formula, the SE of the difference between the Mns of the strength scores of Group I and Group II i is 39.7825 (i.e., $\sqrt{27.6517^2 + 28.6012^2}$).

If $N = 50$ or more, the **SE of the difference between the Mns** of the same test given to the same group at different times, or of correlated tests[10] given to the same group, may be computed by

$$SE_{\text{Dif}_{Mns}} = \sqrt{SE^2_{Mn_1} + SE^2_{Mn_2} - (2r_{12}SE_{Mn_1}SE_{Mn_2})}.{}^{[11]}$$

Computed by this formula, the SE of the difference between the Mns of the strength scores of Group II i and Group II f is 17.1703 [i.e., $\sqrt{28.6012^2 + 34.5366^2 - (2 \times .8686 \times 28.6012 \times 34.5366)}$].

660. The **critical ratio** (CR) (see Sec. 73) is the difference between the same statistics of two groups of subjects, or of two tests administered

---

[8] Table 135 (p. 431).

[9] For example, the strengths of the bicipites femorum and the intelligence quotients of the same group of subjects.

[10] For example, the strengths of the latissimi dorsi and of the teretes majores.

[11] $r_{12} = .8686$; the r was computed according to the method indicated in Section 666.

to the same subjects, divided by the *SE* of that difference. Hence the *CR* of the *Mns* of the strength scores of Group II *f* and Group II *i* is 7.5479 $\left[\text{i.e., } \dfrac{1526.4 \ (Mn\,f) - 1396.8 \ (Mn\,i)}{17.1703}\right]$. This value may, in a normal distribution, be used as follows to determine the best estimate of the upper and the lower limits of various differences between the means of strength scores at the beginning and at the end of an experiment. If experiments comparable to the experiment conducted on Group II were conducted on each of one hundred groups of fifty subjects drawn from the same population from which Group II was drawn, the difference between the means of the strength scores would, in ninety-five of the experiments, be expected to be no larger than 163.2538 [i.e., $129.6(Mn\,f - Mn\,i) +$

Table 134

STANDARD ERROR OF DIFFERENCE BETWEEN CORRELATED
MEANS OF SMALL SAMPLE: WORKSHEET

Strength Score f	Strength Score i	$X_f - X_i - \text{Dif}_{Mns}$	$(X_f - X_i - \text{Dif}_{Mns})^2$
1781	1469	168.7	28459.69
1439	1522	-226.3	51211.69
1612	1377	91.7	8408.89
1599	1563	-107.3	11513.29
1392	1289	- 40.3	1624.09
1951	1708	99.7	9940.09
1782	1587	51.7	2672.89
1416	1287	- 14.3	204.49
1167	1058	- 34.3	1176.49
1394	1240	10.7	114.49
Σ = 15533	Σ = 14100		Σ = 115326.10

Mn = 1553.3   Mn = 1410

Dif$_{Mns}$ = 143.3 (i.e., 1553.3 - 1410.0)

$(1.96\,^{[12]} \times 17.1703)]$ and no smaller than 95.9462 [i.e., $129.6 - (1.96 \times 17.1703)$]; and in ninety-nine of the experiments the difference would be expected to be no larger than 173.8994 [i.e., $129.6 + (2.58 \times 17.1703)$] and no smaller than 85.3006 [i.e., $129.6 - (2.58 \times 17.1703)$].

A *CR* of 1.96 is large enough for most experiments in the area of physical and health education.

661. If $N =$ less than 50, the *SE* of the difference between the *Mns* of the same test given to different groups, or of uncorrelated tests given to the same group, may be computed by

$$SE_{\text{Dif}_{Mns}} = \sqrt{\frac{\Sigma d_1^2 + \Sigma d_2^2}{(N_1 - 1) + (N_2 - 1)}} \times \sqrt{\frac{N_1 + N_2}{N_1 N_2}}.$$

Computed by this formula, the *SE* of the difference between the *Mn*

[12] Table 132 (p. 426).

of the ten strength scores of Group I (Table 131, p. 425) and the Mn of the ten strength scores of Group II i [13] is 95.8792

$$\left(\text{i.e., } \sqrt{\frac{484174 + 343230}{(10 - 1) + (10 - 1)}} \times \sqrt{\frac{10 + 10}{10 \times 10}}\right).$$

If $N =$ less than 50, the SE of the difference between the Mns of the same test given to the same group at different times, or of correlated tests given to the same group, may be computed by

$$SE_{\text{Dif}_{Mns}} = \sqrt{\frac{\Sigma[(X_1 - X_2) - (Mn_1 - Mn_2)]^2}{N(N - 1)}}.$$

Table 135*

TABLE OF t

Degrees of Freedom (N - 1)	Probability		
	.05	.02	.01
1	t = 12.71	t = 31.82	t = 63.66
2	4.30	6.96	9.92
3	3.18	4.54	5.84
4	2.78	3.75	4.60
5	2.57	3.36	4.03
6	2.45	3.14	3.71
7	2.36	3.00	3.50
8	2.31	2.90	3.36
9	2.26	2.82	3.25
10	2.23	2.76	3.17
11	2.20	2.72	3.11
12	2.18	2.68	3.06
13	2.16	2.65	3.01
14	2.14	2.62	2.98
15	2.13	2.60	2.95
16	2.12	2.58	2.92
17	2.11	2.57	2.90
18	2.10	2.55	2.88
19	2.09	2.54	2.86
20	2.09	2.53	2.84
21	2.08	2.52	2.83
22	2.07	2.51	2.82
23	2.07	2.50	2.81
24	2.06	2.49	2.80
25	2.06	2.48	2.79
26	2.06	2.48	2.78
27	2.05	2.47	2.77
28	2.05	2.47	2.76
29	2.04	2.46	2.76
30	2.04	2.46	2.75
35	2.03	2.44	2.72
40	2.02	2.42	2.71
45	2.02	2.41	2.69
50	2.01	2.40	2.68

*Abridged from Table III of Ronald A. Fisher and Frank Yates, Statistical Tables for Biological, Agricultural and Medical Research, published by Oliver and Boyd, Ltd., Edinburgh, by permission of the authors and publishers.

[13] The fifth, tenth, fifteenth . . . fiftieth strength scores (Table 127, p. 419) were used for the sample. $Mn = 1410$.

Computed by this formula, the SE of the difference between the Mn of the ten strength scores of Group II i and the Mn of the ten strength scores of Group II f is 35.7967 $\left[\text{i.e., } \sqrt{\dfrac{115326.10}{10(10-1)}}, \text{ Table 134, p. 430}\right]$.

If $N =$ less than 50, the difference between two statistics divided by the SE of this difference is called a t. Hence the t of the Mns (Table 134, p. 430) of the strength scores of Group II i and Group II f is 4.0032 $\left[\text{i.e., } \dfrac{1553.3 - 1410}{35.7967}\right]$. This value may be interpreted like the CR except that Table 135 is used instead of Table 132. Hence if experiments comparable to the experiment conducted on Group II were conducted on each of one hundred groups of ten subjects drawn from the same population from which Group II was drawn, the difference between the means of the strength scores would, in ninety-five of the experiments, be expected to be no larger than 224.2005 [i.e., $143.3(Mn f - Mn i) + (2.26^{14} \times 35.7967)$] and no smaller than 62.3995 [i.e., $143.3 - (2.26 \times 35.7967)$]; and in ninety-nine of the experiments the difference would be expected to be no larger than 259.6393 [i.e., $143.3 + (3.25 \times 35.7967)$] and no smaller than 26.9607 [i.e., $143.3 - (3.25 \times 35.7967)$].

662. The t, in terms of the ten strength scores of Group I and the ten strength scores of Group II i, is interpreted like the t of the ten strength scores of Group II i and Group II f, except that eighteen degrees of freedom (i.e., $N_1 - 1 + N_2 - 1$) are used instead of nine degrees of freedom.

A t that meets the probability of .05 (Table 135, p. 431) is high enough for most experiments in the area of physical and health education.

663. The **SE of a percentage** may be computed by

$$SE_\% = 100\sqrt{\frac{pq}{N}}.$$

In this formula p is the proportion of the subjects that exceed a certain score, and q is $1 - p$. In Group I, one subject had a strength score that exceeded 1700, and in Group II i, six subjects had strength scores that exceeded 1700. The p of Group I is .02 (i.e., $1 \div 50$), and that of Group II i is .12 (i.e., $6 \div 50$). The q of Group I is .98 (i.e., $1 - .02$), and that of Group II i is .88 (i.e., $1 - .12$). Computed by the preceding formula, the SE of the percentage of Group I is 2.000 $\left(\text{i.e., } 100\sqrt{\dfrac{.02 \times .98}{50}}\right)$, and that of Group II i is 4.5800 $\left(\text{i.e., } 100\sqrt{\dfrac{.12 \times .88}{50}}\right)$.

664. The SE of the difference between two percentages of the same test given to different groups, or of uncorrelated tests, may be computed by

$$SE_{\text{Dif}\%'s} = \sqrt{SE^2_{\%_1} + SE^2_{\%_2}}.$$

[14] Table 135 (p. 431); nine degrees of freedom ($N - 1$).

Computed by this formula, the SE of the difference between the indicated percentages of the strength scores of Group I and Group II i is 4.9976 (i.e., $\sqrt{2.00^2 + 4.58^2}$). The CR is 2.0010 $\left(\text{i.e., } \dfrac{12 - 2}{4.9976}\right)$.

MEASURES OF RELATIONSHIP OF SAMPLES (see Sec. 74) [15]

665. The relationship between two variables (called a **zero-order** correlation) may be determined by a **coefficient of product-moment correlation,** which may be computed by

$$r = \frac{\dfrac{\Sigma XY}{N} - (Mn_x Mn_y)}{SD_x SD_y}.$$

The X and the Y represent the data to be correlated. Computed by this formula, the r between the weights and the strength scores of Group I is

$.6376 \left[\text{i.e., } \dfrac{\dfrac{9318784}{50} - (139.3 \times 1321.2)}{18.7085 \times 195.5280} \right]$. The 9318784 is the sum of the

products of the weights and the strength scores of Group I [i.e., $(139 \times 1231) + (135 \times 1259) \cdots + (139 \times 1287)$]. The fifty products are: 171109; 169965; 169841; 212709; 266074; 149445; 147506; 180340; 149875; 156768; 173844; 176319; 178017; 150429; 127650; 257580; 136276; 150084; 198341; 177689; 198750; 199500; 70585; 161200; 171340; 158460; 150495; 239454; 194740; 127194; 183568; 245284; 119805; 150120; 99216; 194540; 189660; 276640; 233805; 246813: 283860; 145360; 199198; 201761; 262593; 270351; 209747; 224175; 231816; 178893.

666. The r may also be computed from a scattergram. The data must first be plotted, which procedure is like making a two-dimensional frequency distribution for each set of data. In Table 136 (p. 434) is presented a scattergram for the weights and the strength scores of Group I. The r may be computed from a scattergram by

$$r = \frac{\dfrac{\Sigma xy}{N} - \left(\dfrac{\Sigma fd_x}{N} \times \dfrac{\Sigma fd_y}{N}\right)}{\sqrt{\dfrac{\Sigma fd_x^2}{N} - \left(\dfrac{\Sigma fd_x}{N}\right)^2} \times \sqrt{\dfrac{\Sigma fd_y^2}{N} - \left(\dfrac{\Sigma fd_y}{N}\right)^2}}.$$

Computed by this formula, the r between the weights and the strength

scores of Group I is .6957 $\left[\text{i.e., } \dfrac{\dfrac{468}{50} - \left(\dfrac{51}{50} \times \dfrac{43}{50}\right)}{\sqrt{\dfrac{583}{50} - \left(\dfrac{51}{50}\right)^2} \times \sqrt{\dfrac{737}{50} - \left(\dfrac{43}{50}\right)^2}} \right]$. The

[15] If there is no relationship between two sets of data, the best prediction of one set of data from the other is the Mn. There is, for example, no relationship between the length of the nose and the width of the foot of men five feet in height. Hence if, knowing only the length of the nose of a man five feet in height, one wished to predict the width of his foot, the best prediction would be the best estimate of the Mn of the width of the feet of all men in that population who were five feet in height.

Table 136

PRODUCT-MOMENT CORRELATION AND CORRELATION RATIO: SCATTERGRAM

468 is obtained as follows. The values in the d squares are multiplied, and the products are inserted in the Σxy column. Two examples follow.

(1) The first value in the Σxy column of CI 177.5 − 182.4

45 = 5 × 9 (see d). The 5 is obtained as follows. The f (1) in CI 1350 − 1409 is multiplied by the d of that CI, which is +2. The f (1) in CI 1410 − 1469 is multiplied by the d of that CI, which is +3. The sum of the products is 5 (i.e., 2 + 3).

(2) The twelfth value in the Σxy column of CI 122.5 − 127.4

12 = −6 × −2 (see d). The −6 is obtained as follows. The f (1) in CI 1050 − 1109 is multiplied by the d of that CI, which is −3. The f (4) in CI 1170 − 1229 is multiplied by the d of that CI, which is −1. The f (1) in CI 1290 − 1349 is multiplied by the d of that CI, which is +1. The sum of the products is −6 [i.e., −3 + (−4) + 1].

434

From a product-moment r, a **regression equation** can be computed to predict the most probable value of one variable corresponding to the other variable. The equation is

$$X_0 = r_{01} \frac{\sigma_0}{\sigma_1} X_1 - (r_{01} \frac{\sigma_0}{\sigma_1} Mn_1 - Mn_2)$$

667. The relationship between two variables may be determined by an r if the means of the columns and the means of the rows of a scattergram form straight lines. If the means form curves, the degree of relationship between the two variables may be determined by a correlation ratio (η_{yx} and η_{xy}) (eta). The η's may be computed by the following formulas (Table 136, p. 434):

$$\eta^2_{xy} = \frac{\frac{1}{N} \Sigma \left[\frac{(\Sigma f_y d_x)^2}{f_y} \right] - \left(\frac{\Sigma f d_x}{N} \right)^2}{\frac{\Sigma f d^2_x}{N} - \left(\frac{\Sigma f d_x}{N} \right)^2}$$

The η_{xy} is for the smoothed line drawn through the means of the rows.

$$\eta^2_{yx} = \frac{\frac{1}{N} \Sigma \left[\frac{(\Sigma f_x d_y)^2}{f_x} \right] - \left(\frac{\Sigma f d_y}{N} \right)^2}{\frac{\Sigma f d^2_y}{N} - \left(\frac{\Sigma f d_y}{N} \right)^2}$$

The η_{yx} is for the smoothed line drawn through the means of the columns.

The $(\Sigma f_x d_y)^2$ for each row is the square of the value in the upper left corner of each square in the d row.

Hence $\eta^2_{xy} = .6552$ $\left[\text{i.e., } \dfrac{\frac{1}{50}(399.88)^* - \left(\frac{51}{50}\right)^2}{\frac{583}{50} - \left(\frac{51}{50}\right)^2} \right]$, and $\eta_{xy} = .8156$. Hence

$\eta^2_{yx} = .5042$ $\left[\text{i.e., } \dfrac{\frac{1}{50}(407.81)^* - \left(\frac{43}{50}\right)^2}{\frac{737}{50} - \left(\frac{43}{50}\right)^2} \right]$, and $\eta_{yx} = .7101$.

If there are many rows or columns with frequencies of 1 or 2, as in Table 136, η approaches 1.00 and is meaningless. Hence η should not be used in this kind of scattergram.

668. In the **rank-difference method of correlation** only the positions of the items in a series are taken into account. A rank of 1 is assigned to the highest datum, a rank of 2 to the next highest datum, etc. If the values of two or more data are the same, the average of the ranks is assigned to each datum. The rank-difference coefficient may be computed by (Table 137, p. 436)

$$\rho_{(\text{rho})} = 1 - \frac{6 \Sigma D^2}{N(N^2 - 1)}.$$

D is the difference between the ranks. Computed by this formula, the ρ

* Computations carried to three places and rounded off to two places.

APPENDIX A

Table 137

RANK-DIFFERENCE CORRELATION: WORKSHEET

Subject	Group I Weight	Rank	Group I Strength Score	Rank	Difference between Ranks	Difference^2
1	139	22.5	1231	35	12.5	156.25
2	135	29.5	1259	32	2.5	6.25
3	133	31.5	1277	29	2.5	6.25
4	147	15	1447	15	0	0
5	173	3	1538	6	3	9
6	123	43.5	1215	37	6.5	42.25
7	131	35	1126	44	9	81
8	142	20.5	1270	30	9.5	90.25
9	125	40	1199	39	1	1
10	138	24	1136	43	19	361
11	132	33.5	1317	23	10.5	110.25
12	137	26.5	1287	27.5	1	1
13	147	15	1211	38	23	529
14	123	43.5	1223	36	7.5	56.25
15	115	45.5	1110	46	.5	.25
16	180	1	1431	16	15	225
17	124	41.5	1099	47	5.5	30.25
18	132	33.5	1137	42	8.5	72.25
19	143	18.5	1387	18	.5	.25
20	137	26.5	1297	26	.5	.25
21	159	9.5	1250	33	23.5	552.25
22	150	12	1330	21	9	81
23	95	50	743	50	0	0
24	124	41.5	1300	25	16.5	272.25
25	130	36.5	1318	22	14.5	210.25
26	114	47	1390	17	30	900
27	127	39	1185	40	1	1
28	159	9.5	1506	11	1.5	2.25
29	130	36.5	1498	12	24.5	600.25
30	129	38	986	48	10	100
31	149	13	1232	34	21	441
32	178	2	1378	19	17	289
33	105	48	1141	41	7	49
34	135	29.5	1112	45	15.5	240.25
35	104	49	954	49	0	0
36	142	20.5	1370	20	.5	.25
37	145	17	1308	24	7.0	49
38	160	8	1729	1	7.0	49
39	143	18.5	1635	3	15.5	240.25
40	161	7	1533	7	0	0
41	171	4.5	1660	2	2.5	6.25
42	115	45.5	1264	31	14.5	210.25
43	137	26.5	1454	14	12.5	156.25
44	133	31.5	1517	10	21.5	462.25
45	163	6	1611	4	2	4
46	171	4.5	1581	5	.5	.25
47	137	26.5	1531	8	18.5	342.25
48	147	15	1525	9	6.0	36
49	156	11	1486	13	2.0	4
50	139	22.5	1287	27.5	5.0	25

$$\Sigma D^2 = 7101.50$$

for the weights and the strength scores of Group I is .6590

$$\left[\text{i.e., } 1 - \frac{6(7101.50)}{50(2500 - 1)}\right].$$

The ρ is generally used with this kind of data merely as an exploratory device. It may be used profitably in the correlation of traits that cannot be measured accurately, but which can be ranked.

669. The **biserial method of correlation** (see Sec. 76) may be used if one set of data represents a continuous variable and the other set of data

Table 138*

BISERIAL CORRELATION: WORKSHEET

Baskets Made in Thirty Seconds (no.)	Unsuccessful Players (no.)	Successful Players (no.)	f	d	fd	fd²
18		1	1	8	8	64
17			0	7	0	0
16		2	2	6	12	72
15		3	3	5	15	75
14	7	8	15	4	60	240
13	4	5	9	3	27	81
12	6	13	19	2	38	76
11	10	7	17	1	17	17
10	11	8	19	0	0	0
9	23	3	26	-1	-26	26
8	11	3	14	-2	-28	56
7	21		21	-3	-63	189
6	11		11	-4	-44	176
5	15		15	-5	-75	375
4	8		8	-6	-48	288
3	3		3	-7	-21	147
	130	53	183		-128	1882
	N	N	Σf		Σfd	Σfd²

*The data were taken from L. William Johnson, "Objective Basketball Tests for High School Boys" (M.A. Thesis, State University of Iowa, 1934).

represents classifications into two categories. For example, in the first column in Table 138 (p. 437) are the numbers of baskets made in thirty seconds; the number of baskets made is a continuous variable. In the second and the third column are the numbers of baskets made by unsuccessful players[17] and by successful players,[18] respectively; hence the two groups of players constitute the dichotomous variable. The biserial method of correlation should be used with caution, and the results interpreted with reservations unless the distribution of the dichotomous variable (or attribute) can validly be assumed to be approximately normal.

The r of biserial correlation may be computed by

[17] Players who failed to "make the squad."
[18] Players who "made the squad."

$$r_{\text{bis}} = \frac{Mn_p - Mn_q}{SD} \times \frac{pq}{z}.$$

In this formula Mn_p, which is the mean of the continuous variable of the successful group (or the group showing the superior or more valuable characteristics), is 12; Mn_q, which is the mean of the continuous variable of the unsuccessful group (or the contrasting group), is 8.2;

Table 139

z VALUES OF AREA UNDER NORMAL PROBABILITY CURVE

p	.00	.01	.02	.03	.04	.05	.06	.07	.08	.09
.00	.0000	.0267	.0484	.0680	.0862	.1031	.1191	.1343	.1487	.1624
.10	.1755	.1880	.2000	.2115	.2226	.2332	.2433	.2531	.2624	.2714
.20	.2800	.2882	.2961	.3036	.3109	.3178	.3244	.3306	.3366	.3423
.30	.3477	.3528	.3576	.3621	.3664	.3704	.3741	.3776	.3808	.3837
.40	.3863	.3887	.3909	.3928	.3944	.3958	.3969	.3978	.3984	.3988
.50	.3989	.3988	.3984	.3978	.3969	.3958	.3944	.3928	.3909	.3887
.60	.3863	.3837	.3808	.3776	.3741	.3704	.3664	.3621	.3576	.3528
.70	.3477	.3423	.3366	.3306	.3244	.3178	.3109	.3036	.2961	.2882
.80	.2800	.2714	.2624	.2531	.2433	.2332	.2226	.2115	.2000	.1880
.90	.1755	.1624	.1487	.1343	.1191	.1031	.0862	.0680	.0484	.0267

SD, which is the SD of the continuous variable of the entire group, is $3.1297 \left[\text{i.e., } \sqrt{\frac{1882}{183} - \left(\frac{-128}{183}\right)^2 \times 1} \right]$; p, which is the proportion of the successful group to the whole group, is .2896; q, which is $1 - p$, is .7104 (i.e., $1.0000 - .2896$); and z, which is the height of the ordinate between p and q in a normal distribution whose area and SD are together equal to 1, is .3423. The value of z is read from Table 139 (p. 438).

Table 140

TRISERIAL CORRELATION: WORKSHEET

Standing Broad Jump (in.)	Prepubescent Boys (no.)	Pubescent Boys (no.)	Postpubescent Boys (no.)	f	d	fd	fd²
102			1	1	7	7	49
99				0	6	0	0
96	1	1	1	3	5	15	75
93	1	1	3	5	4	20	80
90		2	5	7	3	21	63
87	2	5	7	14	2	28	56
84	2	4	4	10	1	10	10
81	4	8	3	15	0		
78	7	6	1	14	-1	-14	14
75	4	2	1	7	-2	-14	28
72	3	3		6	-3	-18	54
69	2			2	-4	- 8	32
66	2	1		3	-5	-15	75
63	1			1	-6	- 6	36
	29	33	26	88		26	572
	N_1	N_2	N_3	Σf		Σfd	Σfd^2

The r_{bis} between the numbers of baskets made in thirty seconds by successful and by unsuccessful players is .7296

$$\left[\text{i.e., } \frac{12 - 8.2}{3.1297} \times \frac{.2896 \times .7104}{.3423}\right].$$

670. The **triserial method of correlation** may be used if one set of data represents a continuous variable, and the other set of data represents a classification into three categories. In the first column in Table 140 (p. 438) are records in inches for the standing broad jump; the standing broad jump is a continuous variable. In the second, the third, and the fourth column are the numbers of the various records in the standing broad jump made by groups of prepubescent, pubescent, and post-pubescent boys, respectively; hence the three groups of boys constitute the trichotomous variable.

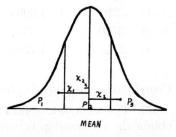

FIGURE LVII. Centroid Deviations of Each Segment of Distribution

To use the method of triserial correlation with confidence, there must be assurance that the trichotomous variable is approximately normally distributed. The r of triserial correlation may be computed by

$$r_{\text{tris}} = \frac{\Sigma pxy}{\Sigma px^2}.{}^{[19]}$$

The p (Fig. LVII, p. 439) is the proportion of the number of boys in each category [i.e., prepubescence (1), pubescence (2), and postpubescence (3)]. Hence $p_1 = .3295$ (i.e., $29 \div 88$), $p_2 = .3750$ (i.e., $33 \div 88$), and $p_3 = .2955$ (i.e., $26 \div 88$).

The x (Fig. LVII) is the deviation of the centroid of each of the three categories of the trichotomous variable from the mean. The x's may be computed by the following formulas:

$$x_1 = \frac{-z_1}{p_1}\left(\frac{-.3621}{.3295} = -1.0989\right); \quad x_2 = \frac{z_1 - z_2}{p_2}\left(\frac{.3621 - .3477}{.3750} = .0384\right);$$

$$x_3 = \frac{z_2}{p_3}\left(\frac{.3477}{.2955} = 1.1766\right).{}^{[20]}$$

The y's are the differences between the Mns of each column and the Mn of the whole group divided by the SD of the whole group. Hence

$$y_1 = \frac{Mn_1 - Mn_0}{SD_0} = \frac{77.5863 - 81.8865}{7.5969} = -.5660;$$

[19] For the derivation of the formula see: Charles H. McCloy, *Appraising Physical Status: Methods and Norms*, pp. 123-24.

[20] The z ordinates from Table 139 (p. 438) are always computed from p_1 and p_3, never from p_2.

$$y_2 = \frac{Mn_2 - Mn_0}{SD_0} = \frac{81.4545 - 81.8865}{7.5969} = -.0569;$$

$$y_3 = \frac{Mn_3 - Mn_0}{SD_0} = \frac{87.2307 - 81.8865}{7.5969} = .7035.$$

The p's, the x's, and the y's for the prepubescent (1), the pubescent (2), and the postpubescent (3) group are assembled in the following tabulation:

	p	x	y	pxy	px^2
(1)	.3295	-1.0989	$-.5660$	.2049	.3979
(2)	.3750	.0384	$-.0569$	$-.0008$	.0006
(3)	.2955	1.1766	.7035	.2446	.4091

$$\Sigma pxy = .4487 \quad \Sigma px^2 = .8076$$

Computed by the preceding formula, the r_{tris} is .5556 (i.e., .4487 ÷ .8076).

671. The **tetrachoric method of correlation** may be used if it is desired to obtain the relationship between two variables both of which are dichotomous. For example, forty high-school seniors tried out for both the

Table 141

TETRACHORIC CORRELATION: WORKSHEET

	Unsuccessful in football	Successful in football
Successful in basketball	b = .25 f = 10	a = .4 f = 16
Unsuccessful in basketball	d = .20 f = 8	c = .15 f = 6

football and the basketball team. They were rated as successful [21] or as unsuccessful [22] in each sport. In Table 141 (p. 440) are given the results of the ratings: ten players who were successful in basketball were unsuccessful in football; sixteen were successful in both football and basketball; eight were unsuccessful in both basketball and football; and six who were unsuccessful in basketball were successful in football.

The full equation for the r of a tetrachoric correlation[23] is seldom used. A satisfactory approximation may be secured by the use of the following formula:

[21] "Made the team."
[22] Failed to "make the team."
[23] Kelley, *op. cit.,* p. 254.

$$\frac{ad - bc}{zz'} = r + \frac{\chi\chi'r^2}{2}$$

The a, which is the proportion of the number of players who were successful in both basketball and football to the total number of players, is .4 (i.e., 16 ÷ 40). The d, which is the proportion of the number of players who were unsuccessful in both basketball and football to the total number of players, is .20 (i.e., 8 ÷ 40). The b, which is the proportion of the players who were successful in basketball and unsuccessful in football to the total number of players, is .25 (i.e., 10 ÷ 40). The c, which is the proportion of the players who were successful in football and unsuccessful in basketball to the total number of players, is .15 (i.e., 6 ÷ 40).

Table 142

χ VALUES OF AREA UNDER NORMAL PROBABILITY CURVE

p	.00	.01	.02	.03	.04	.05	.06	.07	.08	.09
.00		2.3263	2.0537	1.8808	1.7507	1.6649	1.5548	1.4758	1.4051	1.3408
.10	1.2816	1.2265	1.1750	1.1264	1.0803	1.0364	.9945	.9542	.9154	.8779
.20	.8416	.8064	.7722	.7388	.7063	.6745	.6433	.6128	.5828	.5534
.30	.5244	.4959	.4678	.4399	.4125	.3853	.3583	.3319	.3055	.2793
.40	.2533	.2275	.2019	.1764	.1510	.1257	.1004	.0753	.0502	.0251
.50	.0000	.0251	.0502	.0753	.1004	.1257	.1510	.1764	.2019	.2275
.60	.2533	.2793	.3055	.3319	.3583	.3853	.4125	.4399	.4678	.4959
.70	.5244	.5534	.5828	.6128	.6433	.6745	.7063	.7388	.7722	.8064
.80	.8416	.8779	.9154	.9542	.9945	1.0364	1.0803	1.1264	1.1750	1.2265
.90	1.2816	1.3408	1.4051	1.4758	1.5548	1.6649	1.7507	1.8808	2.0537	2.3263

The p, which is $a + b$, is .65 (i.e., .25 + .40); hence the z (Table 139, p. 438) is .3704. The p', which is $a + c$, is .55 (i.e., .40 + .15); hence the z' is .3958.

The χ (chi) is the distance from the mid-point of the curve in terms of standard deviations if the area is 1 and the standard deviation is 1. Hence χ is −.3853 [24] (Table 142, p. 441), and χ' is −.1257.

If the above values are then used in the formula, the result is the following:

$$\frac{(.4 \times .2) - (.25 \times .15)}{.3704 \times .3958} = r + \frac{(-.3853)(-.1257)r^2}{2} \quad or$$

$$.2899 = r + .0242r^2$$

By the quadratic equation[25] the following result is obtained:

[24] Minus because the p is greater than .5. If the p is less than .5, the χ is positive.

[25] A quadratic equation may be solved by the following formula:

$$r = \frac{-b \pm \sqrt{b^2 - 4ac}}{2a}$$

Before this formula is used, the equation must be reduced to the general form of $ar^2 + br + c = 0$. In the example given in Table 141, this would be $.0242r^2 + r - .2899 = 0$. Here $a = .0242$, $b = 1$, and $c = -.2899$.

$$r = \frac{-1 \pm \sqrt{1 - (4 \times .0242 \times -.2899)}}{2 \times .0242} = .2913 \; or \; 41.0310.$$

The latter value is an impossible one for an r.

This method of computing an r of tetrachoric correlation may well be used if only a few dozen r's are computed. If the researcher proposes to use this device extensively, he will be well advised to procure tables that are prepared for the very rapid computation of r's of tetrachoric correlation.[26]

672. An r of partial correlation (see Sec. 78) with one variable held constant may be computed by

$$r_{01.2} = \frac{r_{01} - (r_{02}r_{12})}{\sqrt{1 - r^2_{02}} \times \sqrt{1 - r^2_{12}}}.$$

Computed by this formula, the r between the strength scores (0) and the records in the shot-put (1), with the influence of the weights (2) partialed out, is .3972

$$\left[i.e., \; \frac{.6359 - (.6661 \times .5983)}{\sqrt{1 - .6661^2} \times \sqrt{1 - .5983^2}} \right].^{27}$$

673. The following formula may be used for an r of partial correlation with two variables held constant:

$$r_{01.23} = \frac{r_{01.2} - (r_{03.2}r_{13.2})}{\sqrt{1 - r^2_{03.2}} \sqrt{1 - r^2_{13.2}}}$$

Computed by this formula, the r between the strength scores (0) and the records in the shot-put (1), with the influence of the weights (2) and the records in the standing broad jump (3) partialed out, is .3219

$$\left[i.e., \; \frac{.3972 - (.3418 \times .3250)}{\sqrt{1 - .3418^2} \sqrt{1 - .3250^2}} \right].$$

674. The following is a generalized formula for the r of partial correlation:

$$r_{01.23\cdots n} = \frac{r_{01.23\cdots (n-1)} - \left[r_{0n.23\cdots (n-1)} r_{1n.23\cdots (n-1)} \right]}{\sqrt{1 - r^2_{0n.23\cdots (n-1)}} \sqrt{1 - r^2_{1n.23\cdots (n-1)}}}$$

675. The **coefficient of multiple correlation** (see Sec. 79) may be com-

---

[26] L. Chesire and Others, *Computing Diagrams for the Tetrachoric Correlation Coefficient.*

[27] The following r's from Hutto's study ($N = 406$) were used for the computation of the r's of partial correlation in Sections 672, 673, and 676.

	Weight	Standing broad jump	Shot-put
Strength score	.6661	.4235	.6359
Weight		.2670	.5983
Standing broad jump			.4107

puted by the following formula, which involves the use of r's of partial correlation:

$$R_{0.123\cdots n} = \sqrt{1 - (1 - r^2_{01})(1 - r^2_{02.1})(1 - r^2_{03.12}) \cdots (1 - r^2_{0n.12\cdots(n-1)})}$$

676. The R between the strength scores (0) and the combination of the weights (1), the records in the standing broad jump (2), and the records in the shot-put (3) computed by

$$R_{0.123} = \sqrt{1 - (1 - r^2_{01})(1 - r^2_{02.1})(1 - r^2_{03.12})}$$

is .7481 [i.e., $\sqrt{1 - [(1 - .6661^2)(1 - .3418^2)(1 - .3219^2)]}$].

677. A commonly used method for computing R's is the Doolittle Method,[28] the use of which method is advised, especially if multiple regression equations are to be computed. The values for the r's are inserted in the first row in Table 143 (pp. 444-46), and the directions in the left margin are followed. Seven variables may be used with this table.

After the computations in Part I (Table 143) have been completed, the β (beta) values are computed according to Part II. If there are three independent variables and hence β_1, β_2, and β_3 are to be computed, β_3 is computed first, β_2 is computed second, and β_1 is computed last. β_3 is the value in row 11, column I; since there are only three independent variables, there can be no values for β_6, β_5, and β_4, and hence the items at the left of I 11 are eliminated.

The R, then, may be computed by

$$R_{0.123} = \sqrt{\beta_1 r_{01} + \beta_2 r_{02} + \beta_3 r_{03}}.$$

Computed by this formula, the R between the strength scores (0) and the combination of the weights (1), the records in the standing broad jump (2), and the records in the shot-put (3) is .7481

$$[\text{i.e., } \sqrt{(.4387 \times .6661) + (.1841 \times .4235) + (.2978 \times .6359)}].$$

678. The weighting of the weights, of the records in the standing broad jump, and of the records in the shot-put, in the prediction of the strength scores, may be determined by a **multiple regression equation,** a formula for which is as follows:

$$X_0 = \beta_1 \frac{\sigma_0}{\sigma_1} X_1 + \beta_2 \frac{\sigma_0}{\sigma_2} X_2 + \beta_3 \frac{\sigma_0}{\sigma_3} X_3 + K$$

$$K = Mn_0 - \left(\beta_1 \frac{\sigma_0}{\sigma_1} Mn_1\right) - \left(\beta_2 \frac{\sigma_0}{\sigma_2} Mn_2\right) - \left(\beta_3 \frac{\sigma_0}{\sigma_3} Mn_3\right)$$

Computed by this formula, the multiple regression equation for the pre-

[28] Charles C. Peters and Elizabeth C. Wykes, "Simplified Methods for Computing Regression Coefficients and Partial and Multiple Correlations," *Journal of Educational Research,* May, 1931.

Table 143

MULTIPLE CORRELATION: WORKSHEET FOR DOOLITTLE METHOD*

Part I

Directions	A	B	C	D	E	F	I
1. Insert values for r's	1.0000	r_{12} .2670	r_{13} .5983	r_{14}	r_{15}	r_{16}	r_{01} -.6661
2. Divide line 1 by -1		-.2670	-.5983				.6661
3. Insert values for r's		1.0000	r_{23} .4107	r_{24}	r_{25}	r_{26}	r_{02} -.4235
4. Multiply items in line 1, B to I, by item in line 2, B		-.0713	-.1597				.1778
5. Add algebraically lines 3 and 4		.9287	.2510				-.2457
6. Divide line 5 by negative of item in line 5, B		-1.0000	-.2703				.2646
7. Insert values for r's			1.0000	r_{34}	r_{35}	r_{36}	r_{03} -.6359
8. Multiply items in line 1, C to I, by item in line 2, C			-.3580				.3985
9. Multiply items in line 5, C to I, by item in line 6, C			-.0678				.0664
10. Add algebraically lines 7, 8, and 9			.5742				-.1710
11. Divide line 10 by negative of item in line 10, C			-1.0000				.2978
12. Insert values for r's				1.0000	r_{45}	r_{46}	r_{04}
13. Multiply items in line 1, D to I, by item in line 2, D							

Table 143 (continued)

	Directions	D	E	F	I
14.	Multiply items in line 5, D to I, by item in line 6, D				
15.	Multiply items in line 10, D to I, by item in line 11, D				
16.	Add algebraically lines 12, 13, 14, and 15				
17.	Divide line 16 by negative of item in line 16, D				
18.	Insert values for r's		$\underline{1.0000}$	r_{56}	$-r_{05}$
19.	Multiply items in line 1, E to I, by item in line 2, E				
20.	Multiply items in line 5, E to I, by item in line 6, E				
21.	Multiply items in line 10, E to I, by item in line 11, E				
22.	Multiply items in line 16, E to I, by item in line 17, E				
23.	Add algebraically lines 18, 19, 20, 21, and 22				
24.	Divide line 23 by negative of item in line 23, E				
25.	Insert values for r's			$\underline{1.0000}$	$-r_{06}$
26.	Multiply items in line 1, F to I, by item in line 2, F				
27.	Multiply items in line 5, F to I, by item in line 6, F				
28.	Multiply items in line 10, F to I, by item in line 11, F				
29.	Multiply items in line 16, F to I, by item in line 17, F				
30.	Multiply items in line 23, F to I, by item in line 24, F				
31.	Add algebraically lines 25, 26, 27, 28, 29, and 30				
32.	Divide line 31 by negative of item in line 31, F				

Table 143 (continued)

Part II

To obtain the regression coefficients substitute in the following equations values computed in Part I. I 32 = column I, row 32; F 24 = column F, row 24; etc.

β_6 = I 32

β_5 = (β_6 x F 24) + I 24

β_4 = (β_6 x F 17) + (β_5 x E 17) + I 17

β_3 = (β_6 x F 11) + (β_5 x E 11) + (β_4 x D 11) + I 11 = .2978

β_2 = (β_6 x F 6) + (β_5 x E 6) + (β_4 x D 6) + (β_3 x C 6) + I 6 = .1841
     [i.e., (.2978 x -.2703) + .2646]

β_1 = (β_6 x F 2) + (β_5 x E 2) + (β_4 x D 2) + (β_3 x C 2) + (β_2 x B 2) + I 2 =
     .4387 [i.e., (.2978 x -.5983) + (.1841 x -.2670) + .6661]

* Charles C. Peters and Elizabeth C. Wykes, "Simplified Methods for Computing Regression Coefficients and Partial and Multiple Correlations," *Journal of Educational Research*, May, 1931. Reproduced by permission.

diction of the strength score from the combination of the weight, the standing broad jump, and the twelve-pound shot-put is as follows:[29]

5.5034 weight + 50.3068 standing broad jump

+ 13.4531 shot-put − 90.0073

$$\left[\text{i.e., } .4387 \frac{219.0163}{17.4587} X_1 + .1841 \frac{219.0163}{.8015} X_2 + .2978 \frac{219.0163}{4.8482} + \right.$$

$$\left[1389.5172 - \left(.4387 \frac{219.0163}{17.4587} 137.1946 \right) - \left(.1841 \frac{219.0163}{.8015} 7.2767 \right) - \right.$$

$$\left. \left(.2978 \frac{219.0163}{4.8482} 26.6422 \right) \right].$$

RELIABILITY OF MEASURES OF RELATIONSHIP OF SAMPLES

679. In Table 144 (p. 447) are given values of *r* and *R* required for probabilities of .05 and .01. The degrees of freedom for this table are the number of subjects minus the number of variables. Hence an *r* between two variables must, for fifty-two subjects, be .273 for a probability of .05, and .354 for a probability of .01. An *r* between two variables, with the influence of

[29] The following means and standard deviations from Hutto's study ($N = 406$) were used:

	Mean	Standard Deviation
Strength score (0)	1389.5172	219.0163
Weight (1)	137.1946	17.4587
Standing broad jump (2)	7.2767	.8015
Twelve-pound shot-put (3)	26.6422	4.8482

The β's are from Table 143.

three variables partialed out, must, for fifty subjects, be .288 for a probability of .05, and .372 for a probability of .01. An R between a combination of four variables and another variable must, for fifty subjects, be .288 for a probability of .05, and .372 for a probability of .01.

680. The efficiency with which a test can predict a score in a criterion variable may be computed by

$$E = 1 - \sqrt{1 - r^2}.$$

Computed by this formula, the efficiency with which a test can predict a score in a criterion variable if the r of the test with the criterion variable is .8660 is .50. Hence if a test is used to predict scores in a criterion variable, it would appear that the r of the test with the criterion variable should be more than .8660. If a test is, for an *individual*, used to predict

Table 144*

r AND R VALUES FOR PROBABILITY OF .05 AND .01

Degrees of Freedom	Number of Variables				Degrees of Freedom	Number of Variables			
	2	3	4	5		2	3	4	5
10	.576 .708	.671 .776	.726 .814	.763 .840	45	.288 .372	.353 .430	.397 .470	.432 .501
20	.423 .537	.509 .608	.563 .652	.604 .685	50	.273 .354	.336 .410	.379 .449	.412 .479
25	.381 .487	.462 .555	.514 .600	.553 .633	60	.250 .325	.308 .377	.348 .414	.380 .442
26	.374 .478	.454 .546	.506 .590	.545 .624	80	.217 .283	.269 .330	.304 .362	.332 .389
27	.367 .470	.446 .538	.498 .582	.536 .615	100	.195 .254	.241 .297	.274 .327	.300 .351
28	.361 .463	.439 .530	.490 .573	.529 .606	150	.159 .208	.198 .244	.225 .270	.247 .290
29	.355 .456	.432 .522	.482 .565	.521 .598	200	.138 .181	.172 .212	.196 .234	.215 .253
30	.349 .449	.426 .514	.476 .558	.514 .591	300	.113 .148	.141 .174	.160 .192	.176 .208
35	.325 .418	.397 .481	.445 .523	.482 .556	400	.098 .128	.122 .151	.139 .167	.153 .180
40	.304 .393	.373 .454	.419 .494	.455 .526					

*Taken from Table 13.6 of George W. Snedecor: Statistical Methods[4], published by the Iowa State College Press, Ames, by permission of the author and publisher.

Underlined numbers = probability of .01.

Numbers not underlined = probability of .05.

the score in the criterion variable, the r of the test with the criterion variable *should be* more than .8660. However, a test with an r as low as .6 [30] (see Sec. 74) with a criterion variable, or a battery of tests with an R as low as .8 with a criterion variable may, for *groups*,[31] be useful in the prediction of scores in the criterion variable.

Table 145

z FUNCTION FOR VALUES OF r FROM .00 TO .99[*]

r	.00	.01	.02	.03	.04	.05	.06	.07	.08	.09
.0	.0000	.0100	.0200	.0300	.0400	.0500	.0601	.0701	.0802	.0902
.1	.1003	.1104	.1206	.1307	.1409	.1511	.1614	.1717	.1820	.1923
.2	.2027	.2132	.2237	.2342	.2448	.2554	.2661	.2769	.2877	.2986
.3	.3095	.3205	.3316	.3428	.3541	.3654	.3769	.3884	.4001	.4118
.4	.4236	.4356	.4477	.4599	.4722	.4847	.4973	.5101	.5230	.5361
.5	.5493	.5627	.5763	.5901	.6042	.6184	.6328	.6475	.6625	.6777
.6	.6931	.7089	.7250	.7414	.7582	.7753	.7928	.8107	.8291	.8480
.7	.8673	.8872	.9076	.9287	.9505	.9730	.9962	1.0203	1.0454	1.0714
.8	1.0986	1.1270	1.1568	1.1881	1.2212	1.2562	1.2933	1.3331	1.3758	1.4219
.9	1.4722	1.5275	1.5890	1.6584	1.7380	1.8318	1.9459	2.0923	2.2976	2.6466

[*]Taken from Table 14 of E. F. Lindquist, Statistical Analysis in Educational Research, published by the Houghton Mifflin Company, New York, with the permission of the author and publishers.

681. The upper and lower limits of an r may be determined from the z value[32] (Table 145, p. 448) of r. The z for the r of .70 (i.e., .6957) between the weights and the strength scores of Group I is .8673. The *SE* of z may be computed by

$$SE_z = \frac{1}{\sqrt{N-3}}.$$

Hence the *SE* of the z of .8673 is .1459 (i.e., $1 \div \sqrt{50-3}$). This value may, in a normal distribution, be used as follows to determine the best estimate of the upper and the lower limits of various r's between weights and strength scores. If the weights and the strength scores were obtained on each of one hundred groups of fifty subjects drawn from the same population from which Group I was drawn, the z's between the weights

[30] Increasing the range of ability usually causes a marked increase in the size of an r; this is illustrated by the following r's between a certain test score and basketball ability of various ranges of ages:

College freshman boys	.45	
Senior-high-school boys	.55	.68 .79 .88
Junior-high-school boys	.60	
Fourth-to-sixth-grade boys	.60	

Such increased r's are spurious, and should be interpreted accordingly.

[31] Garrett, *op. cit.*, pp. 163-66.

[32] Discussions and tables of the z function of an r, which function was developed by Fisher, may be found in: Fisher, *Statistical Methods for Research Workers*[11]; Garrett, *op. cit.*; and Lindquist, *Statistical Analysis in Educational Research*.

and the strength scores would, in ninety-five of the groups, be expected to be no larger than 1.1533 [i.e., .8673 + (1.96 [33] × .1459)] and no smaller than .5813 [i.e., .8673 − (1.96 × .1459)]; and in ninety-nine of the groups the z's would be expected to be no larger than 1.2437 [i.e., .8673 + (2.58

Table 146

VARIANCE RATIO: TABLE OF F*

		K-2				
	6	8	10	12	14	16
30	2.42 3.47	2.27 3.17	2.16 2.98	2.09 2.84	2.04 2.74	1.99 2.66
40	2.34 3.29	2.18 2.99	2.07 2.80	2.00 2.66	1.95 2.56	1.90 2.49
50	2.29 3.18	2.13 2.88	2.02 2.70	1.95 2.56	1.90 2.46	1.85 2.39
60	2.25 3.12	2.10 2.82	1.99 2.63	1.92 2.50	1.86 2.40	1.81 2.32
70	2.23 3.07	2.07 2.77	1.97 2.59	1.89 2.45	1.84 2.35	1.79 2.28
80	2.21 3.04	2.05 2.74	1.95 2.55	1.88 2.41	1.82 2.32	1.77 2.24
100	2.19 2.99	2.03 2.69	1.92 2.51	1.85 2.36	1.79 2.26	1.75 2.19
150	2.16 2.92	2.00 2.62	1.89 2.44	1.82 2.30	1.76 2.20	1.71 2.12
200	2.14 2.90	1.98 2.60	1.87 2.41	1.80 2.28	1.74 2.17	1.69 2.09
300	2.13 2.87	1.97 2.57	1.86 2.39	1.79 2.26	1.73 2.15	1.68 2.07
400	2.12 2.85	1.96 2.55	1.85 2.37	1.78 2.23	1.72 2.12	1.67 2.04

(left axis: N − K)

*Taken from Table 10.2 of George W. Snedecor, Statistical Methods[4] published by the Iowa State College Press, Ames, by permission of the author and publisher.

Underlined numbers = probability of .01.

Numbers not underlined = probability of .05.

× .1459)] and no smaller than .4909 [i.e., .8673 − (2.58 × .1459)]. The r's that correspond to the z values of 1.1533 (nearest z value in Table = 1.5568) and .5813 (nearest z value in Table = .5763) are .82 and .52, respectively; and the r's that correspond to z values of 1.2437 and .4909 are .85 and .45, respectively.

[33] Table 132 (p. 426).

682. The **variance ratio,** which may be computed by the following formula, may be used to test for the curvilinearity of a paired distribution:

$$F = \frac{(\eta^2 - r^2)(N - K)}{(1 - \eta^2)(K - 2)}$$

For η_{xy}, K is the number of rows (i.e., 18 in Table 136), and for η_{yx}, K is the number of columns (i.e., 18). Computed by the preceding formula, $F_{xy} = 1.0824$

$$\left[\text{i.e., } \frac{(.8156^2 - .6957^2)(50 - 18)}{(1 - .8156^2)(18 - 2)} \right];$$

and $F_{yx} = .0842$

$$\left[\text{i.e., } \frac{(.7101^2 - .6957^2)(50 - 18)}{(1 - .7101^2)(18 - 2)} \right].$$

If $N = 50$ and $K = 18$, an F of 1.99 [34] (Table 146, p. 449) indicates that if paired distributions were made of the weights and the strength scores of each of one hundred groups of fifty subjects drawn from the same population from which Group I was drawn, 95 per cent of such distributions would be curvilinear; and an F of 2.66, that 99 per cent of such distributions would be curvilinear. Since 1.0824 and .0842, the F values obtained for the paired distribution of Group I, are less than 1.99, the distribution cannot be assumed to be curvilinear.

683. The **SE of p** may be computed by

$$SE_\rho = \frac{1.05(1 - \rho^2)}{\sqrt{N - 1}}.$$

Computed by this formula, the SE of ρ between the weights and the strength scores of Group I is .0849 $\left[\text{i.e., } \dfrac{105(1 - .6590^2)}{\sqrt{50 - 1}} \right]$.

684. The **SE of r_{bis}** may be approximated by the following formula if p and q are each larger than .05:

$$SE_{r_{bis}} = \frac{\dfrac{\sqrt{pq}}{z} - r^2_{bis}}{\sqrt{N}}.$$

Computed by this formula, the SE of the r_{bis} presented in Section 669 is

$$.0586 \left[\text{i.e., } \frac{\dfrac{\sqrt{.2896 \times .7104}}{.3423} - .7296^2}{\sqrt{183}} \right].$$

685. The **SE of r_{tet}** is an exceedingly complex function, and is not given here.[35]

[34] $N - K = 32$ (i.e., $50 - 18$). In Table 146 (p. 449) the row of 30 is the nearest value to 32. $K - 2 = 16$ (i.e., $18 - 2$). Hence the F value is read in row 30 and in column 16.

[35] A method for its computation may be found in: Kelley, *op. cit.*, pp. 257-58.

INCREASE OF RELIABILITY AND VALIDITY

686. If the r of reliability and the r of validity of a test have been determined (see Secs. 104-05), the amount by which the test needs to be lengthened to give a desired r of reliability and of validity may be determined by

$$N = \frac{r_D(1 - r_{12})}{r_{12}(1 - r_D)}.$$

For example, if the r of the reliability of a test with ten trials is .80, and the desired (D) r of reliability is .90, the ten trials need to be increased 2.25 times $\left[\text{i.e., } \frac{.90(1 - .80)}{.80(1 - .90)}\right]$, or to 22.5 trials. If the r of validity of a three-item battery is .70 and the desired r of validity is .85, the three items need to be increased 2.43 times by items of like validity $\left[\text{i.e., } \frac{.85(1 - .70)}{.70(1 - .85)}\right]$, or to 7.29 items.

The Spearman-Brown Prophecy Formula, which is another form of the formula given in the preceding paragraph is as follows:

$$r_D = \frac{Nr_{12}}{1 + (N - 1)r_{12}}$$

Hence the expected r of reliability for the test in the preceding paragraph would, if the number of trials were increased to 23, be .90. Hence the expected r of validity for the same test would, if the number of items were increased to 8, be .86.

OBJECTIVITY

687. The objectivity of a written examination may be determined by the r between two scorings of the same test by the same person or between the scorings of two or more different scorers. The objectivity of a test of physical performance may be determined by the second method.

688. It is repeated that a brief treatise on statistical techniques in a textbook, the chief objective of which is not to discuss statistical techniques, is not a substitute for a detailed textbook, the entire objective of which is to discuss the use of statistical techniques. Furthermore, while the knowledge of statistical techniques gained from a thorough study of many textbooks on statistical techniques is basic to an adequate analysis of data, it is imperative that such knowledge be supplemented by experience in dealing with data in the field of study involved.

APPENDIX B

ANALYSIS OF DIFFICULTY
OF OBJECTIVE ITEMS

689. The purposes of an item analysis are to improve the items of a speed test and to construct a power test. In a speed test, all the items are about equal in difficulty, and no items should be included that everybody marks correctly or that nobody marks correctly. In a power test, the items should be arranged in order of difficulty. A power test should include items that almost everybody marks correctly, items that about two thirds mark correctly, and items that about one third marks correctly; that is, the scores should range from near zero to near perfect.

690. The difficulty of the items of a twenty-item true-false test, administered to thirty students, may be determined by the procedure outlined in Table 147 (p. 453). The first column represents the number of the items to be assessed; the second column, the number of students selecting the correct choice for each item; the third column, the percentage of students selecting the correct choice; the fourth column, the number of students selecting the incorrect choice; the fifth column, the percentage of students selecting the incorrect choice; the sixth column, the number of students not making any choice; and the seventh column, the percentage of students not making any choice. The percentage of students recording correct responses to a question indicates the difficulty of the item relative to that of the other items. Items marked correctly by too high a percentage of the students or by too low a percentage of the students may be ambiguously worded, and should be re-examined.

Item 1 which was marked correctly by everybody, Item 18 which was marked incorrectly by everybody, and Item 10 which was not marked by five students should be re-examined. The remaining twenty-seven items should be re-arranged into the following order: 4, 8, 12, 16, 20, 14, 17, 19, 11, 9, 7, 5, 2, 3, 6, 13, 15.

691. The difficulty of the choices of a multiple-choice test may be determined similarly to the difficulty of the items of a true-false test. In the material presented in Table 148 (p. 453) the first column represents the five choices of each item to be assessed, the second column represents the number of students selecting each choice, and the third column represents the percentage of students selecting each choice. The correct choice for Item 1 is b, that for Item 2 is e, and that for Item 3 is d.

452

Table 147

DIFFICULTY ANALYSIS: TRUE-FALSE TEST ITEMS

Number of Item	Number of Correct Responses	Percentage of Total Responses	Number of Incorrect Responses	Percentage of Total Responses	Number of No Choices	Percentage of Total Responses
1	30	100	0			
2	8	27	22	73		
3	7	23	23	77		
4	29	97	1	3		
5	10	33	20	67		
6	6	20	24	80		
7	12	40	18	60		
8	28	93	2	7		
9	14	47	16	53		
10	10	33	15	50	5	17
11	16	53	14	47		
12	27	90	3	10		
13	4	13	26	87		
14	19	63	11	37		
15	2	7	28	93		
16	26	87	4	13		
17	18	60	12	40		
18	0	0	30	100		
19	17	57	13	43		
20	25	83	5	17		

Table 148

DIFFICULTY ANALYSIS:
MULTIPLE-CHOICE TEST ITEMS

Number of Item		Number of Responses	Percentage of Total Responses
1.	a	10	33.3
	b	5	16.7
	c	12	40.0
	d	2	6.7
	e	1	3.3
2.	a	1	3.3
	b	2	6.7
	c	12	40.0
	d	5	16.7
	e	10	33.3
3.	a	5	16.7
	b	10	33.3
	c	2	6.7
	d	12	40.0
	e	1	3.3

692. The difficulty of the items of a ten-item true-false test administered to twenty students may also be determined by the index of discrimination of each item. In Table 149 (p. 454) are indicated the response of each student to each item and the total number of correct responses of each student. The total number of correct responses of each student is written in the + column of Table 150 (pp. 455-56) if the student answered the question correctly, and in the — column if he answered the question incorrectly. For example, Student 1 had seven correct responses; he answered Questions 1, 2, 3, 4, 5, 6, and 10 correctly. Hence 7 is written under the + for Questions 1, 2, 3, 4, 5, 6, and 10; and under the — for Questions

Table 149

DIFFICULTY ANALYSIS OF TEST ITEMS: PRELIMINARY WORKSHEET
FOR COMPUTATION OF INDEXES OF DISCRIMINATION

Number of Student	Number of Questions										Number of Items Correct
	1	2	3	4	5	6	7	8	9	10	
1	+	+	+	+	+	+	-	-	-	+	7
2	+	-	+	-	+	+	-	-	+	+	6
3	+	+	+	+	+	+	-	-	+	+	8
4	+	+	+	+	-	+	-	+	+	-	7
5	-	-	+	+	+	+	-	+	-	+	6
6	+	+	-	+	-	+	+	-	-	-	5
7	+	+	+	+	+	-	+	+	+	+	9
8	+	-	+	+	-	+	-	+	-	+	5
9	+	+	+	+	-	+	-	-	-	+	6
10	-	-	+	+	-	+	+	-	+	+	6
11	+	+	+	+	-	+	-	-	-	+	6
12	+	-	+	+	-	-	-	+	-	-	4
13	+	-	+	+	+	-	+	-	-	+	6
14	-	-	+	+	-	-	+	-	-	+	4
15	+	+	+	+	-	+	+	-	-	+	7
16	+	-	+	+	+	+	+	-	-	+	7
17	+	+	+	+	+	+	-	-	+	+	8
18	+	+	+	+	-	+	+	-	+	+	8
19	+	-	+	+	+	+	-	-	-	+	6
20	+	-	+	+	+	+	-	+	+	+	8

7, 8, and 9, which he answered incorrectly. If the student omitted the question, the omission is, for the purpose of this analysis, recorded with the incorrect responses.

The number of correct responses for each question is summed. For example, seventeen students answered Question 1 correctly. The value of the correct responses for each question is the sum of the numbers in each column of correct responses (+). For example, the value of the correct responses for Question 1 is 113 (i.e., $7 + 6 + 8 + 7 + 5 + 9 + 5 + 6 + 6 + 4 + 6 + 7 + 7 + 8 + 8 + 6 + 8$).

The number of incorrect responses for each question is summed (e.g., 3 for Question 1). The value of the incorrect responses for each question is the sum of the numbers in each column of incorrect responses (—). The value of the incorrect responses for Question 1 is 16 (i.e., $6 + 6 + 4$).

Table 150

DIFFICULTY ANALYSIS OF TEST ITEMS: SAMPLE WORKSHEET
FOR COMPUTATION OF INDEXES OF DISCRIMINATION

Questions

	1 +	1 −	2 +	2 −	3 +	3 −	4 +	4 −	5 +	5 −	6 +	6 −	7 +	7 −	8 +	8 −	9 +	9 −	10 +	10 −
	7		7		7		7		7		7		7		7			7	7	
	6			6	6			6	6		6		6		6		6		6	
	8		8		8		8		8		8		8		8		8		8	
	7	6	7	6	7		7	7		7	7		7		7	7	7	6		7
	5		5		6	5	6		6		6		6		5			6	6	
	9		9				5			5	5	9		5		9	9	5	9	5
	5			5	5		9					5		9	5	5	5	5	5	5
	6	6			6	5	5			5			5		6		6	6	6	6
			6		6		6			6	6		6	6	6		6			
	6			6	6		6		6	6	6			6	6	4	6	6	6	6
	4	4	4		4		4	4		4		4		4		4	4	4	4	4
	6		6	6	6		6	6	6	6	6				6		6	6	6	
			4				4				4	4	4	4	4			4		4
	7	7	7		7		7	7		7	7	7	7	7	7	7	7	7	7	7
	7				7	5	7	7		7	7	7	7	7	7	7		7	7	7
	8		8	8	8		8		8	8	8		8	8	8			8	8	8
	8		8	8	8		8			8	8		8	8	8		8		8	8

Students

Table 150 (continued)

Questions

	1 (−)	1 (+)	2 (−)	2 (+)	3 (−)	3 (+)	4 (−)	4 (+)	5 (−)	5 (+)	6 (−)	6 (+)	7 (−)	7 (+)	8 (−)	8 (+)	9 (−)	9 (+)	10 (−)	10 (+)
	6	8	6	8	6	8	6	8	6	8	6	8	6	8	6	8	6	8	6	8
Number of correct responses		17		10		19		19		9		16		8		6		8		17
Value of correct responses		113		71		124		123		64		107		54		39		59		113
Number of incorrect responses	3		10		1		1		11		4		12		14		12		3	
Value of incorrect responses	16		58		5		6		65		22		75		90		70		16	
Average value of correct responses		6.65		7.1		6.53		6.47		7.11		6.69		6.75		6.50		7.38		6.65
Average value of incorrect responses	5.33		5.8		5.00		6.0		5.91		5.5		6.25		6.43		5.83		5.33	
Index of discrimination	1.32		1.3		1.53		.47		1.20		1.19		.50		.07		1.55		1.32	

The average value of the correct responses for each question is the value of the correct responses divided by the number of correct responses to the question. The average value of the correct responses for Question 1 is 6.65 (i.e., 113 ÷ 17). Similarly, the average value of the incorrect responses for Question 1 is 5.33 (i.e., 16 ÷ 3).

The index of discrimination of each question is the average value of the correct responses minus the average value of the incorrect responses. Hence the index of discrimination of Question 1 is 1.32 (i.e., 6.65 − 5.33). On the basis of this analysis, at least Item 8, and probably Items 4 and 7, should be re-examined.

APPENDIX C

LABORATORY EXERCISES

To the teacher. The following laboratory exercises should be performed after the indicated chapter has been studied. Frequent reference should be made to Chapter 33 concerning the methods of administering tests.

To the student. All the laboratory records should be preserved in a notebook, for records taken in one period may again be utilized in another period.

CHAPTER 4: DEFINITIONS OF TERMS OF STATISTICS

See the exercises for Appendix A, Statistical Methods (pp. 468-75 ff).

CHAPTER 5: RATING

To the teacher. The ratings made by each student for this unit should be made available to all the students. The ratings made by each method should be averaged and discussed.

(1) Rate one another in general-motor-performance ability by each of the rating devices described in Sections 85 to 91.

To the teacher. If the students are unacquainted with one another, they should rate such a quality as blondness, stockiness, or straightness of posture.

(2) Compute the *r* of reliability (see Secs. 665 and 686) of the ratings of all the students obtained by one method with those obtained by each of the other methods.

CHAPTER 7: SCORING TABLES

Events to be performed. Twenty-second shuttle run (see Sec. 358), standing broad jump, medicine-ball-put for distance, running high jump, and ten stunts on apparatus or on mats.

To the teacher. The records for each student in the events to be performed should be made available to all the students.

(1) Prepare scoring tables of the pass-or-fail type, of the three-or-four-category type, and of the equal-increment type (see Secs. 110-14) for each of the events performed except the stunts.

(2) Using the 100-yard dash and the shuttle run, compute a theoretical world's record for the shuttle run (see Secs. 116-17). On the basis of that world's record and using an exponent of 3, compute a universal scoring table for the shuttle run.

(3) Compute T-scores for the stunts (see Sec. 122).

(4) Prepare smoothed T-scores for the following data.

PULL-UPS

BOYS AGE 13		BOYS AGE 13		BOYS AGE 13		BOYS AGE 13	
Record	Frequency	Record	Frequency	Record	Frequency	Record	Frequency
23	1	17	6	11	48	5	97
22	1	16	5	10	65	4	60
21	1	15	9	9	68	3	65
20	3	14	24	8	84	2	38
19	2	13	21	7	108	1	30
18	2	12	32	6	117	0	13

Number = 900

(5) Compute P-scores for 3 and 4.

CHAPTER 8: SIZE AND MATURITY

(1) Males: Compute your classification index by the McCloy method (see Sec. 120).

(2) Males: Compute your classification index by the Neilson-Cozens method (see Sec. 137).

D.G. (3) Compute (a) the McCloy Classification Indices for the three boys and (b) the Neilson-Cozens Classification Indices for the elementary-school and junior-high-school boys for whom data may be found on pages 471 to 474. All exercises preceded by D.G. (data given) are based on these data. The answer for these exercises are given in parentheses after the exercises. (a: 655, 757, 882; b: 15, Class C; 29, Class E)

To the teacher. X rays of the hands and wrists of boys and of girls of eight, ten, twelve, fourteen, sixteen, and eighteen years of age should be procured. A copy of the Atlas of Skeletal Maturity by T. W. Todd (St. Louis, C. V. Mosby Company, 1937) should be made available to the students.

(4) Assess from X rays the skeletal (maturational) age of boys and of girls of eight, ten, twelve, fourteen, sixteen, and eighteen years of age (see Sec. 129).

CHAPTER 9: POWER

To the teacher. In order that the effect of practice upon performance in the vertical jumps may be indicated, the following procedure is suggested. In the first period have the correct form demonstrated, allow three or four practice trials, and have the heights of the jumps recorded. During each of the following four laboratory periods, have the students practice for five to ten minutes. In the fifth period have the heights of the jumps recorded again and compared with those for the first period.

Events to be performed. Vertical jump (see Sec. 163) with both hands holding to the belt, vertical jump according to the directions in Section 159, vertical jump according to the directions in Section 164, and shot-put from a stand.

(1) Compute your power quotient by the Stansbury method (males) or by the Anderson-McCloy method (females) (see Secs. 166-68).

D.G. (2) Compute (a) the Stansbury Power Quotients for the high-school boys, and (b) the Anderson-McCloy Power Quotients for the high-school girls. (a: 96.05, 108.58; b: 107.37, 84.18)

CHAPTER 10: AGILITY

Events to be performed. Squat thrusts (see Sec. 172), thirty-foot shuttle run (see Sec. 181), side-step test (see Sec. 182), boomerang test (see Sec. 177), maze run (see Sec. 178), loop-the-loop test (see Sec. 179), and auto-tire test (see Sec. 185).

(1) Record the T-score for your performance in the squat-thrust test (Table 14).

(2) Females: Compute your agility score by the Sierakowski method (see Sec. 186).

CHAPTER 11: MOTOR EDUCABILITY

Events to be performed. Brace Test (see Secs. 198, 201, and 205-07), Iowa-Brace Test (see Secs. 199, 201, and 205-08), Hill Test (see Secs. 201, 203, and 205-09), and Johnson Test (see Secs. 210-14).

(1) Record the raw score and the T-score (Table 19, p. 93) for your performance in the Brace Test.

(2) Record the raw score and the T-score (Table 20, p. 94) for your performance in the Iowa-Brace Test.

(3) Record the raw score for your performance in the Hill Test. (See Table 21, p. 95, for T-scores for junior-high-school boys.)

(4) Record the raw score for your performance in each of the ten items of the Johnson Test, and then total these scores.

D.G. (5) Record the T-scores for the Iowa-Brace raw scores of (a) the three boys and (b) the three girls. (a: 54, 34, 56; b: 48, 58, 49)

Events to be performed. Target-throwing test at a concentric-ring target (see Sec. 226). Make fifty throws (not all of them necessarily during the laboratory period). Keep your records in the order of the throws.

To the teacher. The records of the throws of each student should be made available to all the students.

(6) Compute the *r* between the sum of the scores for the first five odd-numbered throws and the sum of the scores for the first five even-numbered throws (see Sec. 666). Correct the *r* by the Spearman-Brown Formula (see Sec. 686). Make similar computations for the first twenty throws, the first thirty throws, the first forty throws, and the fifty throws.

(These results should illustrate the importance of an adequate number of trials.)

Event to be performed. Bass Tests of static balance (see Sec. 235) and of dynamic balance (see Secs. 237-38).

To the teacher. The records of each student should be made available to all the students

(7) Compute the r between the results of the sum of the first and second trials in the static and the dynamic balance tests, between the results of the sum of the first two trials and the sum of the results of the third and fourth trials, and between the results of the sum of the first three trials and the sum of the results of the last three trials.

To the teacher. Records for the Seashore Test of Sensory Rhythm and of Timing may be obtained as indicated in Section 240. A manual with directions for administering and for scoring the tests may be obtained with the records. Each test should be administered three times.

(8) Average the results of your three performances in the Seashore Rhythm Test and in the Seashore Timing Test.

To the teacher. The McCloy Blocks Test (see Sec. 245) should be demonstrated.

(9) Administer the McCloy Blocks Test to two students. Record the time for each of your own performances in the test, and the T-score (Table 24, p. 111) for the average of these times.

To the teacher. The Wiebe Test of Kinesthesis (see Sec. 251) should be demonstrated.

(10) Administer the Wiebe Test to two students. Record the scores of your own performances in each of the items of the test.

CHAPTER 12: GENERAL-MOTOR CAPACITY

The records needed for the computation of the McCloy General-motor-capacity Score should be available from the exercises for Chapters 8 to 11.

(1) Compute your motor quotient (see Secs. 261-63; Tables 27 to 44, pp. 118-25).

D.G. (2) Compute the motor quotients for (a) the three boys and (b) the three girls. (a: 102.84, 90.69, 112.27; b: 101.69, 104.58, 88.94)

CHAPTER 14: STRENGTH

Events to be performed. Gripping-strength test (see Sec. 291), back lift (see Sec. 292), leg lift (see Sec. 293), pull-ups (males, see Sec. 296; females, see Sec. 297), parallel-bar dips (males, see Sec. 294), push-ups (females, see Sec. 295), and pushing-and-pulling-strength test (see Secs. 298-99).

(1) Males: Convert the number of your pull-ups and dips into pounds

of pull-up and dipping strength by (a) Table 45 (p. 130) or Table 49 (p. 132) and (b) Table 46 (p. 130).

(2) Males: Convert your pushing-and-pulling strength into pull-up-dip strength by Table 50 (p. 133).

(3) Males: Compute three versions of your strength quotient, utilizing the values obtained in 1 and in 2 (see Table 52, pp. 136-38).

(4) Males: Compute your athletic-strength score by the long and the short form (see Sec. 282).

(5) Females: Convert the number of your pull-ups into pounds of strength (Table 47, p. 131).

(6) Females: Convert the number of your push-ups into pounds of strength (Table 48, p. 131).

(7) Females: Convert your pulling-and-pushing strength into pull-up-push-up strength (Table 51, p. 134).

(8) Females: Compute two versions of your strength quotient, utilizing the values obtained in 5 to 7 (Table 53, pp. 139-41).

D.G. (9) Compute the McCloy Strength Quotients for the boys. (a) Use Table 46 (p. 130); (b) use Table 49 (p. 132); (c) senior-high-school boy only: use Table 50 (p. 133). (a: 108.33, 94.63, 105.02; b: 113.98, 96.07, 105.74; c: 105.87)

D.G.(10) Compute the McCloy Strength Quotients for the three girls. (a) Use Tables 47 and 48 (p. 131); (b) use Table 51 (p. 134). (a: 98.85, 119.48, 79.02; b: 104.17, 123.54, 76.98)

(11) Males: Compute your physical-efficiency quotient by the Stansbury method (see Sec. 309 and Table 59, p. 161). The records needed should be available from the exercises for Chapter 9.

(12) Females: Compute your physical-efficiency quotient by the Anderson-McCloy method (see Sec. 309 and Table 60, p. 162).

D.G. (13) Compute the Stansbury Physical-efficiency Quotients for the high-school boys. (100.71, 100.73)

D.G. (14) Compute the Anderson-McCloy Physical-efficiency Quotients for the high-school girls. (104.31, 88.54)

Event to be performed. Martin Test (see Sec. 308). Test the strengths of the groups of muscles indicated in Table 57 (p. 160).

(15) Compute, by the Martin method (Table 58, p. 160), the strength of the muscles that extend your lower legs. Make the computation on the basis of the tested strengths of the muscles that extend and flex your thighs, and of the muscles that adduct your upper arms in front of and behind the body.

To the teacher. The manual tests of strength described in Section 303 should be demonstrated.

CHAPTER 15: ENDURANCE

To the teacher. It is suggested that the class be divided into groups for the endurance tests, and that each group perform two of the tests.

Events to be performed. Males: two-minute sit-ups (Table 67, pp. 172-73), squat jumps (see Sec. 328 and Table 72, p. 176), Carlson Test (see Sec. 337), indoor shuttle race (see Sec. 343 and Table 82, p. 188), Cureton Test (see Sec. 346 and Table 84, p. 191). *Females:* sit-ups (see Sec. 326 and Table 76, p. 179), back lifts (see Sec. 327 and Table 76, p. 179), full squats (see Sec. 328 and Table 78, p. 181), Carlson Test for five innings (see Sec. 337), and indoor shuttle race (see Sec. 343 and Table 83, p.189).

(1) Males: Record the endurance score for the number of your pull-ups (Table 75, p. 178) executed in connection with the exercises for Chapter 14.

(2) Females: Record the endurance scores for the number of your pull-ups and push-ups (Table 77, p. 180) executed in connection with the exercises for Chapter 14.

(3) Record the endurance scores for your performances for which there are scoring tables.

CHAPTER 16: TRACK-AND-FIELD ATHLETICS

Events to be performed. 50-yard dash, standing broad jump (the record obtained in connection with the exercises for Chapter 14 may be used), running high jump, basketball throw for distance, and shuttle run (see Sec. 358).

(1) Males: Compute your athletics quotient by Tables 87-89 (pp. 198-203). Multiply the sum of the quotient points by $\dfrac{10}{4}$.

D.G. (2) Compute the athletics quotients for the boys. Use the records for the 50-yard dash, the standing broad jump, the running high jump, and the basketball throw. (90.50, 85.13, 104.33)

CHAPTER 17: GENERAL-MOTOR ACHIEVEMENT

The records needed for the computation of the general-motor-achievement quotient should be available from the exercises for Chapters 14 and 16.

(1) Compute your general-motor-achievement quotient (see Sec. 360 and Tables 91 to 95, pp. 209-13).

D.G. (2) Compute the general-motor-achievement quotients for (a) the boys and (b) the girls. For the boys use the records in the 50-yard dash, the standing broad jump, the running high jump, the shot-put, and the pull-ups. For the girls use the records in the 50-yard dash, the standing broad jump, the basketball throw for distance. (a: 99.36, 91.00, 90.26; b: 77.74, 97.84, 72.05)

CHAPTER 18: MOTOR ABILITY

Events to be performed. Wear Obstacle Race (see Sec. 368), Scott Obstacle Race (see reference cited in Sec. 369), NSWA Test (see reference cited in Sec. 378), University of Illinois Screen Test (see reference cited in Sec. 382), and Phillips JCR Test (see reference cited in Sec. 372).

NOTE. Most of the records needed for the NSWA Test and for the Phillips JCR Test should be available from exercises in connection with Chapters 14 and 15.

(1) Record the raw scores for your performances in the indicated events. Table 96 (p. 217) is a scoring table for the Wear Race for junior-high-school boys. Scorings tables for the other indicated events may be found in the references cited.

CHAPTER 19: SPECIAL ABILITIES

Events to be performed. Tests of flexibility (see Secs. 389 and 394), tests of single- and multiple-response time (see Secs. 395-98), tests of eye dominance (see Sec. 409), dextrality test (see Sec. 411 and Table 98, p. 234), group test of breath-holding (see Sec. 417).

To the teacher. Apparatus for the measurement of response time may be obtainable from a psychology laboratory. It is suggested that response time be measured on the basis of individual appointments.

(1) Record the raw scores of your performances in this laboratory period.

(2) Males: Compute your potential-velocity score by the Coleman method (see Sec. 404).

(3) Females: Compute your potential-velocity score by the Carpenter method (see Sec. 406).

CHAPTER 20: ACHIEVEMENT IN SPORTS

To the teacher. It is suggested that the class be divided into groups, and that each group be responsible for the administration of one of the achievement tests to the class. The directions for the tests may be found in the references cited in the text.

Events to be performed. French-Stalter or Lockhart-McPherson Badminton Test (see Sec. 425), Johnson Basketball Test for Men (complete directions are given in Sec. 427), Young-Moser or Dyer-Apgar Basketball Test for Women (see Sec. 428), Dyer Backboard Tennis Test (revision) or Broer-Miller Tennis Test (see Sec. 443), Brady Volleyball Test for Men (see Sec. 444), French-Cooper or Bassett-Glassow-Locke Volleyball Test for Women (see Sec. 444).

CHAPTER 21: BODY MECHANICS

To the teacher. A photograph should be taken of each student (see Sec. 461), and footprints should be made for each student (see Secs. 466-67).

(1) Rate the posture of six other students according to the Iowa Test (see Sec. 453). Compare scores with one another.

(2) Rate your photograph according to the University of Southern California Posture Standards (see Sec. 456).

(3) Score your photograph according to the Wellesley method (see Sec. 461).

D.G. (4) Score the silhouettes on page 474 according to the Wellesley method. (Males: B+, B, A−; females: A, A, A)

(5) Score your photograph according to the Massey method (see Sec. 463).

D.G. (6) Score the silhouettes on page 474 according to the Massey method. (Males: B, D, D; females: E, D, D)

(7) Score your footprints according to the Clarke method (see Sec. 468).

(8) Score your footprints according to the scales in Section 469.

(9) Score your footprints for pronation according to the Ewing method (see Sec. 470 and Tables 100 and 101, pp. 273-74).

(10) Score your footprints for pronation according to the second Danford method (see Sec. 471).

CHAPTER 22: CHARACTER

(1) Rate, according to the O'Neel Scale (see Sec. 475), five persons whom you know well (see Sec. 474). Re-rate the same persons a week later, and compare the ratings.

(2) Rate yourself according to the factors of emotions (see Sec. 479 and Table 102, p. 286).

CHAPTER 23: CARDIOVASCULAR TESTS

Directions for Reading Blood Pressure

A Bowles or other type of disk stethoscope is preferable to the bell type.

Wrap the cuff snugly around the upper arm. Connect one tube with the sphygmomanometer and one tube with the bulb used to inflate the cuff. Place the stethoscope directly over the artery in the upper arm (or at the bend in the elbow). Inflate the cuff until the pressure is 160 mm. If a sound is heard at this point, raise the pressure until the sound disappears. Then gradually lower the pressure until the first sound, which is a sharp staccato sound and which corresponds to the systolic pressure, is heard. The second sound is louder but less decisive than the first sound. Then there is a sudden fall-off in loudness, which fall-off corresponds to the diastolic pressure at the fourth point.

The following is a guide as to what to expect to hear through the stethoscope. Rest the index finger of the left hand lightly on the cartilaginous flap of the right ear just in front of the ear canal. Then gently tap that finger with the index finger of the right hand. The resulting sound is much like the sound that corresponds to the systolic pressure. Then brush the tip of the finger and nail of the right hand against the finger of the left hand. The resulting sound is much like the sound following the sound that corresponds to the systolic pressure. Increase the intensity of the brushing, and then suddenly decrease it. The sound heard is much like the sound that corresponds to the diastolic pressure.

Precautions. The subject should have rested ten minutes before any of the tests are begun. There should be no excitement. The subject should rest between the different exercise periods until the pulse rate returns to normal.

Readings to be obtained. Reclining pulse rate (for all the pulse rates, the pulse is counted for fifteen seconds, and the number of beats is multiplied by 4), reclining systolic pressure, sitting pulse rate, standing pulse rate, standing systolic pressure, standing diastolic pressure, pulse rate after fifteen seconds of the Schneider exercise (see Sec. 486), pulse rate one minute after the exercise, pulse rate one and one-half minutes after the exercise, and pulse rate two minutes after the exercise.

(1) Score the present status of your functional health according to the Crampton method (see Sec. 485 and Table 103, p. 291).

(2) Score the present status of your functional health according to the Schneider method (see Secs. 486-87 and Tables 104-05, pp. 293-94).

(3) Score the present status of your functional health according to the McCloy method (see Sec. 488).

Event to be performed. Tuttle Pulse-ratio Test for the detection of abnormal hearts (see Sec. 495).

(4) Compute graphically the number of steps you need for a 2.5 ratio.

Event to be performed. Males: Harvard Test (see Sec. 498); females: Clarke Test (see Sec. 500).

(5) Males: Record your score for the Harvard Test (Table 107, p. 303).

(6) Females: Record your score for the Clarke Test (Table 107, p. 303).

To the teacher. The methods for measuring basal metabolic rate described in Sections 505 to 507 (Table 109, p. 309) should be demonstrated.

To the teacher. If there are students of physical reconditioning or corrective therapy in the class, it is suggested that they demonstrate the Karpovich Tests (see Secs. 490-92) and the Barringer Test (see Sec. 496).

CHAPTER 24: KNOWLEDGE

To the teacher. A unit in hygiene or a sport should be assigned for the objective test items. The test prepared by each student should be made available to all the students.

Prepare the following for the assigned material:

(1) Twenty true-false items

(2) Five true-false-doubtful items

(3) Five true-false—corrected-false items

(4) Five correct-incorrect diagrams

(5) Five true-false-reason items

(6) Twenty multiple-choice items

(7) Five tabular series of items

(8) Five matching series of items

(9) Five completion items

CHAPTER 25: POTENTIALITY FOR DIFFERENT SPORTS

Events to be performed. Pendulum test for batting skill (see Sec. 551, a board-and-string pendulum may be suspended from a basketball backboard), Johnson Test (see Sec. 553), McCloy Revision of Edgren Test (see Sec. 554), baseball throw for distance.

(1) Males: Compute your baseball-potentiality score by the Everett method (see Sec. 550).

(2) Males: Compute your basketball-potentiality score by the Johnson method (see Sec. 553).

(3) Males: Compute your football-potentiality score by (a) the Brechler method (see Sec. 556) and (b) the Cormack method (see Sec. 557).

(4) Males: Compute your track-and-field-potentiality score (see Sec. 564).

D.G. (5) Compute the track-and-field-potentiality score (see Sec. 564) of the high-school boys. Count age as of last full year. (70th-80th percentile, 80th percentile)

CHAPTER 27: MEDICAL EXAMINATIONS

To the teacher. It is suggested that a physician, following the procedure outlined in Section 575, demonstrate a complete medical examination.

Tests to be administered. One or more tests of vision (see Sec. 575 (7)) and one or more tests of hearing (see Sec. 575 (8)).

CHAPTER 28: ANTHROPOMETRY

To the teacher. Photographs of thirty males and of thirty females should be taken according to the directions in Section 586, and made available to the male and the female students respectively.

(1) Somatotype the photographs according to the criteria in Table 111 (pp. 348-53, see also Secs. 581-86).

(2) Rate the photographs for somatic androgyny according to the criteria in Table 113 (pp. 356-60) and in Section 588.

Measurements to be taken. Height (see Sec. 591 (2)), weight (see Sec. 591 (1)), chest girth (see Sec. 591 (4)), hip width (see Sec. 591 (3)), knee width (see Sec. 591 (5)), chest front fat, chest back fat, abdomen fat, supra-ilium fat (see Sec. 591 (6)), breathing capacity (see Sec. 603).

(1) Compute your normal weight (Tables 114-17, pp. 366-67 and Tables 119-20, pp. 371-72).

D.G. (2) Compute the normal weight (in kgm.) of each of the boys and the girls. (Boys: 39.10, 46.55, 62.75; girls: 35.6, 37.43, 58.41)

(3) Compute your normal fat (Table 118, p. 369).

D.G. (4) Compute the normal fat of each of the boys and the girls. (Boys: 82, 84, 87; girls: 94, 103, 107)

(5) Determine the relationship of your breathing capacity to the norm for your sex, age, height, and weight (Tables 125-26, pp. 386-95).

D.G. (6) Same as 5 for the three boys and the three girls. (Boys: 107.58 (extrapolated), 96.26, 101.98; girls: 96.77 (extrapolated), 112, 101.60)

APPENDIX A: STATISTICAL METHODS

IN THE following problems A = the fifty weights of Group I (Table 127, p. 419), B = the fifty strength scores of Group I, C = the fifty strength scores of Group II i, D = the fifty strength scores of Group II f, E = the first ten weights of Group I, F = the first ten strength scores of Group I, G = the first ten strength scores of Group II i, and H = the first ten strength scores of Group II f. In problems 1 to 26 and 38 to 44 answers are given in parentheses for computations carried to three places and rounded off to two places. In problems 27 to 31 answers are given in parentheses for computations carried to five places and rounded off to four places, and for computations carried to three places and rounded off to two places. In problems 32 to 36 answers are given in parentheses for computations carried to five places and rounded off to four places.

(1) Compute, (a) by the long method and (b) from a frequency distribution, the Mn of B, of C, and of D. (a: 1320.22, 1393.60, 1528.94; b: 1321.20, 1396.80, 1526.40)

(2) What is the middle datum of B, of C, and of D? (1298.5, 1372, 1513)

(3) Compute from a frequency distribution the Mdn of B, of C, and of D. (1300, 1380, 1500)

(4) What is the mode of B and of D determined from B and from D unclassified? (1287; 1612 or 1402)

(5) What is the mode of B, of C, and of D determined from a frequency distribution? (1260; 1380 or 1260; 1500)

(6) Compute the mode of B, of C, and of D. (1257.60, 1346.40, 1447.20)

(7) Compute from a frequency distribution the SD of B, of C, and of D. (195.6, 202.2, 244.2)

(8) Compute the Sk of B, of C, and of D. (.33, .25, .32)

(9) Compute the SD of E, of F, of G, and of H. (14.13, 129.79, 177.34, 244.44)

(10) Compute the PE of B, of C, and of D. (131.93, 136.38, 164.71)

(11) Compute the Q of B, of C, and of D. (138, 126.16, 171.25)

(12) Compute the SE of the Mn of B, of C, and of D. (27.67, 28.60, 34.54)

(13) Compute the SE of the Mn of E, of F, of G, and of H. (4.47, 41.07, 56.12, 77.35)

(14) Compute the SE of the difference between the Mn of B and the Mn of D. (44.26)

(15) Compute the CR of the Mns of B and D. (4.64)

(16) Compute the SE of the difference between the Mn of F and the Mn of G. (69.93)

(17) Compute the SE of the difference between the Mn of G and the Mn of H. (55.52)

(18) Compute the t of the Mns of F and G. (.11)

(19) Compute the t of the Mns of G and H. (2.59)

(20) Compute from a scattergram the r between C and D. (.87)

(21) Compute the SE of the difference between the Mn of the first thirty scores of C and the Mean of the first thirty scores of D. Consider this sample to be large. Compute from a scattergram the SD's and the r. (25.58)

(22) Compute the η's for C and D. (.91, .91)

(23) Compute the ρ between C and D. (.82)

(24) Divide B into two groups: (1) scores above 1321 and (2) scores below 1321. Compute the r_{bis} between A and the two groups of B. (.73)

(25) Divide B into three groups: (1) scores above 1400, (2) scores from 1250 to 1400, and (3) scores below 1250. Compute the r_{tris} between A and the three groups of B. (.67)

(26) Divide B into two groups as in 24. Divide A into two groups: (1) weights above 140 and (2) weights below 140. Compute the r_{tet} between the two dichotomous groups of B and A. (.75)

For problems 27 to 35 use the following r's ($N = 406$):

(27) Compute the r between the shot-put and the strength score, with the influence of weight partialed out (held constant). (.3972; .41)

	Velocity (factor)	Strength score	Sixty-yard dash	Standing broad jump	Running high jump	Twelve-pound shot-put	Age	Height	Weight
Velocity (factor)									
Strength score	.0871								
Sixty-yard dash	-.5909	-.4456							
Standing broad jump	.6811	.4235	-.5797						
Running high jump	6329	.3479	-.4260	.5548					
Twelve-pound shot-put	.3771	.6359	-.4318	.4107	.4404				
Age	1694	.3689	-.1836	.2605	.2825	.3828			
Height	.3117	.4901	-.3367	.3659	.4011	.4202	.2926		
Weight	.0251	.6661	-.2383	.2670	.2244	.5983	.3146	.6032	
Mean	50*	1389.5172	7.9889	7.2767	4.4095	26.6422	16.4389	68.0813	137.1946
SD	10*	219.0163	.6755	.8015	.3918	4.8482	1.0936	2.7734	17.4587

*T-score

(28) Compute the r between the shot-put and weight, with the influence of the strength score partialed out. (.3035; .30)

(29) Compute the r between the shot-put and weight, with the influence of height partialed out. (.4764; .48)

(30) Compute the r between the dash and the standing broad jump, with the influence of the strength score partialed out. (−.4821; −.48)

(31) Compute the r between the running high jump and the standing broad jump, with the influence of height and of the strength score partialed out. (.4503; .44)

(32) Compute by the Doolittle Method the R between the strength score and the following variables: weight, shot-put, and standing broad jump. (.7481)

(33) Compute by the Doolittle Method the R between the shot-put and the following variables: weight, strength score, and velocity factor. (.7554)

(34) Compute by the Doolittle Method the R between the shot-put and tne following variables: age, height, and weight. (.6342)

(35) Compute by the Doolittle Method the R between the velocity factor and the following variables: standing broad jump, dash, and strength score. (.7817)

(36) Compute the multiple regression equations for 32, 33, 34, and 35. (32: $X_0 = 5.5034X_1 + 13.4531X_2 + 50.3068X_3 − 90.0073$. 33: $X_0 = 0927X_1 + .0085X_2 + .1625X_3 − 6.0116$. 34: $X_0 = .9270X_1 + .1040X_2 + .1379X_3 − 14.5963$. 35: $X_0 = 7.4236X_1 − 5.9008X_2 − .0156X_3 + 64.7981$)

(37) At what levels are the r's and the R's of 20, 21, and 27 to 35 statistically significant? (.01)

(38) What is the prediction efficiency of the tests in 20, 21, and 32 to 35? (.51, .37, .34, .36, .22, .37)

(39) What are the upper and the lower limits of the parameter r's of the

DATA

Elementary School Boy

				Strength		
Age	11	yr. 3 mo.				
Height	146	cm. (57.5 in.)		Right grip	55	lb.
Weight	41	kgm. (90.2 lb.)		Left grip	50	lb.
Chest girth	72	cm.		Back lift	180	lb.
Hip width	23.6	cm.		Leg lift	330	lb.
Knee width	8.8	cm.		Pull-ups	8	times
Fat				Dips	5	times
Chest front	22	mm.		Sargent Jump	36	cm.
Chest back	24	mm.		10-second squat		
				thrusts	6¼	times
Abdomen	21	mm.		Iowa-Brace Test	15	points
Supra-ilium	24	mm.		50-yard dash	8.5	sec.
Breathing capacity	142	cu. in.		Feet run in 6		
				seconds	64	ft.
				200-yard run	36	sec.
				Standing broad		
				jump	5	ft. 5 in.
				Running high		
				jump	3	ft. 3 in.
				8-pound shot-put	25	ft.
				Basketball throw		
				for distance	70	ft.

Elementary School Girl

				Strength		
Age	11	yr. 0 mo.				
Height	147	cm. (57.9 in.)		Right grip	45	lb.
Weight	33.5	kgm. (73.7 lb.)		Left grip	42	lb.
Chest girth	64	cm.		Back lift	142	lb.
Hip width	23	cm.		Leg lift	200	lb.
Knee width	8.4	cm.		Pull-ups	16	times
Fat				Push-ups	5	times
Chest front	25	mm.		Pushing		
Chest back	28	mm.		strength	49	lb.
Abdomen	28	mm.		Pulling		
Supra-ilium	31	mm.		strength	42	lb.
Breathing capacity	120	cu. in.		Sargent Jump	37	cm.
				10-second squat		
				thrusts	5½	times
				Iowa-Brace Test	11	points
				50-yard dash	8.8	sec.
				Standing broad		
				jump	5	ft.10 in.
				Basketball throw		
				for distance	60	ft.
				6-pound shot-put	16	ft. 8 in.

Junior High School Boy

			Strength		
Age	13	yr. 9 mo.			
Height	162	cm. (63.8 in.)	Right grip	58	lb.
Weight	48	kgm. (105.6 lb.)	Left grip	56	lb.
Chest girth	73.5	cm.	Back lift	195	lb.
Hip width	25.6	cm.	Leg lift	370	lb.
Knee width	9.1	cm.	Pull-ups	6	times
Fat			Dips	4	times
Chest front	21	mm.	Sargent Jump	42	cm.
Chest back	22	mm.	10-second squat		
Abdomen	21	mm.	thrusts	5½	times
Supra-ilium	22	mm.	Iowa-Brace Test	9	points
Breathing capacity	180	cu. in.	50-yard dash	8.2	sec.
			Feet run in 6		
			seconds	96	ft.
			200-yard run	33	sec.
			Standing broad		
			jump	6	ft. 0 in.
			Running high		
			jump	3	ft. 8 in.
			8-pound shot-put	25	ft.
			Basketball throw		
			for distance	72	ft.

Junior High School Girl

			Strength		
Age	14	yr. 1 mo.			
Height	147	cm. (57.9 in.)	Right grip	65	lb.
Weight	34	kgm. (74.6 lb.)	Left grip	60	lb.
Chest girth	64	cm.	Back lift	220	lb.
Hip width	23	cm.	Leg lift	390	lb.
Knee width	8.4	cm.	Pull-ups	21	times
Fat			Push-ups	9	times
Chest front	25	mm.	Pushing		
Chest back	28	mm.	strength	57	lb.
Abdomen	28	mm.	Pulling		
Supra-ilium	31	mm.	strength	46	lb.
Breathing capacity	140	cu. in.	Sargent Jump	35	cm.
			10-second squat		
			thrusts	6¼	times
			Iowa-Brace Test	18	points
			50-yard dash	7.4	sec.
			Standing broad		
			jump	6	ft. 3 in.
			Basketball throw		
			for distance	62	ft.
			6-pound shot-put	18	ft. 4 in.

Senior High School Boy

			Strength		
Age	17	yr. 4 mo.	Right grip	106	lb.
Height	173	cm. (68.1 in.)	Left grip	100	lb.
Weight	61	kgm. (134.2 lbs.)	Back lift	390	lb.
Chest girth	83	cm.	Leg lift	600	lb.
Hip width	27.4	cm.	Pull-ups	11	times
Knee width	9.5	cm.	Dips	9	times
Fat			Pushing strength	48	lb.
Chest front	20	mm.	Pulling strength	29	lb.
Chest back	21	mm.	Sargent Jump	61	cm.
Abdomen	19	mm.	10-second squat		
Supra-ilium	22	mm.	thrusts	8	times
Breathing capacity	258	cu. in.	Iowa-Brace Test	17	points
			50-yard dash	7	sec.
			Feet run in 6		
			seconds	120	ft.
			200-yard run	28	sec.
			Standing broad		
			jump	7	ft. 9 in.
			Running high jump	4	ft. 7 in.
			8-pound shot-put	35	ft.
			12-pound shot-put	29	ft.
			Basketball throw		
			for distance	98	ft.

Senior High School Girl

			Strength		
Age	16	yr. 7 mo.	Right grip	72	lb.
Height	171	cm. (67.3 in.)	Left grip	70	lb.
Weight	57	kgm. (125.6 lb.)	Back lift	200	lb.
Chest girth	75	cm.	Leg lift	320	lb.
Hip width	29	cm.	Pull-ups	13	times
Knee width	9.5	cm.	Push-ups	2	times
Fat			Pushing		
Chest front	22	mm.	strength	55	lb.
Chest back	24	mm.	Pulling		
Abdomen	26	mm.	strength	44	lb.
Supra-ilium	28	mm.	Sargent Jump	28	cm.
Breathing capacity	190	cu. in.	10-second squat		
			thrusts	4 3/4	times
			Iowa-Brace Test	12	points
			50-yard dash	8.8	sec.
			Standing broad		
			jump	4	ft. 9 in.
			Basketball throw		
			for distance	62	ft.
			6-pound shot-put	21	ft. 2 in.

Posture Silhouettes

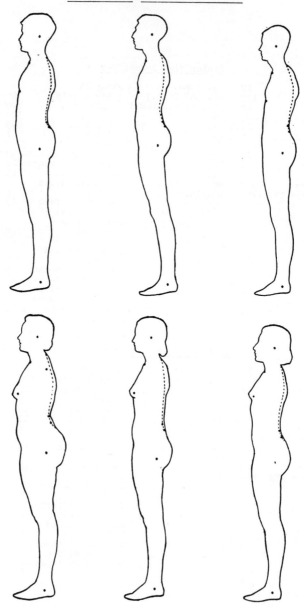

r's in 20 and 21 at the .05 and .01 levels? (.05: .92, .78; .01: .93, .73; .05: .89, .59; .01: .91, .51)

(40) Test the curvilinearity of the η computed in 22. (F: .75, .91)

(41) Compute the SE of the ρ computed in 23. (.05)

(42) Compute the SE of the r_{bis} computed in 24. (.10)

(43) How many tests would need to be added to each of the batteries in 32 to 35 for the r of the validity of each of the batteries to be .95? Assume that the r's of validity of the added tests are at least as high as those of the tests in the original battery. (32: 6 times as many tests, or 15 tests added. 33: 5.5 times as many tests, or 14 tests added. 34: 11.67 times as many tests, or 32 tests added. 35: 5.25 times as many tests, or 13 tests added)

(44) What would the r of the validity of each of the batteries be in 32 to 35 if each of the batteries consisted of six tests? Assumption of r's of validity, same as for 43. (.86, .87, .77, .88)

APPENDIX B: ANALYSIS OF DIFFICULTY OF OBJECTIVE ITEMS

(1) COMPUTE THE INDEX of discrimination for each of the twenty true-false items prepared in connection with the exercises for Chapter 24.

(2) Analyze the difficulty of the responses for each of the twenty multiple-choice items prepared in connection with the exercises for Chapter 24.

SELECTED BIBLIOGRAPHY

See also bibliographies of tests of health knowledge in Chapter 29, of tests of physical-education knowledge in Chapter 24, and of psychological tests in Chapter 19.

RQ = Research Quarterly of the American Association for Health, Physical Education, and Recreation.

JHPE = Journal of Health and Physical Education of the same Association.

Adkins, Dorothy C., and Others. *Construction and Analysis of Achievement Tests.* Wash.: U. S. Gov't Print. Of., 1947.

Alden, Florence D., and Others. "A Motor Ability Test for University Women for the Classification of Entering Students into Homogeneous Groups," *RQ,* III (Mar., 1932).

The American National Red Cross, *Instructor's Manual—Life Saving and Water Safety Courses.* Wash.: The American National Red Cross, 1937.

The American National Red Cross, *Instructor's Manual—Swimming and Diving Courses.* Wash.: The American National Red Cross, 1939.

The American National Red Cross, *Instructor's Guide—Functional Swimming and Water Safety Training Course.* Wash.: The American National Red Cross, 1943.

Andersen, Leonora. *An Athletic Program for Elementary Schools.* N. Y.: A. S. Barnes & Co., 1927.

Anderson, Charlotte W. "Achievement Records in Swimming," *JHPE,* I (May, 1930).

Anderson, Lou E. *Basketball for Women.* N. Y.: Macmillan Co., 1929.

———. *Tennis for Women.* N. Y.: A. S. Barnes & Co., 1926.

Anderson, Theresa, and C. H. McCloy. "The Measurement of Sports Ability in High School Girls," *RQ,* XVIII (Mar., 1947).

Arkin, Herbert, and Raymond R. Colton. *An Outline of Statistical Methods*[4]. N. Y.: Barnes & Noble, Inc., 1939.

———. *Tables for Statisticians.* N. Y.: Barnes & Noble, Inc., 1950.

Armfield, Helen. "Some Ideas for a Hockey Practice," *Sportswoman,* V (Oct., 1928).

Arnold, Dorothy M. "A Study of the Response of the Heart to Different Dosages of Exercise That Are Similar." M.A. Thesis; Iowa City, State Univ. of Iowa, 1935.

Aschner, B. "Die praktische Bedeutung der Lehre vom Habitus und die Renaissance der Humoralpathologie als therapeutische Konsequenz der Konstitutionslehre," *Wiener klinische Wochenschrift,* XXXV (Jan. 26, 1922).

Bancroft, Jessie H. *The Posture of School Children.* N. Y.: Macmillan Co., 1914.

Barach, J. H. "The Energy Index," *Jr. Amer. Med. Assoc.,* LXII (Feb. 14, 1914).

Barringer, Jr., T. B. "Studies of the Heart's Functional Capacity as Estimated by the Circulatory Reaction to Graduated Work," *Archives of Internal Medicine,* XVII (May, 1916).

Barton, Gertrude. "A Comparative Study of the Brace Type of Test and the Johnson Type of Test as Measurers of Motor Educability in the Junior High School Girl." M.A. Thesis; Iowa City, State Univ. of Iowa, 1935.

Bass, Ruth I. "An Analysis of the Components of Tests of Semicircular Canal Function and of Static and Dynamic Balance," *RQ,* X (May, 1939).

Bassett, Gladys, and Others. "Studies in Testing Volleyball Skills," *RQ*, VIII (Dec., 1937).

Bates, Frank H. "The Relationship of Hand and Eye Coordinations to Accuracy in Baseball Batting." M.A. Thesis; Iowa City, State Univ. of Iowa, 1948.

Bayley, Nancy, and Leona M. Bayer. "The Assessment of Somatic Androgyny," *Amer. Jr. Physical Anthropology*, IV New Series (Dec., 1946).

Beall, Elizabeth. "Essential Qualities in Certain Aspects of Physical Education with Ways of Measuring and Developing the Same," *Amer. Physical Educ. Review*, XXXIII (June, Sept., Oct., Nov., and Dec., 1928).

Bean, R. Bennett. "The Two European Types," *Amer. Jr. Anatomy*, XXXI (March, 1923).

Bennett, La Verne M. "A Test of Diving for Use in Beginning Classes," *RQ*, XIII (Mar., 1942).

Bethe, Albrecht, "Aktive und passive Kraft menschlicher Muskeln," *Ergebnisse der Physiologie*, XXIV: 71 (1925).

Blanchard, Jr., B. E. "A Behavior Frequency Rating Scale for the Measurement of Character and Personality in Physical Education Classroom Situations," *RQ*, VII (May, 1936).

Bliss, J. G. *Basketball*. Phila.: Lea & Febiger, 1929.

Bookwalter, Karl W. "An Assessment of the Validity of Height-Weight Class Divisions for High School Girls," *RQ*, XV (May, 1944).

————. "Further Studies of Indiana University Motor Fitness Index," *Bull. of the School of Educ.*, XIX. Bloomington: Ind. Univ., Sept., 1943.

————. "Test Manual for Indiana Motor Fitness Indices for High School and College Age Men," *RQ*, XIV (Dec., 1943).

————, and Carolyn W. Bookwalter. "A Measure of Motor Fitness for College Men," *Bull. of the School of Educ.*, XIX. Bloomington: Ind. Univ., Mar., 1943.

Boulware, Lois. "Study of the Physical Efficiency of Freshman Women as Indicated by the Pulse Ratio." M.A. Thesis; Iowa City, State Univ. of Iowa, 1932.

Bovard, J. F., and F. W. Cozens. *The Leap-meter*. University of Oregon Physical Education Series I:2. Eugene, Ore.: Univ. of Ore., 1928.

————, and Others. *Tests and Measurements in Physical Education³*. Phila.: W. B. Saunders Co., 1949.

Bowen, B. D., and D. L. Platt. "The Relation of Age and Obesity to Vital Capacity," *Archives of Internal Medicine*, XXXI (April, 1923).

Boynton, Bernice. "Individual Differences in the Structure of Pelvis and Lumbar Spine as a Factor in Body Mechanics." M.A. Thesis; Iowa City, State Univ. of Iowa, 1934.

Brace, David K. *Measuring Motor Ability*. N. Y.: A. S. Barnes & Co., 1927.

————. "Studies in Motor Learning of Gross Bodily Motor Skills," *RQ*, XVII (Dec., 1946).

————. "Studies in the Rate of Learning Gross Bodily Motor Skills," *RQ*, XII (May, 1941).

————. "Testing Basket Ball Technique," *Amer. Physical Educ. Review*, XXIX (Apr., 1924).

Brady, George F. "The Effect of Excess Weight upon Motor Skills." Ph.D. Dissertation; Iowa City, State Univ. of Iowa, 1951.

————. "Preliminary Investigations of Volleyball Playing Ability," *RQ*, XVI (Mar., 1945).

Brechler, Paul W. "A Test to Determine Potential Ability in Football (Backs and Ends)." M.A. Thesis; Iowa City, State Univ. of Iowa, 1940.

Broer, Marion R., and Donna M. Miller. "Achievement Tests for Beginning and Intermediate Tennis," *RQ*, XXI (Oct., 1950).

Brophy, Kathleen. "A New Target for Testing Accuracy in Throwing," *Spalding's Athletic Library*, 121R. N. Y.: Amer. Sports Pub. Co., 1934.

Brouha, Lucien. "The Step Test: A Simple Method of Measuring Physical Fitness for Muscular Work in Young Men," *RQ*, XIV (Mar., 1943).

Brown, Harriet M. "The Game of Ice Hockey," *JHPE*, VI (Jan., 1935).

Brownell, Clifford L. *A Scale for Measuring the Antero-posterior Posture of Ninth Grade Boys*. N. Y.: Bur. of Publications, Teachers College, Columbia Univ., 1928.

Brugsch, Theodor. "Masse und Proportionen zur Charakterisierung des Individuums in seinem Habitus," *Zsch für exper. Pathol.*, XIX (1918).

Bryant, John. "The Carnivorous and Herbivorous Types in Man: The Possibility and Utility of their Recognition. I. Introduction and Outline," *Boston Medical and Surgical Jr.*, CLXXII (Mar. 4, 1915).

Buck, Nadine. "A Comparison of Two Methods of Testing Response to Auditory Rhythms," *RQ*, VII (Oct., 1936).

Camp Fire Girl's Book of Aquatics. N. Y.: Camp Fire Outfitting Co., 1925.

Camp Fire Girl's Manual. N. Y.: Camp Fire Outfitting Co., 1948.

Capen, Edward K. "The Effect of Systematic Weight Training on Power, Strength, and Endurance," *RQ*, XXI (May, 1950).

Carlson, H. C. "Fatigue Curve Test," *RQ*, XVI (Oct., 1945).

Carpenter, Aileen. "An Analysis of the Relationships of the Factors of Velocity, Strength, and Dead Weight to Athletic Performance," *RQ*, XII (Mar., 1941).

——. "A Critical Study of the Factors Determining Effective Strength Tests for Women," *RQ*, IX (Dec., 1938).

——. "Factors in Motor Educability," *RQ*, XIV (Dec., 1943).

——. "The Measurement of General Motor Capacity and General Motor Ability in the First Three Grades," *RQ*, XIII (Dec., 1942).

——. "Strength, Power, and 'Femininity' as Factors Influencing the Athletic Performance of College Women," *RQ*, IX (May, 1938).

——. "Strength Testing in the First Three Grades," *RQ*, XIII (Oct., 1942).

——. "Tests of Motor Educability for the First Three Grades," *Child Development*, XI (Dec., 1940).

Carter, Frances H. "A Mechanical Analysis of the Relationships of Positive and Negative Loads to Performance in the Vertical Jump." M.A. Thesis; Iowa City, State Univ. of Iowa, 1945.

Chailley-Bert. *Education Physique et Contrôle Médical*. Paris: Librairie J. B. Baillière, 1943.

Chamberlain, Carl G., and Dean F. Smiley. "Functional Health and the Physical Fitness Index," *RQ*, II (Mar., 1931), Part II.

Chesire, L., and Others. *Computing Diagrams for the Tetrachoric Correlation Coefficient*. Chicago: Univ. of Chicago Bookstore, 1933.

Chui, Edward. "The Effect of Systematic Weight Training on Athletic Power," *RQ*, XXI (Oct., 1950).

Clarke, Harriet L. "A Functional Physical Fitness Test for College Women," *JHPE*, XIV (Sept., 1943).

Clarke, H. Harrison. *Application of Measurement to Health and Physical Education*[2]. N. Y.: Prentice-Hall, Inc., 1950.

——. *Cable-Tension Strength Tests*. Chicopee, Mass.: Brown-Murphy Co., 1953.

——. "An Objective Method of Measuring the Height of the Longitudinal Arch in Foot Examinations," *RQ*, IV (Oct., 1933).

——. "Objective Strength Tests of Affected Muscle Groups Involved in Orthopedic Disabilities," *RQ*, XIX (May, 1948).

————, and Others. "Relationship between Body Position and the Application of Muscle Power to Movements of the Joints," *Archives of Physical Medicine*, XXXI (Feb., 1950).

Clevett, Melvin A. "An Experiment in Teaching Methods of Golf," *RQ*, II (Dec., 1931).

Coleman, James W. "The Differential Measurement of the Speed Factor in Large Muscle Activities," *RQ*, VIII (Oct., 1937).

Collins, Vivian D., and Eugene C. Howe. "A Preliminary Selection of Tests of Fitness," *Amer. Physical Educ. Review*, XXIX (Dec., 1924).

Colvin, Valerie. "Achievement Tests for Speedball," *Spalding's Official Soccer and Speedball Guide*, 116R. N. Y.: Amer. Sports Pub. Co., 1936.

Combs, Lex V. "A Comparison of the Efficacy of the Whole Method and of the Whole-Part-Whole Method of Teaching Track Activities." M.A. Thesis; Iowa City, State Univ. of Iowa, 1932.

The Construction and Use of Achievement Examinations (ed. by Herbert E. Hawkes and Others). N. Y.: Houghton Mifflin Co., 1936.

Cope, Esther E. "A Study of the Component Factors of the Iowa Revision of the Brace Motor Ability Test." M.A. Thesis; Iowa City, State Univ. of Iowa, 1938.

Cormack, Herbert P. "A Test to Determine Potential Ability in Football (Linemen)." M.A. Thesis; Iowa City, State Univ. of Iowa, 1940.

Cornish, Clayton. "A Study of Measurement of Ability in Handball," *RQ*, XX (May, 1949).

Cozens, Frederick W. *Achievement Scales in Physical Education Activities for College Men*. Phila.: Lea & Febiger, 1936.

————. *The Measurement of General Athletic Ability in College Men*. Physical Education Series, I (April, 1929). Eugene, Ore.: Univ. of Ore. Press.

————. "Ninth Annual Report of the Committee on Curriculum Research of the College Physical Education Association. (Part III)," *RQ*, VIII (May, 1937).

————. "A Study of Stature in Relation to Physical Performance," *RQ*, I (Mar., 1930).

————, and Hazel J. Cubberley. "Achievement Tests in Soccer and Speedball," *Spalding's Official Soccer and Speedball Guide*, 116R. N. Y.: Amer. Sports Pub. Co., 1936.

————, and Others. *Achievement Scales in Physical Education Activities for Secondary School Girls and College Women*. N. Y.: A. S. Barnes & Co., 1937.

————. *Physical Education Achievement Scales for Boys in Secondary Schools*. N. Y.: A. S. Barnes & Co., 1936.

Crampton, C. Ward. "A Test of Condition: Preliminary Report," *Medical News*, LXXXVII (Sept. 16, 1905).

Crook, Billie L. "A Scale for Measuring the Antero-posterior Posture of the Preschool Child," *RQ*, VII (Dec., 1936).

Cross, Thomas J. "A Comparison of the Whole Method, the Minor Game Method, and the Whole Part Method of Teaching Basketball to Ninth-Grade Boys," *RQ*, VIII (Dec., 1937).

Cubberley, Hazel J. *Field Hockey Analyzed*. N. Y.: A. S. Barnes & Co., 1928.

————, and Frederick W. Cozens. "The Measurement of Achievement in Basketball," *Spalding's Athletic Library*, 17R. N. Y.: Amer. Sports Pub. Co., 1935-36.

Cureton, Jr., Thomas K. *Beginning and Intermediate National Y.M.C.A. Progressive Aquatic Tests*. N. Y.: Association Press, 1938.

————. "Flexibility as an Aspect of Physical Fitness," *Supplement to RQ*, XII (May, 1941).

————. *How to Teach Swimming and Diving*, I. N. Y.: Association Press, 1934.

──────. *Objective Scales for Rating Swimming Performance and Diagnosing Faults*. Springfield, Mass.: Springfield College, 1935. (Mimeographed.)

──────. "Objective Tests of Swimming." M.P.E. Thesis; Springfield, Mass., Springfield College, 1930.

──────, and Others. *Physical Fitness Appraisal and Guidance*. St. Louis: C. V. Mosby Co., 1947.

──────. *Standards for Testing Beginning Swimming*. N. Y.: Association Press, 1939.

──────. "A Test for Endurance in Speed Swimming," *Supplement to RQ*, VI (May, 1935).

──────, and J. Stuart Wickens. "The Center of Gravity of the Human Body in the Antero-posterior Plane and Its Relation to Posture, Physical Fitness, and Athletic Ability," *Supplement to RQ*, VI (May, 1935).

──────, and Others. "Reliability and Objectivity of the Springfield Postural Measurements," *Supplement to RQ*, VI (May, 1935).

Dane, C. Wesley. "A Study of Circulatory-Respiratory Changes as Indicated by the McCurdy-Larson Organic Efficiency Test in Relation to Physiological Age," *RQ*, XV (May, 1944).

Danford, Harold R. "A Comparative Study of Three Methods of Measuring Flat and Weak Feet," *Supplement to RQ*, VI (Mar., 1935).

Daniels, Lucille, and Others. *Muscle Testing, Techniques of Manual Examination*. Phila.: W. B. Saunders Co., 1947.

Davenport, Charles B. "Body-Build and Its Inheritance," *Carnegie Institute of Wash. Publications* 329, Paper 35 of the Dept. of Eugenics, 1923.

Daviess, Grace B. *Swimming*. Phila.: Lea & Febiger, 1932.

Davison, Arthur H. "The Relationship between Unimanual and Bimanual Handedness," *Jr. of Experimental Psychology*, XXXVIII (June, 1948).

Delaney, Mary. "Age, Height, Weight, and Pubescence Standards for the Athletic Handicapping of Girls," *Amer. Physical Educ. Review*, XXXIII (Oct., 1928).

DeLorme, Thomas L., and Arthur L. Watkins. *Progressive Resistance Exercise*. N. Y.: Appleton-Century-Crofts, Inc., 1951.

Dimock, Hedley S. *Rediscovering the Adolescent*. N. Y.: Association Press, 1937.

Draper, George. "The Mosaic of Androgyny," *New Eng. Medical Jr.*, CCXXV (Sept. 11, 1941).

──────, and Others. *Human Constitution in Clinical Medicine*. N. Y.: Paul B. Hoeber, Inc., 1944.

Driver, Helen I. *Tennis for Teachers*. Phila.: W. B. Saunders Co., 1936.

Duke-Elder, William S. *Text-book of Ophthalmology I*. London: H. Kimpton, 1932.

Dunder, Victor C. "A Multiple Strength Index of General Motor Ability," *RQ*, IV (Oct., 1933).

Dyer, Joanna T. "The Backboard Test of Tennis Ability," *Supplement to RQ*, VI (Mar., 1935).

──────. "Revision of the Backboard Test of Tennis Ability," *RQ*, IX (Mar., 1938).

──────, and Others. "A Basketball Motor Ability Test for College Women and Secondary School Girls," *RQ*, X (Oct., 1939).

Ebel, Robert L. "Writing the Test Item," in *Educ'l Measurement*. Wash.: Amer. Council on Educ., 1951.

Edgren, H. D. "An Experiment in the Testing of Ability and Progress in Basketball," *RQ*, III (Mar., 1932).

──────, and G. G. Robinson. *Individual Skill Tests in Physical Activities*. 5315 Drexel Ave., Chicago: Authors, 1937.

Evaluative Procedures in Physical Activities for Girls and Young Women. N. Y. State Div. of Health and Physical Educ., Sept., 1944.

Everett, Peter W. "The Prediction of Baseball Ability," *RQ*, XXIII (Mar., 1952).

Everts, Edgar W., and Gordon J. Hathaway. "The Use of a Belt to Measure Leg Strength Improves the Administration of Physical Fitness Tests," *RQ*, IX (Oct., 1938).

Ewing, Neil. "A Study of the Possibly Significant Functional Angles of the Pronated and Non-pronated Foot." M.A. Thesis; Iowa City, State Univ. of Iowa, 1937.

Felderman, Lyle E. "The Effect of Variations in Body Weight on the Scores of the General Motor Capacity Test." M.A. Thesis: Iowa City, State Univ. of Iowa, 1948.

Fisher, Ronald A. *Statistical Methods for Research Workers*[11]. N. Y.: Hafner Pub. Co., 1950.

———, and Frank Yates. *Statistical Tables for Biological, Agricultural and Medical Research.* London: Oliver and Boyd, Ltd., 1948.

Flack, Martin W. *The Medical Problems of Flying.* Special Report Series No. 53, Medical Research Council, Great Britain.

———. "Some Simple Tests of Physical Efficiency," *Lancet*, CXCVI (I: Feb. 8, 1919).

Foster, Wilfred L. "A Test of Physical Efficiency," *Amer. Physical Educ. Review*, XIX (Dec., 1914).

Franklin, C. C., and N. G. Lehsten. "Indiana Physical Fitness Test for the Elementary Level (Grades 4 to 8)," *Physical Educator*, V (May, 1948).

Franzen, Raymond. *Physical Measures of Growth and Nutrition*, School Health Research Monograph 2. N. Y.: Amer. Child Health Assoc., 1929.

French, Esther L., and Bernice I. Cooper. "Achievement Tests in Volleyball for High School Girls," *RQ*, VIII (May, 1937).

———, and Evelyn Stalter. "Study of Skill Tests in Badminton for College Women," *RQ*, XX (Oct., 1949).

Friermood, H. T. "Basketball Progress Tests Adaptable to Class Use," *JHPE*, V (Jan., 1934).

Fritsch, Raymond M. "An Evaluation of Fitness Tests for Junior High School Boys." M.A. Thesis; Iowa City, State Univ. of Iowa, 1947.

Frymir, Alice W. *Basketball for Women.* N Y.: A. S. Barnes & Co., 1928.

Gale, Annabella M., and G. H. Gale. "Estimation of the Basal Metabolic Rate," *Lancet*, CCXX (I: June 13, 1931).

Gallagher, J. Roswell, and Lucien Brouha. "A Simple Method of Testing the Physical Fitness of Boys," *RQ*, XIV (Mar., 1943).

Garrett, Henry E. *Statistics in Psychology and Education*[4]. N. Y.: Longmans, Green and Co., 1953.

Gates, Donald D., and R. P. Sheffield. "Tests of Change of Direction as Measurements of Different Kinds of Motor Ability in Boys of the Seventh, Eighth, and Ninth Grades," *RQ*, XI (Oct., 1940).

Gire, Eugenia, and Anna Espenschade. "The Relationship between Measures of Motor Educability and the Learning of Specific Motor Skills," *RQ*, XIII (Mar., 1942).

Girl Scout Handbook. N. Y.: National Headquarters, Girl Scouts, Inc., 1947.

Glassow, Ruth B., and Marion R. Broer. *Measuring Achievement in Physical Education.* Phila.: W. B. Saunders Co., 1938.

Gray, Jr., William S. "Standards for the Appraisement of Antero-posterior Posture." M.A. Thesis; Iowa City, State Univ. of Iowa, 1942.

Group Examination Alpha. Div. of Psychology, Medical Dept., U.S.A., May 20, 1918.

Handbook on Physical Fitness for Students in Colleges and Universities, U. S. Of. of Educ. Wash.: U. S. Gov't Print. Of., 1943.

Handy, Elvin R. "A Further Validation of the Pulse-Ratio Test as a Measure of Physical Efficiency and Endurance." Ph.D. Dissertation; Iowa City, State Univ. of Iowa, 1937.

Happ, William P., and Others. "The Physiologic Effects of Abdominal Cold Packs," *RQ,* XX (May, 1949).

Harris, J. A., and Others. *The Measurement of Man.* Minneapolis: Univ. of Minnesota Press, 1930.

Harris, Jane E. "The Differential Measurement of Force and Velocity for Junior High School Girls," *RQ,* VIII (Dec., 1937).

Harshbarger, Don W. "The Brace Test and Elements Selected from the Brace Test as a Measure of Motor Skills Educability." M.A. Thesis; Iowa City, State Univ. of Iowa, 1936.

Hartley, Grace. "Motivating the Physical Education Program for High School Girls," *Amer. Physical Educ. Review,* XXXIV (May, June, and Sept., 1929).

Hartshorne, Hugh, and M. A. May. *Studies in Deceit.* N. Y.: Macmillan Co., 1928.

Hatlestad, S. Lucille. "Motor Educability Tests for Women College Students," *RQ,* XIII (Mar., 1942).

Hatley, Fred J. "A Battery of Functional Tests for the Prediction of Football Potentiality." M.A. Thesis; Iowa City, State Univ. of Iowa, 1942.

Heath, Marjorie L., and Elizabeth G. Rodgers. "A Study in the Use of Knowledge and Skill Tests in Soccer," *RQ,* III (Dec., 1932).

Heinlein, C. P. "A New Method of Studying the Rhythmic Responses of Children Together with an Evaluation of the Method of Simple Observation," *The Pedagogical Seminary and Jr. Genetic Psychology,* XXXVI (June, 1929).

Henderson, Yandell. "The Time the Breath Can Be Held as an Index for Acidosis," *Jr. Amer. Medical Assoc.,* LXIII (July 25, 1914).

Hernlund, V. F. "The Selection of Physical Tests for Measuring Y.M.C.A. Secretaries," *Supplement to RQ,* VI (Mar., 1935).

Hewitt, Jack E. "Achievement Scale Scores for High School Swimming," *RQ,* XX (May, 1949).

———. "Achievement Scale Scores for Wartime Swimming," *RQ,* XIV (Dec., 1943).

———. "Swimming Achievement Scale Scores for College Men," *RQ,* XIX (Dec., 1948).

Hill, A. V. *Muscular Movement in Man: The Factors Governing Speed and Recovery from Fatigue.* N. Y.: McGraw-Hill Book Co., Inc., 1927.

Hill, Kenneth. "The Formulation of Tests of Motor Educability for Junior High School Boys." M.A. Thesis; Iowa City, State Univ. of Iowa, 1935.

Hillas, Marjorie, and Marian Knighton. *An Athletic Program for High School and College Women.* N. Y.: A. S. Barnes & Co., 1929.

Hindman, Darwin A. "Nomographs for Interpolating Scores on the Schneider Test," *RQ,* I (Dec., 1930).

Holzinger, Karl J. *Statistical Methods for Students in Education.* N. Y.: Ginn and Co., 1928.

Howard, Harvey J. "A Test for the Judgment of Distance," *Amer. Jr. Ophthalmology,* Series 3, II (Sept., 1919).

Howell, William H. *A Textbook of Physiology*[14]. Phila.: W. B. Saunders Co., 1940.

How to Make the Picture Test Item, DA AGO PRT-873. Wash.: Dept. of the Army, 1948.

Humiston, Dorothy. "Humiston Motor-Ability Test," in *Handbook on Physical Fitness for Students in Colleges and Universities,* U. S. Of. of Educ. Wash.: U. S. Gov't Print. Of., 1943.

Hupprich, Florence L. "Volleyball Practice Tests," *Spalding's Athletic Handbook for Women,* 115R. N. Y.: Amer. Sports Pub. Co., 1929-30.

———, and Peter O. Sigerseth. "The Specificity of Flexibility in Girls," *RQ,* XXI (Mar., 1950).

Hyde, Edith I. "An Achievement Scale in Archery," *RQ,* VIII (May, 1937).

———. "The Measurement of Achievement in Archery," *Jr. of Educ'l Research,* XXVII (May, 1934).

———. "National Research Study in Archery," *RQ,* VII (Dec., 1936).

The Iowa Program of Physical Education for Boys. Des Moines: Dept. of Public Instruction, 1945.

Johnson, Granville B. "Physical Skill Tests for Sectioning Classes into Homogeneous Units," *RQ,* III (Mar., 1932).

Johnson, L. William. "Objective Basketball Tests for High School Boys." M.A. Thesis; Iowa City, State Univ. of Iowa, 1934.

Johnson, Wendell, and Darlene Duke. "Revised Iowa Hand Usage Dextrality Quotients of Six-Year-Olds," *Jr. of Educ'l Psychology,* XXXI (Jan., 1940).

Karpovich, Peter V. "Analysis of the Propelling Force in the Crawl Stroke," *Supplement to RQ,* VI (May, 1935).

———. "Water Resistance in Swimming," *RQ,* IV (Oct., 1933).

Keithly, Rowlen B. "The Relationship between Physiological Age and Motor and Physical Development." M.A. Thesis; Iowa City, State Univ. of Iowa, 1939.

Keller, Jr., Arthur T. "An Attempt to Determine, through the Use of the McCloy Cardiovascular Test and the Pulse-Ratio Test, the 'Present Health' of Students Recovering from Illness." M.A. Thesis; Iowa City, State Univ. of Iowa, 1952.

Keller, Louis F. "The Relation of 'Quickness of Bodily Movement' to Success in Athletics," *RQ,* XIII (May, 1942).

Kelley, Truman L. *Statistical Method.* N. Y.: Macmillan Co., 1923.

Kellogg, J. H. "The Value of Strength Tests in the Prescription of Exercise," *Modern Medicine Library,* II. Battle Creek, Mich., 1896.

Kelly, Helen G. *A Study of Individual Differences in Breathing Capacity in Relation to Some Physical Characteristics,* Univ. of Iowa Studies in Child Welfare VII. Iowa City: State Univ. of Iowa, 1933.

Kempt, Grover A., and Others. "A Special Study of the Vision of School Children," *Public Health Reports,* XLIII (July 6, 1928). U. S. Public Health Service, Wash.: U. S. Gov't Print. Of.

Kendall, M. G., and B. B. Smith. *Tables of Random Sampling Numbers.* London: Cambridge University Press, 1939.

Kistler, Joy W. "A Comparative Study of Methods of Classifying Pupils into Homogeneous Groups for Physical Education," *RQ,* V (Mar., 1934).

———. "The Establishment of Bases for Classification of Junior and Senior High School Boys into Homogeneous Groups for Physical Education," *RQ,* VIII (Dec., 1937).

Klein, Armin, and Leah C. Thomas. *Posture Exercises,* Children's Bureau Pub. 165. Wash.: U. S. Gov't Print. Of., 1926.

Klotz, Donald D. "A Mechanical Analysis of the Vertical Jump as Affected by Variations in Weight and Strength." Ph.D. Dissertation; Iowa City, State Univ. of Iowa, 1948.

Knighton, Marian. "Soccer Questions," *JHPE,* I (Oct., 1930).

Koob, Clarence G. "A Study of the Johnson Skills Test as a Measure of Motor Educability." M.A. Thesis; Iowa City, State Univ. of Iowa, 1937.

Kummer, Veva M. "A Study of the Distributions and Relationships of Certain Bony Structures as Related to Static Body Mechanics." M.A. Thesis; Iowa City, State Univ. of Iowa, 1932.

Lapp, V. W. "An Analysis of Movement on the Basis of Latent Times and Variabilities," *Supplement to RQ*, VI (Oct., 1935).

Larson, Leonard A. "A Factor Analysis of Motor Ability Variables and Tests, with Tests for College Men," *RQ*, XII (Oct., 1941).

————. "A Note on Scaling Some Measures of Circulation and Respiration," *RQ*, XIX (Dec., 1948).

————, and Rachael D. Yocom. *Measurement and Evaluation in Physical, Health, and Recreation Education*. St. Louis: C. V. Mosby Co., 1951.

Laveaga, Robert E. *Volleyball; A Man's Game*. N. Y.: A. S. Barnes & Co., 1933.

Layman, Emma McCloy. "An Item Analysis of the Adjustment Questionnaire," *Jr. of Psychology*, X (July, 1940).

Leighton, Jack R. "A Simple Objective and Reliable Measure of Flexibility," *RQ*, XIII (May, 1942).

Lemon, Eloise, and Elizabeth Sherbon. "A Study of the Relationships of Certain Measures of Rhythmic Ability and Motor Ability in Girls and Women," *Supplement to RQ*, V (Mar., 1934).

Lindenmeyer, Frederick T. "The Physical Efficiency Index as a Measure of Athletic Development." M.A. Thesis; Iowa City, State Univ. of Iowa, 1947.

Lindquist, Everett F. *A First Course in Statistics*. N. Y.: Houghton Mifflin Co., 1938.

————. *Statistical Analysis in Educational Research*. N. Y.: Houghton Mifflin Co., 1940.

Lockhart, Aileene, and Frances A. McPherson. "The Development of a Test of Badminton Playing Ability," *RQ*, XX (Dec., 1949).

Lookabaugh, Guy. "The Prediction of Total Potential Strength of Adult Males from Skeletal Build," *RQ*, VIII (May, 1937).

Lowsley, O. S. "The Effects of Various Forms of Exercise on the Systolic, Diastolic and Pulse Pressures and Pulse Rate," *Amer. Jr. of Physiology*, XXVII (Mar. 1, 1911).

McCall, William A. *How to Measure in Education*. N. Y.: Macmillan Co., 1922.

McCloy, Charles H. "An Analysis for Multiple Factors of Physical Growth at Different Age Levels," *Child Development*, XI (Dec., 1940).

————. "An Analytical Study of the Stunt Type Test as a Measure of Motor Educability," *RQ*, VIII (Oct., 1937).

————. "The Apparent Importance of Arm Strength in Athletics," *RQ*, V (Mar., 1934).

————. *Appraising Physical Status: Methods and Norms*, Univ. of Iowa Studies in Child Welfare, XV. Iowa City: State Univ. of Iowa, 1938.

————. *Appraising Physical Status: The Selection of Measurements*, Univ. of Iowa Studies in Child Welfare, XII. Iowa City: State Univ. of Iowa, 1936.

————. "'Blocks Test' of Multiple Response," *Psychometrika*, VII (Sept., 1942).

————. "A Cardiovascular Rating of 'Present Condition,'" *Arbeitsphysiologie*, IV (Mar., 1931).

————. "Character Building through Physical Education," *RQ*, I (Oct., 1930).

————. "A Combination of Weight, Height, and Chest Girth," *Chinese Jr. of Physical Educ. and Hygiene*, III (1926). (In Chinese.)

————. "Endurance," *Physical Educator*, V (Mar., 1948).

————. "The Factor Analysis as a Research Technique," in *Research Methods*

Applied to Health, Physical Education, and Recreation. Wash.: Amer. Association for Health, Physical Educ., and Recreation, 1949.

————. "How about Some Muscle?" *JHPE,* VII (May, 1936).

————. "Individual Weight Standards for Adults," *Jr. of Physical Educ.,* XXVI (Jan., 1929).

————. "The Influence of Chronological Age on Motor Performance," *RQ,* VI (May, 1935).

————. *The Measurement of Athletic Power.* N. Y.: A. S. Barnes & Co., 1932.

————. "The Measurement of General Motor Capacity and General Motor Ability," *Supplement to RQ,* V (Mar., 1934).

————. "The Measurement of Speed in Motor Performance," *Psychometrika,* V (Sept., 1940).

————. "A New Method of Scoring Chinning and Dipping," *RQ,* II (Dec., 1931).

————. "The Organization and Teaching of Apparatus Work and Tumbling," *Jr. of Physical Educ.,* XXXIV (Jan.-Feb., Mar.-Apr., 1937).

————. *Philosophical Bases for Physical Education.* N. Y.: Appleton-Century-Crofts Co., 1940.

————. "A Program of Athletic Activities for Boys," *JHPE,* XII (Dec., 1941).

————. "Recent Studies in the Sargent Jump," *RQ,* III (May, 1932).

————. "A Study of Cardiovascular Variables by the Method of Factor Analysis," *Proceedings,* Second Biennial Meeting, Society for Research in Child Development, II (Oct., 1936).

————. "Weight Standards for the Individual," *Amer. Physical Educ. Review,* XXXI (Sept., 1926).

————. "X-ray Studies of Innate Differences in Straight and Curved Spines," *RQ,* IX (May, 1938).

McCristal, K. J. "Experimental Study of Rhythm in Gymnastic and Tap Dancing," *RQ,* IV (May, 1933).

McCurdy, J. H., and L. A. Larson. "Measurements of Organic Efficiency for the Prediction of Physical Condition," *Supplement to RQ,* VI (May, 1935).

————. "The Measurement of Organic Efficiency for the Prediction of Physical Condition in Convalescent Patients," *RQ,* VI (Dec., 1935).

————. *The Physiology of Exercise.* Philadelphia: Lea and Febiger, 1939.

————. "The Reliability and Objectivity of Blood-Pressure Measurements," *Supplement to RQ,* VI (May, 1935).

McKee, Mary E. "A Test for the Full-Swinging Shot in Golf." *RQ,* XXI (Mar., 1950).

MacCurdy, Howard L. *A Test for Measuring the Physical Capacity of Secondary School Boys.* Yonkers, N. Y.: Author, 1933.

MacEwan, Charlotte G., and Eugene C. Howe. "An Objective Method of Grading Posture," *RQ,* III (Oct., 1932).

Manual of Examination Methods[2]. Chicago: Univ. of Chicago Bookstore, 1937.

Maris, Elizabeth. "Hockey from Fourth Grade through Advanced High School," *Official Field Hockey Guide,* 38R:19. N. Y.: Amer. Sports Pub. Co., 1932.

Martin, E. G. "Tests of Muscular Efficiency," *Physiological Reviews,* I (July, 1921).

Martin, Rudolf. *Lehrbuch der Anthropologie.* Jena: G. Fischer, 1928.

Massey, Wayne W. "A Critical Study of Objective Methods for Measuring Anterior Posterior Posture with a Simplified Technique," *RQ,* XIV (Mar., 1943).

Master, Arthur M., and Enid T. Oppenheimer. "A Simple Exercise Tolerance Test for Circulatory Efficiency with Standard Tables for Normal Individuals," *Amer. Jr. of Medical Science,* CLXXVII (Feb., 1929).

Meredith, Howard V. "Stature of Massachusetts Children of North European and Italian Ancestry," *Amer. Jr. of Physical Anthropology,* XXIV (Jan.-Mar., 1939).

Metheny, Eleanor. "Studies of the Johnson Test as a Test of Motor Educability," *RQ,* IX (Dec., 1938).

———. "The Variability of the Percentage Index of Build as Applied to the Prediction of Normal Weight," *Human Biology,* XI (Dec., 1939).

Meusel, H. *Körperliche Grundansbildung,* Berlin, 1939.

Miles, Walter R. "The Pursuitmeter," *Jr. of Experimental Psychology,* IV (Apr., 1921).

———. "Pursuit Pendulum," *Psychological Review,* XXVII (Sept., 1920).

———. "Static Equilibrium as a Useful Test of Motor Efficiency," *Jr. of Industrial Hygiene,* III (Feb., 1922).

Miller, Frances A. "A Badminton Wall Volley Test," *RQ,* XXII (May, 1951).

Millikin, Rex M. "The Physical Efficiency Rating of Sixth, Seventh, and Eighth Grade Boys as Shown by the Pulse-Ratio Test." M.A. Thesis; Iowa City, State Univ. of Iowa, 1933.

Moffett, D. C. "A Study of Accuracy of Direction in Motor Skills at Different Distances as Determined by the Relative Size of the Angle of Error," *RQ,* XIII (Dec., 1942).

Money, C. V. "Tests for Evaluating the Abilities of Basketball Players," *Athletic Jr.,* XIV (Nov. and Dec., 1933).

Montessori, Maria. *Pedagogical Anthropology* (trans. by F. T. Cooper). N. Y.: Stokes, 1913.

Montoye, Henry J. "Breath-Holding as a Measure of Physical Fitness," *RQ,* XXII (Oct., 1951).

———, and John Brotzmann. "An Investigation of the Validity of Using the Results of a Doubles Tournament as a Measure of Handball Ability," *RQ,* XXII (May, 1951).

Morton, Dudley J. *The Human Foot; Its Evolution, Physiology and Functional Disorders.* N. Y.: Columbia Univ. Press, 1935.

Mosbek, Ellen. "Baseball Skill Tests," *Spalding's Athletic Library,* 121R. N. Y.: Amer. Sports Pub. Co., 1937.

Moser, Helen A. "The Use of Basketball Skill Tests for Girls and Women," *JHPE,* VI (Mar., 1935).

Moser, Jake H. "An Attempt to Devise a Simple Method of Measuring Potential Football Intelligence." M.A. Thesis; Iowa City, State Univ. of Iowa, 1938.

"Motor Ability Tests," Report of the Committee of the Amer. Physical Educ. Assoc., Feb., 1929.

Moyle, William J. "A Study of Speed and Heart Size as Related to Endurance in Swimming." M.A. Thesis; Iowa City, State Univ. of Iowa, 1936.

Murphy, Mary A. "A Study of the Primary Components of Cardiovascular Tests," *RQ,* XI (Mar., 1940).

Muzzey, Dorothy M. "Group Progress of White and Colored Children in Learning a Rhythm Pattern," *RQ,* IV (Oct., 1933).

Myers, J. A. *Vital Capacity of the Lungs.* Baltimore: Williams & Wilkins Co., 1925.

National Physical Achievement Standards. Nat'l Physical Achievement Standards Committee. N. Y.: A. S. Barnes & Co., 1929.

National Physical Achievement Standards for Girls. Prepared by Amy R. Howland. N. Y.: Nat'l Recreation Assoc., Inc., 1936. Reprint, 1946.

Neal, Charlotte F. "The Value of Variations of Grip in Selected Sports for Women as Compensating Factors for Sex Differences in Strength." M.A. Thesis; Iowa City, State Univ. of Iowa, 1951.

Neilson, N. P., and Frederick W. Cozens. *Achievement Scales in Physical Education Activities for Boys and Girls in Elementary and Junior High Schools.* Sacramento: Calif. State Dept. of Educ., 1934.

Nevers, John E. "The Effects of Physiological Age on Motor Achievement," *RQ,* XIX (May, 1948).

Nibbe, Raymond W. "The Relationship Existing between the Heart Rate and the Intensity of Exercise." M.A. Thesis; Iowa City, State Univ. of Iowa, 1931.

Niehaus, Marian. "A Study of Tests for Dividing Junior High School Girls into Homogeneous Groups for Physical Education." M.A. Thesis; Iowa City, State Univ. of Iowa, 1935.

Oliphant, Harve A. "A Study of Improvement in Shooting Baskets as Related to the Amount of Practice." M.A. Thesis; Iowa City, State Univ. of Iowa, 1939.

O'Neel, F. W. "A Behavior Frequency Rating Scale for the Measurement of Character and Personality in High School Physical Education Classes for Boys," *RQ,* VII (May, 1936).

Palmer, Gladys E. *Baseball for Girls and Women.* N. Y.: A. S. Barnes & Co., 1929.

Parkhurst, Mary G. "Achievement Tests in Swimming," *JHPE,* V (May, 1934).

Peters, Charles C., and Elizabeth C. Wykes. "Simplified Methods for Computing Regression Coefficients and Partial and Multiple Correlations," *Jr. of Educational Research,* XXIII (May, 1931).

Phillips, Bernath E. "The JCR Test," *RQ,* XVIII (Mar., 1947).

——. "The Relationship between Certain Phases of Kinesthesis and Performance during the Early Stages of Acquiring Two Perceptuo-Motor Skills," *RQ,* XII (Oct., 1941).

Phillips, Marjorie, and Dean Summers. "Bowling Norms and Learning Curves for College Women," *RQ,* XXI (Dec., 1950).

Physical Defects, The Pathway to Correction. N. Y.: Amer. Child Health Association, 1934.

Physical Fitness Manual for High School Boys, Bull. 136. Ind. State Dept. of Public Instruction, 1944.

Physical Fitness Manual for High School Girls, Bull. 137 (Revised). Ind. State Dept. of Public Instruction, 1944.

Physical Fitness through Physical Education for the Victory Corps, U. S. Of. of Educ. Wash.: U. S. Gov't Print. Of., 1942.

"Physical Performance Levels for High School Girls," A Summary Report of the Research Committee, Nat'l Section on Women's Athletics, *JHPE,* XVI (June, 1945).

Physical Reconditioning, War Dept. Technical Manual 8-292. Wash.: U. S. Gov't Print. Of., 1944.

Physical Training, War Dept. Field Manual 21-20. Wash.: U. S. Gov't Print. Of., 1950.

"Popularizing the Swimming Badge Tests," *Recreation,* XXVII (July, 1933).

Pryor, Helen B. *As the Child Grows.* N. Y.: Silver Burdett Co., 1943.

Read, J. Marion. "Basic Pulse Rate and Pulse Pressure Changes Accompanying Variations in the Metabolic Rate," *Archives of Internal Medicine,* XXXIV (Oct. 15, 1924).

——, and Charles W. Barnett. "A New Formula for Prediction of Basal Metabolism from Pulse Rate and Pulse Pressure," *Proceedings* of the Society for Experimental Biology and Medicine, XXXI (March, 1934).

Reichart, Natalie, and Jeanette Brauns. *The Swimming Work Book*. N. Y.: A. S. Barnes & Co., 1937.

Reynolds, Herbert J. "Volleyball Tests," *JHPE*, I (Mar., 1930).

Roads, Hazel M. "A Comparative Study of the Brace Type of Test and the Johnson Type of Test as Measurers of Motor Educability in the Senior High School Girls as Shown by Two Selected Criteria." M.A. Thesis; Iowa City, State Univ. of Iowa, 1936.

Rodgers, Elizabeth G. "Evaluation of the Fundamentals of Motor Performance," *JHPE*, XVIII (Apr., 1947).

————, and Marjorie L. Heath. "An Experiment in the Use of Knowledge and Skill Tests in Playground Baseball," *RQ*, II (Dec., 1931).

Rogers, Frederick R. *Physical Capacity Tests in the Administration of Physical Education*. N. Y.: Teachers College, Columbia Univ., 1925.

————. *Tests and Measurement Programs in the Redirection of Physical Education*. New York: Bureau of Publications, Teachers College, Columbia Univ., 1927.

Ruch, Giles M. *The Objective or New-Type Examination*. Chicago: Scott, Foresman & Co., 1929.

Rump, August H. "The Relative Contribution of Arm, Back, Abdomen and Leg Strength to the General Athletic Ability of High School Boys." M.A. Thesis; Iowa City, State Univ. of Iowa, 1931.

Russell, Naomi, and Elizabeth Lange. "Achievement Tests in Volleyball for Junior High School Girls," *RQ*, XI (Dec., 1940).

Sargent, Dudley A. "The Physical Test of a Man," *Amer. Physical Educ. Review*, XXVI (Apr., 1921).

————. *The Universal Test for Strength, Speed and Endurance of the Human Body*. Cambridge, Mass.: pub. privately, 1902.

Sargent, L. W. "Some Observations on the Sargent Test of Neuromuscular Efficiency," *Amer. Physical Educ. Review*, XXIX (Feb., 1924).

Schneider, E. C. "A Cardiovascular Rating as a Measure of Physical Fatigue and Efficiency," *Jr. Amer. Medical Assoc.*, LXXIV (May 29, 1920).

Schrock, H. D., and C. H. McCloy. "A Study of the Best Combination of Age, Height and Weight for Basketball Classification," *Jr. of Physical Educ.*, XXVII (Oct., 1929).

Schwartz, Helen. "Knowledge and Achievement Tests in Girls' Basketball on the Senior High School Level," *RQ*, VIII (Mar., 1937).

Scott, M. Gladys, and Esther French. *Evaluation in Physical Education*. St. Louis: C. V. Mosby Co., 1950.

Scouting for Girls. N. Y.: Nat'l Headquarters, Girl Scouts, Inc., 1926.

Seashore, Carl E. *The Measurement of Musical Talent*. N. Y.: G. Schirmer, 1915.

Seashore, Harold G. "The Development of a Beam-Walking Test and Its Use in Measuring Development of Balance in Children," *RQ*, XVIII (Dec., 1947).

Seashore, Robert H. "Stanford Motor Skills Unit," *Psychological Monographs*, XXXIX:2 (1928).

Seaver, Jay W. *Anthropometry and Physical Examination*. Meriden, Conn.: Curtiss-Way Co., 1909.

Seltzer, Carl C., and Lucien Brouha. "The 'Masculine' Component and Physical Fitness," *Amer. Jr. of Physical Anthropology*, I New Series (Mar., 1943).

Shambaugh, Mary E. "The Objective Measurement of Success in the Teaching of Folk Dancing to University Women," *RQ*, VI (Mar., 1935).

Sheffield, Lyba and Nita. *Swimming Simplified*. N. Y.: A. S. Barnes & Co., 1931.

Sheldon, W. H., and Others. *The Varieties of Human Physique*. N. Y.: Harper & Bros., 1940.

————, and Others. *Atlas of Men.* N. Y.: Harper & Bros., 1954.

Shirley, Mabel J. "The Response of the Normal Prepubescent Heart to Exercise of Graded Intensities." M.A. Thesis; Iowa City, State Univ. of Iowa, 1934.

Sierakowski, Frances. "A Study of Change-of-Direction Tests for High School Girls." M.A. Thesis; Iowa City, State Univ. of Iowa, 1940.

Sievers, Harry L. "The Measurement of Potential Wrestling Ability." M.A. Thesis; Iowa City, State Univ. of Iowa, 1934.

Sievers, Henry. "A Simple Method of Detecting Abnormal Hearts by the Use of the Pulse-Ratio Test," *RQ,* VI (May, 1935).

Slater-Hammel, Arthur T., and R. L. Stumpner. "Batting Reaction-Time," *RQ,* XXI (Dec., 1950).

Smith, Ann A. "Aids to Efficient Swimming Instruction for Girls and Women," *JHPE,* II (Sept., 1931).

Smith, Stanley M. "The 'Blocks Test' as a Measurement of Adaptive Athletic Response." M.A. Thesis; Iowa City, State Univ. of Iowa, 1943.

Snedecor, George W. *Statistical Methods*[4]. Ames, Iowa: Iowa State College Press, 1946.

Spearman, Charles E. *The Abilities of Man, Their Nature and Measurement.* N. Y.: Macmillan Co., 1927.

Spindler, Evelyn. "Do You Grade or Guess?" *JHPE,* II (Oct., 1931).

Sprow-Howland, Ivalclare. "A Study of the Position of the Sacrum in the Adult Female Pelvis and Its Relationship to Body Mechanics." M.A. Thesis; Iowa City, State Univ. of Iowa, 1933.

Stansbury, Edgar B. "A Simplified Method of Classifying Junior and Senior High School Boys into Homogeneous Groups for Physical Education Activities," *RQ,* XII (Dec., 1941).

Stockard, Charles R. "Human Types and Growth Reactions," *Amer. Jr. of Anatomy,* XXXI (Jan., 1923).

Stone, W. J. "The Clinical Significance of High and Low Pulse Pressures with Special Reference to Cardiac Load and Overload," *Jr. Amer. Medical Assoc.,* LXI (Oct. 4, 1913).

Stuber, George M. "The Measurement of Potential Velocity in Post-Pubescent High School Boys." M.A. Thesis; Iowa City, State Univ. of Iowa, 1940.

"Swimming Badge Tests for Boys and Girls," *Amer. Physical Educ. Review,* XXXIV (May, 1929).

Symonds, Percival M. *The Nature of Conduct.* N. Y.: Macmillan Co., 1928.

Taylor, Craig. "A Maximal Pack Test of Exercise Tolerance," *RQ,* XV (Dec., 1944).

Thompson, Betty L. *Fundamentals of Rhythm and Dance.* N. Y.: A. S. Barnes & Co., 1933.

Thurstone, L. L. *A Factorial Study of Perception.* Chicago: Univ. of Chicago Press, 1944.

————. *Mechanical Aptitude III, Analysis of Group Tests.* Chicago: Psychometric Lab., Univ. of Chicago, 1949.

————. "The Perceptual Factor," *Psychometrika,* III (Mar., 1938).

————. *Primary Mental Abilities.* Chicago: Univ. of Chicago Press, 1938.

————. *A Simplified Multiple Factor Method and an Outline of the Computations.* Chicago: Univ. of Chicago Bookstore, 1933.

————, and Thelma G. Thurstone. *Factorial Studies of Intelligence.* Chicago: Univ. of Chicago Press, 1941.

Todd, Thomas W. *Atlas of Skeletal Maturation.* St. Louis: C. V. Mosby Co., 1937.

Travers, Robert M. W. *How to Make Achievement Tests.* N. Y.: Odyssey Press, 1950.

Troemel, Ernestine A. "Swimming—On an Efficient Grading Basis." *Amer. Physical Educ. Review*, XXXIII (June, 1928).

Tuttle, W. W. "The Efficiency of High School Boys as Shown By the Pulse Ratio Test," *RQ*, I (Oct., 1930).

————. "The Use of the Pulse-Ratio Test for Rating Physical Efficiency," *RQ*, II (May, 1931).

————, and Henryetta Frey. "A Study of the Physical Efficiency of College Women as Shown by the Pulse-Ratio Test," *RQ*, I (Dec., 1930).

Van Dalen, Debold. "The Contribution of Breathing Capacity to the Physical Fitness Index," *RQ*, VII (Dec., 1936).

————. "New Studies in the Sargent Jump," *RQ*, XI (May, 1940).

Vickers, Vernette S., and Others. "The Brace Scale Used with Young Children," *RQ*, XIII (Oct., 1942).

Voigt, Gunter. "Über die Richtungspräzision einer Fernhandlung," *Psychologische Forschung*, XVI: 1 and 2 (1932).

Wagner, Miriam M. "An Objective Method of Grading Beginners in Tennis," *JHPE*, VI (Mar., 1935).

War Department Training Circular, No. 40, June, 1944.

Wardlaw, Charles D. *Fundamentals of Baseball*. N. Y.: C. Scribner's Sons, 1929.

Wayman, Agnes R. *Education through Physical Education*[2]. Phila.: Lea & Febiger, 1938.

Wear, Carlos L. "The Construction of a Multiple Obstacle Run for Classifying Junior High School Boys into Homogeneous Groups for Physical Education Activities," *RQ*, XI (May, 1940).

Wedemeyer, Ross. "A Differential Analysis of Sit-ups for Strength and Muscular Endurance," *RQ*, XVII (Mar., 1946).

Weitzman, Ellis, and Walter J. McNamara. *Constructing Classroom Examinations . . . A Guide for Teachers*. Chicago: Science Research Associates, 1949.

Wells, Katharine F., and Evelyn K. Dillon. "The Sit and Reach—A Test of Back and Leg Flexibility," *RQ*, XXIII (Mar., 1952).

Wells, P. V. *Flarimeter Manual*. Princeton, N. J.: Princeton Univ. Press, 1953.

Wendler, Arthur J. "A Critical Analysis of Test Elements Used in Physical Education," *RQ*, IX (Mar., 1938).

Wettstone, Eugene. "Tests for Predicting Potential Ability in Gymnastics and Tumbling," *RQ*, IX (Dec., 1938).

Wetzel, Norman C. "Physical Fitness in Terms of Physique, Development and Basal Metabolism," *Jr. Amer. Medical Assoc.*, CXVI (Mar. 22, 1941).

Weymouth, F. W., and M. J. Hirsch. "Reliability of Certain Tests for Determining Distance Discrimination," *Amer. Jr. of Psychology*, LVIII (July, 1945).

Wickens, J. Stuart, and Oscar W. Kiphuth. "Body Mechanics Analysis of Yale University Freshmen," *RQ*, VIII (Dec., 1937).

Wiebe, Vernon R. "A Study of Tests of Kinesthesis." M.A. Thesis; Iowa City, State Univ. of Iowa, 1951.

Willgoose, Carl E., and Millard L. Rogers. "Relationship of Somatotype to Physical Fitness," *Jr. of Educ'l Research*, XLII (May, 1949).

Wilson, Colin T. "Coordination Tests in Swimming," *RQ*, V (Dec., 1934).

Y.M.C.A. Swimming and Life Saving Manual. N. Y.: Association Press, 1929.

Young, Genevieve, and Helen Moser. "A Short Battery of Tests to Measure Playing Ability in Women's Basketball," *RQ*, V (May, 1934).

Young, Kathryn E. "An Analytic Study of the Tests of Change of Direction." M.A. Thesis; Iowa City, State Univ. of Iowa, 1937.

Young, Olive G. "A Study of Kinesthesis in Relation to Selected Movements," *RQ*, XVI (Dec., 1945).

INDEX